Exploring
Anatomy&Physiology
in the Laboratory

FOURTH EDITION

Erin C. Amerman

Florida State College at Jacksonville

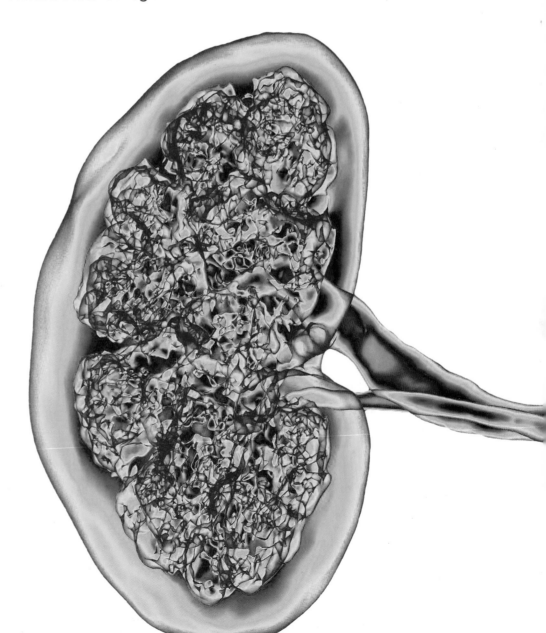

MORTON
PUBLISHING

925 W. Kenyon Avenue, Unit 14
Englewood, CO 80110

morton-pub.com

Book Team

President and CEO	David M. Ferguson
Senior Acquisitions Editor	Marta R. Pentecost
Supervising Editor	Michelle A. Schulte
Editorial Project Managers	Trina Lambert, Rayna S. Bailey
Editorial Assistant	Sasha L. Robeson
Production Manager/Cover	Will Kelley
Production Associate	Joanne Saliger
Indexer	Teri Jurgens
Illustrations	Imagineeringart.com

Dedication

For Doug Morton, whose support of my vision, commitment to this book, and belief in the value of higher education to transform lives will not be forgotten.

For Elise, who was 12 weeks old when I dedicated my first book to her. At 17 years old now, she remains my favorite reason for missing deadlines.

Printed in the United States of America

10 9 8 7 6 5 4 3 2 1

ISBN-13: 978-1-64043-398-4
ISBN-10: 1-64043-398-8

Library of Congress Control Number: 2021946637

Preface

Having just put the finishing touches on the fourth edition of *Exploring Anatomy and Physiology in the Laboratory*, or *EAPL*, I find it interesting to reflect upon how we arrived here. It feels like just yesterday, even though it was 2003, that I first met David Ferguson at a meeting of the Human Anatomy and Physiology Society (HAPS). At that initial meeting, we discussed our shared vision for an activity-based lab manual that would keep students engaged, improve their lab grades, and solve teaching problems.

We started with the text *Exercises for the Anatomy and Physiology Laboratory*, a simple black and white manual with focused activities. *Exercises* was enthusiastically received, and so we set out to produce an expanded, full-color version of the exercises that would include more explanations, new activities, a complete art program, and new pedagogy. In 2010, we released this reimagined book as the first edition of *EAPL*. Like its predecessor, it was warmly received.

With each subsequent edition of *EAPL*, we have worked to improve the text and give students and professors a better experience. And now we introduce the fourth edition. We think it's the best version of *EAPL* so far, and we hope you agree. As you peruse the new fourth edition, please take note of the following updates:

- **Lab practical review quizzes.** We know from decades of educational research that answering questions is one of the best ways to enhance student learning and retention. With that in mind, we have added four lab practical review quizzes to this new edition. These quizzes will help students review for practical exams and will highlight areas in which they need further review.

- **Concept overview figures.** Students sometimes struggle to appreciate the big picture—they focus on the puzzle pieces, having difficulty appreciating how they fit together to form a larger whole. To address this problem, we added several full-page concept overview figures to the fourth edition. These figures serve as visual summaries of important material, and help students assemble the puzzle pieces.

- **Model photos.** A goal for each new edition of *EAPL* has been to improve the art program. For years, we have wanted to include photos of the models students examine in labs, but our selection has been limited for reasons of copyright. However, with this fourth edition, two model companies—Denoyer-Geppert Science Company and 3B Scientific—granted us permission to use their model photos. This addition of 27 new model photos will help students better connect what they are

seeing in the laboratory with what they see in the artwork of the book. In addition, we have included model photos among the quiz questions to help students better prepare for lab practical exams.

- **All new quiz questions.** With each edition, we aim to refresh 70–80% of the assessments, including the "Check Your Recall" and "Check Your Understanding" questions. But with this new edition, we went for a full overhaul—every single question in the book has been replaced or updated.

- **Active reading sections.** One reason the laboratory is such a useful learning tool is because it is an active learning process. However, the reading done prior to the laboratory is largely passive. This isn't ideal—research has demonstrated that students develop better understanding and retention of complex material when reading is an active process. To make reading more active, we have added problem-solving exercises to select text sections. In these exercises, students use logic and previously learned material to work through a specific physiological concept.

- **Added etymologies.** When students are learning anatomy and physiology, it can feel like they are learning an entirely new language. In the previous edition, we added phonetic pronunciation keys to help students with this new language. With this fourth edition, we have expanded into adding word etymologies so students can better understand new vocabulary and learn how to build their own words.

- **Focus on the scientific method.** With the advent of the COVID-19 pandemic, we have seen science, particularly the science of the human body, become a topic of popular conversation. This has made developing science literacy, and an appreciation of the scientific method, more relevant to students' lives than ever before. With that in mind, we added an introductory exercise on the scientific method. In addition, students are asked to provide a hypothesis prior to each experiment they perform from the manual. At the end of the experiment, students are challenged to compare their hypothesis to their results.

We hope you enjoy the fourth edition of *EAPL* and find that it is indeed the best edition yet. Please continue to share your feedback with us—we are always looking for additional ways to improve the experience for you and your students.

Erin Amerman, author

About the Author

Erin C. Amerman has been involved in anatomy and physiology education for over 20 years as an author and professor. She is presently teaching at Florida State College at Jacksonville. She is an alumna of the University of West Florida and Des Moines University (University of Osteopathic Medicine and Health Sciences). Dr. Amerman is presently the author of six textbooks, four of which are with Morton Publishing Company. She is deeply committed to helping students succeed in the world of science, and to generating curiosity and excitement about the material.

When she's not writing or in the classroom, Dr. Amerman is tending to her crew of rescued farmed animals as founder and president of the nonprofit Critter Creek Farm Sanctuary. Founded in 2016, Critter Creek Farm Sanctuary has quickly grown to become the largest bovine sanctuary in the United States. Learn more about Critter Creek Farm Sanctuary at crittercreekfarmsanctuary.org.

Acknowledgments

Textbooks are an enormous undertaking. Many people were integral to the production and development of this edition, and I would like to take this brief opportunity to express my gratitude.

First and foremost, I would like to thank my family and friends, particularly my daughter Elise, my mother Cathy, and my husband Chris. Without your unwavering support and patience, none of my work would be possible. I'd also like to thank Dr. Lourdes Norman-McKay, whose advice, wisdom, and friendship helps to keep me (mostly) sane. Lastly, I can't forget the animals and the wonderful team of humans at Critter Creek Farm Sanctuary, who provide a wonderful distraction from work (except the dogs and cats, who "help" by being completely in the way of whatever I'm doing).

Next, I would like to extend my gratitude to the talented book team with whom I was fortunate enough to work: Joanne Saliger, who expertly designed and produced the book as she always does; Will Kelley, who designed the wonderful cover; Trina Lambert, who skillfully copyedited the text; Marta Pentecost, who oversaw the project as senior acquisitions editor; Rayna Bailey, Adam Jones, Sasha Robeson, and Miki Schulte for adding "extra eyes" throughout the project; Teri Jurgens, who provided the index; the team at Imagineering, who provided the beautiful illustrations; Denoyer-Geppert Science Company and 3B Scientific, which allowed me to use photos of their anatomical models; and John Crawley, Michael Leboffe, Justin Moore, Lorraine Jadeski, and James Turgeon, who allowed me to use several of their excellent photos and photomicrographs. I truly appreciate all your hard work and generosity.

I would also like to thank the following reviewers for their invaluable suggestions that helped to improve this edition:

Diana M. Coffman, Lincoln Land Community College
Angela Corbin, Nicholls State University
Dr. Cassy Cozine, University of Saint Mary
Molli Crenshaw, Texas Christian University
Kathryn A. Durham, RN, PhD, Lorain County Community College
Jill E. Feinstein, Richland Community College
Nancy E. Fitzgerald, MD, Alvin Community College
Carrie L. Geisbauer, Moorpark College
Carol Haspel, PhD, Laguardia Community College
Stephanie Ann Havemann, PhD, Alvin Community College
Elizabeth Hodgson, York College of Pennsylvania
Steven Leadon, Durham Technical Community College
Eddie Lunsford, Southwestern Community College
Dr. Shawn Macauley, Muskegon Community College
Darren Mattone, Muskegon Community College
John David Matula, Alvin Community College
Justin Moore, American River College

Tommy D. Morgan, Alvin Community College
Dr. Anita Naravane, St. Petersburg College
Michele Robichaux, Nicholls State University
Deanne Roopnarine, Nova Southeastern University
Amy Fenech Sandy, Columbus Technical College in Columbus, GA
Lori Smith, American River College
Valory Thatcher, Mt. Hood Community College
Dr. Donald R. Tredway, Tulsa Community College
Cathy Whiting, The University of North Georgia–Gainesville

The acknowledgments would be incomplete without thanking Doug Morton, to whom I will be eternally grateful for adding me to the Morton family. And, finally, I extend a special thank you to President and CEO David Ferguson for his support, patience, friendship, and willingness to give cookies to cows, even if it meant getting covered in cow slobber.

Be Prepared

Objectives set learning goals to prepare students for what they are expected to know after completing the lab. The numbered objectives also aid in the review of material.

Pre-Lab Exercises encourage students to actively prepare for the lab by defining key terms, doing labeling and coloring exercises to learn anatomical structures, and reviewing vital material from previous units, saving instructors from having to spend extra time reviewing material from the lecture. These exercises have updated terms and figures and can be completed using information available in the lab manual. The pre-lab exercises are designed to help students retain information and build a deeper understanding of the content through asking students to draw their own leader lines and write definitions.

Scientific Method Exercise introduces students to the systematic series of steps collectively known as the scientific method. Before proceeding with the anatomy and physiology (A&P) content, students learn how to develop a hypothesis and analyze its results. This exercise is new to this edition as are the 36 opportunities for students to develop hypotheses within existing and new procedures.

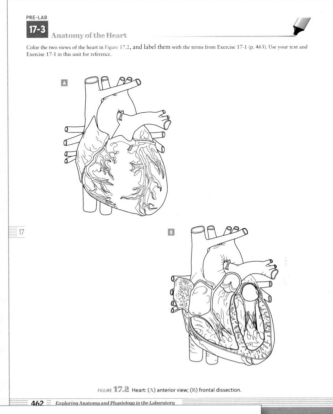

Color the two views of the heart in Figure 17.2, and label them with the terms from Exercise 17-1 (p. 463). Use your text and Exercise 17-1 in this unit for reference.

A

B

FIGURE **17.2** Heart: (A) anterior view; (B) frontal dissection.

Name _____ Section _____ Date _____

PRE-LAB EXERCISES

Complete the following exercises prior to coming to lab, using your lab manual and textbook for reference.

You should be familiar with the following terms before coming to lab.

Term	Definition
Layers of the Heart Wall	
Pericardium	
Pericardial cavity	
Myocardium	
Endocardium	
Structures of the Heart	
Atria (right and left)	
Ventricles (right and left)	
Tricuspid valve	
Mitral (bicuspid) valve	
Pulmonary valve	
Aortic valve	
Chordae tendineae	
Great Vessels	
Superior vena cava	

Be Organized

Model Inventories provide organized and easily referenced lists of anatomical structures students are responsible for identifying. These lists help students catalog the specimens they see in the lab. The emphasis on examination, description, pronunciation, and writing the names of anatomical structures encourages students to be actively involved in the learning process and allows them to better retain the material. A pronunciation guide at the beginning of the manual and pronunciation keys throughout the exposition help students gain confidence and learn the correct pronunciation of terms. An added feature includes etymologies, which are provided for many terms in order to aid with assimilating the vocabulary of A&P.

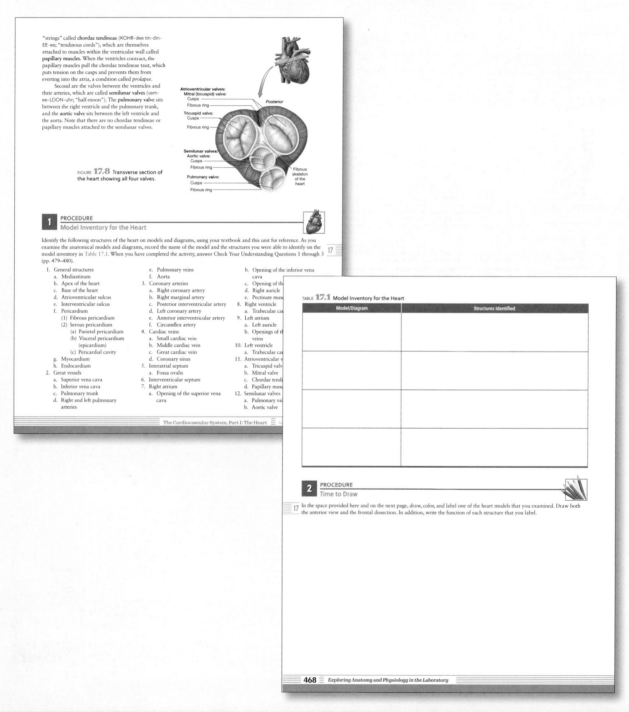

Be Focused

Illustrations and ***Photographs*** support the lab exercises and improve student understanding of significant concepts and the procedural instructions in the laboratory setting. The images were specifically designed for Exploring Anatomy & Physiology in the Laboratory. (Many lab manuals simply reproduce artwork and exposition from the related textbook, unnecessarily increasing the redundancy, size, and price of the manual.) This fourth edition contains many new and revised illustrations and photographs, including images of plastic anatomical models, which offer a variety of detailed and realistic views of human anatomy. The histology images provide consistency with what students are likely to see in the lab, and include those from the best sources of commercially available slides.

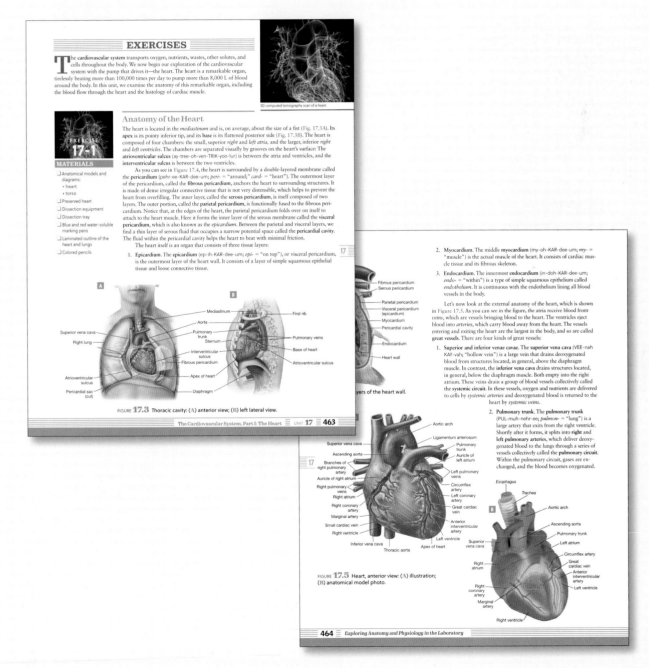

Be Active

Focused Activities demonstrate the guiding philosophy of this lab manual. Students learn best when they are actively engaged in the laboratory. In this manual, students are asked to be active by describing, labeling, writing, coloring, and drawing. Several activities have been edited for clarity to add terms and more detail. Additional procedures provide fresh learning activities.

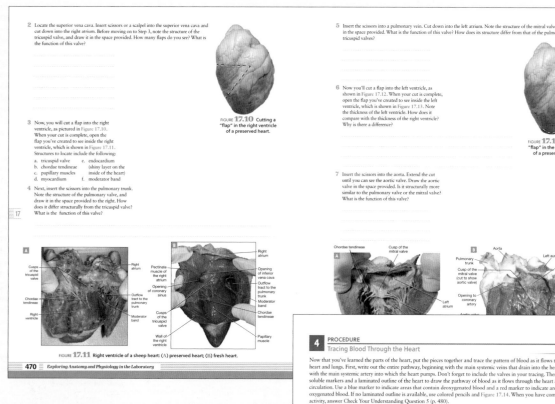

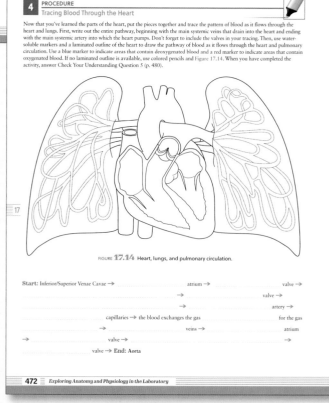

Tracing Exercises ask students to write step-by-step, turn-by-turn directions to follow substances (a blood cell, food molecule, waste by-product, or electrical event) through the human body, and then trace the substances' paths on a "map" of the body. These exercises allow students to see the big picture of how the body systems interact and to understand the relationship between structure and function.

Hints & Tips sidebars appear throughout the book to help students navigate some of the more difficult topics in A&P.

Be Sure

Check Your Recall quizzes test the students' ability to retain the material they completed in the lab. These review sections consist of labeling, fill-in-the-blank, multiple-choice, and sequencing questions. These sheets can be used as graded lab quizzes and/or to check attendance in the lab.

Check Your Understanding tests ask students to use the information they have learned to answer critical thinking questions, often as applied in clinical scenarios. The ability to synthesize and apply knowledge is the desired outcome of any A&P course. These questions check students' deeper understanding by challenging them to provide answers they cannot find verbatim in either the lab manual or the textbook. Check Your Understanding questions have been updated throughout the manual.

Lab Practical Practice Quizzes provide additional opportunities for students to prepare for their lab practical exams. This new feature consists of four multiple-choice quizzes.

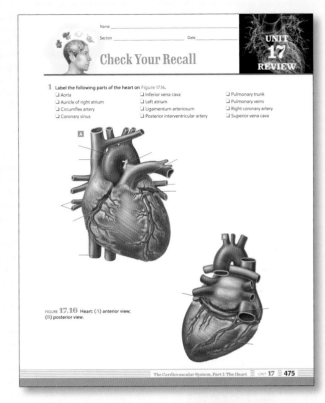

Name _____

Section _____ Date _____

Check Your Recall

UNIT 17 REVIEW

1 Label the following parts of the heart on Figure 17.16.
- ❑ Aorta
- ❑ Auricle of right atrium
- ❑ Circumflex artery
- ❑ Coronary sinus
- ❑ Inferior vena cava
- ❑ Left atrium
- ❑ Ligamentum arteriosum
- ❑ Posterior interventricular artery
- ❑ Pulmonary trunk
- ❑ Pulmonary veins
- ❑ Right coronary artery
- ❑ Superior vena cava

FIGURE **17.16** Heart: (A) anterior view; (B) posterior view.

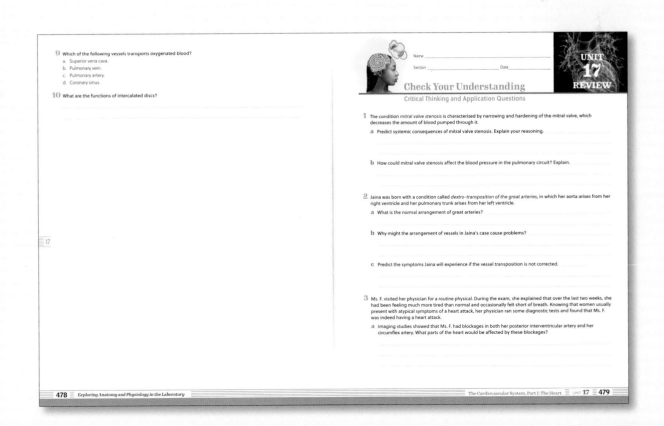

9 Which of the following vessels transports oxygenated blood?
- a. Superior vena cava.
- b. Pulmonary vein.
- c. Pulmonary artery.
- d. Coronary sinus.

10 What are the functions of intercalated discs?

17

Name _____

Section _____ Date _____

Check Your Understanding
Critical Thinking and Application Questions

UNIT 17 REVIEW

1 The condition *mitral valve stenosis* is characterized by narrowing and hardening of the mitral valve, which decreases the amount of blood pumped through it.
- a Predict systemic consequences of mitral valve stenosis. Explain your reasoning.

- b How could mitral valve stenosis affect the blood pressure in the pulmonary circuit? Explain.

2 Jaina was born with a condition called *dextro-transposition of the great arteries*, in which her aorta arises from her right ventricle and her pulmonary trunk arises from her left ventricle.
- a What is the normal arrangement of great arteries?

- b Why might the arrangement of vessels in Jaina's case cause problems?

- c Predict the symptoms Jaina will experience if the vessel transposition is not corrected.

3 Ms. F. visited her physician for a routine physical. During the exam, she explained that over the last two weeks, she had been feeling much more tired than normal and occasionally felt short of breath. Knowing that women usually present with atypical symptoms of a heart attack, her physician ran some diagnostic tests and found that Ms. F. was indeed having a heart attack.
- a Imaging studies showed that Ms. F. had blockages in both her posterior interventricular artery and her circumflex artery. What parts of the heart would be affected by these blockages?

Be Aware

Morton Publishing understands that textbooks are expensive, and the last thing students need is to spend too much for a lab manual. Morton Publishing is committed to providing high-quality products at reasonable prices. It is our sincere hope that *Exploring Anatomy & Physiology in the Laboratory*, 4e, will provide you the tools necessary for a productive and engaging laboratory experience. We welcome all comments and suggestions for future editions of this book. Please feel free to contact us at eapl@morton-pub.com or visit us at morton-pub.com

Be Choosy

MortyPak Options Bundle *Exploring Anatomy & Physiology in the Laboratory*, 4e, with one or more of the following supplemental titles:

- *A Visual Analogy Guide to Human Anatomy*
- *A Visual Analogy Guide to Human Physiology*
- *A Visual Analogy Guide to Human Anatomy and Physiology*
- *A Photographic Atlas for the A&P Laboratory*
- *Mammalian Anatomy: The Cat*
- *A Dissection Guide and Atlas to the Fetal Pig*
- *A Dissection Guide and Atlas to the Mink*
- *A Dissection Guide and Atlas to the Rabbit*
- *A Dissection Guide and Atlas to the Rat*
- *A Photographic Atlas of Histology*
- *Discovering Anatomy: A Guided Examination of the Cadaver*
- *An Illustrated Atlas of the Skeletal Muscles*

Morton CustomLab enables creation of affordable personalized lab manuals and other materials, tailored to the needs of instructors and students. Instructors may remove or combine material from our existing lab manuals and photographic atlases, use photographs and illustrations from our extensive online library, and/or produce original material while utilizing our professional publishing services. Enrollment minimums apply.

Digital Delivery

Top Hat Active Learning Platform Enhance the learning experience with **Top Hat**. This title and others are available on the **Top Hat** active learning platform, which provides the added features of customizing content, embedding video, delivering secure online assessments, managing the classroom, and engaging students with interactive content.

eBooks Access this title and others through our vendor partners: VitalSource, RedShelf, Chegg, and GooglePlay.

Pronunciation Guide

Note: Accented syllables are capitalized; for example, "uh-NĂT-oh-mee and fiz-ee-AHL-oh-jee." (The phonetic symbol Ă [or ă] references the sound the "a" makes in the word "apple.")

abdominal (ab-DAH-mih-nuhl)

abdominis (ab-DAHM-in-iss)

abdominopelvic
(ab-dahm-ih-noh-PEL-vik)

abducens (ab-DOO-senz)

acetabulum (ă-seh-TAB-yoo-lum)

acetylcholine (ah-SEE-til-koh-leen)

acetylcholinesterase
(ah-see-til-kohl-in-ESS-ter-ayz)

acidosis (ă-sih-DOH-sis)

acinar (AY-sin-ahr)

acromial (ah-KROH-mee-uhl)

acromioclavicular
(ah-KROH-mee-oh-klah-VIK-yoo-lur)

acromion (ah-KROH-mee-ahn)

acrosomal (ak-roh-ZOH-muhl)

actin (AK-tin)

adenohypophysis
(ăd-in-oh-hy-PAHF-ih-sis)

adipocytes (ĂD-ih-poh-syt'z)

adipose (Ă-dih-pohs)

adrenal (uh-DREE-nuhl)

adrenocorticotropic
(uh-dree-noh-kohr-tih-koh-TROH-pik)

adventitia (ad-ven-TISH-uh)

afferent (AF-uhr-int)

agglutination (uh-gloo-tin-AY-shun)

agranulocytes (AY-gran-yoo-loh-syt'z)

ala (AY-luh)

alae (AY-lee)

albuginea (al-byoo-JIN-ee-uh)

albumin (al-BYOO-min)

aldosterone (al-DAHS-tur-ohn)

alimentary (al-uh-MEN-tuh-ree)

alkaline (AL-kuh-lyn'e)

alkalosis (al-kuh-LOH-sis)

alleles (uh-LEELZ)

alveolar (al-vee-OH-luhr)

alveoli (al-vee-OH-lye)

amino (uh-MEE-noh)

amnion (AM-nee-ahn)

amphiarthroses
(am-fee-ar-THROH-seez)

amphipathic (am-fih-PATH-ik)

amphiphilic (am-fih-FIL-ik)

ampulla (am-PULL-uh)

amygdala (uh-MIG-duh-luh)

amylase (AM-uh-layz)

anions (AN-aye-ahnz)

antebrachial (an-tee-BRAY-kee-uhl)

antecubital (an-tee-KYOO-bih-tuhl)

anterior (an-TEER-ee-ur)

antidiuretic (an-tee-dy-yoo-RET-ik)

antigens (AN-tih-jenz)

aorta (ay-OHR-tah)

aponeurosis (ap-oh-noo-ROH-sis)

arachnoid mater
(ah-RAK-noyd MAH-tur)

arbor vitae (AHR-bohr VEE-tay)

arcuate (ARK-yoo-it)

areola (aehr-ee-OH-lah)

arrector pili (ah-REK-tohr PIL-aye)

arrhythmia (ay-RITH-mee-uh)

arytenoid (uh-RIT-uh-noyd)

arteriosus (ahr-teer-ee-OH-suhs)

astigmatism (uh-STIG-muh-tiz'm)

atelectasis (ă-tuh-LEK-tuh-sis)

atrioventricular
(ay-tree-oh-ven-TRIK-yoo-lur)

atrium (AY-tree-um)

auricle (OHR-ih-kuhl)

auscultation (ahs-kuhl-TAY-shun)

autosomes (AH-toh-sohmz)

avascular (ay-VASS-kyu-lur)

axillary (AX-il-ehr-ee)

axolemma (ax-oh-LEM-uh)

axon (AX-ahn)

azygos (ay-ZY-guhs)

baroreceptor (BEHR-oh-reh-sep-ter)

basal lamina (BAY-zul LAM-in-uh)

basale (bay-SAY-lee)

basilar (BAY-zih-lur)

basilic (buh-SIL-ik)

basophils (BAY-zoh-filz)

biceps brachii (BY-seps BRAY-kee-aye)

blastocyst (BLAST-oh-sist)

brachial (BRAY-kee-uhl)

brachialis (bray-kee-AL-iss)

brachiocephalic
(bray-kee-oh-seh-FAL-ik)

brachioradialis
(bray-kee-oh-ray-dee-AL-iss)

bradycardia (bray-dih-KAR-dee-uh)

bronchi (BRONG-kye)

bronchial (BRONG-kee-uhl)

bronchioles (BRONG-kee-ohlz)

bronchomediastinal
(brongk-oh-mee-dee-uh-STYN-uhl)

bruits (broo-eez)

buccal (BYOO-kuhl)

buccinator (BUK-sin-ay-tur)

bulbourethral
(bul-boh-yoo-REETH-ruhl)

bursae (BURR-see)

calcaneal (kal-KAY-nee-uhl)

calcaneus (kal-KAYN-ee-uhs)

calcitonin (kal-sih-TOH-nin)

calvaria (kal-VEHR-ee-uh)

calyces (KAY-lih-seez)

calyx (KAY-lix)

canaliculi (kan-ah-LIK-yoo-lee)

canines (KAY-nynz)

capitulum (kah-PIT-yoo-lum)

carbonic anhydrase (kar-BAH-nik
an-HY-dray'z)

cardiac (KAR-dee-ak)

carina (kuh-RY-nuh)

carotid (kuh-RAHT-id)

carpal (KAR-puhl)

carpals (KAR-pulz)

carpi radialis (KARP-aye ray-dee-AL-iss)

caruncle (kar-UN-kuhl)
catalyst (KAT-uh-list)
cations (KAT-aye-ahnz)
cauda equina (KOW-dah eh-KWY-nah)
caudate (KAH-dayt)
cecum (SEE-kum)
celiac (SEE-lee-ak)
centrioles (SIN-tree-ohlz)
centromere (SIN-troh-meer)
centrosome (SIN-troh-sohm)
cephalic (sef-AL-ik)
cerebellum (sehr-eh-BELL-um)
cerebrospinal (seh-ree-broh-SPY-nuhl)
cerebrum (seh-REE-brum)
cervical (SUR-vih-kuhl)
cervicis (SUR-vih-sis)
chiasma (ky-AZ-mah)
chiasmata (ky-az-MAH-tah)
chondrocytes (KAHN-droh-syt'z)
chordae tendineae
    (KOHR-dee tin-din-EE-ee)
chorion (KOHR-ee-ahn)
chorionic villi
    (KOHR-ee-ahn-ik VILL-aye)
choroid (KOHR-oyd)
chromatids (KROH-muh-tidz)
chromatin (KROH-mah-tin)
chromosomes (KROH-moh-sohmz)
chylomicrons (ky-loh-MY-krahnz)
chyme (KY'M)
cilia (SIL-ee-uh)
ciliary body (SILL-ee-ehr-ee)
circumflex (SIR-kum-flex)
cisterna chyli (sis-TUR-nuh KY-lee)
cisternae (sis-TUR-nee)
clitoris (KLIT-uhr-iss)
coccyx (KAHX-iks)
cochlea (KOHK-lee-ah)
collagen (KAHL-eh-jen)
colliculi (kahl-IK-yoo-lye)
colloid (KAHL-oyd)
conceptus (kuhn-SEPT-uhs)
conchae (KAHN-kee)
conjunctiva (kahn-junk-TY-vah)
conus medullaris
    (KOHN-uhs med-yoo-LEHR-uhs)
coracohumeral
    (kohr'-uh-koh-HYOO-muhr-uhl)
coracoid (KOHR-ah-koyd)
cornea (KOHR-nee-ah)

corniculate (kor-NIK-yoo-lit)
coronal (koh-ROH-nuhl)
coronary (KOHR-oh-nehr-ee)
corpora cavernosa
    (kohr-POHR-uh kă-ver-NOH-suh)
corpus callosum
    (KOHR-puhs kal-OH-sum)
corpuscle (KOHR-puhs-uhl)
corpuscles (KOHR-puhs-uhlz)
corpus luteum
    (KOHR-puhs LOO-tee-um)
corpus spongiosum
    (KOHR-puhs spun-jee-OH-sum)
cortisol (KOHR-tih-sahl)
cranial (KRAY-nee-uhl)
cremaster (kreh-MASS-ter)
cribriform (KRIB-rih-form)
cricoid (KRY-koyd)
cricothyroid (kry-koh-THY-royd)
cricothyroidotomy
    (kry-koh-thy-royd-AH-toh-mee)
crista galli (KRIS-tah GAL-ee)
cruciate (KROO-shee-iht)
crural (KROO-ruhl)
cubital (KYOO-bit-uhl)
cuneiform (kyoo-NEE-ih-form)
cystic (SIS-tik)
cytokines (SY-toh-kyn'z)
cytokinesis (sy-toh-kin-EE-sis)
cytology (sy-TAHL-oh-gee)
cytoplasm (SY-toh-plaz-m)
cytosol (SY-toh-sahl)
deciduous (dih-SIJ-oo-uhs)
dendrites (DEN-dryt'z)
denticulate (den-TIK-yoo-lit)
deoxyribonucleic acid
    (dee-ahk-see-ry-boh-noo-KLAY-ik)
deoxyribose (dee'-ahks-ee-RY-bohs)
detrusor (dee-TROO-sur)
diaphragm (DY-uh-fram)
diaphysis (dy-Ă-fih-sis)
diarthroses (dy-ar-THROH-seez)
diastole (dy-Ă-stoh-lee)
diastolic (dy-uh-STAHL-ik)
diencephalon (dy-en-SEF-ah-lahn)
digital (DIJ-it-uhl)
diploid (DIP-loyd)
disaccharide (dy-SAK-uh-ry'd)
dorsalis pedis (dohr-SAL-iss PEE-diss)

ductus deferens
    (DUHK-tuhs DEF-er-ahnz)
duodenum (doo-AH-den-um)
dura mater (DOO-rah MAH-tur)
dynamometer (dy-nuh-MAH-muh-tur)
dysrhythmia (dis-RITH-mee-uh)
efferent (EF-uhr-int)
embryo (IHM-bree-oh)
embryogenesis
    (ihm-bree-oh-JEN-ih-sis)
endocardium (in-doh-KAR-dee-um)
endolymph (IN-doh-limf)
endometrium (in-doh-MEE-tree-um)
endomysium (in-doh-MY-see-um)
endoneurium (in-doh-NOOR-ee-um)
endoplasmic reticulum
    (in-doh-PLAZ-mik reh-TIK-yoo-lum)
endosteum (in-DAH-stee-um)
endotracheal (in-doh-TRAY-kee-uhl)
enterocytes (IN-tuh-roh-syt'z)
eosinophils (ee-oh-SIN-oh-filz)
ependymal (eh-PEN-dih-muhl)
epicardium (ep-ih-KAR-dee-um)
epicondyles (ep-ih-KAHN-dyl'z)
epicranius (eh-pih-KRAY-nee-uhs)
epidermis (ep-ih-DER-miss)
epididymis (ep-ih-DID-ih-miss)
epidural (ep-ih-DOO-ruhl)
epiglottis (ep-ih-GLAH-tiss)
epimysium (ep-ih-MY-see-um)
epineurium (ep-ih-NOOR-ee-um)
epiphyseal (eh-PIF-ih-seel)
epiphysis (eh-PIF-ih-sis)
epiploic (ep-ih-PLOH-ik)
epithalamus (ep-ih-THAL-ih-muhs)
epithelial (ep-ih-THEE-lee-uhl)
eponychium (ep-oh-NIK-ee-um)
erector spinae (eh-REK-tohr SPY-nee)
erythrocytes (eh-RITH-roh-syt'z)
esophagus (eh-SAHF-uh-guhs)
facets (fuh-SETZ)
falciform (FALL-sih-form)
falx cerebelli (FALS sehr-eh-BELL-ee)
falx cerebri (FALS seh-REE-bree)
fascia (FASH-uh)
fascicles (FASS-ih-kullz)
fasciculata (fah-SIK-yoo-lah-tah)
femoral (FEM-oh-ruhl)
fibroblasts (FY-broh-blastz)

fibula (FIB-yoo-luh)

fibularis (fib-yoo-LEHR-iss)

filum terminale
(FY-lum ter-mee-NAL-ay)

fimbriae (FIM-bree-ay)

flagella (flah-JEL-uh)

fossa ovalis (FAHS-uh oh-VAL-is)

fovea capitis (FOH-vee-uh CAP-ih-tiss)

fovea centralis
(FOH-vee-uh sin-TRAL-iss)

frontal (FRUHN-tuhl)

frontalis (frun-TAL-iss)

funiculi (fun-IK-yoo-lye)

gametes (GAM-eetz)

gametogenesis
(gah-meet-oh-JEN-uh-sis)

ganglion (GAYN-glee-ahn)

gastrocnemius
(gas-trahk-NEE-mee-uhs)

gastroesophageal
(gas-troh-eh-sahf-uh-JEE-uhl)

genotype (JEE-noh-type)

gingivae (JIN-jih-vay)

glenohumeral
(glen'-oh-HYOO-mur-uhl)

glenoid labrum (GLEN-oyd LAY-brum)

glomerulosa (gloh-mehr-yoo-LOH-sah)

glomerulus (gloh-MEHR-yoo-luhs)

glossopharyngeal
(glah-soh-fehr-IN-jee-uhl)

glucagon (GLOO-kah-gahn)

glucocorticoids
(gloo-koh-KORT-ih-koydz)

gluteal (GLOO-tee-uhl)

gluteus (GLOO-tee-uhs)

glycerol (GLISS-er-ahl)

glycogen (GLY-koh-jen)

glycoproteins (GLY-koh-proh-teenz)

Golgi (GOHL-jee)

gomphosis (gahm-FOH-sis)

gonadocorticoids
(goh-nad-oh-KORT-ih-koydz)

gonads (GOH-nadz)

gracilis (gruh-SILL-iss)

granulocytes (GRAN-yoo-loh-syt'z)

granulosum (gran-yoo-LOH-sum)

gustation (guh-STAY-shun)

gustatory (GUHS-tuh-tohr-ee)

gyri (JY-ree)

haploid (HAP-loyd)

haustra (HAH-struh)

hematocrit (heh-MĂ-toh-krit)

hemoglobin (HEE-moh-glohb-in)

hemolysis (heem-AH-luh-sis)

hepatopancreatic ampulla (heh-PĂ-
toh-payn-kree-at-ik am-POOL-ah)

heterozygous (het-er-oh-ZY-guhs)

hilum (HY-lum)

hippocampus (hip-poh-CAM-pus)

homologous (huh-MAH-luh-guhs)

homozygous (hoh-moh-ZY-guhs)

humerus (HYOO-mur-uhs)

hyaline (HY-ah-lin)

hydrophilic (hy-droh-FIL-ik)

hydrophobic (hy-droh-FOH-bik)

hyoid (hy-OYD)

hypertonic (hy-per-TAHN-ik)

hypodermis (hy-poh-DER-miss)

hypoglossal (hy-poh-GLAHS-uhl)

hyponychium (hy-poh-NIK-ee-um)

hypophyseal (hy-PAH-fih-see-uhl)

hypothalamus (hy-poh-THAL-uh-muhs)

hypotonic (hy-poh-TAHN-ik)

ileocecal (ill-ee-oh-SEE-kuhl)

ileum (ILL-ee-um)

iliac (ILL-ee-ak)

iliacus (ill-ee-AK-uhs)

iliocostalis (ill-ee-oh-kahst-AL-iss)

iliohypogastric
(ill-ee-oh-hy-poh-GAS-trik)

ilioinguinal (ill-ee-oh-IN-gwin-uhl)

iliopsoas (ill-ee-oh-SOH-uhs)

ilium (ILL-ee-um)

incus (ING-kuhs)

infraspinatus (in-frah-spy-NAY-tuhs)

infundibulum (in-fun-DIB-yoo-lum)

inguinal (IN-gwin-uhl)

integument (in-TEG-yoo-ment)

integumentary
(in-teg´-yoo-MEN-tuh-ree)

interatrial (in-ter-AY-tree-uhl)

intercalated (in-TER-kuh-lay-t'd)

interferons (in-ter-FEER-ahnz)

intertrochanteric
(in-ter-troh-kan-TEHR-ik)

intertubercular sulcus
(in-ter-too-BUR-kyoo-lur SUL-kuhs)

intraperitoneal
(in-trah-pehr-ih-toh-NEE-uhl)

ions (AYE-ahnz)

iris (AYE-riss)

ischium (ISS-kee-um)

islets (AYE-lets)

isomers (AYE-soh-merz)

isotonic (aye-soh-TAHN-ik)

isthmus (ISS-th-muhs)

jejunum (jeh-JOO-num)

jugular (JUG-yoo-lur)

juxtaglomerular
(jux-tah-gloh-MEHR-yoo-lur)

keratin (KEHR-ah-tin)

keratinocyte (kehr-ah-TIN-oh-sy't)

keratinocytes (kehr-ah-TIN-oh-syt'z)

Korotkoff (kuh-RAHT-koff)

labia (LAY-bee-ah)

labial frenulum
(LAY-bee-uhl FREN-yoo-lum)

lacerum (LAS-er-um)

lacrimal (LAK-ruh-muhl)

lacteal (lak-TEEL)

lacunae (lah-KOO-nee)

lambdoid (LAM-doyd)

lamellae (lah-MELL-ee)

laminae (LAM-ih-nee)

laryngopharynx
(lah-ring-oh-FEHR-inks)

larynx (LEHR-inks)

lateral (LAT-er-uhl)

latissimus dorsi
(lah-TISS-ih-muhs DOHR-sye)

leukocytes (LOO-koh-syt'z)

ligamentum arteriosum (lig-uh-MEN-
tum ahr-teer-ee-OH-sum)

linea aspera (LIN-ee-ah ASS-per-ah)

lingual (LING-yoo-uhl)

lipase (LYE-payz)

lipids (LIP-idz)

longissimus (lahn-JISS-ih-muhs)

lucidum (LOO-sid-um)

lumbar (LUHM-bahr)

lunula (LOON-yoo-luh)

luteinizing (LOO-tee-in-aye-zing)

lymph (LIMF)

lymphatic (limf-Ă-tik)

lymphocytes (LIMF-oh-syt'z)

lysosomes (LY-soh-zohmz)

macrophages (MAK-roh-feyj-uhz)

macula densa (MAK-yoo-lah DEN-sah)

macula lutea
(MAK-yoo-lah LOO-tee-ah)

malleolus (mal-ee-OH-luhs)

malleus (MAL-ee-uhs)

mammary (MAM-uh-ree)

manual (MAN-yoo-uhl)

manubrium (mah-NOO-bree-um)

masseter (MASS-uh-tur)

maxillae (mak-SILL-ee)

mechanoreceptors
(mek-uh-noh-reh-SEP-terz)

medial (MEE-dee-uhl)

mediastinum (mee-dee-uh-STY-num)

medius (MEE-dee-uhs)

medulla (meh-DOOL-uh)

medulla oblongata
(meh-DOOL-uh ahb-lahn-GAH-tuh)

medullary (MED-yoo-lehr-ee)

meiosis (my-OH-sis)

melanin (MEL-uh-nin)

melanocytes (mel-AN-oh-syt'z)

melatonin (mel-uh-TOH-nin)

meninges (meh-NIN-jeez)

menisci (men-ISS-kee)

mental (MEN-tuhl)

mesenchyme (MEZ-en-ky'm)

mesenteric (mez-en-TEHR-ik)

mesentery (MEZ-en-tehr-ee)

metatarsals (met-uh-TAHR-sulz)

metopic (met-AHP-ik)

micelles (my-SELLZ)

microglial (my-kroh-GLEE-uhl)

microvilli (my-kroh-VIL-aye)

micturition (mik-choo-RISH-un)

midsagittal (mid-SAJ-ih-tuhl)

mineralocorticoids
(min-er-al-oh-KORT-ih-koydz)

mitochondria (my-toh-KAHN-dree-ah)

mitosis (my-TOH-sis)

mitral (MY-truhl)

molecule (MAHL-eh-kyool)

monocytes (MAHN-oh-syt'z)

monomer (MAHN-oh-mer)

monosaccaride
(mahn'-oh-SAK-uh-ry'd)

mons pubis (MAHNS PYOO-biss)

morula (MOHR-yoo-luh)

musculocutaneous
(musk-yoo-loh-kyoo-TAY-nee-uhs)

myelin (MY-lin)

myocardium (my-oh-KAR-dee-um)

myocytes (MY-oh-syt'z)

myofibrils (my-oh-FY-brillz)

myometrium (my-oh-MEE-tree-um)

myosin (MY-oh-sin)

nasal (NAY-zuhl)

nasopharynx (nayz-oh-FEHR-inks)

nephrons (NEF-rahns)

neurilemma (noor-ih-LEM-uh)

neuroglial (noor-oh-GLEE-uhl)

neurohypophysis
(noor-oh-hy-PAHF-ih-sis)

neurolemmocytes
(noor-oh-LEM-oh-syt'z)

neurons (NOOR-ahnz)

neutrons (NOO-trahnz)

neutrophils (NOO-troh-filz)

nuchal (NOO-kuhl)

nucleolus (noo-klee-OH-luhs)

nucleotides (NOO-klee-oh-tyd'z)

nucleus (NOO-klee-uhs)

obturator (AHB-too-ray-tur)

occipital (ahk-SIP-ih-tuhl)

occipitalis (ahk-sip-ih-TAL-iss)

ocular (AHK-yoo-lur)

oculomotor (ahk-yoo-loh-MOH-tohr)

olecranon (oh-LEK-ruh-nahn)

olfactory (ohl-FAK-toh-ree)

oligodendrocytes
(oh-lig-oh-DEN-droh-syt'z)

omentum (oh-MEN-tum)

oocytes (OH-oh-syt'z)

oogenesis (oh-oh-JEN-ih-sis)

oogonia (oh-oh-GOHN-ee-uh)

ophthalmic (ahf-THAL-mik)

optic (AHP-tik)

oral (OH-ruhl)

orbicularis oculi
(ohr-bik-yoo-LEHR-iss AHK-yoo-lye)

orbital (OHR-bit-uhl)

organelles (ohr-gan-ELLZ)

oris (OHR-iss)

oropharynx (ohr-oh-FEHR-inks)

osmosis (oz-MOH-sis)

osseous (AHS-see-uhs)

ossicles (AH-sih-kullz)

osteoblasts (AH-stee-oh-blasts)

osteoclasts (AH-stee-oh-klasts)

osteocytes (AHS-tee-oh-syt'z)

osteogenic (ah-stee-oh-JEN-ik)

osteons (AHS-tee-ahnz)

otic (OH-tik)

ovale (oh-VAL-ay)

oxytocin (ahks-ee-TOH-sin)

palate (PAL-it)

palatine (PAL-uh-ty'n)

palmar (PAHL-mur)

palpebrae (pal-PEE-bree)

pancreas (PAYN-kree-uhs)

papillae (pah-PILL-ee)

parasagittal (pehr-uh-SAJ-ih-tuhl)

parietal (puh-RY-ih-tuhl)

parotid (puh-RAHT-id)

patella (puh-TEL-uh)

patellar (puh-TEL-ur)

pectinate (PEK-tin-et)

pectineus (pek-TIN-ee-uhs)

pectoral (pek-TOHR-uhl)

pectoralis (PEK-tohr-AL-iss)

pedal (PEE-duhl)

pedicles (PED-ih-kullz)

pelvic (PEL-vik)

pericardial (pehr-ee-KAR-dee-uhl)

pericardium (pehr-ee-KAR-dee-um)

perilymph (PEHR-ee-limf)

perimetrium (pehr-ee-MEE-tree-um)

perimysium (pehr-ih-MY-see-um)

perineurium (pehr-ih-NOOR-ee-um)

periodontal (pehr-ee-oh-DAHN-tuhl)

periosteum (pehr-ee-AH-stee-um)

peristalsis (pehr-ih-STAHL-sis)

peritoneal (pehr-ih-toh-NEE-uhl)

peroxisomes (per-AHKS-ih-zohmz)

phagocytes (FAY-go-syt'z)

phalanges (fuh-LAN-jeez)

pharyngotympanic
(fah-ring-oh-tim-PAN-ik)

pharynx (FEHR-inks)

phenotype (FEE-noh-type)

phosphate (FAHS-fayt)

phospholipid (FAHS-foh-lip-id)

phospholipids (fahs-foh-LIP-idz)

photons (FOH-tahns)

phrenic (FREN-ik)

pia mater (PEE-ah MAH-tur)

pineal (pin-EE-uhl)

pituitary (pih-TOO-ih-tehr-ee)

placenta (plah-SIN-tuh)

plantar (PLAN-tahr)

platelets (PLAYT-letz)

platysma (plah-TIZ-muh)

pleural (PLOO-ruhl)

pneumothorax (noo-moh-THOHR-ax)

podocytes (POH-doh-syt'z)

polymer (PAHL-ih-mer)

polysaccharide (pahl-ee-SAK-uh-ry'd)

pons (PAHNZ)

popliteal (pahp-lih-TEE-uhl)

porta hepatis (POHR-tuh heh-PĂ-tis)

prostate (PRAH-stayt)

proximal (PRAHKS-ih-muhl)

pseudostratified (SOO-doh-strat-ih-fy'd)

pseudounipolar
    (soo-doh-yoo-nih-POHL-uhr)

psoas (SOH-uhs)

pterygoid (TEHR-ih-goyd)

pubic (PYOO-bik)

pubis (PYOO-bis)

pudendal (poo-DEN-duhl)

pulmonary (PUL-muh-nehr-ee)

pulmonary ventilation
    (PUL-muh-nehr-ee)

purines (PYOOR-eenz)

Purkinje (pur-KIN-jee)

pylorus (py-LOHR-uhs)

pyrimidines (per-IM-ih-deenz)

pyrogens (PY-roh-jenz)

radius (RAY-dee-uhs)

rami (RAY-mee)

Ranvier (rahn-vee-ay)

renal (REE-nuhl)

renal fascia (REE-nuhl FASH-uh)

rete testis (REE-tee TES-tis)

reticular (reh-TIK-yoo-luhr)

retina (RET-in-ah)

retroperitoneal
    (reh-troh-pehr-ih-toh-NEE-uhl)

ribose (RY-bohs)

ribosomes (RY-boh-zohmz)

Rinne (rinn-ay)

risorius (ry-ZOHR-ee-uhs)

rugae (ROO-ghee)

saccule (SAK-yool)

sacroiliac (say-kroh-ILL-ee-ak)

sacrum (SAY-krum)

sagittal (SAJ-ih-tuhl)

saltatory (sahl-tuh-TOHR-ee)

saphenous (SAF-en-uhs)

sarcolemma (sar-koh-LEM-uh)

sarcomere (SAR-koh-meer)

sarcoplasm (SAR-koh-plazm)

sarcoplasmic reticulum
    (sar-koh-PLAZ-mik reh-TIK-yoo-lum)

sartorius (sar-TOHR-ee-uhs)

scapula (SKAP-yoo-luh)

scapular (SKAP-yoo-lur)

sciatic (sy-Ă-tik)

sclera (SKLEHR-ah)

sebaceous (seh-BAY-shuhs)

sebum (SEE-bum)

sella turcica (SELL-uh TUR-sih-kuh)

semilunar (sem-ee-LOON-uhr)

semimembranosus
    (sem-aye-mem-brah-NOH-suhs)

seminiferous (sem-ih-NIF-er-uhs)

semitendinosus
    (sem-aye-ten-din-OH-suhs)

seromucous (seer-oh-MYOO-kuhs)

serous (SEER-uhs)

serratus (ser-AY-tuhs)

sinoatrial (sy-noh-AY-tree-uhl)

soleus (SOHL-ee-uhs)

spermatogenesis
    (sper-mat-oh-JEN-ih-sis)

spermatogonia
    (sper-mat-oh-GOH-nee-ah)

sphenoid (SFEE-noyd)

sphygmomanometer
    (sfig-moh-muh-NAH-muh-tur)

spinalis (spy-NAL-iss)

spinosum (spin-OH-sum)

spirometer (spih-RAH-meh-ter)

splenic (SPLEN-ik)

splenius capitis
    (SPLEN-ee-uhs CAP-ih-tiss)

squamous (SKWAY-muhs)

stapes (STAY-peez)

stenosis (sten-OH-sis)

stereocilia (stehr-ee-oh-SILL-ee-uh)

sternal (STUR-nuhl)

sternocleidomastoid (stern-oh-kly-doh-
    MASS-toy'd)

stethoscope (STETH-oh-skohp)

stratified (STRAT-ih-fy'd)

stratum corneum
    (STRAT-um KOHR-nee-um)

striated (STRY-ayt-ed)

styloid (STY-loyd)

subclavian (sub-KLAY-vee-in)

sublingual (sub-LING-gwuhl)

subscapularis (sub-skap-yoo-LEHR-uhs)

sulci (SUL-kee)

supracondylar (soo-prah-KAHN-duh-lar)

suprarenal (soo-prah-REE-nuhl)

supraspinatus (soo-prah-spy-NAY-tuhs)

sural (SOO-ruhl)

sutural (SOO-tchur-uhl)

sutures (SOO-tchurz)

symphysis (SIM-fih-sis)

synapse (SIN-ăpz)

synapsis (sin-ĂP-sis)

synarthroses (sin-ar-THROH-seez)

synchondroses (sin-khan-DROH-seez)

syndesmoses (sin-dez-MOH-seez)

synovial (sih-NOH-vee-uhl)

systole (SIS-toh-lee)

systolic (sis-TAHL-ik)

tachycardia (tak-ih-KAR-dee-uh)

taeniae coli (TEE-nee-ee KOHL-aye)

talus (TAY-luhs)

tarsal (TAR-suhl)

tarsals (TAHR-sulz)

telodendria (tee-loh-DEN-dree-uh)

telophase (TEL-oh-fayz)

temporalis (tem-pur-AL-iss)

teres (TEHR-eez)

thalamus (THAL-uh-muhs)

thoracic (thoh-RĂ-sik)

thymopoietin (thy-moh-POY-eh-tin)

thyroid (THY-royd)

tibia (TIB-ee-uh)

tibialis (tib-ee-AL-is)

titin (TY-tin)

trabeculae (trah-BEK-yoo-lee)

trabeculae carneae
    (trah-BEK-yoo-lee kar-NEE-ee)

trachea (TRAY-kee-uh)

trapezius (trah-PEE-zee-uhs)

trigeminal (try-JEM-in-uhl)

triglycerides (try-GLISS-er-aye'dz)

trigone (TRY-gohn)

triiodothyronine
    (try-aye-oh-doh-THY-roh-neen)

trochanter (TROH-kan-tur)

trochlea (TROH-klee-uh)

trochlear (TROH-klee-ur)

trophoblast (TROHF-oh-blast)

tropomyosin (trohp-oh-MY-oh-sin)

troponin (TROH-poh-nin)

tympanic (tim-PAN-ik)

ulnaris (uhl-NEHR-iss)

umbilical (um-BIL-ih-kuhl)

ureteral (yoo-REE-ter-uhl)

ureters (YOOR-eh-terz)

urethra (yoo-REETH-ruh)

uterosacral (yoo-ter-oh-SAY-kruhl)

uterus (YOO-ter-uhs)

utricle (YOO-trih-kuhl)

uvea (YOO-vee-uh)

uvula (YOO-vyoo-luh)

vagus (VAY-guhs)

vena cava (VEE-nah KAY-vah)

venosus (veh-NOH-suhs)

vermis (VER-miss)

vertebral (vur-TEE-bruhl)

vestibulocochlear
    (ves-tib-yoo-loh-KOHK-lee-ur)

villi (VILL-aye)

visceral (VISS-er-uhl)

vitreous (VIT-ree-uhs)

vomer (VOH-muhr)

xiphoid (ZY-foyd)

zygomatic (zy-goh-MAT-ik)

zygomaticus (zy-goh-MAT-ih-kuhs)

zygote (ZY-goh't)

Contents

Introduction to Anatomical Terms

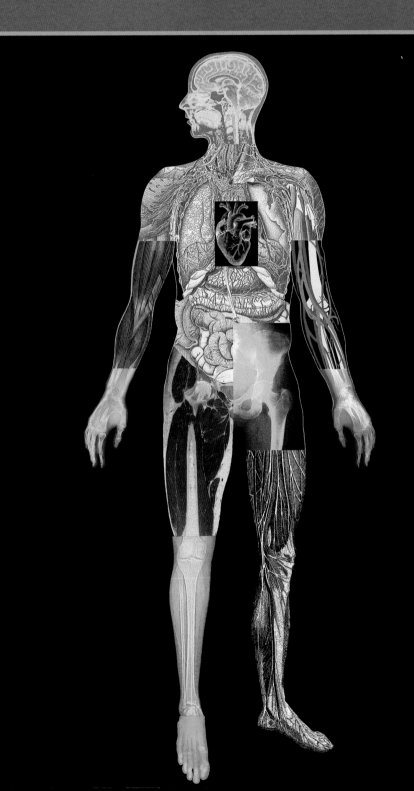

When you have completed this unit, you should be able to:

1 Describe the scientific method.

2 Demonstrate and describe anatomical position.

3 Apply directional terms to descriptions of body parts.

4 Use regional terms to describe locations on the body.

5 Locate and describe the divisions of the major body cavities and the membranes lining each cavity.

6 Demonstrate and describe anatomical planes of section.

7 Identify the organ systems, their functions, and the major organs in each system.

PRE-LAB EXERCISES

Complete the following exercises prior to coming to lab, using your lab manual and textbook for reference.

PRE-LAB

1-1 Key Terms

You should be familiar with the following terms before coming to lab.

Term	Definition
Directional Terms	
Anterior	
Posterior	
Superior	
Inferior	
Proximal	
Distal	
Medial	
Lateral	
Superficial	
Deep	
Body Cavities and Membranes	
Cranial cavity	
Vertebral cavity	
Thoracic cavity	
Abdominopelvic cavity	
Serous membrane (parietal and visceral layers)	
Planes of Section	
Midsagittal plane	
Parasagittal plane	
Frontal (coronal) plane	
Transverse plane	

Body Cavities

Color the body cavities in Figure 1.1, and label them with the terms from Exercise 1-5 (p. 16). Use Exercise 1-4 in this unit and your text for reference.

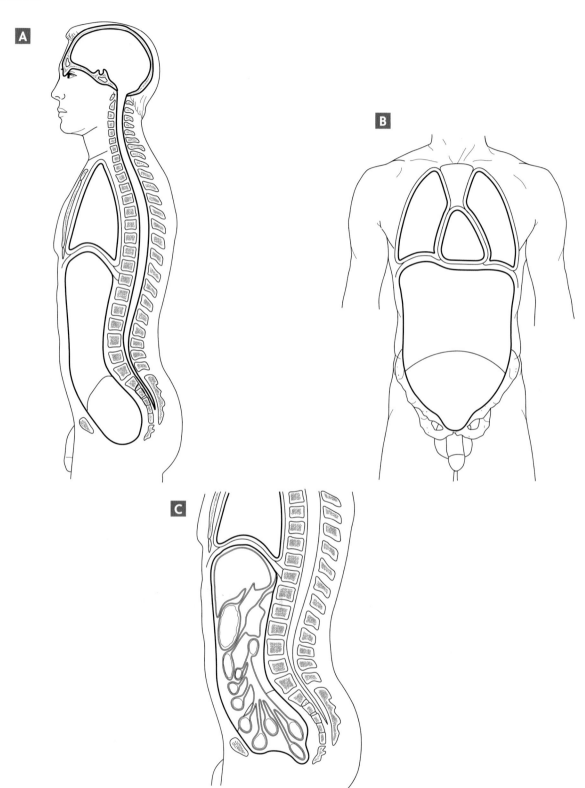

FIGURE **1.1** Body cavities: (**A**) posterior body cavity; (**B**) anterior body cavity; (**C**) peritoneal cavity (subdivision of abdominopelvic cavity).

The bullet entered the right posterior scapular region, 3 centimeters (cm)
lateral to the vertebral region, 4 cm inferior to the cervical region,
and penetrated deep to the muscle and bone,
but superficial to the lung and parietal pleura . . .

MRI, x-ray, dissection, and artwork of a human body.

Would you believe that by the end of this unit, you'll be able to translate the above sentence and also locate the hypothetical wound? Unit 1 introduces you to the world of **anatomy** and **physiology,** or A&P, which is the study and science of the structure and function of the human body. We start this unit with an introduction to science and the *scientific method.* We then move on to the language of A&P. Like learning any new language, this may seem overwhelming at first. The key to success is repetition and application: The more you use the terms, the easier it will be for them to become part of your normal vocabulary.

From terminology, we move on to the organization of the internal body into spaces called **body cavities,** and to how we can examine the body's cavities and organs with specific cuts known as **anatomical sections.** Finally, we look at how the body's organs are combined into functional groups called **organ systems.** When you have completed this unit, return to the opening statement, and challenge yourself to use your new knowledge of anatomical terms, body cavities, and organs to locate the precise position of the bullet wound on an anatomical model.

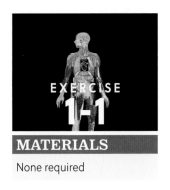

EXERCISE
1-1

MATERIALS

None required

The Scientific Method

We tend to treat the word "science" as a noun, but, in practice, **science** is actually best viewed as a verb—the *process* we use to gain knowledge. The process of science occurs through a systematic series of steps collectively known as the **scientific method.** The scientific method has seven steps:

1. **Make observations.** We observe the world around us all the time and plan our lives based on those observations. When you observe there are dark clouds and it's thundering, you know rain is usually approaching and you don't plan outdoor activities. Similarly, if you observe that classmates who regularly attend class make higher grades, you are more likely to attend class. The scientific method starts with observations like these. From these observations, we can make predictions that we can test in the next steps.

2. **Do research.** Before moving on to the next step, background research is needed to see whether your observation already has been explored. Say you're curious about the correlation between class attendance and grades. Background research could let you know that many studies have found that better attendance is correlated with better grades. This background research wouldn't preclude you from further testing and observing this phenomenon, but it gives you a good place to start.

3. **Develop a hypothesis.** Our observations can be used to develop a **hypothesis,** which is a statement about how we think the world works. It's important to note that a hypothesis *must* be testable—a hypothesis that is not testable is little more than a guess. What's more, the best hypotheses are testable under multiple conditions. If you hypothesize that class attendance and grades are correlated, you could test this with different student populations, different class sizes, and different teaching styles.

4. **Perform an experiment.** The next step in the scientific method is to design an experiment, which is a carefully controlled manipulation of certain natural variables. In this sense, the term **variable** refers to factors that might change during an experiment. If you are studying class attendance and grades, variables may include the students' ages; the students' educational backgrounds; and the format of the courses. In a **controlled experiment,** the researcher controls all possible variables so that only one—the *independent variable*—changes and is tested. To control your experiment, you could ensure that all students were in a similar age range; that all students had a similar educational background; and that all students were taking the same type of course. Many experiments we do in this manual use a scientific **control,** which is a sample that doesn't include the variable being tested.

   A key point in experimental design is that you should aim to *falsify* your hypothesis—you should aim to prove yourself *wrong,* not prove yourself right. This means that at least one of the possible outcomes of the experiment could demonstrate the hypothesis is incorrect.

5. **Analyze the experimental data.** After you have performed your experiment, you must analyze the data you collected and check your experiment for possible flaws that could have affected your data. At this time, you compare the outcome to your hypothesis. If the evidence falsified the hypothesis, you could either reject the hypothesis, try to design a new, better experiment to test it, or modify the hypothesis. If you failed to falsify your hypothesis, you have some evidence that it's likely to be correct. Note here that your experiment won't have *proved* your hypothesis correct or incorrect. A single experiment can provide good evidence that something is likely to be true or false, but it cannot definitively prove something.

6. **Publish conclusions.** The field of science relies on scientists sharing data and findings—this is crucial for Step 2 of the scientific method. If your experiment provided good evidence that your hypothesis was correct, it's important to share these data. However, it's equally important to share the data if your experiment provided evidence that your hypothesis was false. All newly gathered information is valuable and adds to the general body of knowledge.

7. **Repeat the experiment.** A single experiment is a good first step, but it's only a first step. For any hypothesis to gain credibility—or to be fully debunked—the results must be repeated by other scientists. Scientists may repeat the experiment exactly or they may try to improve on the initial study. In this way, experiments that lead to flawed results are eventually corrected. At this stage, scientists often debate and argue over their findings. This is not only expected, but encouraged. It's only through this process of ongoing debate and experimentation that we can have good confidence in our conclusions.

    The importance of repeatability cannot be understated. History is full of hypotheses that were supported by the results of an initial experiment but that ultimately failed the test of repeatability. It's only after many scientists have failed to falsify a hypothesis that it will gain general acceptance.

After a hypothesis has gained a significant amount of experimental evidence demonstrating its truth, it may become a theory. Many people use the word theory to mean an educated guess or simple speculation. But to scientists, a **theory** is a hypothesis that has been repeatedly tested over time and that explains a wide range of scientific findings. Calling a hypothesis a theory is the highest "promotion"—or the biggest endorsement from the overall scientific community—that a hypothesis can receive.

It's important to remember in our study of science that hypotheses and even theories may be modified. Science as a process is ongoing, and new and better information may be discovered. This is part of the beauty of science: It's an inherently self-correcting process. The answer to an incorrect hypothesis isn't a distrust of science—it's more science, as the process allows for the correction of these mistakes.

---

1 PROCEDURE

Designing an Experiment

Let's put what we just learned into practice and design an experiment based on the following observation: *People develop a fever when they have a bacterial infection.*

1 First, start with some background research. Use your textbook to discover how a fever develops. Record relevant details in the space provided.

2 Develop a hypothesis to explain the observation. Ensure your hypothesis is testable and falsifiable.

3 Design an experiment to test your hypothesis. Be sure your experiment can falsify your hypothesis.

4 Suppose you perform the experiment you designed.

a If you analyze your data and they confirm your hypothesis, does this "prove" it is correct? Why or why not?

b If your data support your hypothesis, what should be your next steps?

c If your experiment falsifies your hypothesis, what should be your next steps?

d What role will other scientists play in testing your hypothesis?

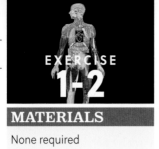

MATERIALS

None required

Anatomical Position

In the study of the human body, most specimens are presented in a standard position called **anatomical position**. In anatomical position, shown in Figure 1.2, the body is presented facing forward, with the toes pointing forward, the feet shoulder-width apart, and the palms facing forward. This presentation of the human body creates a standard point of reference that facilitates communication among scientists and healthcare professionals.

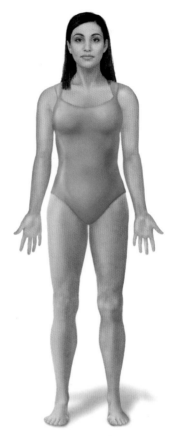

FIGURE **1.2** Woman standing in anatomical position.

1 PROCEDURE

Demonstrating Anatomical Position

Have your lab partner stand in a normal, relaxed way, and then adjust your partner's position so it matches anatomical position. When you have completed this procedure, answer Check Your Understanding Question 1 (p. 31).

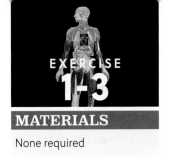

EXERCISE 1-3

MATERIALS

None required

Directional Terms

Another strategy that makes communication easier and less prone to errors is to use **directional terms** to define the location of body parts and body markings. For example, when describing a wound on the chest, we could say either of the following:

- The wound is near the middle and top of the chest; or
- The wound is on the right *anterior* thoracic region, 4 cm *lateral* to the sternum, and 3 cm *inferior* to the acromial region.

The second option is precise and allows the reader to pinpoint the wound's exact location. Remember that these descriptions are referring to a body in anatomical position.

Most directional terms are arranged into pairs of opposite directions. Some of the common pairs you'll use in this course are illustrated in Figure 1.3, and include the following:

- **Anterior/Posterior.** The term **anterior** (an-TEER-ee-ur; *ante-* = "before"), also known as **ventral,** refers to the front of the body or of a body part. For example, we could say that the nose is on the anterior side of the body, or we may describe the surface of a bone that faces the front of the body as its *anterior surface*. However, we may also use the term anterior to describe a structure whose anatomical course takes it toward the front of the body. For example, branches of spinal nerves called *anterior rami* (RAY-mee; *ramus* = "branch") are named this way because they travel toward the anterior side of the body. The opposite term of anterior/ventral is **posterior/dorsal** (*post-* = "after"). Just as with the term anterior, the term posterior can have two meanings. It may refer to the back side of the body or of a body part, or to a structure that travels toward the back side of the body (such as the *posterior rami*).

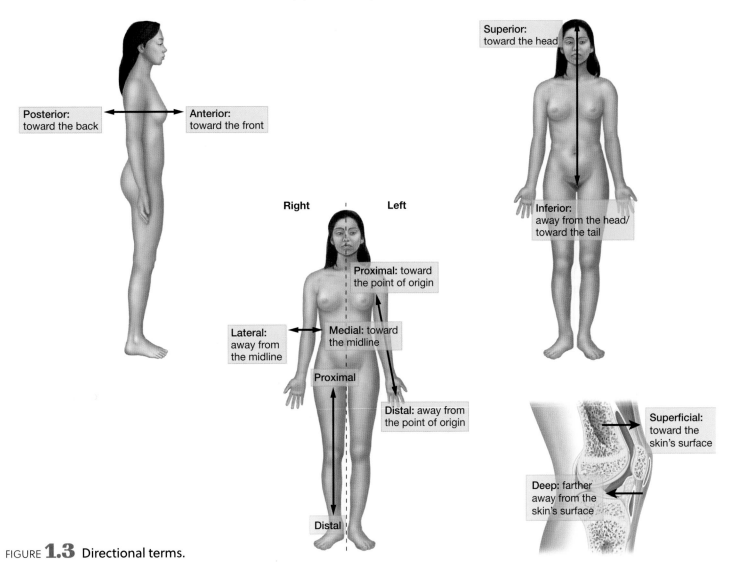

FIGURE **1.3** Directional terms.

■ **Superior/Inferior.** The directional term **superior** (*super-* = "above") is used to describe structures toward or closer to the head. The opposite term of superior is **inferior** (*infer-* = "below"), which means away from the head or toward the tail. Both superior and inferior may be used to describe a structure's absolute position in the body or the position of a structure relative to another structure. For example:

- The two largest veins in the body are the *superior vena cava* and the *inferior vena cava*. The superior vena cava is the vessel located nearer the head, and the inferior vena cava is the one located farther away from the head (or closer to the tail).

- We can describe the head as being *superior* to the neck, and we can say that the abdomen is *inferior* to the chest.

  With superior and inferior, we must remember a very important rule: These terms are used to describe structures only on the head, neck, and trunk. This is a part of the body known as the *axial region*. With very few exceptions, we do not use superior and inferior on the upper and lower limbs, a part of the body known as the *appendicular region*.

■ **Proximal/Distal.** When discussing the appendicular region, we use the terms proximal and distal instead of superior and inferior. The directional term **proximal** (PRAHKS-ih-muhl; *prox-* = "near") refers to the closeness—or *proximity*—of a structure to its point of origin. For the upper limb, this refers to the shoulder; for the lower limb, this refers to the hip. You know this from the everyday term *approximate*, which refers to closeness. The opposite term, **distal** (*dist-* = "far"), refers to the farness—or *distance*—of a structure from the shoulder or hip. As with superior and inferior, the terms can describe a structure's absolute position, or the position of a structure relative to another structure. Here are a couple of examples:

- The part of the femur (thigh bone) that is closest to the hip is called the *proximal* end of the bone. The end of the femur that is farthest away from the hip is its *distal* end.

- We can describe the knee as being *proximal* to the ankle, because it is closer to the hip than is the ankle. Similarly, the fingers are *distal* to the wrist because they are farther away from the shoulder than is the wrist.

■ **Medial/Lateral.** The terms medial and lateral reference an imaginary line running down the middle of the body called the *midline*. A structure is described as **medial** (MEE-dee-uhl; *med-* = "middle") when its position is closer to this midline, and its position becomes more **lateral** (LAT-er-uhl; *lat-* = "side") as it moves farther away from the midline. Again, we can use these terms to describe a structure's absolute location or its location relative to another structure. For example:

- The ulna, or the inner forearm bone, is the *medial* bone of the forearm because it is closest to the midline of the body. The radius, or the outer forearm bone, is the *lateral* bone of the forearm because it is farthest away from the midline of the body.

HINTS & TIPS

Sorting Out Superior and Inferior versus Proximal and Distal

One of the most common problems students have with respect to directional terms is how to use the terms superior/inferior and proximal/distal. Superior and inferior are easy enough on the head, neck, and trunk, but many students forget the rules and want to use them on the upper and lower limbs. So, to start, here's a mnemonic to help: "Use *your superior mind* to remember when to use *superior and inferior*." This will remind you to use these terms only on the head, neck, and trunk, as these are the locations in the body that house structures associated with your "mind" (the brain and spinal cord).

Now, let's think about proximal and distal for a minute. To start, why even have different terms on the upper and lower limbs? Well, stand with your hands by your side. If we were to use superior and inferior, we would say that your hand is inferior to your shoulder. But lift your arm in the air above your head—where is your hand now? It's superior to your shoulder, right? This is the problem with limbs: They can change position. Ideally, every specimen we describe is in anatomical position, but we can't guarantee that every patient we treat or body we find will be in anatomical position. So, for the upper and lower limbs, we need a different set of terms.

Once you understand the "why" of proximal and distal, all that's left is to understand how to apply them. That part is easy, because both are words that you already know, even if you don't immediately recognize them. You use words with the word root *prox-* all the time, such as "proximity" and "approximate." The word root *dist-* is also very common—you use it in words such as "distant," "distinct," "distance," and "distend."

Knowing the meanings of the word roots for the terms proximal and distal makes it very simple to come up with mnemonics for their use. Here are a couple of easy ones:

ℹ The more *proximal* structure is the one in the closest *proximity* to the hip (or shoulder).

ℹ The more *distal* structure is the one that is the most *distant* from the hip (or shoulder).

However, don't forget that these terms are only used on the upper and lower limbs, with very few exceptions. Just as you can't use superior and inferior on the upper and lower limbs, you also can't use proximal and distal on the head, neck, and trunk.

- We can describe the ears as being *lateral* to the eyes because the ears are farther away from the midline than are the eyes. Conversely, we could say that the eyes are *medial* to the ears for the same reason.
- **Superficial/Deep.** You are probably already familiar with the final pair of directional terms just from your everyday language: superficial and deep. As you might expect, the term **superficial** refers to a position that is closer to the surface of the body or closer to the skin. Structures that are **deep** are farther away from the skin's surface.

Review the definitions of the directional terms that you just read and that are illustrated in Figure 1.3. When you think you understand how to use them, fill in the correct directional terms in the following practice procedure.

PROCEDURE

Practicing Directional Terms

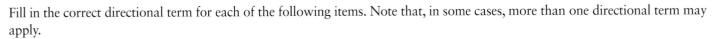

Fill in the correct directional term for each of the following items. Note that, in some cases, more than one directional term may apply.

The wrist is _____ to the elbow.

The forehead is _____ to the nose.

The sternum is _____ to the shoulder.

The mouth is _____ to the forehead.

The bone is _____ to the skin.

The ribs are _____ to the lungs.

The nose is on the _____ side of the body.

The scapula is _____ to the spine.

The ears are _____ to the cheeks.

The knee is _____ to the ankle.

MATERIALS

❏ Laminated outline of the human body

❏ Water-soluble marking pens

Regional Terms

You may have noticed in the example of Exercise 1-2 that we said *thoracic region* and *acromial region* instead of using generic words such as "chest" and "shoulder." These more specific words are known as **regional terms.** We use regional terms to make descriptions as specific as possible and to reduce the potential for errors in communication. Think about it—the "shoulder" could consist of a large area, whereas the "acromial region" refers to one specific location.

The following regional terms, illustrated in Figure 1.4 and defined in Table 1.1, are among the more common terms you'll encounter in your study of anatomy and physiology. Note that most of these terms are adjectives rather than nouns. This means the term is not complete unless it is paired with the term "region." For example, we cannot say, "The wound is in the antebrachial." We instead must say, "The wound is in the antebrachial *region*."

The following list may look daunting, but you are probably familiar with several of the terms already. For example, you likely know the locations of the "oral," "nasal," and "abdominal" regions. Watch for other terms that you may know.

1. Cranial
2. Frontal
3. Orbital
4. Nasal
5. Buccal
6. Otic
7. Oral
8. Occipital
9. Nuchal
10. Mental
11. Cervical
12. Acromial
13. Scapular
14. Sternal
15. Thoracic
16. Axillary
17. Mammary
18. Brachial
19. Antecubital
20. Vertebral
21. Abdominal

22. Umbilical
23. Antebrachial
24. Carpal
25. Manual
26. Palmar
27. Digital
28. Pelvic
29. Lumbar
30. Gluteal
31. Inguinal
32. Pubic
33. Femoral
34. Patellar
35. Popliteal
36. Crural
37. Sural
38. Tarsal
39. Pedal
40. Calcaneal
41. Plantar

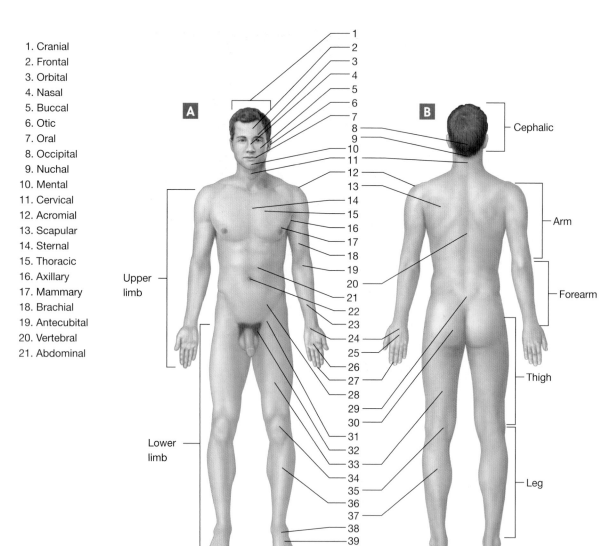

FIGURE **1.4** Regional terms: (**A**) anterior view; (**B**) posterior view.

TABLE **1.1** Regional Terms

Term	Word Root	Definition
Adjectives		
Abdominal region	Abdomin- = "abdomen"	Area over the abdomen that is inferior to the diaphragm and superior to the bony pelvis
Acromial region	Acrom- = "highest point," "peak"	Area over the lateral part of the shoulder that contains the acromion of the scapula
Antebrachial region	Brach- = "arm"	Anterior forearm
Antecubital region	Cubit- = "elbow"	Anterior upper limb between the forearm and arm, over the elbow joint
Axillary region	Axill- = "armpit"	Area in and around the axilla (armpit)
Brachial region	Brach- = "arm"	Anterior and posterior arm (between the elbow and the shoulder)
Buccal region	Bucca- = "cheek"	Lateral portions of the face corresponding to the cheeks
Calcaneal region	Calcan- = "heel"	Heel of the foot
Carpal region	Carp- = "wrist"	Wrist
Cephalic region	Cephal- = "head"	Entire head from the chin to the top of the head
Cervical region	Cerv- = "neck"	Neck
Cranial region	Cran- = "head," "skull"	Top of the head, or the portion of the skull that encases the brain
Crural region	Crur- = "leg"	Anterior leg (or the shin)
Digital region	Digit- = "fingers"	Fingers or the toes
Femoral region	Fem- = "thigh"	Thigh
Frontal region	Fron- = "forehead"	Forehead
Gluteal region	Glut- = "the rump"	Buttock
Inguinal region	Inguin- = "groin"	Area along the inguinal ligament that divides the pelvis from the thigh
Lumbar region	Lumb- = "loin"	Lower back
Mammary region	Mamm- = "breast"	Area around the breast
Manual region	Manu- = "hand"	General area of the hand
Mental region	Ment- = "chin," "mind"	Chin
Nasal region	Nas- = "nose"	Nose
Nuchal region	Nuch- = "nape"	Ridge that runs along the back of the skull at the superior boundary of the occipital region
Occipital region	Occipit- = "back of the skull"	General area of the back of the skull
Oral region	Or- = "mouth"	Mouth
Orbital region	Orbit- = "circle"	Area around the eye
Otic region	Ot- = "ear"	Area around the ear
Palmar region	Palm- = "palm of the hand"	Anterior hand (the palm of the hand)
Patellar region	Patell- = "little plate"	Anterior part of the knee over the patella (kneecap)
Pedal region	Ped- = "foot"	Foot
Pelvic region	Pelv- = "basin" or "bowl"	Anterior pelvis
Plantar region	Plant- = "sole"	Bottom of the foot

(continues)

TABLE **1.1** Regional Terms *(cont.)*

Term	Word Root	Definition
Adjectives		
Popliteal region	*Poplit-* = "knee"	Posterior side of the knee joint
Pubic region	*Pub-* = "genital area/groin"	Area over the pubic bone of the pelvis
Scapular region	*Scapul-* = "shoulder"	Area over the scapula in the superior back
Sternal region	*Stern-* = "chest"	Area in the middle of the chest over the sternum
Sural region	*Sur-* = "calf"	Posterior part of the leg (the calf)
Tarsal region	*Tars-* = "ankle"	Proximal foot and ankle region
Thoracic region	*Thorac-* = "chest/thorax"	General chest area
Umbilical region	*Umbil-* = "navel"	Area around the umbilicus (belly button)
Vertebral region	*Vertebr-* = "spine"	Area over the vertebral column (spine)

Term	Definition
Nouns	
Arm	Portion of the upper limb from the elbow to the shoulder
Forearm	Portion of the upper limb from the elbow to the wrist
Leg	Portion of the lower limb from the knee to the ankle
Lower limb	Entire portion of the body from the hip to the digits of the foot
Thigh	Portion of the lower limb from the hip to the knee
Upper limb	Entire portion of the body from the shoulder to the digits of the hand

PROCEDURE

1

Labeling Body Regions

Locate each of the listed regions on laminated outlines of the human body. Use water-soluble markers to label the regions. If outlines are unavailable, label the regions on **Figure 1.5**.

Adjectives

- ❑ Abdominal (ab-DAH-mih-nuhl)
- ❑ Acromial (ah-KROH-mee-uhl)
- ❑ Antebrachial (an-tee-BRAY-kee-uhl)
- ❑ Antecubital (an-tee-KYOO-bih-tuhl)
- ❑ Axillary (AX-il-ehr-ee)
- ❑ Brachial (BRAY-kee-uhl)
- ❑ Buccal (BYOO-kuhl)
- ❑ Calcaneal (kal-KAY-nee-uhl)
- ❑ Carpal (KAR-puhl)
- ❑ Cephalic (sef-AL-ik)
- ❑ Cervical (SUR-vih-kuhl)
- ❑ Cranial (KRAY-nee-uhl)
- ❑ Crural (KROO-ruhl)
- ❑ Digital (DIJ-it-uhl)
- ❑ Femoral (FEM-oh-ruhl)
- ❑ Frontal (FRUHN-tuhl)
- ❑ Gluteal (GLOO-tee-uhl)

- ❑ Inguinal (IN-gwin-uhl)
- ❑ Lumbar (LUHM-bahr)
- ❑ Mammary (MAM-uh-ree)
- ❑ Manual (MAN-yoo-uhl)
- ❑ Mental (MEN-tuhl)
- ❑ Nasal (NAY-zuhl)
- ❑ Nuchal (NOO-kuhl)
- ❑ Occipital (awk-SIP-ih-tuhl)
- ❑ Oral (OH-ruhl)
- ❑ Orbital (OHR-bit-uhl)
- ❑ Otic (OH-tik)
- ❑ Palmar (PAHL-mur)
- ❑ Patellar (puh-TEL-ur)
- ❑ Pedal (PEE-duhl)
- ❑ Pelvic (PEL-vik)
- ❑ Plantar (PLAN-tahr)
- ❑ Popliteal (pahp-lih-TEE-uhl)

- ❑ Pubic (PYOO-bik)
- ❑ Scapular (SKAP-yoo-lur)
- ❑ Sternal (STUR-nuhl)
- ❑ Sural (SOO-ruhl)
- ❑ Tarsal (TAR-suhl)
- ❑ Thoracic (thoh-RĂ-sik)
- ❑ Umbilical (um-BIL-ih-kuhl)
- ❑ Vertebral (vur-TEE-bruhl)

Nouns

- ❑ Arm
- ❑ Forearm
- ❑ Leg
- ❑ Lower limb
- ❑ Thigh
- ❑ Upper limb

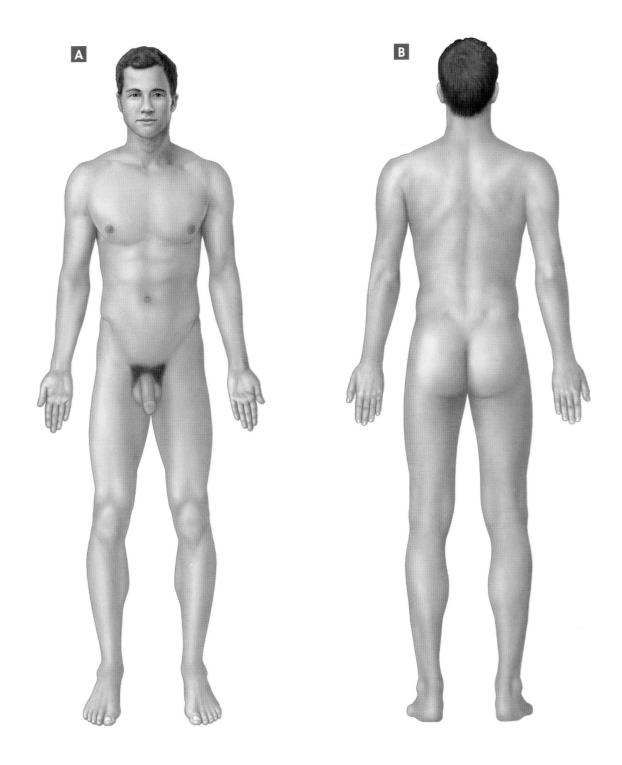

FIGURE **1.5** Human body in anatomical position: (**A**) anterior view; (**B**) posterior view.

EXERCISE

1-5

MATERIALS

☐ Anatomical models and diagrams: human torso

Body Cavities and Membranes

The body is divided into several cavities, many of which are fluid-filled and each of which contains specific organs. In this exercise, you will identify the body cavities and the organs contained within each cavity.

Several of the fluid-filled body cavities are formed by thin sheets of tissue called **serous membranes** (SEER-uhs; *ser-* = "liquid"). Cells of these membranes produce a thin, watery liquid called **serous fluid** that lubricates organs so they move within the cavity with little friction. Serous membranes are composed of two layers: an outer **parietal layer** (puh-RY-ih-tuhl; *pariet-* = "wall") that is attached to the body wall and surrounding structures, and an inner **visceral layer** (VISS-er-uhl; *viscer-* = "organ") that is attached to specific organs. Between the parietal and visceral layers is a thin potential space that contains serous fluid. This potential space is referred to as a cavity.

As you can see in Figure 1.6, there are two major body cavities, each of which is subdivided into smaller cavities, as follows:

1. **Posterior (dorsal) body cavity.** As implied by its name, the **posterior body cavity** is largely on the posterior side of the body (Fig. 1.6A). It is divided into two smaller cavities:

   a. **Cranial cavity.** The **cranial cavity** is the area encased by the skull. It contains the brain and a fluid called *cerebrospinal fluid*.

   b. **Vertebral** (or **spinal**) **cavity.** The **vertebral cavity** is the area encased by the vertebrae. It contains the spinal cord and is also filled with cerebrospinal fluid.

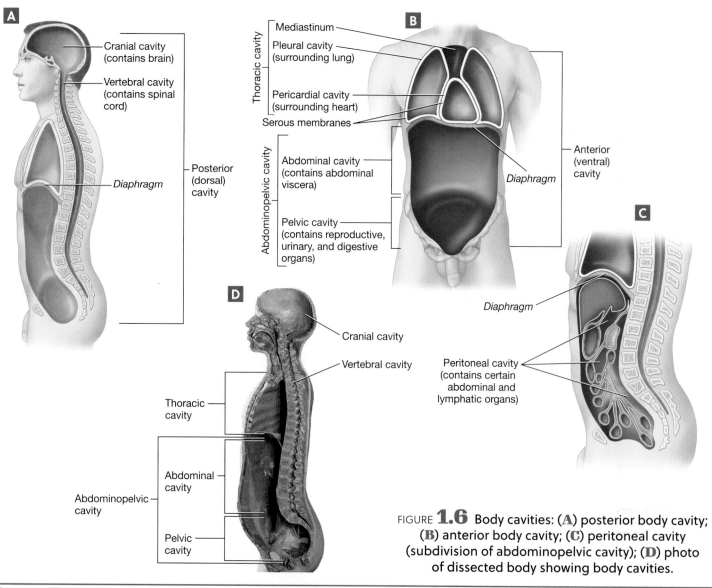

FIGURE **1.6** Body cavities: (**A**) posterior body cavity; (**B**) anterior body cavity; (**C**) peritoneal cavity (subdivision of abdominopelvic cavity); (**D**) photo of dissected body showing body cavities.

2. **Anterior (ventral) body cavity.** The **anterior body cavity** is largely on the anterior side of the body (Fig. 1.6B). It has two main divisions: the *thoracic* and *abdominopelvic cavities*, each of which is divided into smaller subcavities.

a. **Thoracic cavity.** The **thoracic cavity** (thoh-RĂ-sik*) is located superior to a muscle called the diaphragm where it encompasses the area encased by the ribs. We find the following smaller cavities within the thoracic cavity:

(1) **Pleural cavities.** Each **pleural cavity** (PLOO-ruhl; *pleur-* = "side of the body," "rib") surrounds one of the lungs, and is located between two layers of a serous membrane called the **pleural membrane**. The **parietal pleurae** are attached to the body wall and the surface of the diaphragm, and the **visceral pleurae** are attached to the surface of the lungs. Between the two layers we find a thin layer of serous fluid.

(2) **Mediastinum.** The cavity between the pleural cavities, called the **mediastinum** (mee-dee-uh-STY-num; *media-* = "middle"), contains the great vessels, the esophagus, the trachea and bronchi, and other structures. It houses another cavity formed by a second double-layered serous membrane called the **pericardial membrane** (pehr-ee-KAR-dee-uhl; *peri-* = "around;" *card-* = "heart"). The **parietal pericardium** is attached to surrounding structures, and the inner **visceral pericardium** is attached to the heart muscle. Between the two layers, we find the **pericardial cavity**, which is filled with a thin layer of serous fluid.

b. **Abdominopelvic cavity.** The **abdominopelvic cavity** (ab-dahm-ih-noh-PEL-vik) is located inferior to the diaphragm and extends into the bony pelvis. There are three subcavities within the abdominopelvic cavity:

(1) **Abdominal cavity.** The area superior to the bony pelvis, called the **abdominal cavity,** houses many organs including the liver, gallbladder, small intestine, stomach, pancreas, kidneys, adrenal glands, spleen, and much of the colon (large intestine).

(2) **Pelvic cavity.** The cavity housed within the bony pelvis, the **pelvic cavity**, contains certain sex organs, the urinary bladder, the rectum, and part of the colon.

(3) **Peritoneal cavity.** The third subcavity of the abdominopelvic cavity, shown in Figure 1.6C, is formed by a serous membrane called the **peritoneal membrane** (pehr-ih-toh-NEE-uhl; "stretched around"). The outer **parietal peritoneum** is attached to the body wall and surrounding structures, and the inner **visceral peritoneum** is attached to the surface of many of the abdominal and pelvic organs. Between these two layers of peritoneal membrane we find the **peritoneal cavity**, which is filled with serous fluid. Organs that are within the peritoneal cavity are **intraperitoneal** (in-trah-pehr-ih-toh-NEE-uhl; *intra-* = "within") and include the liver, most of the small intestine, much of the colon, the stomach, the spleen, and part of the pancreas. Those organs that are posterior to the peritoneal cavity are said to be **retroperitoneal** (reh-troh-pehr-ih-toh-NEE-uhl; *retro-* = "behind"), and include the kidneys, adrenal glands, the sex organs, the urinary bladder, part of the colon, and part of the pancreas.

We often divide the abdominopelvic cavity into four surface quadrants: the right upper, right lower, left upper, and left lower quadrants, as shown in Figure 1.7. Take note in the figure of which organs are located in each quadrant, as you will be identifying them in an upcoming procedure. Be aware, though, that certain structures are deep to the labeled organs and so aren't visible in the figure. These deeper organs are listed to the side of each quadrant.

---

* The phonetic symbol Ă (or ă) references the sound the "a" makes in the word "apple."

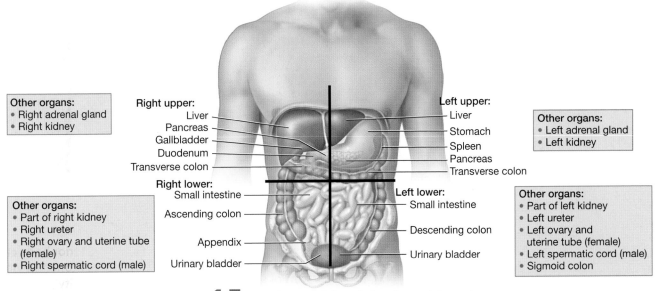

Other organs:
- Right adrenal gland
- Right kidney

Right upper:
- Liver
- Pancreas
- Gallbladder
- Duodenum
- Transverse colon

Left upper:
- Liver
- Stomach
- Spleen
- Pancreas
- Transverse colon

Other organs:
- Left adrenal gland
- Left kidney

Other organs:
- Part of right kidney
- Right ureter
- Right ovary and uterine tube (female)
- Right spermatic cord (male)

Right lower:
- Small intestine
- Ascending colon
- Appendix
- Urinary bladder

Left lower:
- Small intestine
- Descending colon
- Urinary bladder

Other organs:
- Part of left kidney
- Left ureter
- Left ovary and uterine tube (female)
- Left spermatic cord (male)
- Sigmoid colon

FIGURE **1.7** Quadrants of the abdominopelvic cavity.

We can also divide the abdominopelvic cavity into nine regions based on a series of lines drawn over the surface of the abdomen. The regions are listed and labeled in Figure 1.8.

FIGURE **1.8** Regions of the abdominopelvic cavity.

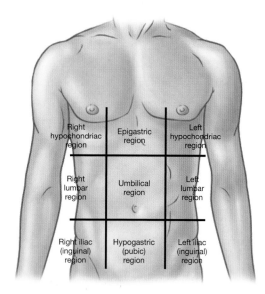

PROCEDURE

Examining Body Cavities

In this procedure, you will use a human torso model to examine the body cavities. If you are using a preserved small mammal, your lab will provide a dissection guide specific for that animal with directions for opening and examining the animal.

1 Identify the organs of the thoracic, abdominal, and pelvic cavities, and list these organs in Table 1.2. See Figures 1.9 through 1.11 for reference.

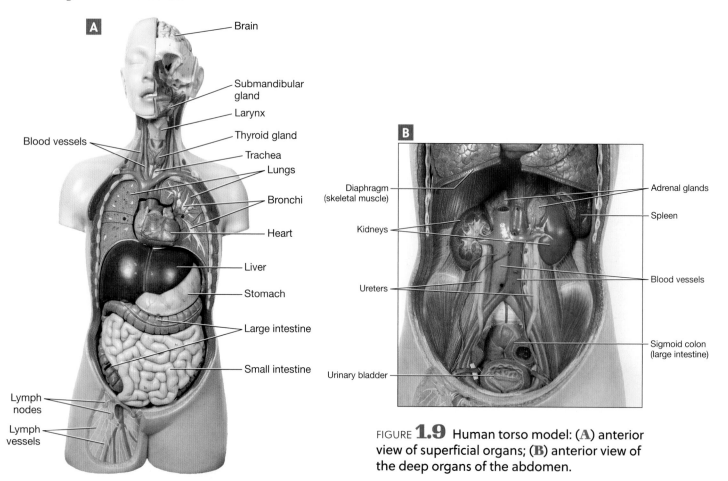

FIGURE **1.9** Human torso model: (**A**) anterior view of superficial organs; (**B**) anterior view of the deep organs of the abdomen.

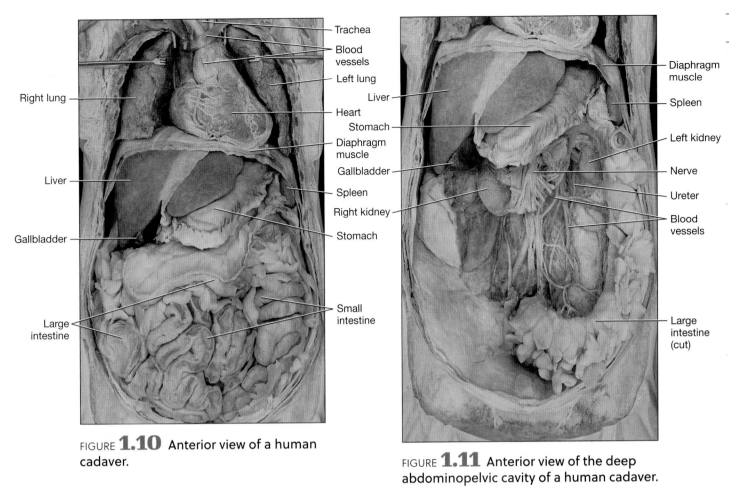

FIGURE **1.10** Anterior view of a human cadaver.

Labels (Figure 1.10): Trachea, Blood vessels, Left lung, Liver, Heart, Stomach, Diaphragm muscle, Gallbladder, Spleen, Right kidney, Stomach, Small intestine, Right lung, Liver, Gallbladder, Large intestine

FIGURE **1.11** Anterior view of the deep abdominopelvic cavity of a human cadaver.

Labels (Figure 1.11): Diaphragm muscle, Spleen, Left kidney, Nerve, Ureter, Blood vessels, Large intestine (cut)

2 Mark each quadrant of the abdominopelvic cavity with marking tape. Note which organs are located in each quadrant, and add this information to Table 1.2.

TABLE **1.2** Divisions of the Anterior Body Cavity and Quadrants of the Abdominopelvic Cavity

Cavity	Organ(s)
1. Thoracic cavity	
a. Pleural cavities	
b. Mediastinum	
(1) Pericardial cavity	

(continues)

TABLE 1.2 Divisions of the Anterior Body Cavity and Quadrants of the Abdominopelvic Cavity *(cont.)*

Cavity	Organ(s)
2. Abdominopelvic cavity	
a. Subdivisions	
(1) Abdominal cavity	
(2) Pelvic cavity	
(3) Peritoneal cavity	
b. Quadrants	
(1) Right upper quadrant	
(2) Right lower quadrant	
(3) Left upper quadrant	
(4) Left lower quadrant	

2 PROCEDURE
Examining Serous Membranes

Part A

On a human torso model, look for the serous membranes listed in Table 1.3. As you identify each membrane, name the structure to which the membrane is attached (the lungs, heart, abdominal wall, etc.) and record it in the table. (Note that sometimes models don't show the membranes well, so you may have to use your imagination.)

TABLE **1.3** Serous Membranes

1

Membrane	Cavity	Structure(s)
Parietal pleura		
Visceral pleura		
Parietal pericardium		
Visceral pericardium		
Parietal peritoneum		
Visceral peritoneum		

Part B

Draw in the body cavities on your laminated outlines of the human body (using water-soluble markers) or on Figure 1.12. Label each body cavity, as well as the serous membranes surrounding the cavity, where applicable.

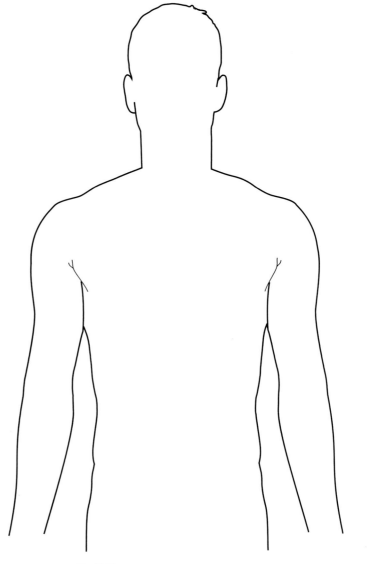

FIGURE **1.12** Anterior view of the human torso.

3 PROCEDURE

Applying Terms, Cavities, and Membranes

Remember this from the unit opener?

> *The bullet entered the right posterior scapular region, 3 cm lateral to the vertebral region,*
> *4 cm inferior to the cervical region, and penetrated deep to the muscle and bone,*
> *but superficial to the lung and parietal pleura.*

Now, it's your turn to describe a "bullet wound" by combining the different anatomical terms you've learned. Assume you are acting as coroner, and you have a victim with three gunshot wounds. In this scenario, your victim will be a human torso model or preserved small mammal that your instructor has "shot." For each "bullet wound," describe the location of the wound using at least three directional terms and as many regional terms as possible, following the example provided. As coroner, you need to be as specific as possible, and don't forget to keep your patient in anatomical position. When you have completed the activity, answer Check Your Understanding Questions 2 through 5 (pp. 31–33).

Shot 1	
Shot 2	
Shot 3	

EXERCISE
1-6

MATERIALS

- ❏ Modeling clay
- ❏ Knife or scalpel
- ❏ Anatomical models demonstrating various planes of section

Planes of Section

Often, in anatomy and physiology, we need to obtain different views of the internal structure of an organ or a body cavity. These views are obtained by making an **anatomical section** along a specific plane. The commonly used planes of section, shown in Figures 1.13 and 1.14, are as follows:

1. **Sagittal plane.** A section along the **sagittal plane** (SAJ-ih-tuhl) divides the specimen into right and left parts. The sagittal section has two variations:

   a. **Midsagittal sections** (mid-SAJ-ih-tuhl; *mid-* = "middle") divide the specimen into equal right and left halves.

   b. **Parasagittal sections** (pehr-uh-SAJ-ih-tuhl; *para-* = "next to") divide the specimen into unequal right and left parts.

2. **Frontal plane.** The **frontal plane**, also known as the **coronal plane** (koh-ROH-nuhl), divides the specimen into an anterior (front) part and a posterior (back) part.

3. **Transverse plane.** The **transverse plane**, also known as a **cross section** or the **horizontal plane**, divides the specimen into a superior (or proximal) part and an inferior (or distal) part.

Note that there is a single midsagittal plane, but there are a near infinite number of possible parasagittal, frontal, and transverse planes. In your study of anatomy and physiology, you will see many different examples of these planes of section.

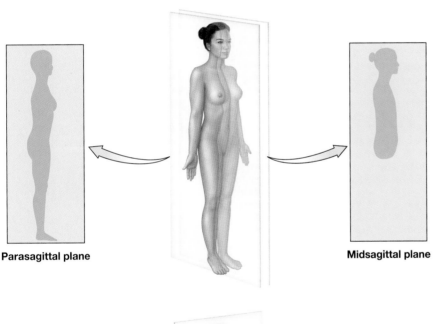

Parasagittal plane

Midsagittal plane

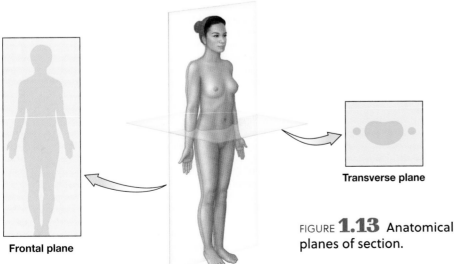

Frontal plane

Transverse plane

FIGURE **1.13** Anatomical planes of section.

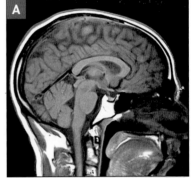

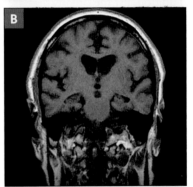

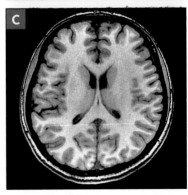

FIGURE **1.14** Planes of anatomical section visible on computed tomography scans of the brain: (**A**) midsagittal section; (**B**) frontal section; (**C**) transverse section.

1 PROCEDURE

Sectioning Along Anatomical Planes

Mold a ball of modeling clay into the shape of a head, and draw eyes on the head to denote anterior and posterior sides. Then, use a scalpel to cut the ball in each of the numbered anatomical planes. When you have finished cutting the planes, sketch a model "head" in the space provided next to the list, and draw each of the anatomical planes. Use Figures 1.13 and 1.14 for reference. When you have completed this exercise, answer Check Your Understanding Questions 6 and 7 (p. 34).

1. Sagittal
   a. Midsagittal
   b. Parasagittal
2. Frontal
3. Transverse

2 PROCEDURE

Identifying Examples of Anatomical Planes of Section

In Table 1.4, identify at least two examples of each plane of section on the anatomical models provided by your instructor. In addition, list the organs that are visible in the section.

TABLE **1.4** Anatomical Models and Planes of Section

Examples of Midsagittal and/or Parasagittal Sections	
Model Name or Description	Organ(s) Visible
1.	
2.	
Examples of Frontal Sections	
Model Name or Description	Organ(s) Visible
1.	
2.	
Examples of Transverse Sections	
Model Name or Description	Organ(s) Visible
1.	
2.	

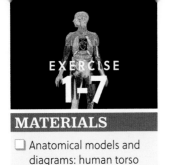

EXERCISE 1-7

MATERIALS

❑ Anatomical models and diagrams: human torso

Organs and Organ Systems

The organs that you have identified in this lab are organized into functional groups called **organ systems**. The human body has 11 organ systems, each with specific organs and functions (Fig. 1.15). In this exercise, you will examine the organ systems and identify their major organs.

1 PROCEDURE
Identifying Organs

Identify the following organs on human torso models. Check off each organ as you identify it, and record the organ system to which it belongs in Table 1.5, using Figure 1.15 for reference (also refer back to Figs. 1.9–1.11). Remember that some organs may function in more than one system.

❑ Adrenal glands
❑ Blood vessels
❑ Bones
❑ Brain
❑ Esophagus
❑ Gallbladder
❑ Heart

❑ Joints
❑ Kidneys
❑ Large intestine
❑ Larynx
❑ Liver
❑ Lungs
❑ Lymph nodes

❑ Pancreas
❑ Skeletal muscles
❑ Skin
❑ Small intestine
❑ Spinal cord
❑ Spleen
❑ Stomach

❑ Testes (male) or ovaries (female)
❑ Thymus
❑ Thyroid gland
❑ Trachea
❑ Urinary bladder
❑ Uterus

TABLE **1.5** Organs and Organ Systems

Organ System	Major Organ(s)
Integumentary system	
Skeletal system	
Muscular system	
Nervous system	
Endocrine system	
Cardiovascular system	
Lymphatic system	
Respiratory system	
Digestive system	
Urinary system	
Reproductive system	

2 PROCEDURE
Researching Organ Systems

The body's organ systems are illustrated in Figure 1.15. Fill in the blanks next to each organ system to identify the major organs shown. Then, use your textbook or other resources to research the principal functions of each system.

Main Organs:

Main Functions:

Integumentary System

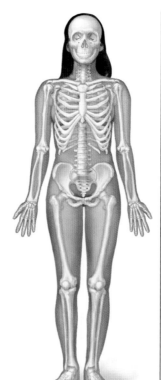

Main Organs:

Main Functions:

Skeletal System

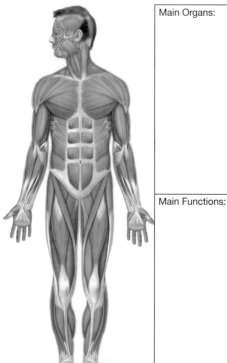

Main Organs:

Main Functions:

Muscular System

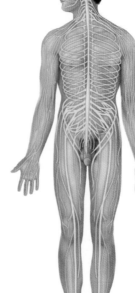

Main Organs:

Main Functions:

Nervous System

FIGURE **1.15** Organ systems of the body (continues)

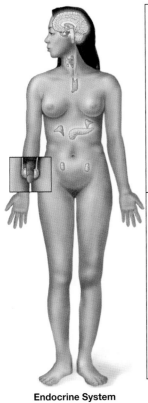

Endocrine System

Main Organs:

Main Functions:

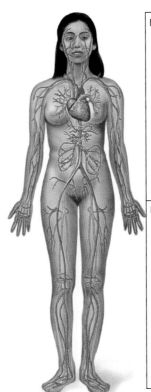

Cardiovascular System

Main Organs:

Main Functions:

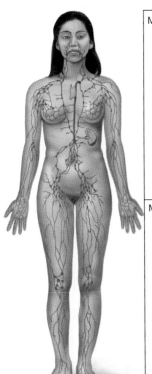

Lymphatic System

Main Organs:

Main Functions:

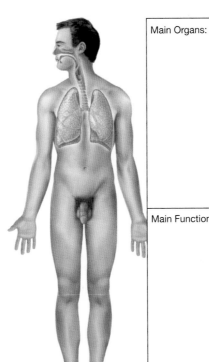

Respiratory System

Main Organs:

Main Functions:

FIGURE **1.15** (*cont.*) **Organ systems of the body** (*continues*)

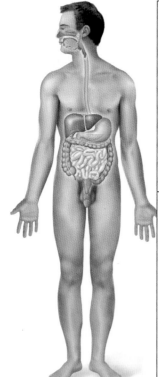

Main Organs:

Main Functions:

Digestive System

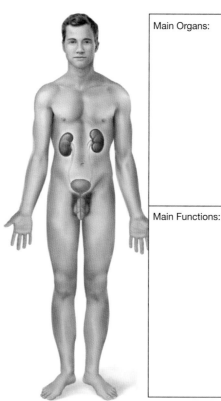

Main Organs:

Main Functions:

Urinary System

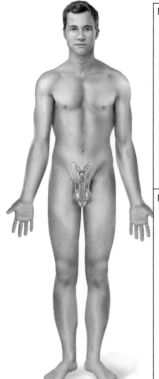

Main Organs:

Main Functions:

Male Reproductive System

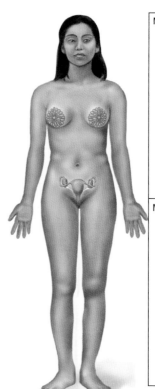

Main Organs:

Main Functions:

Female Reproductive System

FIGURE **1.15** (*cont.*) Organ systems of the body.

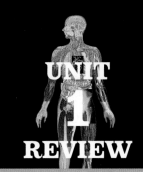

Check Your Recall

1 *Circle all that apply.* Which of the following is/are components of anatomical position?

  a. Palms facing forward.

  b. Feet together.

  c. Palms facing backward.

  d. Body facing forward.

  e. Feet shoulder-width apart.

  f. Upper limbs raised over the head.

2 How do the directional terms proximal and distal differ from the terms superior and inferior in how they're used to describe locations on the body?

_____

_____

_____

3 Medial is defined as

  a. away from the surface or toward the body's interior.

  b. toward the front of the body or body part.

  c. toward the body's midline.

  d. away from the head/toward the tail.

4 Label the following anatomical regions on Figure 1.16.

  ❏ Antecubital region

  ❏ Arm

  ❏ Brachial region

  ❏ Cephalic region

  ❏ Cervical region

  ❏ Inguinal region

  ❏ Leg

  ❏ Lower limb

  ❏ Occipital region

  ❏ Sternal region

  ❏ Thigh

  ❏ Umbilical region

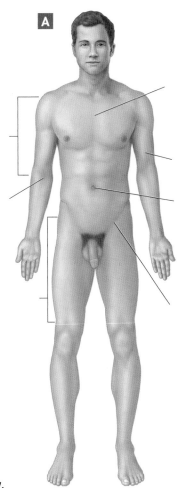
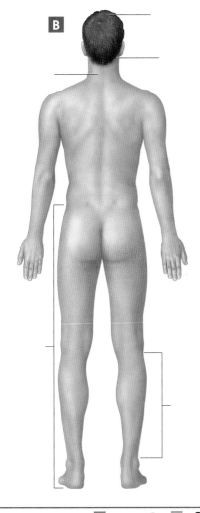

FIGURE **1.16** Human body in anatomical position: (**A**) anterior view; (**B**) posterior view.

5 Label the following body cavities on Figure 1.17.

- ❏ Abdominopelvic cavity
- ❏ Anterior body cavity
- ❏ Cranial cavity
- ❏ Mediastinum
- ❏ Pelvic cavity
- ❏ Pericardial cavity
- ❏ Peritoneal cavity
- ❏ Pleural cavity
- ❏ Thoracic cavity

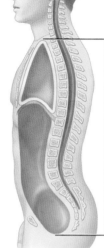
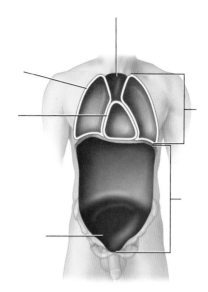
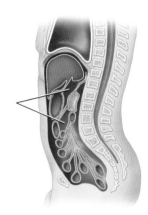

FIGURE **1.17** Body cavities.

6 Which of the following body cavities is located within a double-layered serous membrane?

a. Peritoneal cavity.

b. Mediastinum.

c. Cranial cavity.

d. All of the above are located within a double-layered serous membrane.

7 *Fill in the blanks:* **A parasagittal plane divides the body or body part into** _____

_____ **, whereas a midsagittal plane divides the body or body part into** _____

_____ .

8 Which of the following planes of section divides the body or body part into superior and inferior (or proximal and distal) parts?

a. Midsagittal plane.

b. Transverse plane.

c. Parasagittal plane.

d. Frontal plane.

9 *Circle all that apply.* Which of the following organs belong to the endocrine system?

a. Thyroid gland.

b. Adrenal gland.

c. Trachea.

d. Liver.

e. Pancreas.

10 *Circle all that apply.* Which of the following organs belong to the integumentary system?

a. Bone.

b. Skin.

c. Adrenal gland.

d. Nails.

e. Uterus.

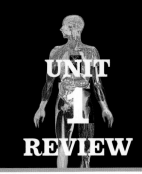

Check Your Understanding

Critical Thinking and Application Questions

1 Figure 1.18 is not in anatomical position. List all of the deviations from anatomical position.

_____

_____

_____

FIGURE **1.18**
Figure not in anatomical position.

2 Locate the following wounds, and mark them on the body in Figure 1.19.

  a The wound is located in the right inferior lumbar region. It is 3 cm lateral to the vertebral region and 4 cm superior to the gluteal region.

  b The wound is located on the left anterior, lateral forearm, 2 cm distal to the antecubital region.

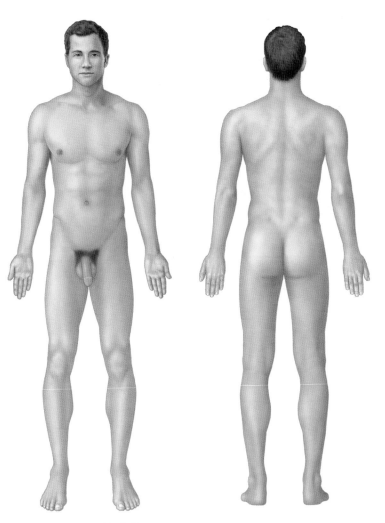

FIGURE **1.19** Anterior and posterior views of the human body in anatomical position.

You are reading a surgeon's operative report. During the surgery, she made several incisions. Your job is to read her operative report and determine where the incisions were made. Draw and label the incisions on Figure 1.20.

a The first incision was made in the left posterior scapular region, 3 cm inferior to the acromial region and 2 cm lateral to the axillary region. The cut extended horizontally in a medial direction, ending 2 cm lateral to the vertebral region.

b The second incision began in the anterior umbilical region. It extended vertically in a superior direction, ending 2 cm inferior to the sternal region. Here, the cut turned and extended horizontally in a left lateral direction for 4 cm.

c The third incision was made in the left posterior, medial sural region, 2 cm distal to the popliteal region. The cut extended in a distal direction to 2 cm proximal to the tarsal region.

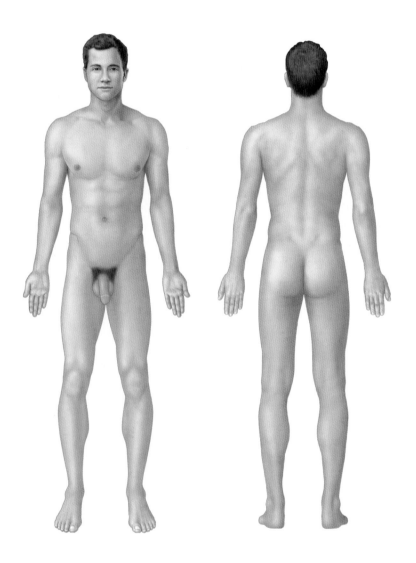

FIGURE **1.20** Anterior and posterior views of the human body in anatomical position.

4 You are riding with an ambulance crew who had been called to the scene of a motor vehicle accident, which was caused by texting while driving. As the paramedics are loading one of the victims into the ambulance, you are asked to describe his most serious wounds to the emergency department so they can be prepared for his arrival. Describe the location of his wounds, indicated on Figure 1.21 by three X marks, using at least three correct regional and directional terms.

 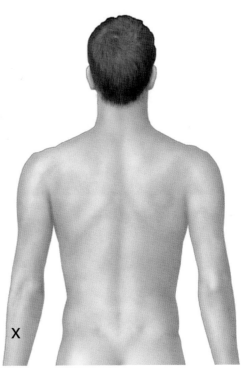

FIGURE **1.21** Anterior and posterior views of the human torso.

a _____

_____

_____

b _____

_____

c _____

_____

5 A female patient presents to the emergency department complaining of pain in the left lower quadrant of her abdomen. List the organs and structures that could possibly be involved in causing her pain.

_____

_____

_____

6 Identify the plane of section of each of the following medical imaging scans in Figure 1.22.

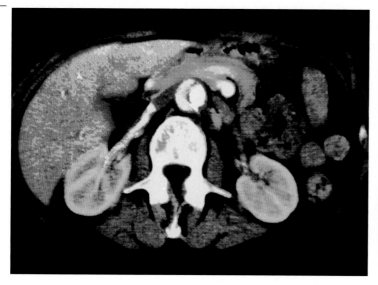

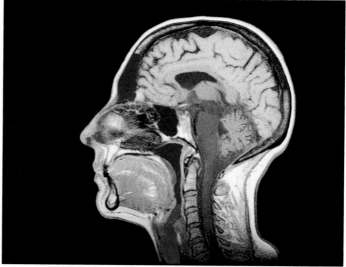

a _____

b _____

FIGURE **1.22** Computed tomography
scans in different anatomical sections.

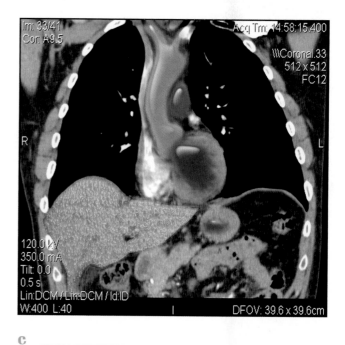

c _____

7 Identify some of the major organs you can see in each of the sections from Question 6, and name the organ
system to which each belongs.

a _____

_____

b _____

_____

c _____

Chemistry

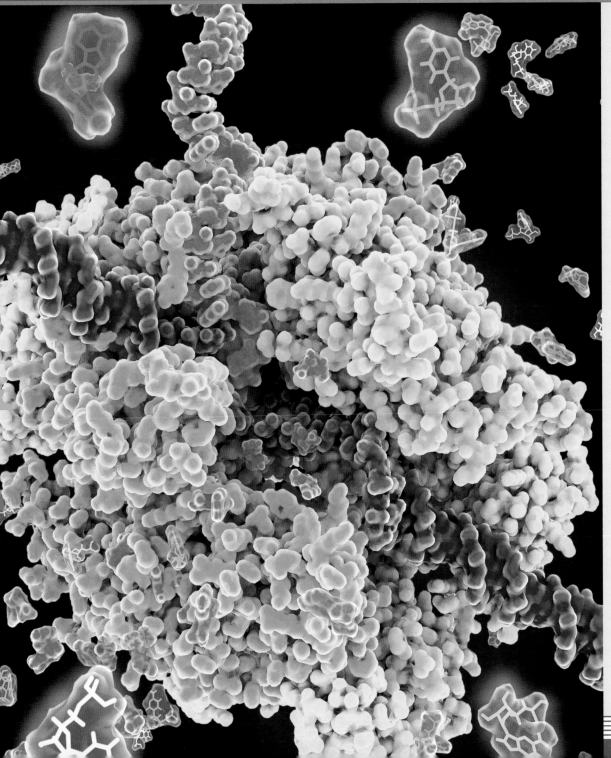

When you have completed this unit, you should be able to:

1 Describe and apply the pH scale.

2 Describe the purpose and effects of a buffer.

3 Describe the differences between ionic, polar, and nonpolar compounds, and explain why they are soluble in different solvents.

4 Explain the factors that affect the rate of chemical reactions, and describe the purpose of an enzyme in chemical reactions.

5 Explain the properties of the main organic compounds found in the human body: carbohydrates, proteins, lipids, and nucleotides.

PRE-LAB EXERCISES

2

Complete the following exercises prior to coming to lab, using your lab manual and textbook for reference.

PRE-LAB

2-1 **Key Terms**

You should be familiar with the following terms before coming to lab.

Term	Definition
Element	
Metal	
Nonmetal	
Ion (cation and anion)	
Acid	
Base	
pH scale	
Neutral	
Buffer	
Ionic bond	
Polar covalent bond	
Nonpolar covalent bond	
Solute	
Solvent	

Solubility _____

Hydrophilic _____

Hydrophobic _____

Chemical reaction _____

Enzyme _____

Carbohydrate _____

Lipid _____

Protein _____

Denatured _____

Nucleotide _____

Deoxyribonucleic acid (DNA) _____

Ribonucleic acid (RNA) _____

2-2 The pH Scale and –logarithms

The **pH scale** is a numerical scale from 0 through 14 that represents the hydrogen ion concentration of a solution. Solutions with a pH of less than 7 are considered *acidic*; those with a pH of exactly 7 are *neutral*; and those with a pH greater than 7 are *basic*. Solutions with a pH of 0 have the highest hydrogen ion concentration and are the most acidic, whereas solutions with a pH of 14 have the lowest hydrogen ion concentration and are the most basic.

The pH is calculated by taking the negative logarithm of a solution's hydrogen ion concentration. Grab your calculator and enter the following:

–log(0.01) = _____   –log(0.0001) = _____

–log(0.001) = _____   –log(0.00001) = _____

Notice the general trend here: *As the number gets smaller, its negative log gets bigger.*

Let's do an example using hydrogen ions: Solution X has a hydrogen ion concentration of 0.05 M. Solution Y has a hydrogen ion concentration of 0.0002 M.

■ Which solution has more hydrogen ions? (**Hint:** It's just the solution with the bigger number.) _____

■ What is the –log of solution X? _____

■ What is the –log of solution Y? _____

As you can see, the solution with the *higher* hydrogen ion concentration has the *lower* –log. This means that:

■ Solution X is the more _____ (acidic/basic) solution and has a _____ (lower/higher) pH.

■ Solution Y is the more _____ (acidic/basic) solution and has a _____ (lower/higher) pH.

In Exercise 2-1, we'll discuss the pH further, and explain why this scale seems backward.

2-3 Chemical Bonding

One of the more challenging concepts to grasp in chemistry is chemical bonding, a topic that pops up again and again in A&P. We can make this easier by reviewing some basics, first. Use your textbook and this unit to answer the following questions.

1. Do metals donate or accept electrons? What do they become after they donate/accept electrons? _____

2. Do nonmetals donate or accept electrons? What do they become after they donate/accept electrons? _____

3. Electron shells:

   How many electrons can go in the first shell? _____

   How many electrons can go in the second shell? _____

   How many electrons can go in the third shell? _____

4. How many electrons does each element require in its valence shell to become stable? _____

EXERCISES

The simplest level of organization is the chemical level. Our cells, tissues, organs, and extracellular environments are all composed of chemicals that undergo countless chemical reactions every second. So, to understand our anatomy and physiology, we first must understand our bodies' most basic structures—chemicals (or **matter**, which is defined as anything that has mass and takes up space). To see a big picture view of the relevance of chemistry to the human body, refer to **Figure 2.1**.

RNA polymerase II transcribing DNA.

5 Four main types of organic compounds make up cellular structures: carbohydrates, proteins, lipids, and nucleotides. (Ex. 2-5)

1 Acids and bases play important roles in human physiology. Cells in the stomach secrete acid to assist with digestion. (Ex. 2-1)

4 About 37 thousand billion-billion enzyme-catalyzed chemical reactions occur in the human body per second. (Ex. 2-4)

2 Acids and bases are found in all body fluids, including blood. Large swings in the pH are prevented by buffer systems. (Ex. 2-2)

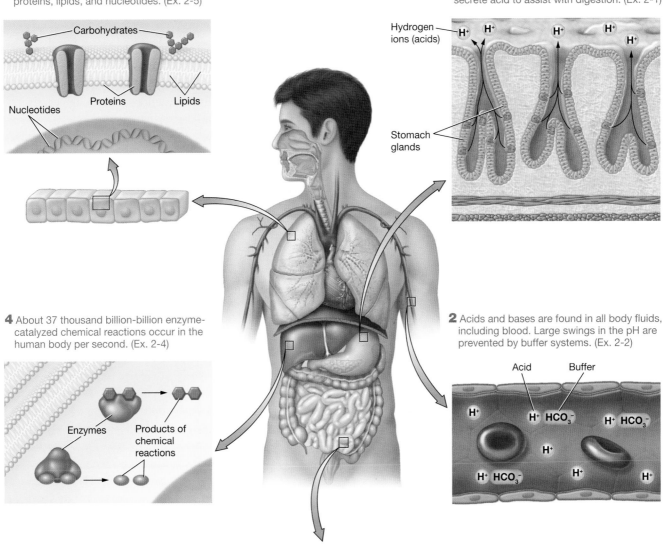

3 Water is the body's solvent. Water can dissolve and transport chemicals with polar covalent and ionic bonds. Chemicals with nonpolar covalent bonds cannot dissolve and must be transported on carriers. (Ex. 2-3)

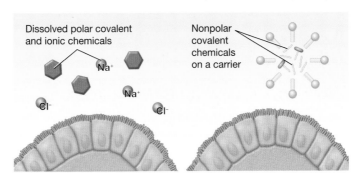

FIGURE **2.1** Why study chemistry in an A&P course?

The smallest unit of matter that still retains its original properties is the **atom**. Atoms are composed of even smaller **subatomic particles**, including:

- **Protons,** positively charged particles that reside in the **atomic nucleus** (NOO-klee-uhs);
- **Neutrons** (NOO-trahnz), particles with no charge that also reside in the atomic nucleus; and
- **Electrons,** tiny, negatively charged particles that inhabit regions around the nucleus known as *electron shells*.

Each atom contains an equal number of positively charged protons and negatively charged electrons. As a result, atoms overall have no charge. However, an atom may have a different number of protons and neutrons.

We discuss atoms in terms of **elements,** which are substances composed of identical atoms with a unique number of protons. An element's characteristic number of protons is called its **atomic number.** The **periodic table of the elements,** shown in Figure 2.2, arranges the elements in order of increasing atomic number, and lists them by an abbreviation called a *chemical symbol.*

Notice the blue "staircase" on the right side of the periodic table. To the left of the staircase, we find elements called **metals,** which are shiny substances that conduct electricity. In chemical reactions, a metal tends to donate electrons. In doing so, the number of electrons and protons is no longer equal—such charged particles are called **ions** (AYE-ahnz). Metals become positive ions called **cations** (KAT-aye-ahnz). To the right of the staircase, we find the **nonmetals,** which are gases or brittle solids that usually conduct electricity poorly. Unlike metals, nonmetals tend to accept electrons during chemical reactions, becoming negatively charged **anions** (AN-aye-ahnz).

Hydrogen (H), with an atomic number of one, is on the "metal" side of the periodic table. However, hydrogen requires extreme temperatures and pressures to behave as a metal, and those conditions don't exist on Earth (you'd need to go to the core of Jupiter). For this reason, hydrogen generally acts like a nonmetal in chemical reactions and exists as a gas on Earth.

When we combine two or more elements in a *chemical bond*, the resulting substance is called a **molecule** (MAHL-eh-kyool). If two or more different elements are united by a chemical bond, this is called a molecule of a **compound.** Many important substances in the body, including *carbohydrates, proteins, lipids,* and *nucleotides,* are very large compounds, which are known as **macromolecules.**

In the following exercises, you'll learn about different compounds and macromolecules that are important in human anatomy and physiology. We start with **inorganic compounds**—those that do not contain carbon and hydrogen. We then move onto the **organic compounds** of the human body—those that do contain carbon and hydrogen.

Periodic Table of the Elements

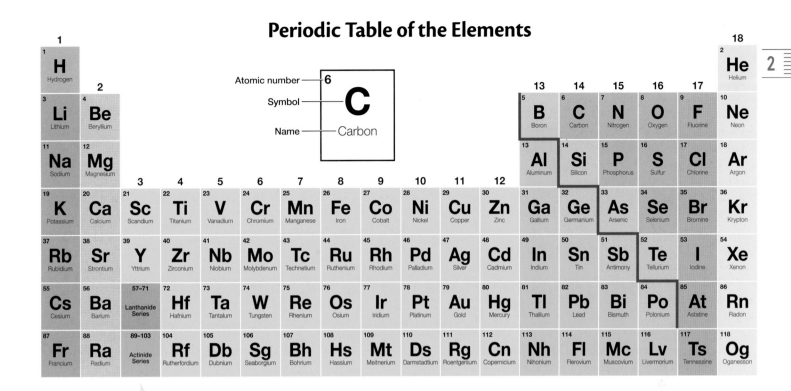

FIGURE **2.2** Periodic table of the elements.

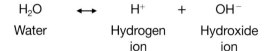

EXERCISE 2-1

MATERIALS

- ❏ Glass test tubes (3)
- ❏ Test tube rack
- ❏ Graduated cylinder
- ❏ Dropping pipette
- ❏ pH paper
- ❏ Samples of various acids and bases
- ❏ 0.1 M hydrochloric acid
- ❏ Samples of Tums, Rolaids, and Alka-Seltzer antacid tablets
- ❏ Glass stirring rods
- ❏ Permanent marker

pH, Acids, and Bases

Most of the time, hydrogen behaves like a nonmetal. But, sometimes a hydrogen atom in certain compounds can act like a metal when placed in water, donating its lone electron to become a positive hydrogen cation (H^+; usually simply called a *hydrogen ion*). Even the hydrogen in water can do this. Notice how, in the following reaction, water breaks apart, or *dissociates*, producing a hydrogen ion and an anion called the **hydroxide ion (OH^-)**:

$$H_2O \longleftrightarrow H^+ + OH^-$$

Water ⟷ Hydrogen ion + Hydroxide ion

Hydrogen ions define the class of inorganic compounds known as acids and bases.

- **An acid donates a hydrogen ion.** When you place an **acid** in water, it splits into a hydrogen ion (H^+) and an anion. We can see this with the reaction of nitric acid (HNO_3):

$$\overset{\text{In } H_2O}{HNO_3 \rightleftharpoons H^+ + NO_3^-}$$

Nitric acid ⇌ Hydrogen ion + Nitrate ion

- **A base accepts a hydrogen ion.** When you mix a **base** (or **alkali**; AL-kuh-lye) with water, it binds to the hydrogen ions in the solution. This causes the number of hydrogen ions in the solution to decrease.

Every solution has a certain number of hydrogen ions and a certain number of base ions. A solution's hydrogen ion concentration is represented via a value on the **pH scale**. You can see in Figure 2.3 that the pH scale ranges from 0 to 14, and the number on the scale defines a solution as *acidic, neutral,* or *basic.*

- **An acidic solution has a pH less than 7.** A solution that has more hydrogen ions than base ions has a pH less than 7 and is defined as **acidic**. The lower the number, the more hydrogen ions and the more acidic the solution—a solution with a pH of 1 is considered a *strong acid*, whereas one with a pH of 6 is a *weak acid*.

- **A neutral solution has a pH of exactly 7.** When the numbers of hydrogen ions and base ions are equal, the solution has a pH of 7 and is defined as **neutral**. Few solutions other than pure water are neutral.

- **A basic, or alkaline, solution has a pH greater than 7.** A solution that has more base ions than hydrogen ions has a pH greater than 7 and is defined as **basic** or **alkaline** (AL-kuh-lyn'e). The higher the number, the more basic the solution—a solution with a pH of 14 is a *strong base*, while one with a pH just above 7 is a *weak base*. Human blood falls into this category, with a pH range of 7.35–7.45.

⚠ SAFETY NOTE

Many of the chemicals you will use in this lab are poisons that can burn your skin, eyes, and mucous membranes. Take care in handling all chemicals. Do not handle any chemicals without safety glasses and gloves.

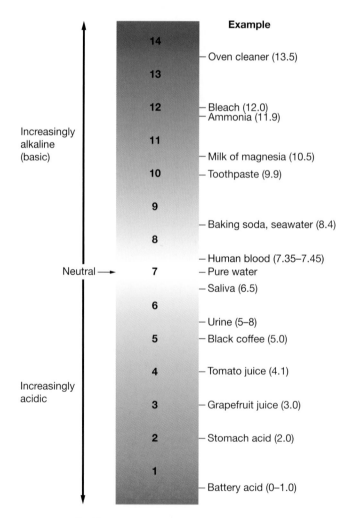

	Example
14	— Oven cleaner (13.5)
13	
12	— Bleach (12.0)
	— Ammonia (11.9)
11	
	— Milk of magnesia (10.5)
10	— Toothpaste (9.9)
9	
	— Baking soda, seawater (8.4)
8	
	— Human blood (7.35–7.45)
7	— Pure water
	— Saliva (6.5)
6	
	— Urine (5–8)
5	— Black coffee (5.0)
4	— Tomato juice (4.1)
3	— Grapefruit juice (3.0)
2	— Stomach acid (2.0)
1	
	— Battery acid (0–1.0)

Increasingly alkaline (basic) — Neutral → 7 — Increasingly acidic

FIGURE **2.3** pH scale and examples of solutions with different pH values.

HINTS & TIPS

Sorting Out the pH Scale

The pH scale seems backward—as the number of hydrogen ions in a solution increases, its pH *decreases*, and as the number of hydrogen ions decreases, its pH *increases*. This inverse relationship is a consequence of how we calculate the pH, which is to take the negative log of the hydrogen ion concentration ($-\log[H^+]$).

First, why do we even use the pH scale in the first place? Well, when dealing with hydrogen ion concentrations, the actual numbers are usually pretty difficult to deal with. You probably don't want to have to repeatedly write out numbers like 0.0000000000094582244 or 0.00066594482. So instead, we use a shorthand type of notation, which is to take the logarithm (or log).

The log is very simple—it just states the number of zeroes that follow a number 1. So, the log of 1 billion is 9, because 9 zeroes follow the 1, and the log of 10,000 is 4, because 4 zeroes follow the 1. When there are zeroes in *front* of the 1, like 0.001, we simply move the decimal backward until it's behind the 1. This number is our log—but, we are moving the decimal backward, so the number is negative. For 0.001, we move the decimal backward three times, and the log is −3. Easy, right?

So, the log offers a nice shortcut to represent unruly numbers like hydrogen ion concentrations. But, remember that a hydrogen ion concentration is a number such as 0.00000000089254428, which means we have to move the decimal backward. This gives us a negative number, which seems awkward—how do you represent a positive quantity with a negative number? We can easily fix this negative number problem, though.

Remember from basic math what happens when you multiply a negative by a negative? The result is a positive number ($-2 \times -2 = +4$). So, all we have to do to make this number positive is to pop a negative sign in front of the log. This multiplies the negative answer by a negative, which makes it positive. But, look what happens when we do this:

	Hydrogen Ion Concentration	Log	Negative Log
Solution A	0.01	−2	2
Solution B	0.00000000000001	−14	14

Solution A, with a concentration of 0.01, has a higher hydrogen ion concentration than Solution B because 0.01 is a larger number than 0.00000000000001. Solution A also has a higher log: −2 is a higher number than −14. But, Solution A, which has more hydrogen ions, has a *lower negative log*. Solution B, which has almost no hydrogen ions, has a *higher negative log*.

So, why does the pH seem backward? It's all because of that negative log. Knowing this gives you a trick you can use if you get confused: Just imagine the numbers are negative. Then we are back to −2 and −14, and the higher number has the higher number of hydrogen ions.

1 PROCEDURE
Reading the pH

A simple way to measure pH is to use pH paper (Fig. 2.4). To test the pH with pH paper, drop one or two drops of the sample solution on the paper, and compare the color change

⚠ SAFETY NOTE
Safety glasses and gloves are required!

with the colors on the side of the pH paper container. The pH is read as the number that corresponds to the color the paper turned.

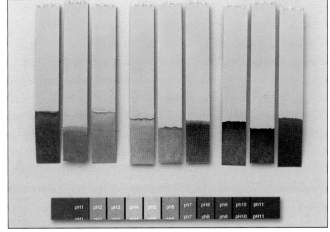

FIGURE 2.4 pH paper and indicator strip.

1 Obtain two samples each of known acids and bases, and record their molecular formulae in Table 2.1 (the molecular formula should be on the side of each bottle).

2 Measure the pH of each acid and base using pH paper, and record their pH values in Table 2.1.

3 Obtain two randomly selected unknown samples, and measure their pH using pH paper.

4 Record the pH values in Table 2.1, and determine whether this substance is an acid, a base, or neutral based upon its pH.

TABLE 2.1 Samples of Acids and Bases

Samples	Molecular Formula	pH
Acid #1		
Acid #2		
Base #1		
Base #2		
Unknown Samples	pH	Acid, Base, or Neutral?
Unknown #1		
Unknown #2		

2 PROCEDURE

Applying the pH Scale

Now, let's apply the pH scale to physiological systems. The stomach contains concentrated hydrochloric acid, and the pH of the stomach contents ranges between 1 and 3. **Antacids** are a group of medications that raise the pH of the stomach contents to treat a variety of conditions, including *gastroesophageal reflux*, commonly known as *heartburn*. Antacids generally consist of a metal bonded to a base. In this activity, you will compare the effectiveness of three widely available antacids in raising the pH of concentrated hydrochloric acid.

Hypothesis: Which antacid do you think will be most effective?

1   Obtain three glass test tubes, and label them 1, 2, and 3 with a permanent marker.

2   Obtain a bottle of 0.1 M hydrochloric acid (HCl), and record its pH in the blank that follows.

pH of 0.1 M HCl: _____

3   In each tube, place 2 mL of the 0.1 M HCl.

4   Add about one-fourth of one crushed Tums tablet to Tube 1 and stir the contents with a clean glass stirring rod.

5   Add about one-fourth of one crushed Rolaids tablet to Tube 2 and stir the contents with a clean glass stirring rod.

6   Add about one-fourth of one crushed Alka-Seltzer tablet to Tube 3 and stir the contents with a clean glass stirring rod.

7   Allow the tubes to sit undisturbed for 3 minutes.

8   Measure the pH of the contents of each tube, and record the values in Table 2.2.

9   What effect did the antacids have on the acid?

⚠ **SAFETY NOTE**

Safety glasses and gloves are required!

10   Based upon your observations, which antacid is the most effective at neutralizing the acid?

TABLE **2.2** Effectiveness of Three Antacids

Antacid	Active Ingredient	pH
Tums		
Rolaids		
Alka-Seltzer		

11   Compare your results to your hypothesis.

EXERCISE 2-2

MATERIALS

- ☐ Well plates
- ☐ Stirring rods
- ☐ Dropping pipettes
- ☐ 0.1 M hydrochloric acid
- ☐ Buffered solution
- ☐ Distilled water
- ☐ 0.1 M NaOH
- ☐ pH paper
- ☐ Permanent marker

Buffers

You may have noticed that the pH range in our cells and blood is very narrow: 7.35–7.45. This narrow range must be maintained because even slight changes in hydrogen ion concentration can disrupt the functions of many important compounds. Such a narrow range is also necessary because a change in one pH unit represents a tenfold change in hydrogen ion concentration. So, blood with a pH of 6.45 has 10 times more hydrogen ions than blood with a pH of 7.45.

How does the body maintain such a narrow pH range? It can do this thanks to built-in **buffers,** chemical systems that resist large or dramatic changes in pH. A solution to which a buffer has been added is a **buffered solution.** A buffer generally consists of a weak acid and its corresponding anion, known as its *conjugate base.* For example, one of the body's main buffers is the *carbonic acid–bicarbonate buffer system.* Here, the weak acid is carbonic acid (H_2CO_3) and its conjugate base is the bicarbonate ion:

$$H_2CO_3 \rightleftharpoons H^+ + HCO_3^-$$

Carbonic acid   Hydrogen ion   Bicarbonate ion

Here's how a buffer such as the carbonic acid–bicarbonate buffer system works. When acid is added to a buffered solution, the buffer's conjugate base binds the added hydrogen ions and removes them from the solution. Similarly, when a base is added to a buffered solution, the buffer's weak acid releases hydrogen ions into the solution. Both effects minimize the pH changes that otherwise would occur in the solution if the buffer were not present.

Buffer systems in the body are critical for keeping the blood pH in the normal range. If the buffer systems are overwhelmed, we may see *acidosis* (ă-sih-DOH-sis)—a decrease in the pH of body fluids (*acidemia* is specifically a decrease in blood pH below 7.35). Acidosis causes nervous system depression, leading to signs and symptoms such as slurred speech, drowsiness, unresponsiveness, coma, and even death. A pH swing in the opposite direction causes *alkalosis* (al-kuh-LOH-sis; *alkalemia* is specifically an increase in blood pH above 7.45). Alkalosis increases nervous system excitability, leading to numbness and tingling, muscle spasms, seizures, and potentially death.

1   PROCEDURE

Testing Buffered Solutions

In this experiment, you'll examine the effects of adding an acid or a base to buffered solutions and nonbuffered solutions. You will use distilled water as your nonbuffered solution, and your instructor will choose an appropriate buffered solution for you to use. When you have completed the activity, answer Check Your Understanding Questions 1 and 2 (p. 65).

⚠ **SAFETY NOTE**

Safety glasses and gloves are required!

> **Hypothesis:** How do you think buffered solutions will compare to nonbuffered solutions when acid or base are added?

1   Obtain a well plate, and number four wells 1, 2, 3, and 4 with a permanent marker.

2   Fill Wells 1 and 2 about half-full of distilled water. Measure the pH of the distilled water, and record that value in Table 2.3.

3   Fill Wells 3 and 4 about half-full of buffered solution. Measure the pH of the buffered solution, and record that value in Table 2.3.

4   Add two drops of 0.1 M HCl to Wells 1 and 3. Stir the solutions with a clean stirring rod (or a toothpick), and measure the pH of each well. Record the pH in Table 2.3.

5 Add two drops of 0.1 M NaOH (a base) to Wells 2 and 4. Stir the solutions with a clean stirring rod (or a toothpick), and measure the pH of each well. Record the pH in Table 2.3.

TABLE **2.3** pH of Buffered and Nonbuffered Solutions

Well	Initial Solution		Solution After Adding Acid or Base	
	Contents	pH	Contents	pH
1	Water		Water + 0.1 M HCl	
2	Water		Water + 0.1 M NaOH	
3	Buffered solution		Buffered solution + 0.1 M HCl	
4	Buffered solution		Buffered solution + 0.1 M NaOH	

6 Interpret your results. What effect did the buffer have on the pH changes you saw?

7 Compare your results to your hypothesis.

EXERCISE 2-3

MATERIALS

- ☐ Glass test tubes (13)
- ☐ Rubber stoppers (13)
- ☐ Graduated cylinders
- ☐ Test tube rack
- ☐ Distilled water
- ☐ Paint thinner (such as acetone)
- ☐ Table salt
- ☐ Sucrose
- ☐ Iodine crystals
- ☐ Unknown solids
- ☐ Starch
- ☐ Pink glucose
- ☐ Oil dyed with Sudan red
- ☐ Lab scoops or spatulas
- ☐ Lugol's iodine
- ☐ Permanent marker

Chemical Solubilities

When two or more atoms combine, they may interact physically, forming a *mixture*, or they may interact *chemically*, forming a **chemical bond**. In writing and in figures, we represent a bond as a horizontal line between atoms or ions, but note that a bond isn't a physical structure. Instead, it's an attractive force between atoms or ions. There are three different types of chemical bonds: *ionic*, *polar covalent*, and *nonpolar covalent bonds*. The type of bond determines much about how the compound or molecule behaves.

Ionic Bond

Why do certain atoms form certain types of bonds? This is best explained with an example. Let's take a look at sodium (Na) and chlorine (Cl). Look to Pre-Lab Exercise 2-3 and the periodic table in Figure 2.1 to answer the following questions:

A sodium atom has how many protons? _____

A sodium atom has how many electrons? _____

How many electrons will go in the first shell? _____

How many in the second shell? _____

How many in the third? _____

Now, draw this out on the diagram in Figure 2.5, and look in particular at the third shell. This outermost shell is known as the **valence shell**, and the electrons it contains are called **valence electrons.** In general, an atom must follow the **octet rule** to be stable, meaning it must have eight electrons in its valence shell. Note that atoms with five or fewer electrons instead follow the *duet rule*, meaning they are most stable with their first electron shell filled with two electrons.

So, sodium requires eight electrons in its valence shell to become stable.

But how many does it have? _____

Sodium obviously doesn't obey the octet rule. This makes it a very *reactive* element. Indeed, sodium metal placed in water is so reactive that it explodes. For sodium to become stable, will it be easier for sodium to: (1) steal seven more electrons from another atom, or (2) give up that one electron and get rid of that third shell? Option 2 is much simpler, and so sodium is simply going to *give away* that last electron. This means that it will lose an electron (negative charge) but will keep the same number of protons (positive charges). What

will the sodium ion's overall charge be now? _____

Now, let's look at an atom of chlorine:

A chlorine atom has how many protons? _____

Therefore, we know that a chlorine atom has how many electrons? _____

_____

How many electrons will go in the first shell? _____

How many in the second shell? _____

How many in the third? _____

Draw this in Figure 2.6.

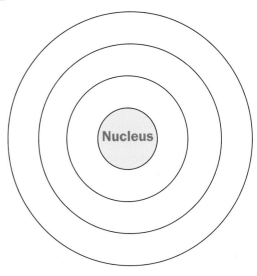

FIGURE **2.5** Orbital model of an atom.

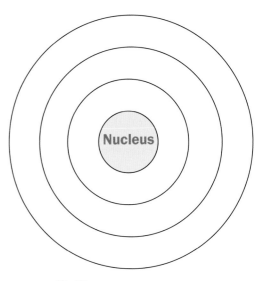

FIGURE **2.6** Orbital model of an atom.

Like sodium, the chlorine atom is also unstable, as it doesn't obey the octet rule. To obey the octet rule, will it be easier for chlorine to: (1) steal one electron from another atom, or (2) give away seven electrons? Option 1 is much easier: Chlorine will take an electron from another atom. This means that chlorine will gain an electron (negative charge) but will keep the same number of protons (positive charges). What charge will chlorine, as the newly formed *chloride ion*, have now? _____

Let's tie this in with what we've learned about metals and nonmetals.

We said that metals

_____ electrons to

become _____ .

Is sodium a metal or a nonmetal?

_____

Looking at our example, did sodium donate or

accept an electron? _____

We also said that nonmetals _____

electrons to become _____ .

Is chlorine a metal or a nonmetal?

_____

Looking at our example above, did chlorine

donate or accept an electron? _____

Why is this important? Well, when electrons are transferred between a metal atom and a nonmetal atom, we end up with a positively charged *cation* and a negatively charged *anion*. The positive and negative charges attract each other, which forms an **ionic bond** (Fig. 2.7). See how simple that is?

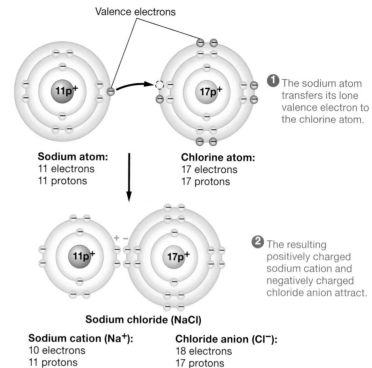

Valence electrons

Sodium atom:
11 electrons
11 protons

Chlorine atom:
17 electrons
17 protons

❶ The sodium atom transfers its lone valence electron to the chlorine atom.

❷ The resulting positively charged sodium cation and negatively charged chloride anion attract.

Sodium chloride (NaCl)

Sodium cation (Na⁺):
10 electrons
11 protons

Chloride anion (Cl⁻):
18 electrons
17 protons

FIGURE **2.7** Sodium chloride (NaCl): an example of an ionic bond.

Polar Covalent Bond

Next, let's tackle another bonding concept, the **polar covalent bond**. The classic example of a polar covalent bond is represented by the two bonds in a water molecule (Fig. 2.8A). Let's look at how this works, using the periodic table (seen in Fig. 2.1).

A hydrogen (H) atom has how many protons? _____

A hydrogen atom has how many electrons? _____

How many electrons will go in the first shell? _____

How many electrons would hydrogen require to obey the duet rule? _____

An oxygen (O) atom has how many protons? _____

An oxygen atom has how many electrons? _____

How many electrons will go in the first shell? _____

How many electrons will go in the second shell? _____

How many electrons would oxygen require to obey the octet rule? _____

Both hydrogen and oxygen are nonmetals, and neither element will give up electrons in this situation. So, instead of one element taking the electrons, the elements share them. But oxygen requires two electrons to obey the octet rule, and hydrogen has only one electron to

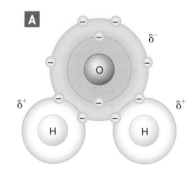

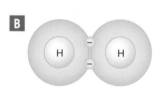

FIGURE **2.8** Covalent bonds: (**A**) water, an example of a polar covalent compound; (**B**) hydrogen, an example of a nonpolar covalent molecule.

share, so oxygen forms a partnership with two hydrogen atoms, forming H_2O. This electron sharing is known as a **covalent bond**.

Although the electrons are shared between oxygen and the hydrogen atoms, they aren't shared equally. Oxygen has a higher **electronegativity**, which means it attracts electrons more strongly than hydrogen does. As a result, the electrons spend more time around the oxygen atom and less around the hydrogen atoms. This means that:

Oxygen will have a partial _____ charge, and the two hydrogens will have a partial

_____ charge (look to **Fig 2.8A**).

This type of bond, in which a compound has a positive pole and a negative pole, is appropriately known as a **polar covalent bond**.

Nonpolar Covalent Bond

A **nonpolar covalent bond** involves the same principles as the polar covalent bond does, except that the atoms share the electrons equally. So, there are no partial positive or negative charges because the electrons don't spend any more time around one or more of the atoms. You can see this in **Figure 2.8B** with the example of a molecule of hydrogen (H_2)—both hydrogen atoms have the same electronegativity, and so they have the same pull on the electrons. This causes the electrons to spend an equal amount of time around each atom.

Chemicals are not limited to having only ionic, polar covalent, or nonpolar covalent bonds. Certain chemicals have both polar and nonpolar parts—these compounds are said to be **amphipathic** (am-fih-PATH-ik; "experiencing both") or *amphiphilic* (am-fih-FIL-ik; "liking both"), meaning that they have both polar and nonpolar parts. Many important biological compounds, including phospholipids and bile salts, are amphipathic.

Solubility

Determining the types of bonds present in a molecule is important, because of this general rule:

Like interacts with like.

This means that chemicals with charged ends—polar and ionic compounds—prefer to interact with chemicals that also have charged ends (other polar and ionic compounds). Chemicals without charged ends—nonpolar molecules and compounds—prefer to interact with chemicals that also have no charged ends (other nonpolar molecules and compounds). Conversely, ionic and polar covalent compounds won't interact with nonpolar molecules and compounds. This is something you have seen in action if you have ever tried to combine nonpolar oil and polar water. In their natural conditions, oil and water don't mix.

The degree to which one substance, called a **solute**, will interact with another substance (usually a liquid), called a **solvent**, is known as its **solubility**. A solute that interacts strongly and dissolves completely in a solvent is said to be highly *soluble* in that solvent. Conversely, a solute that does not interact with and dissolve in a solvent is said to be *insoluble* in that solvent. The rules for solubility are simple:

- Polar and ionic solutes are soluble in most polar solvents.
- Nonpolar solutes are soluble in most nonpolar solvents.

The solvent in the human body is water. This means that polar and ionic solutes are soluble, or can dissolve, in liquid water and be carried around the body relatively easily and safely. Such solutes are said to be **hydrophilic** (hy-droh-FIL-ik; "water loving"). On the other hand, nonpolar substances are insoluble in water and are said to be **hydrophobic** (hy-droh-FOH-bik; "water fearing"). When hydrophobic substances are placed in water, they are attracted to one another instead of to the water molecules. This causes them to clump together, separated from the water.

HINTS & TIPS

How to Determine the Types of Bonds in a Molecule

Following are some simple rules for determining whether a compound or molecule is polar, nonpolar, or ionic.

- ⓘ Any metal (except hydrogen) bound to a nonmetal is an ionic compound.
- ⓘ All compounds that contain only C and H are nonpolar.
- ⓘ Any molecule containing multiple atoms of the same element (e.g., H_2) is nonpolar.
- ⓘ A compound containing C and/or H bound to a significant amount of O, N, P, Cl, or F is polar.
- ⓘ Any compound containing mostly C and H is overall a nonpolar compound, even if it contains a few polar bonds such as C-O or O-H.

1 PROCEDURE

Testing Chemical Solubilities

You can determine whether solutes are nonpolar or polar/ionic based upon the type of solvent in which they dissolve. In this procedure, you will have two solvents—one that is polar and one that is nonpolar. You will attempt to dissolve three known samples of solute and two unknown samples of solute in these solvents in order to identify them as nonpolar or polar/ionic.

After you test them, your instructor may wish to give you the molecular formulae of your unknown samples so you may determine the types of molecules more precisely.

Hypothesis: Which types of solute do you think will dissolve in a polar solvent? What types of solute do you think will dissolve in a nonpolar solvent?

1 Obtain 10 glass test tubes, a test tube rack, and 10 rubber stoppers. Number the test tubes 1 through 10 with a permanent marker.

2 Add 2 mL of distilled water to Tubes 1 through 5. Add 2 mL of paint thinner to Tubes 6 through 10.

   a Which solvent is the polar solvent? _____

   b Which solvent is the nonpolar solvent? _____

3 Add a pinch of table salt to Tubes 1 and 6. What is the molecular formula for salt? _____

4 Add a pinch of sucrose to Tubes 2 and 7. What is the molecular formula for sucrose? _____

5 Add a pinch of iodine crystals to Tubes 3 and 8. What is the molecular formula for iodine? _____

6 Add a pinch of Unknown substance A to Tubes 4 and 9.

7 Add a pinch of Unknown substance B to Tubes 5 and 10.

8 Place a stopper firmly in each of the tubes. Shake each tube for several seconds until you are certain that no further change will take place in the solute.

9 Examine each tube, and determine whether the solute dissolved or remained separate. Record your results in Table 2.4.

10 Now, use your results to determine whether the solute is an ionic, polar, or nonpolar molecule. For your unknowns, you will only be able to determine whether the solute is ionic/polar or nonpolar.

   a What type of compound is salt? _____

   b What type of compound is sucrose? _____

   c What type of molecule is iodine? _____

   d What type of molecule is Unknown substance A (polar/ionic or nonpolar)? _____

   e What type of molecule is Unknown substance B (polar/ionic or nonpolar)? _____

TABLE **2.4** Results for Solubility Experiment

Tube	Tube Contents	Dissolved in Polar Solvent? (Y/N)
1	Salt + water	
2	Sucrose + water	
3	Iodine + water	
4	Unknown substance A + water	
5	Unknown substance B + water	

Tube	Tube Contents	Dissolved in Nonpolar Solvent? (Y/N)
6	Salt + paint thinner	
7	Sucrose + paint thinner	
8	Iodine + paint thinner	
9	Unknown substance A + paint thinner	
10	Unknown substance B + paint thinner	

11 Compare your results to your hypothesis.

_____

_____

_____

2 PROCEDURE

Testing for Hydrophobic and Hydrophilic Solutes

You will now see what happens when we add a hydrophilic solute and a hydrophobic solute to water. When you have completed the activity, answer Check Your Understanding Question 3 (p. 66).

> **Hypothesis:** What will happen to the hydrophilic solute in water? What will happen to the hydrophobic solute in water?

1 Obtain two test tubes with rubber stoppers. Label one "sugar" and the other one "oil."

2 Place about 3 mL of distilled water in each test tube.

3 Add a pinch of pink glucose to the "sugar" test tube, place the rubber stopper on it, and shake the tube vigorously until the pink color is evenly distributed. Set the tube in a test tube rack and leave it undisturbed for 10 minutes.

4 Add about 1 mL of oil stained with Sudan red to the "oil" test tube, place the rubber stopper on it, and shake the tube vigorously until the red color is evenly distributed. Set the tube in a test tube rack and leave it undisturbed for 10 minutes.

5 After 10 minutes:

    a What is the color of the water in the "sugar" tube? _____

    b What is the color of the water in the "oil" tube? _____

6 Interpret your results:

    a What types of bonds are in glucose ($C_6H_{12}O_6$)? How does this help explain the color of the water in this tube?

_____

_____

_____

    b What types of bonds are in oil? How does this help explain the color of the water in this tube?

_____

_____

_____

    c Which substance was hydrophilic? Which substance was hydrophobic? How do you know?

_____

_____

_____

7 Compare your results to your hypothesis.

_____

_____

EXERCISE 2-4

MATERIALS

- ☐ Test tubes (13)
- ☐ Test tube rack
- ☐ Catalase
- ☐ 3% hydrogen peroxide
- ☐ 0.1% hydrogen peroxide
- ☐ Distilled water
- ☐ Hot plate (for boiling water)
- ☐ Ice-water bath
- ☐ pH 3 buffer
- ☐ pH 7 buffer
- ☐ pH 10 buffer
- ☐ Permanent marker
- ☐ Ruler

Enzymes and Chemical Reactions

We just discussed chemical bonds, but chemical bonds are not permanent forces: new bonds can be formed; they can be broken; they can be rearranged; and electrons can be transferred between atoms or compounds. Any time this happens, a **chemical reaction** is said to have taken place. We have already seen examples of chemical reactions in this unit; for example, we discussed this reaction of the carbonic acid–bicarbonate buffer system in Exercise 2-2:

$$H_2CO_3 \rightleftharpoons H^+ + HCO_3^-$$

Carbonic acid   Hydrogen   Bicarbonate
                            ion   ion

Chemical reactions are represented through a series of symbols known as a *chemical equation*. There are two parts to a chemical equation:

- **Reactants.** In our example, carbonic acid is the **reactant**—the starting substance that will undergo the reaction.

- **Products.** The **products** are the end result of the reaction—in this case, the products are a hydrogen ion and a bicarbonate ion. By convention, we place products on the right-hand side of the equation.

Most reactions have an arrow between the products and reactants, indicating that the reaction proceeds in one direction only. In our example, however, the arrow points in both directions. This indicates that the reaction is *reversible* and can proceed in both directions.

Chemical reactions do not proceed spontaneously—all require some input of energy known as the **activation energy** (E_a). You can imagine the activation energy as an "energy barrier" that all reactions must overcome in order to occur. This is because reactants must collide with sufficient force to react. But, reactants' electrons repel one another, and so they must collide with enough force to overcome this repulsion.

The reaction rate is influenced by the likelihood of strong collisions between atoms. Three factors influence these collisions:

- **The concentration of the reactants.** The higher the concentration of the reactants, the higher the chances for particle collisions and the higher the reaction rate. Conversely, the lower the reactant concentration, the lower the chances for particle collisions and the lower the reaction rate.

- **The temperature.** Raising the temperature of the reactants increases the kinetic energy of their atoms, resulting in more forceful and effective collisions. Note that for biological reactions, however, this works only up to a point, because many substances in the human body are destroyed at high temperatures.

- **Particle size and phase of the reactants.** Smaller particles tend to move faster, which makes them collide more strongly and have faster reaction rates than we see with larger particles. Similarly, particles in the gaseous phase also move more rapidly and have stronger collisions than those in the liquid phase, and they move very slowly in the solid phase. As a result, we generally see faster reaction rates in gaseous reactants than in liquids, and very slow reaction rates in solids.

However, the most important factor that affects reaction rate is the activation energy, which can be lowered with a *catalyst* (KAT-uh-list). In the body, biological catalysts called **enzymes** speed up essentially all our chemical reactions. Nearly all enzymes in the body are *proteins* that work by binding to their reacting components, which are known as **substrates**. Each enzyme has a unique region called the **active site** that not only is specific for its substrate, but it also usually only catalyzes a single reaction. Note that enzymes don't change the reaction itself, and are not consumed in the reaction—when the reaction has finished, the enzyme is free to catalyze another reaction.

1 PROCEDURE
Testing Enzyme-Catalyzed Reactions

Certain structures within human cells, which are known as *peroxisomes*, produce hydrogen peroxide, H_2O_2, as a byproduct of chemical reactions that break down fats. The hydrogen peroxide itself is toxic, and an enzyme within the peroxisomes, *catalase*, catalyzes the breakdown of hydrogen peroxide into water and oxygen:

$$2H_2O_2 \longrightarrow 2H_2O + O_2$$

Hydrogen   Water   Oxygen
peroxide

In this experiment, you'll examine the role of catalase in the breakdown of hydrogen peroxide. You'll also study the effects of pH, temperature, and concentration on the ability of the enzyme to function.

Part A

Hypothesis: How will temperature affect the rate of the enzyme-catalyzed reaction?

1 Obtain six test tubes and label them 1–6 with a permanent marker.

2 Add 1 mL of catalase to each test tube.

3 Pre-incubate the tubes at different temperatures for 5 minutes:

  ▪ Incubate Tubes 1 and 4 in ice water.

  ▪ Incubate Tubes 2 and 5 in a test tube rack at room temperature.

  ▪ Incubate Tubes 3 and 6 in a boiling-water bath.

4 After 5 minutes, remove all tubes and place them in a test tube rack. Use tongs to remove the tubes from the boiling water bath to avoid burns.

5 Add 10 drops of 3% hydrogen peroxide to Tubes 1–3.

6 Add 10 drops of distilled water to Tubes 4–6.

7 After 60 seconds, use a ruler to measure the height of any bubbling in each tube. Record your results in Table 2.5.

TABLE **2.5** Results of Catalase Temperature Experiment

Tube	Tube Contents	Height of Bubbling (mm)
1	Hydrogen peroxide + catalase in ice water	
2	Hydrogen peroxide + catalase at room temperature	
3	Hydrogen peroxide + catalase in boiling water	
4	Water + catalase in ice water	
5	Water + catalase at room temperature	
6	Water + catalase in boiling water	

8 Interpret your results: What effect does temperature have on catalase activity?

9 Compare your results to your hypothesis.

Part B

Hypothesis: How will concentration affect the rate of the enzyme-catalyzed reaction?

1 Obtain three test tubes and label them 1–3 with a permanent marker.

2 Add 1 mL of catalase to each test tube.

3 Add 10 drops of 3% hydrogen peroxide to Tube 1.

4 Add 10 drops of 0.1% hydrogen peroxide to Tube 2.

5 Add 10 drops of distilled water to Tube 3.

6 After 60 seconds, use a ruler to measure the height of any bubbling in each tube. Record your results in Table 2.6.

7 Interpret your results: What effect does concentration have on catalase activity?

_____

_____

8 Compare your results to your hypothesis.

_____

_____

TABLE **2.6** Results of Catalase/Hydrogen Peroxide Concentration Experiment

Tube	Tube Contents	Height of Bubbling (mm)
1	Hydrogen peroxide 3% + catalase	
2	Hydrogen peroxide 0.1% + catalase	
3	Water + catalase	

Part C

Hypothesis: How will pH affect the rate of the enzyme-catalyzed reaction?

_____

1 Obtain four test tubes and label them 1–4 with a permanent marker.

2 Add 1 mL of catalase to each test tube.

3 Add 1 mL of the appropriate buffer to the tubes:
- Add 1 mL of pH 3 buffer to Tube 1.
- Add 1 mL of pH 7 buffer to Tube 2.
- Add 1 mL of pH 10 buffer to Tube 3.
- Add 1 mL of distilled water to Tube 4.

4 Add 10 drops of 3% hydrogen peroxide to Tubes 1–3.

5 After 60 seconds, use a ruler to measure the height of any bubbling in each tube. Record your results in Table 2.7.

6 Interpret your results: What effect does pH have on catalase activity?

_____

_____

7 Compare your results to your hypothesis.

_____

_____

TABLE **2.7** Results of Catalase pH Experiment

Tube	Tube Contents	Height of Bubbling (mm)
1	Hydrogen peroxide + catalase in pH 3 buffer	
2	Hydrogen peroxide + catalase pH 7 buffer	
3	Hydrogen peroxide + catalase in pH 10 buffer	
4	Water + catalase	

EXERCISE 2-5

MATERIALS

- [ ] For starch experiment:
  - Glass test tubes (5)
  - Test tube rack
  - Lugol's iodine
  - Onion juice
  - Potato juice
  - Starch solution
  - Distilled water
  - Agave nectar
- [ ] For lipase experiment:
  - Glass test tubes (6)
  - Test tube rack
  - Lipase
  - Boiled lipase
  - Bile salts
  - Vegetable oil
  - 0.1 M NaOH
  - Ice-water bath
  - Warm-water bath (set to 37°C)
  - Phenol red
  - Permanent marker
- [ ] For DNA extraction:
  - 50 mL beaker
  - Test tube
  - Glass stirring rod
  - Graduated cylinder
  - Pea mixture
  - Isopropyl alcohol
  - Meat tenderizer
  - Liquid detergent
  - Wooden applicator stick

Organic Compounds: Carbohydrates, Proteins, Lipids, and Nucleotides

We turn now to organic compounds, those that contain both hydrogen and carbon atoms. Four organic compounds are critical in the human body: *carbohydrates, proteins, lipids* (fats), and *nucleotides*. Each class of organic compound can exist as a single subunit, or **monomer** (MAHN-oh-mer; "one part"), or as a larger structure composed of linked monomers called a **polymer** (PAHL-ih-mer; "many parts"). Each type of organic compound we discuss here has its own monomer and a corresponding polymer built from those subunits.

Carbohydrates make up very little of the body's mass—only about 1%. Instead, they function mostly as a source of energy for our cells. Carbohydrate monomers contain carbon, hydrogen, and oxygen atoms in a 1C:2H:1O ratio (meaning we have two hydrogen atoms for every one carbon and one oxygen atom). The many oxygen atoms, which are found in −OH groups, make carbohydrates polar compounds that are hydrophilic.

A carbohydrate monomer is referred to as a **monosaccharide** (mahn'-oh-SAK-uh-ry'd; *mono-* = "one," *sacchar-* = "sugar") or "simple sugar" (Fig. 2.9). Most monosaccharides in the body have five or six carbons. Examples include *deoxyribose* (dee'-ahks-ee-RY-bohs) and *ribose* (RY-bohs), which have five carbons, and *glucose, galactose,* and *fructose*, which have six. You may notice in Figure 2.9 that glucose, galactose, and fructose all have the same molecular formula, $C_6H_{12}O_6$, but different chemical structures. This makes these compounds **isomers** (AYE-soh-merz; "same parts")—chemicals with the same types and numbers of atoms but different atomic arrangements.

When two monosaccharides are linked, they form a **disaccharide** (dy-SAK-uh-ry'd; *di-* = "two"). Examples of disaccharides include sucrose (table sugar) and lactose (milk sugar). When many monosaccharides are linked together, they form a polymer called a **polysaccharide** (pahl-ee-SAK-uh-ry'd; *poly-* = "many"). Although polysaccharides are technically hydrophilic, they aren't very soluble in water due to their large size. Their structure and low solubility provide a good way for plant and animal cells to store glucose. The plant storage form of glucose is the polysaccharide *starch*; the animal storage form is the polysaccharide **glycogen** (GLY-koh-jen; Fig. 2.10). Glycogen, located primarily in the cells of the liver and skeletal muscles, has a heavily branched structure.

Our next class of organic compounds is the **lipids** (LIP-idz), which include the fats and oils. On average, about 16–25% of the human body is composed of different types of lipids. They perform structural roles, store energy, regulate body temperature, and absorb shock. Like carbohydrates, lipids consist of carbon, hydrogen, and oxygen atoms. However, lipids are mostly carbon and hydrogen with very little oxygen. This makes lipids nonpolar and hydrophobic, which you saw demonstrated with the oil in Procedure 2 of Exercise 2-3. Recall from that exercise, though, that nonpolar compounds such as lipids will dissolve in other nonpolar compounds. In addition, lipids can act as a solvent for nonpolar compounds. For this reason, nonpolar compounds are said to be *lipid-soluble*.

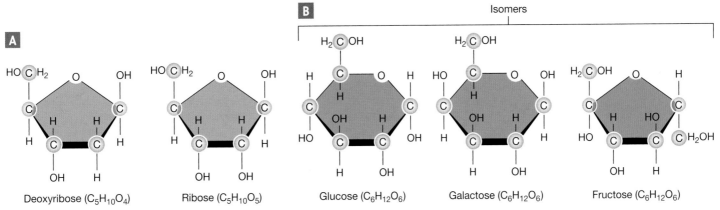

FIGURE **2.9** Examples of monosaccharides: (**A**) five-carbon sugars: deoxyribose and ribose; (**B**) six-carbon sugars: glucose, galactose, and fructose.

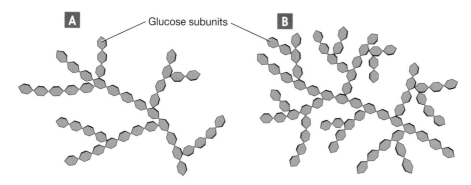

FIGURE **2.10** Polysaccharides: (**A**) starch; (**B**) glycogen.

The **fatty acid** is a lipid monomer. It consists of a long chain of carbon and hydrogen atoms; at the end of this chain is a *carboxylic acid group* (−COOH). Fatty acids are classified based on the number of double bonds between carbon atoms in the chain: a *saturated fatty acid* has no double bonds; a *monounsaturated fatty acid* has one double bond; and a *polyunsaturated fatty acid* has two or more double bonds. We typically find saturated fatty acids in animal fats, and they are typically solid at room temperature. Both monounsaturated and polyunsaturated fatty acids are found in high concentrations in plants. They have a low melting point, and so are liquid (oils) at room temperature.

Our bodies store fatty acids as polymers called **triglycerides** (try-GLISS-er-aye'dz; Fig. 2.11A). These compounds are formed by linking fatty acids to **glycerol** (GLISS-er-ahl), a three-carbon sugar alcohol. The properties of individual triglycerides vary based on which fatty acids are attached.

Special lipids called **phospholipids** (fahs-foh-LIP-idz) have a glycerol backbone, two fatty acids, and a large, strongly polar *phosphate group* (FAHS-fayt) in place of the third fatty acid (Fig. 2.11B). Because the two fatty acids are strongly nonpolar and the phosphate group is strongly polar, we have a two-sided compound: a polar, hydrophilic *phosphate head*, and nonpolar, hydrophobic *fatty acid tails*. Recall from Exercise 2-3 that compounds with polar and nonpolar parts are known as amphipathic. As we will see in Unit 4, phospholipids are a key component of the membrane surrounding our cells.

The third class of organic compounds in the body is called **proteins**, which account for about 16–20% of the body's mass. We produce up to 100,000 different proteins, which have a variety of roles in the body, including playing multiple structural roles,

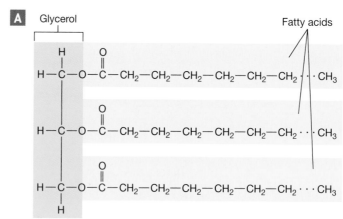

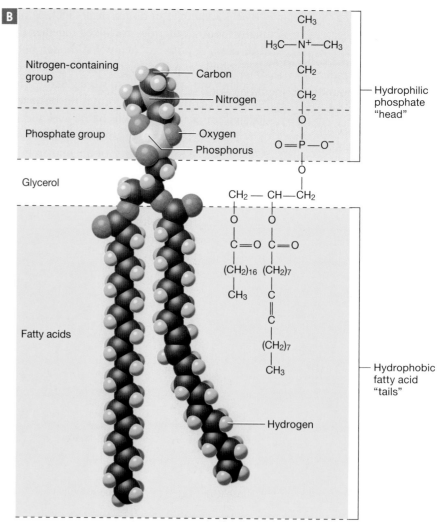

FIGURE **2.11** Lipids: (**A**) a triglyceride; (**B**) a phospholipid.

functioning in immunity, enabling cellular communication, acting as enzymes, making up muscles, and being used for energy. Each protein is a polymer composed of a unique sequence of monomers called **amino acids** (uh-MEE-noh) linked by a polar covalent bond called a **peptide bond**. When two amino acids are joined by a peptide bond, the resulting structure is a *dipeptide*; three amino acids are a *tripeptide*; and 10 or more amino acids are a *polypeptide*. The polypeptide is considered a protein when it is folded into a unique structure.

There are 21 different amino acids in the human body, all of which share the same core structure, as shown in Figure 2.12. Notice that it features a central carbon atom bonded to: (1) a hydrogen atom, (2) an *amino group* ($-NH_2$), (3) a carboxylic acid group ($-COOH$), and (4) the R-group. ("R" just stands for "residue," and is a generic abbreviation for the specialized chemical group bound to the carbon in this position. Note that it is the R-group that gives each amino acid its unique properties. R-groups vary in whether they are polar or nonpolar and acidic or basic.)

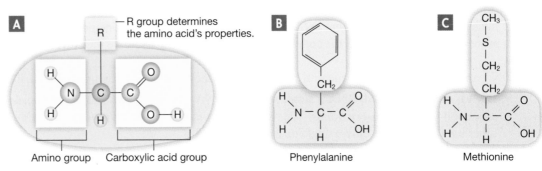

FIGURE **2.12** Amino acids: (**A**) a generic amino acid; (**B**) the amino acid phenylalanine; (**C**) the amino acid methionine.

The amino acids' R-groups tend to give proteins highly complex shapes, and a protein must be folded into this correct shape to be fully functional. Indeed, it is a protein's shape that determines its function. Think back to enzymes—even a minor change in the amino acid sequence can change the enzyme's shape in a way such that it can no longer bind its substrate. A protein that loses its shape is said to be **denatured**, and the process that destroys this shape is called **denaturation**. Proteins are sensitive to many variables, like heat, pH swings, and the presence of chemicals such as those in common disinfectants. Any of these variables can denature proteins and render them nonfunctional—this is largely why humans can't tolerate high temperatures or pH values much outside our normal range.

Before we move on to the fourth and final major class of organic compounds, we should mention a type of modified protein and lipid, **glycoproteins** and **glycolipids**, which consist of proteins and lipids covalently bound to carbohydrates. Glycoproteins and glycolipids are located in the membranes surrounding our cells where they play important structural roles. They also allow cells to recognize one another and enable cell-cell communication.

Let's now turn to our final class of organic compounds in the body, the **nucleotides** (NOO-klee-oh-tyd'z), which account for about 2% of the body's mass. As you might suspect from the name, we find many nucleotides in the central core of the cell, or what is called the *nucleus*. Nucleotides make up our genetic material; the nucleotide adenosine is found in the body's main energy "currency"—*adenosine triphosphate* (*ATP*).

Notice in Figure 2.13 that a nucleotide consists of three parts: (1) a nitrogenous base, (2) a five-carbon sugar (either ribose or deoxyribose), and (3) a phosphate group (the same compound we saw in phospholipids). There are two types of nitrogenous bases: *purines* (PYOOR-eenz), double-ringed compounds that include **adenine** (**A**) and **guanine** (**G**), and *pyrimidines* (per-IM-ih-deenz), single-ringed compounds that include **cytosine** (**C**), **thymine** (**T**), and **uracil** (**U**).

Nucleotide monomers link together to form polymers called **nucleic acids**. The two nucleic acids are **deoxyribonucleic acid** (**DNA**; dee-ahk-see-RY-boh-noo-klay'-ik) and **ribonucleic acid** (**RNA**). Together, they hold and execute the genetic code.

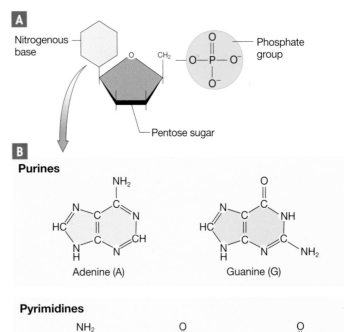

FIGURE **2.13** Nucleotides: (**A**) generic nucleotide structure; (**B**) the five nucleic acid bases.

You can see in Figure 2.14 how the nucleotides in nucleic acids are linked: the phosphate group of one nucleotide forms a polar covalent bond with the sugar of the next nucleotide. These sugar-phosphate group linkages form the nucleic acid's "backbone," and bases stick out to the side.

We said that DNA and RNA are involved in the genetic code, but what does that mean, exactly? Well, recall that proteins are made of strings of amino acids in a unique sequence. How does a cell "know" the correct sequence of amino acids to put together to make a specific protein? The answer is the code in DNA. Within DNA, we find segments of nucleotides called *genes*, and the nucleotide sequence of one gene specifies the amino acid sequence of one protein. But it takes more than just DNA to make a protein—DNA may contain the code, but it is RNA that must assemble the correct sequence of amino acids to make the protein.

DNA and RNA share many structural similarities, but they have key differences, as well, including the following:

- **DNA is double stranded; RNA is single stranded**. DNA consists of two strands of nucleic acids held together by weak attractions called *hydrogen bonds*. The two strands wind around each other in a **double helix** formation. RNA, on the other hand, consists of only a single nucleic acid strand.

- **DNA contains the sugar deoxyribose; RNA contains the sugar ribose**. The sugars found in DNA and RNA are implied by their names—note *deoxyribo*nucleic points to **deoxyribose** and *ribo*nucleic to **ribose**.

- **DNA contains the bases G, C, A, and T; RNA contains the bases G, C, A, and U**. DNA and RNA both contain the bases A, G, and C; DNA contains the base T, while RNA contains U (uracil) instead of T.

- **DNA is located only in the nucleus; RNA can move between the nucleus and the cytosol**. DNA is an absolutely massive polymer, and as such, it cannot leave its home in the nucleus of the cell. RNA molecules are smaller and can move between the nucleus and the fluid environment of the cell, the *cytosol*.

If you take a look at Figure 2.14, you'll notice that the bases in DNA bond in an unusual way: The purine G always bonds with the pyrimidine C, and the purine A always bonds with the pyrimidine T. We refer to this as **complementary base pairing**, and it has to do with the number of hydrogen bonds that each base can form. The bases G and C can both form three hydrogen bonds, so they pair together; the bases A and T can both form only two hydrogen bonds, so they form a pair. RNA lacks the base T, so when RNA binds to DNA or other RNA strands, U forms two hydrogen bonds with A in its place.

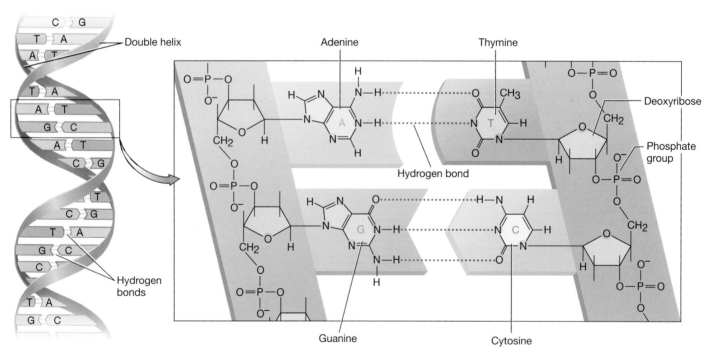

FIGURE **2.14** Deoxyribonucleic acid (DNA).

Testing for the Presence of Starch

The chemical structure of starch allows us to distinguish it chemically from mono-saccharides, disaccharides, and other polysaccharides. To do this, we use a solution known as Lugol's iodine, which contains iodine (I_2) and potassium iodide (KI). Lugol's iodine interacts with the coiled portions of starch, turning the solution a bluish-black color. This bluish-black color is considered a positive test for starch. Compounds that lack these coils, including mono- and disaccharides, won't react with Lugol's iodine, and the solution will remain a yellowish-brown color—this color result is considered a negative test for starch.

⚠ **SAFETY NOTE**

Safety glasses and gloves are required!

Hypothesis: Which solutions will test positive for starch?

1 Obtain five test tubes and number them 1–5.

2 Add to each tube the following:
   - Add 10 drops of onion juice to Tube 1.
   - Add 10 drops of agave nectar to Tube 2.
   - Add 10 drops of potato juice to Tube 3.
   - Add 10 drops of distilled water to Tube 4.
   - Add 10 drops of starch solution to Tube 5.

3 Add three to five drops of Lugol's iodine to each tube and mix by swirling the tube gently.

4 Record your results in Table 2.8.

5 Interpret your results:

   a How much starch is present in onions versus in potatoes?

   b Agave nectar is a commonly used sweetener. From the results of this test, what can you infer about the types of carbo-hydrates present in agave nectar?

6 Compare your results to your hypothesis.

TABLE **2.8** Results of Lugol's Iodine and Starch Experiment

Tube	Tube Contents	Color of Tube Contents
1	Onion juice	
2	Agave nectar	
3	Potato juice	
4	Distilled water	
5	Starch solution	

2 PROCEDURE

Testing Enzymatic Digestion of Lipids

This procedure allows us to examine both lipids and the importance of protein structure. You'll be comparing the ability of two enzymatic solutions—lipase and boiled lipase—to digest vegetable oil at three different temperatures. **Lipase** (LYE-payz) is a protein enzyme found in the human digestive tract that catalyzes the digestion of triglycerides into two free fatty acids and a *monoglyceride*.

⚠ **SAFETY NOTE**

Safety gloves and glasses are required!

You will check for the presence of digestion using an indicator called **phenol red**. Phenol red appears pink at an alkaline (basic) pH, changes to an orange-red color at a neutral pH, and changes to a yellow color when the pH becomes acidic. If triglycerides have been digested, fatty acids will be released that will decrease the pH of the contents of your tube and turn them orange-red or yellow. You may interpret your results in the following way (Fig. 2.15):

- Yellow color = the pH is acidic, and significant triglyceride digestion occurred.

- Red-orange color = the pH is neutral, and some triglyceride digestion occurred.

- Pink color = the pH is basic, and no (or limited) triglyceride digestion occurred.

Note that you also must add another component, called **bile**, to your mixture for digestion to occur. Bile is not an enzyme itself, but it does increase the ability of lipase to catalyze triglyceride digestion. When you have completed this experiment, answer Check your Understanding Questions 4 and 5 (p. 66).

FIGURE **2.15** Possible results from the lipid digestion experiment.

Hypothesis: How will temperature affect the rate of the lipid digestion?

1 Obtain six glass test tubes and label them 1 through 6 with a permanent marker.

2 Add 3 mL of vegetable oil to each test tube.

3 Add 8–10 drops of the pH indicator phenol red to each test tube. The oil now should appear pink. If it does not, add drops of 0.1 M NaOH (a base) to each tube until the indicator turns pink.

4 Add the following ingredients to each test tube:
- Tubes 1, 3, and 5: 1 mL lipase, 1 mL bile.
- Tubes 2, 4, and 6: 1 mL boiled lipase, 1 mL bile.

5 Place Tubes 1 and 2 in an ice bath, and incubate them for 30 minutes.

6 Leave Tubes 3 and 4 in your test tube rack to incubate at room temperature for 30 minutes.

7 Place Tubes 5 and 6 in a warm-water bath set to 37°C, and incubate them for 30 minutes.

8 After 30 minutes have passed, remove the tubes from the ice bath and warm-water bath, and place them in your test tube rack.

9 Record the color of each tube in Table 2.9 and interpret your results.

TABLE **2.9** Enzymatic Activity of Lipase

Tube Number	Color	pH (Acidic, Neutral, or Alkaline)	Amount of Digestion that Occurred
1			
2			
3			
4			
5			
6			

10 Answer the following questions about your results:

   a What effect does temperature have on enzyme activity?

   b Were your results with the boiled lipase different from the results with nonboiled lipase? Why?

11 Compare your results to your hypothesis.

3 PROCEDURE
Extracting DNA

In this procedure, you'll be extracting DNA from dried green peas. Although this obviously is not animal DNA, it's composed of the same nucleic acid bases as animal DNA. The first part of the extraction involves removing the DNA from the cell and the nucleus using a mild detergent. Then you will use enzymes to catalyze reactions that degrade the proteins around the DNA—this frees up the nucleic acids. Finally, you will take advantage of DNA's weak polarity to extract it from strongly polar water into weakly polar isopropyl alcohol.

⚠ SAFETY NOTE

Safety glasses and gloves are required!

1 Obtain about 10 mL of the blended pea mixture (which contains only dried peas and water), and scoop it into a 50 mL beaker.

2 Add 1.6 mL of liquid detergent to the pea mixture. Stir gently with a glass stirring rod, and let the mixture sit undisturbed for 5 to 10 minutes.

3 After 5 to 10 minutes, fill about one-third of a test tube with the pea-soap mixture.

4 Add a pinch of meat tenderizer (which contains enzymes) to the test tube, and stir with a glass stirring rod *very gently* (rough stirring will break up the DNA, making it harder to see).

5 Tilt the test tube, and slowly add isopropyl alcohol with a dropping pipette (or directly from a plastic squeeze bottle) so the alcohol forms a layer on the top of the pea mixture. The amount of alcohol you add should be approximately equal to the volume of the pea mixture.

6 Watch as the DNA rises to the alcohol layer (it looks long and stringy, as shown in Fig. 2.16).

7 Use an applicator stick to fish out the DNA, and set it on a paper towel. Voila! You have just extracted DNA!

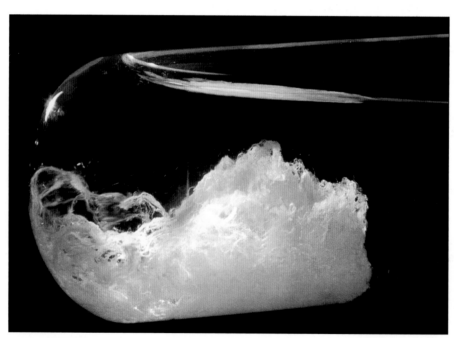

FIGURE **2.16** Extracted DNA in alcohol.

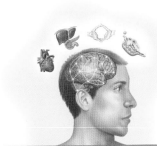

UNIT
2
REVIEW

Check Your Recall

1 An acid is defined as a substance that
   a. donates electrons.
   b. accepts a hydrogen ion.
   c. donates a hydrogen ion.
   d. has a pH greater than 7.

2 Adding base ions to a solution will make the solution more _____ , and its pH will _____ .
   a. acidic; increase
   b. alkaline; increase
   c. acidic; decrease
   d. alkaline; decrease

3 What does a buffer do when base ions are added to a solution?
   a. The buffer keeps the pH of a solution neutral.
   b. The buffer binds hydrogen ions in the solution.
   c. The buffer releases hydrogen ions into the solution.
   d. The buffer binds the base ions to remove them from the solution.

4 *True/False:* Mark the following statements as true (T) or false (F). If the statement is false, correct it to make it a true statement.

   _____ a. Most atoms must follow the octet rule in order to be stable.

   _____ b. Electrons are shared in an ionic bond.

   _____ c. Electrons are shared unequally in a polar covalent bond between two metals.

   _____ d. Electrons are shared unequally in a nonpolar covalent bond between two nonmetals.

5 Predict whether each of the following is an ionic, polar covalent, or nonpolar covalent compound or molecule.

$C_{15}H_{28}$ _____

$C_2H_5NO_2$ _____

CaBr _____

I_2 _____

SO_2 _____

LiF _____

6 Which of the following substances would you expect to dissolve in water?

a. Polar compounds.
b. Ionic compounds.
c. Nonpolar compounds.
d. Both a and b are correct.
e. Both a and c are correct.

7 *Fill in the blanks:* An _____ is a biological catalyst that speeds up a reaction rate by lowering the

_____.

8 Which of the following statements about carbohydrates is false?

a. Carbohydrate monomers are known as polysaccharides.
b. The monosaccharides fructose, glucose, and galactose are isomers.
c. Animals store carbohydrates as glycogen.
d. Carbohydrates consist of carbon, hydrogen, and oxygen in a 1C:2H:1O ratio.

9 *True/False:* Mark the following statements as true (T) or false (F). If the statement is false, correct it to make it a true statement.

_____ a. Two fatty acids plus glycerol form a triglyceride.

_____ b. Phospholipids are amphipathic, having polar and nonpolar parts.

_____ c. Lipids are composed primarily of carbon and hydrogen, and so are nonpolar compounds.

_____ d. Proteins are polymers composed of fatty acids.

_____ e. A protein that loses its shape is denatured and nonfunctional.

10 *Circle all that apply.* Which of the following are properties of DNA?

a. Double helix.
b. Confined to the nucleus.
c. Contains the sugar ribose.
d. Contains the base thymine (T).
e. Single stranded.
f. Can move between the nucleus and the cytosol.
g. Contains the base uracil (U).
h. Contains the sugar deoxyribose.

Name _____

Section _____ Date _____

Check Your Understanding

Critical Thinking and Application Questions

1 Valentina Blackhorse presents to the emergency department with respiratory distress due a diagnosis of COVID-19. The respiratory therapist measures the pH of her blood and determines that it is 7.05.

   a Is the pH of her blood acidic, basic, or neutral? _____

   b The normal pH of human blood is 7.35–7.45. Is Valentina's blood pH more acidic or more basic than normal? Has the number of hydrogen ions in her blood increased or decreased? Explain.

   c While Valentina is recovering, a friend on social media tells her to eat only "alkaline foods," claiming eating alkaline foods will correct her pH disturbance. But Valentina is taking an A&P course, and she knows the foods we eat don't affect our blood pH due to our buffer systems. How are the buffer systems in Valentina's blood responding to her pH disturbance?

2 Let's suppose that the foods we eat really could affect the pH of our blood, and you chose to eat an "alkaline diet" with only foods that are highly basic in pH.

   a What would happen to the number of hydrogen ions in your blood if this were possible?

   b How would this affect the pH of the blood?

   c Could this have potential health repercussions?

3 *Decompression sickness* (also known as *the bends*) is a condition that affects divers and others operating under pressurized conditions. It occurs when gases such as nitrogen (N_2) come out of solution in the blood. This can lead to symptoms including joint pain, shortness of breath, and paralysis. Severe cases may result in death.

a What type of molecule (ionic, polar covalent, nonpolar covalent) is nitrogen gas?

b The liquid medium of blood is water. What type of compound (ionic, polar covalent, nonpolar covalent) is water?

c What happens when molecules such as nitrogen gas mix with water? How does this explain the problems we see with decompression sickness?

4 You prepare four solutions:

Solution 1: Reactants + enzyme at 40°C (about 100°F) and pH 7

Solution 2: Reactants + enzyme at 40°C (about 100°F) and pH 1

Solution 3: Reactants + enzyme at 20°C (about 70°F) and pH 7

Solution 4: Reactants + enzyme at 100°C (about 212°F) and pH 7

a Predict which solution will have the fastest reaction rate. Explain your answer.

b You run the experiment and discover Solutions 2 and 4 have no detectable products after incubating overnight (meaning no significant reaction occurred). What has likely happened in those solutions?

5 A hypothetical amino acid has the same core amino acid structure, but a four-carbon hydrocarbon chain as its R-group. Will this compound be ionic, polar covalent, nonpolar covalent, or amphipathic? Explain.

Introduction to the Microscope

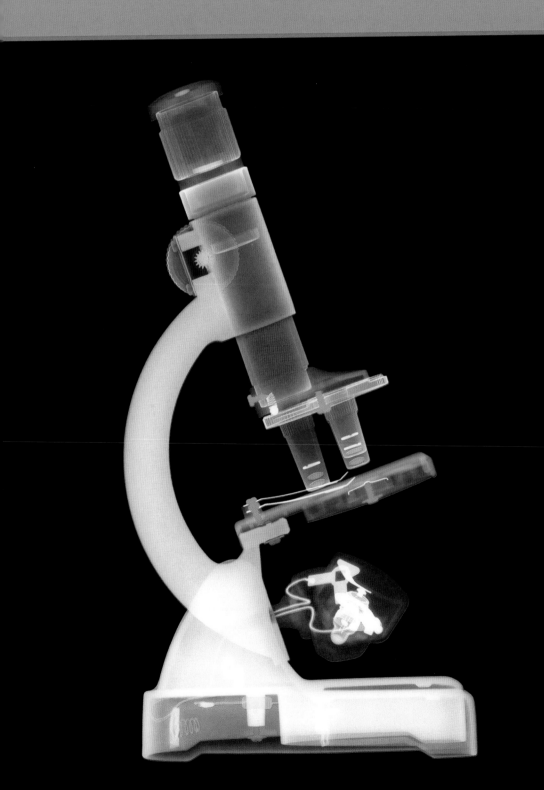

When you have completed this unit, you should be able to:

1 Identify the major parts of the microscope.

2 Define the magnification of high, medium, and low power.

3 Demonstrate proper use of the microscope.

4 Focus the microscope on low, medium, and high power.

5 Define depth of field.

PRE-LAB EXERCISES

Complete the following exercises prior to coming to lab, using your lab manual and textbook for reference.

PRE-LAB

3-1 Key Terms

You should be familiar with the following terms before coming to lab.

Term	Definition
Ocular lens	
Field of view	
Objective lenses	
Oil-immersion lens	
Stage	
Coarse adjustment knob	
Fine adjustment knob	
Iris diaphragm	
Depth of field	

3 Label the parts of the microscope in Figure 3.1 with the terms from Exercise 3-1 (p. 71). Use your text and Exercise 3-1 in this unit for reference.

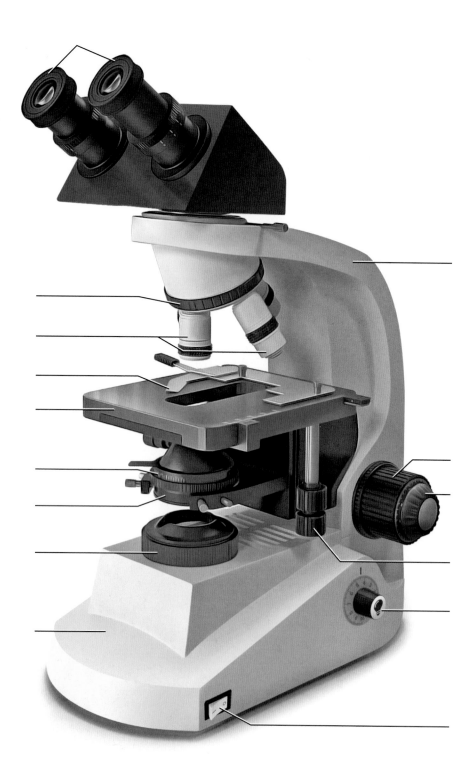

FIGURE **3.1** Compound light microscope.

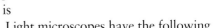

Colored x-ray of an optical microscope.

W orking with the microscope and slides may seem daunting at first. But with a bit of help, a fair amount of patience, and a lot of practice, the use of microscopes becomes progressively easier with each unit.

EXERCISE 3-1

MATERIALS

- ☐ Light microscopes with three objective lenses
- ☐ Slides:
  - ▪ letter "e"
  - ▪ colored threads
  - ▪ blank
- ☐ Fetal pigs or other preserved small mammals
- ☐ Sterile cotton swabs
- ☐ Methylene blue dye
- ☐ Distilled water
- ☐ Lens paper
- ☐ Wooden applicator sticks
- ☐ Coverslip

Introduction to the Microscope

The microscopes that you'll use in this lab are called **light microscopes** (Fig. 3.2). This type of microscope shines light through the specimens to illuminate them, and the light is refracted through objective lenses to magnify the image. Light microscopes have the following components:

- **Ocular lens.** The **ocular lens** (AWK-yoo-lur; *ocul-* = "eye") is the lens through which you look to examine the slide. It generally has a 10× power of magnification, meaning it magnifies the image you are examining 10 times. The microscope may have one ocular lens (a **monocular** microscope) or two ocular lenses (a **binocular** microscope). Many ocular lenses have pointers that can be moved by rotating the black **eyepiece**. The area of the slide visible when you look into the ocular is known as the **field of view**.

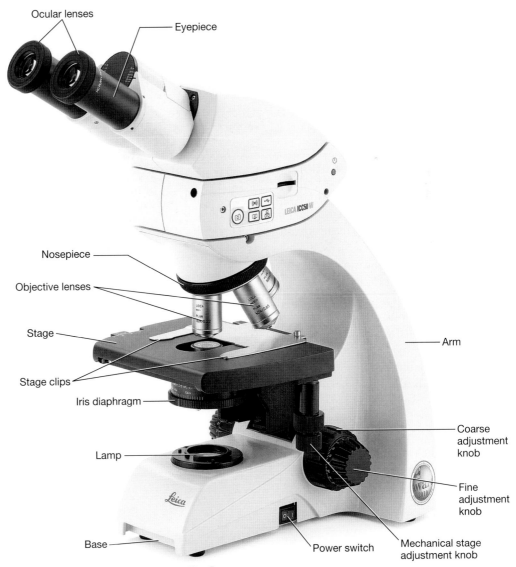

FIGURE **3.2 Compound light microscope.**

Ocular lenses
Eyepiece
Nosepiece
Objective lenses
Stage
Stage clips
Iris diaphragm
Lamp
Base
Power switch
Arm
Coarse adjustment knob
Fine adjustment knob
Mechanical stage adjustment knob

- **Objective lenses.** The **objective lenses** are lenses with various powers of magnification. Most microscopes have low-(4×), medium- (10×), and high-power (40×) objective lenses. Note that, sometimes, the 4× objective is referred to as the scan objective. On such microscopes, the 10× objective is actually called the low-power objective. The objective lenses are attached to the **nosepiece**, which allows the user to switch between objectives. Certain microscopes have a higher-power objective (100×), called the **oil-immersion lens**, which requires the user to place a drop of oil between the slide and objective lens. Without this drop of oil, you will not be able to focus the image.
- **Stage.** The **stage** is the surface on which the slide sits. It typically has stage clips to hold the slide in place. The stages of many microscopes are movable thanks to the **mechanical stage adjustment knob**. On such microscopes, you can move the slide by turning this knob. Other microscopes have stages that are not adjustable, and these require you to move the slide manually.
- **Arm.** The **arm** supports the body of the microscope and typically houses the adjustment knobs.
- **Coarse adjustment knob.** The large knob on the side of the arm is the **coarse adjustment knob**. Turning it moves the stage up and down to change the distance of the stage from the objective lenses. This allows you to grossly focus the image.
- **Fine adjustment knob.** The smaller knob underneath the coarse adjustment knob is the **fine adjustment knob**. You turn it to fine-tune of the image's focus. Note that occasionally the fine adjustment knob is situated on top of the coarse adjustment knob.
- **Lamp.** The **lamp**, also called the *illuminator*, provides the light source. It rests on the base of the microscope. Light from the lamp is focused on the specimen by the **condenser**, a lens that sits under the stage.
- **Iris diaphragm.** On the underside of the stage is an adjustable wheel called the **iris diaphragm** that controls the amount of light allowed to pass through the slide. It is important to check the iris diaphragm when you are focusing an image. Too much light will wash out the image, and too little light will make it harder to see details. You may also be able to adjust the amount of light coming into the image with a **light adjustment dial** (or knob), which is found on the arm or base of the microscope. This dial allows you to control the brightness of the lamp.

1 PROCEDURE
Calculating Magnification

Light is refracted through two lenses to obtain magnification: the ocular lens and the objective lens. Magnification of the ocular lens is usually 10×. This means that if you were to view a slide with only the ocular lens, the image would be magnified 10 times. Magnification of the objective lenses varies, but typically is 4× for low power, 10× for medium power, and 40× for high power. (To verify that this is the case for your microscope, look at the side of the objective lens, which usually is labeled with its magnification.) Remember that oil immersion provides even greater magnification at 100×. When calculating the total magnification, you must multiply the magnification of the ocular lens (10) by the power of the objective lens.

Fill in Table 3.1 to determine total magnification at each of the different objective lenses on your microscope. Remember that the magnification of the objective lens is usually printed on the side of the lens itself.

TABLE **3.1** Total Magnification at Each Power

Magnification of Ocular Lens	Power	Magnification of Objective Lens	Total Magnification
	Low		
	Medium		
	High		
	Oil Immersion		

How to Handle the Microscope

As I'm certain your professor will tell you, microscopes are expensive! Care must be taken to ensure that the microscopes stay in good working condition. Taking proper care of microscopes makes the histology sections of your labs run more smoothly (and also ensures you stay on your lab instructor's good side). Keeping that in mind, following are some general guidelines for handling the microscopes:

- Use two hands to support the microscope when carrying it—one hand to hold the arm and the other hand to support the base.

- Gather up the cord so it does not dangle off the lab table after you have plugged in the microscope. This will help to prevent people from tripping over loose cords.

- Clean the lenses with lens paper only. Do not use paper towels or cloth to clean a lens, because this will scratch its surface.

- Make sure the *lowest* power objective is in place before you begin. This will prevent you from cracking the slide and, possibly, the lens.

- Get the image in focus on low power, then switch to higher power and adjust with the **fine** adjustment knob. Be careful not to use the coarse adjustment knob with the high-power objective in place, because you could break the slide and damage the lens.

- When you are finished with the microscope, turn the nosepiece to the lowest-power objective, and remove the slide. Be sure to clean off the objective if you used oil, because oil left on the objective tends to harden. Turn off the power to the microscope, and unplug it. This will decrease the chances of a blown bulb or fuse next time the microscope is used. Before putting the microscope away, wrap the electrical cord around the base or secure with a Velcro strap, and cover it with a dust cover.

If you follow these general guidelines, you can rest assured that the microscopes (and your grade) will not suffer any harm.

How to Approach Microscopy

Before you try to focus the microscope, read the following hints and tips to make it easier.

ⓘ **Always start on low power.** You are supposed to start on low power, anyway, to avoid damaging the objective lenses. Sometimes, though, students forget, and jump straight to medium or high power. Doing this risks damaging the lenses and also makes it harder on you. Bear in mind that most slides will have more than one structure. Starting on low power allows you to scroll through a large area of the slide, and then to focus in on the desired part of the section.

ⓘ **Make sure the specimen is over the condenser.** This tip may sound simplistic, but I can't count the number of times that my students have declared in frustration that the slide is blank—because they either forgot to move the stage around or the specimen is small and they couldn't find it. The easy solution to this problem is to examine the slide with the naked eye first, and then place it on the stage so that the specimen is right over the condenser (the light). This way, you're guaranteed to see something when you look through the ocular.

ⓘ **Beware of too much light.** It is easy to wash out the specimen with too much light. If you are having difficulty making out details, first adjust the focus with the fine adjustment knob. If this doesn't help, use the iris diaphragm to reduce the amount of light illuminating the specimen. This will increase the contrast and allow you to observe more details. It also helps to reduce headaches and eyestrain.

ⓘ **Keep both eyes open.** It is tempting to close one eye when looking through a monocular microscope. Admittedly, keeping both eyes open isn't easy at first, but it helps to reduce headaches and eyestrain.

ⓘ **Compare your specimen to the photos in your lab manual.** Although the slides you are examining will not necessarily be identical to the photos in this book, they should be similar in appearance. Generally speaking, if you are looking at something that is vastly different from what is in this book, you probably should move the slide around a bit or change to a different power objective to find the correct tissue or cell type on the slide. Other good sources for micrographs include atlases, your textbook, and images on the internet.

ⓘ **Remember that the slides aren't perfect.** Some slides won't clearly demonstrate what you need to see. Some aren't stained adequately or properly. Some are sectioned at a funny angle. Some don't contain all the tissue or cell types you need to see. What should you do about this? See the next hint for the answer.

ⓘ **Look at more than one slide of each specimen.** This will help you in the face of subpar slides and also will assist you overall in gaining a better understanding of the specimens you are examining.

ⓘ **Draw what you see.** Although you may tend to resist drawing, even the most basic picture is helpful for two reasons. First, it allows you to engage more parts of your brain in the learning process. The more areas of your brain that are engaged, the better the chances are that you'll retain the information. Also, drawing is helpful in that you actually have to look at the specimen long enough to draw it.

ⓘ **Have patience!** It really does get easier. Don't get frustrated, and don't give up. By the end of the semester, you may come to appreciate the microscope and the fascinating world it reveals.

2 PROCEDURE
Focusing the Microscope

Now that we know how to handle the microscope properly, let's practice using it. We will start with a simple slide: an image of a newsprint letter "e."

1   Obtain a slide of the letter "e."

2   Examine the letter "e" slide macroscopically (with the naked eye) before placing it on the stage. How is the "e" oriented on the slide? Is it right side up, upside down, backward, etc.?

_____

3   Switch the nosepiece to the low-power objective, place the slide on the stage, and secure it with the stage clips. Move the slide using the stage adjustment knob until the "e" is over the condenser.

4   Use the coarse adjustment knob to bring the slide into focus slowly. After it is grossly in focus, use the fine adjustment knob to sharpen the focus. Note that you might need to adjust the iris diaphragm to allow more light to pass through the specimen, as the newsprint is relatively thick. How is the "e" oriented in the field of view? Is it different from the way it was when you examined it in Step 2?

_____

5   Move the nosepiece to medium power. You should only have to adjust the focus with the fine adjustment knob; no adjustment of the coarse focus should be necessary.

6   Once you have examined the slide on medium power, move the nosepiece to high power. Again, focus only with the fine adjustment knob.

Wasn't that easy?

3 PROCEDURE
Understanding Depth of Field

At times you will look at a slide and see something brown or black and kind of neat-looking with interesting swirls and specks. What is this fascinating discovery you've made? It's dirt on top of the slide. This happens because students tend to focus the objective on the first thing they can make out, which usually is the top of the coverslip on the slide, and this has a tendency to be dirty.

These "dirt discoveries" can be avoided by appreciating what is known as **depth of field**. Also called the _depth of focus_, the depth of field is the thickness of a specimen that is in sharp focus. Thicker specimens will require you to focus up and down to look at all levels of the specimen. This takes practice and skill. Let's get some practice doing this. Here we will use a slide that has three differently colored threads stacked on top of one another.

1   Obtain a slide with three colored threads. The threads are located on the slide at varying depths, and you will have to focus on each thread individually.

2   Examine the slide macroscopically prior to putting it on the stage.

3   Switch the nosepiece to the low-power objective, place the slide on the stage, and secure it with the stage clips. Move the slide using the stage adjustment knob until the threads are in your field of view.

4   Use the coarse adjustment knob to get the slide into focus on low power.

5   Switch to medium power, and use the fine adjustment knob to sharpen the focus. Which thread(s) is (are) in focus?

_____

6   Move the objective up and down slowly with the coarse adjustment knob, focusing on each individual thread. Figure out which color thread is on the bottom, in the middle, and on the top, and write the color order here:

Bottom _____   Middle _____   Top _____

PROCEDURE

Preparing a Cell Sample

Now, let's do some actual laboratory microscopy. In this procedure, you will prepare what is known as a cell smear (Fig. 3.3). To prepare a cell smear, obtain a sample of cells (in this case from the mouth) with a cotton applicator swab and "smear" these cells on a blank slide. However, cells and cell structures aren't visible unless they are first stained, so the next step in preparing a smear is to apply a stain, in this case methylene blue, to the sample.

1   Obtain a blank slide and a coverslip.

2   Clean the slide with lens paper.

3   Swab the inside of your cheek with a sterile cotton swab. As an alternative, swab the inside cheek of a fetal pig or other preserved small mammal. Do not get large chunks of tissue on the swab, or individual cells will not be visible.

4   Wipe the swab of cheek cells on the blank slide. If you are using your own cheek cells, dispose of the swab in a biohazard bag.

5   Place one drop of methylene blue dye onto the slide. Wait 1 minute.

6   Rinse the dye off the slide with distilled water and pat dry. The blue dye should be barely visible on the slide. If you see large areas of blue, rinse the slide again, or get a new sample of cheek cells.

7   Place a coverslip over the stained area, and place the slide on the stage of a microscope. Focus the image grossly on low power, then switch to the high-power objective lens to find individual cells (use oil immersion if available).

8   Identify and draw some of the cells in your smear in the space provided.

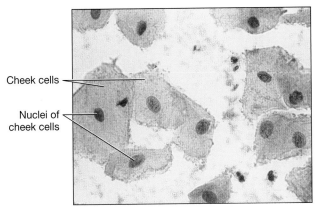

Cheek cells

Nuclei of cheek cells

FIGURE **3.3** Cell smear.

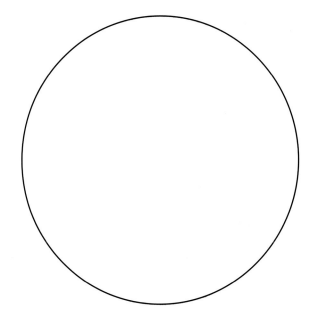

UNIT 3 REVIEW

Check Your Recall

1 *Matching:* Match the following terms with the correct definition from the column.

_____ Oil-immersion lens

_____ Light adjustment dial

_____ Fine adjustment knob

_____ Iris diaphragm

_____ Coarse adjustment knob

_____ Field of view

_____ Nosepiece

_____ Ocular lens

A. Moves the stage up and down; provides gross focusing
B. An objective with 100× magnification
C. The area of the slide visible under the ocular
D. The lens through which you look to view the slide
E. The knob that controls the brightness of the lamp
F. Controls the amount of light that passes through the slide
G. Microscope part to which the objective lenses are attached
H. Allows precise focusing of the image

2 *Fill in the blank:* Magnification of the low-power objective lens is usually _____ .

3 An oil-immersion lens requires
a. oil to be placed on the ocular lens.
b. oil to be placed between the slide and the objective.
c. oil to be placed between the slide and the condenser.
d. oil to be placed between the ocular and objective lenses.

4 Which objective lens should be in place before you begin? Why?

_____

_____

5 When you finish with the microscope, you should turn the nosepiece to the
a. oil-immersion lens.
b. highest-power objective.
c. middle-power objective.
d. lowest-power objective.

6 *Circle all that apply.* Which of the following statements is/are false?
a. It reduces eye strain and headaches when you examine the slide with only one eye.
b. Drawing engages more parts of the brain in the learning process, thus increasing retention.
c. Some slides won't clearly show the structures you are seeking, and so you may need to examine more than one slide.
d. Increasing the amount of light will increase the details visible on the slide.

7 Why should you compare the slide you're viewing to the images in your lab manual?

8 What are two strategies you can use if you're having trouble making out details on your slide?

9 What should you do if you make a "dirt discovery" on your slide?

10 Will depth of field be more relevant for thick specimens or for thin specimens? Explain.

Cytology

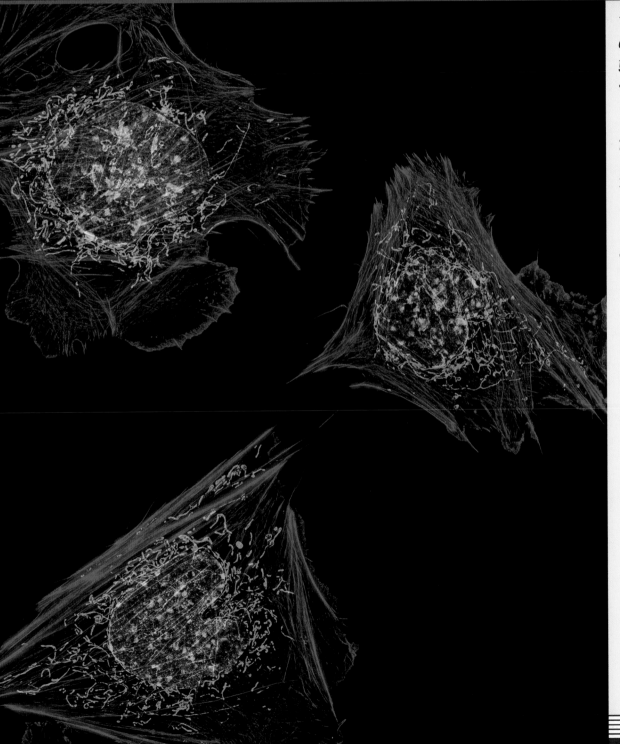

When you have completed this unit, you should be able to:

1 Identify parts of the cell and organelles, and describe their functions.

2 Describe the processes of diffusion and osmosis.

3 Describe the effects of hypotonic, isotonic, and hypertonic environments on cells.

4 Identify the stages of the cell cycle and mitosis.

PRE-LAB EXERCISES

Complete the following exercises prior to coming to lab, using your lab manual and textbook for reference.

4 PRE-LAB

4-1 Key Terms

You should be familiar with the following terms before coming to lab.

Term	Definition

Cell Structures and Organelles

Phospholipid bilayer _____

_____

Cytoplasm _____

_____

Nucleus _____

_____

Nucleolus _____

_____

Mitochondrion _____

_____

Ribosome _____

_____

Peroxisome _____

_____

Smooth endoplasmic reticulum _____

_____

Rough endoplasmic reticulum _____

_____

Golgi apparatus (or complex) _____

_____

Lysosome _____

_____

Centriole _____

_____

Name ______________________ Section __________ Date __________

Cilia ______________________

____

Flagella ______________________

____

Vesicle ______________________

____

Membrane Transport

Diffusion ______________________

____

Osmosis ______________________

____

Tonicity ______________________

____

Cell Cycle and Mitosis

Cell cycle ______________________

____

Interphase ______________________

____

Mitosis ______________________

____

The Plasma Membrane

Color the parts of the plasma membrane in Figure 4.1, and label them with the terms from Exercise 4-1 (p. 85). Use your text and Exercise 4-1 in this unit for reference.

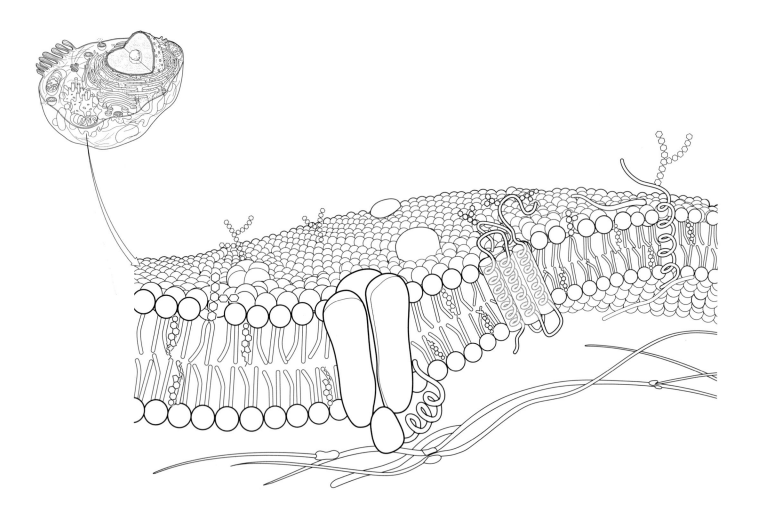

FIGURE **4.1** Plasma membrane.

PRE-LAB

4-3   The Parts of the Cell

Color the parts of the cell in Figure 4.2, and label them with the terms from Exercise 4-1 (p. 85). Note that you may not see all structures in this diagram. Use your text and Exercise 4-1 in this unit for reference.

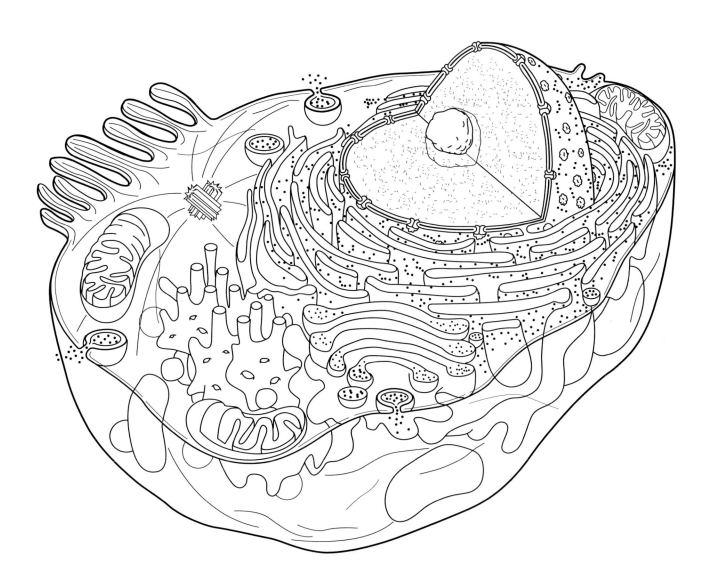

FIGURE **4.2** Generalized cell.

The Cell Cycle

Use your text and lab manual to answer the following questions about the cell cycle and mitosis.

4

1 Describe the following parts of the cell cycle:

a G_1: _____

_____

_____

b S: _____

_____

_____

c G_2: _____

_____

_____

d M: _____

_____

_____

2 Describe the events that are occurring in the cell in each of the phases of mitosis in Table 4.1.

TABLE **4.1** Stages of Mitosis

Stage of Mitosis	Events Taking Place in the Cell	Cell Appearance
Prophase		
Metaphase		
Anaphase		
Telophase		

EXERCISES

W̲e now move on to **cytology** (sy-TAHL-oh-gee; *cyto-* = "cell;" *-logy* = "study of"), which is the study of the next level of organization—the **cell**, the smallest unit of life. This unit introduces you to the cell, its structures, and how the cell reproduces itself via the process of cell division. We also examine two important physiological processes that occur at the chemical and cellular level: *diffusion* and *osmosis*.

Note that this is the first unit in which you will use a *Model Inventory*—something you will use throughout this lab manual. In this inventory, you will list the anatomical models or diagrams that you use in lab—if the model is not named, make up a descriptive name for it. You will then record in a table the structures you are able to locate on each model. This is particularly helpful for study purposes, as it allows you to return to the proper models to locate specific structures.

In this unit, you will also do your first "Time to Draw" procedure, in which you sketch and label one of your anatomical models. Now, I know you might not see the point of drawing. But give it a try. Studies have shown that drawing anatomical structures helps you form a mental map of what you've learned and helps you to better remember it. If you're still hesitant to draw, know that your drawings don't have to be works of art—a simple sketch is all that's needed.

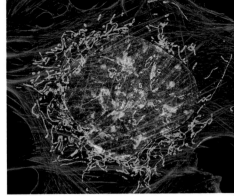

Fluorescent micrograph of cell structure.

EXERCISE 4-1

MATERIALS

- ❏ Anatomical models and diagrams: cell
- ❏ Light microscope
- ❏ Slides:
  - red blood cells
  - skeletal muscle cells
  - sperm cells
- ❏ Colored pencils

Organelles and Cell Structures

Most cells in the body are composed of three basic parts: the plasma membrane, the cytoplasm, and the nucleus.

1. **Plasma membrane.** The **plasma membrane** is the outer boundary of the cell (Fig. 4.3). As you can see in Figure 4.3, it is composed of a **phospholipid bilayer** (FAHS-foh-lip-id). Why do the phospholipids form a bilayer like this? Let's think about it. Refer back to Unit 2 (p. 35) to answer the following questions:

   Is a phospholipid's phosphate head polar or nonpolar? _____

   Are a phospholipid's fatty acid tails polar or nonpolar? _____

   Do polar solutes prefer to interact with polar or nonpolar solvents? _____

   Do nonpolar solutes prefer to interact with polar or nonpolar solvents? _____

   Water is the body's solvent. Is water polar or nonpolar? _____

   So, will the phosphate heads interact with water? _____

   Will the fatty acid tails interact with water? _____

Now, look to Figure 4.3 and notice how the phospholipids align.

What do the phosphate heads face? _____

What do the fatty acid tails face? _____

When we think about the "like interacts with like" rule, this alignment makes sense. The cytosol and extracellular fluid are water-based, so the phosphate heads are attracted to these solvents and face them. The fatty acid tails are repelled by the water-based fluid but attracted to each other. As a result, they face each other.

Phospholipids aren't the only component of the plasma membrane. Scattered among the phospholipids, we find other components, including **integral proteins**, which span the width of the membrane; **peripheral proteins**, which are located on only one face of the membrane; **cholesterol**, a steroid that stabilizes the membrane's structure in the face of changing temperatures; and **glycoproteins** and **glycolipids**, which function in cell recognition.

The plasma membrane is a dynamic, fluid structure that acts as a selectively permeable barrier. This means it acts as a gatekeeper, only allowing certain solutes to pass into or out of the cell. In parts of the body where rapid absorption is necessary, the plasma membrane is folded into projections called **microvilli** (my-kroh-VIL-aye; *micro-* = "small;" *villus* = "hair"), which increase its surface area.

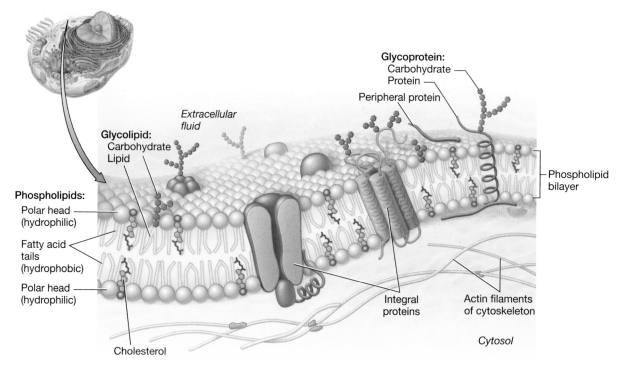

Glycolipid:
Carbohydrate
Lipid

Extracellular
fluid

Glycoprotein:
Carbohydrate
Protein
Peripheral protein

Phospholipid
bilayer

Phospholipids:
Polar head
(hydrophilic)

Fatty acid
tails
(hydrophobic)

Polar head
(hydrophilic)

Cholesterol

Integral
proteins

Actin filaments
of cytoskeleton

Cytosol

FIGURE **4.3** Plasma membrane.

2. **Cytoplasm.** The **cytoplasm** (SY-toh-plaz-m) is the material inside the cell. It consists of three parts: *cytosol*, the *cytoskeleton*, and *organelles* (Fig. 4.4).

a. **Cytosol** (SY-toh-sahl; *sol* = "solution") is the fluid portion of the cytoplasm and contains water, solutes, RNA, enzymes, and other proteins.

b. The **cytoskeleton** is a collection of protein filaments including actin filaments, intermediate filaments, and microtubules. **Actin filaments** are small filaments located along the plasma membrane and in the core of microvilli. They maintain the shape of the cell and function in cell movement. The larger **intermediate filaments** are ropelike structures that maintain the shape of organelles and the nucleus and give the cell mechanical strength. **Microtubules**, the largest filaments, are hollow tubes that maintain the shape of the cell, hold organelles in place, move substances within the cell, and function in cell division. In addition, microtubules form the core of motile extensions from the cell, which are called cilia (SIL-ee-uh) and flagella (flah-JEL-uh). **Cilia** are small, hairlike extensions that beat rhythmically together to propel substances past the cell. They are especially abundant in the respiratory tract, where they act like tiny brooms, removing debris that has been inhaled and trapped in mucus. **Flagella** are single extensions that propel the cell itself (sperm cells are the only flagellated cells in the human body).

c. **Organelles** (ohr-gan-ELLZ) are specialized cellular compartments that carry out a variety of functions. The organelles we cover in this unit include the following:

- **Peroxisomes.** The small, membrane-enclosed organelles known as **peroxisomes** (per-AHKS-ih-zohmz) contain enzymes that catalyze reactions that metabolize certain types of fatty acids. Fatty acid metabolism generates ATP (energy) for the cell and prevents these fatty acids from accumulating in the cells and in the blood. These metabolic reactions generate large quantities of the toxic byproduct hydrogen peroxide, for which peroxisomes are named. To prevent cell damage, peroxisomes produce an enzyme to break down hydrogen peroxide. Peroxisomes also synthesize phospholipids that are critical for the normal functioning of the nervous system.

- **Mitochondria.** The bean-shaped **mitochondria** (my-toh-KAHN-dree-ah) produce the bulk of the cell's ATP (energy) through the breakdown of glucose and fatty acids. Notice in Figure 4.5 that mitochondria are surrounded by a double plasma membrane, which encloses a central space called the **matrix**. Within the matrix, mitochondria contain their own circular mitochondrial DNA and ribosomes, which enables them to produce their own proteins.

- **Ribosomes.** The small, granular **ribosomes** (RY-boh-zohmz) are the sites of protein synthesis in the cell. Each ribosome consists of two subunits and is composed of proteins and RNA known as **ribosomal RNA**. Some ribosomes float freely in the cytosol, whereas others are bound to the membrane of another organelle or the nucleus. They are one of the few organelles that are not enclosed by a membrane.

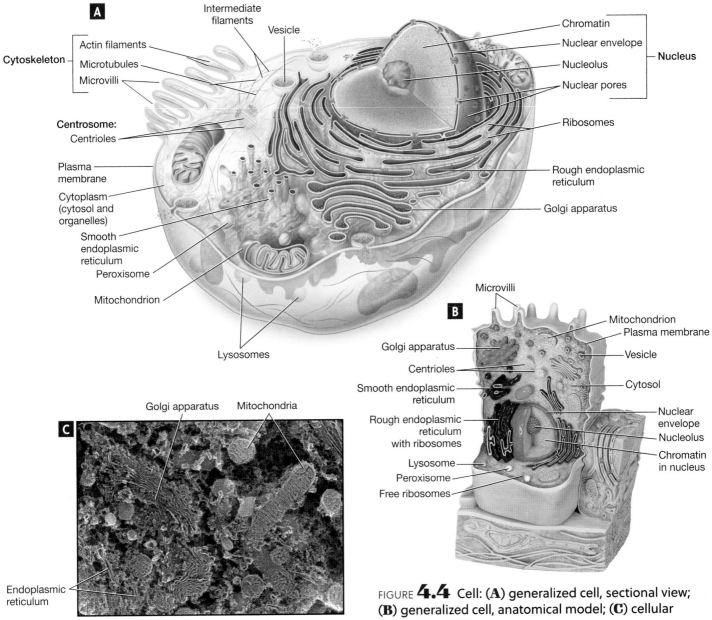

A

Cytoskeleton
- Actin filaments
- Microtubules
- Microvilli

Intermediate filaments

Vesicle

Centrosome:
- Centrioles

Plasma membrane

Cytoplasm (cytosol and organelles)

Smooth endoplasmic reticulum

Peroxisome

Mitochondrion

Lysosomes

Chromatin

Nuclear envelope

Nucleolus — Nucleus

Nuclear pores

Ribosomes

Rough endoplasmic reticulum

Golgi apparatus

4

B

Microvilli

Golgi apparatus

Centrioles

Smooth endoplasmic reticulum

Rough endoplasmic reticulum with ribosomes

Lysosome

Peroxisome

Free ribosomes

Mitochondrion

Plasma membrane

Vesicle

Cytosol

Nuclear envelope

Nucleolus

Chromatin in nucleus

C

Golgi apparatus

Mitochondria

Endoplasmic reticulum

FIGURE **4.4** Cell: (**A**) generalized cell, sectional view; (**B**) generalized cell, anatomical model; (**C**) cellular organelles, SEM.

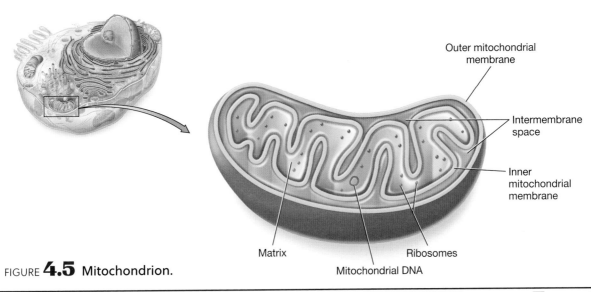

Outer mitochondrial membrane

Intermembrane space

Inner mitochondrial membrane

Matrix

Mitochondrial DNA

Ribosomes

FIGURE **4.5** Mitochondrion.

- **Endoplasmic reticulum.** The series of membrane-enclosed sacs known as the **endoplasmic reticulum** (in-doh-PLAZ-mik reh-TIK-yoo-lum; "reticulum" = "network") may be of two types: **rough endoplasmic reticulum**, or **RER**, which has ribosomes on its surface, and **smooth endoplasmic reticulum**, or **SER**, which lacks ribosomes. The RER performs some of the final steps of protein synthesis, modifying proteins the ribosomes have made—particularly integral membrane proteins and proteins secreted from the cell. The SER catalyzes the detoxification of metabolic waste products, alcohol, and drugs. The cells of the liver—the body's main organ of detoxification—have abundant SER to carry out these reactions. The SER is also involved in lipid synthesis and it stores calcium ions.
- **Golgi apparatus.** The **Golgi apparatus** (GOHL-jee) is a stack of flattened sacs near the RER. Its membrane-enclosed sacs receive vesicles from the RER and other places in the cell. Reactions within the Golgi apparatus modify and sort the products within the vesicles.
- **Lysosomes. Lysosomes** (LY-soh-zohmz; *lyse* = "split") are membrane-enclosed vesicular organelles filled with digestive enzymes. These enzymes catalyze reactions that digest particles brought into the cell, old and worn-out organelles, and even the cell itself. Immune cells known as *phagocytes* (FAY-go-syt'z; *phago -* = "eat"), which ingest and digest damaged cells, foreign cells such as bacteria, and cells infected with viruses, have a large number of lysosomes.
- **Centrioles. Centrioles** (SIN-tree-ohlz) are paired organelles composed primarily of microtubules that are located in the central area of the cell, which is called the **centrosome** (SIN-troh-sohm). They appear to be microtubule organizing centers and are important in facilitating the assembly and disassembly of microtubules.

3. **Nucleus.** The third component in nearly all cells is a specialized structure called the **nucleus** (NOO-klee-uhs). The nucleus is the cell's biosynthetic center that directs the synthesis of nearly all the body's proteins, as well as the synthesis of certain nucleic acids. The nucleus is surrounded by a double membrane called the **nuclear envelope,** which contains holes called **nuclear pores.** Within the nucleus we find **chromatin** (KROH-mah-tin), a ball-like mass of tightly coiled DNA and proteins; RNA; and a dark-staining region called the **nucleolus** (noo-klee-OH-luhs). The nucleolus, which is the "birthplace" of ribosomes, contains ribosomal RNA.

Note that the cell shown in Figure 4.4 is a **generalized cell** that contains each organelle in average numbers. Most cells in the body don't look like this and instead are specialized so their structure follows their functions.

---

1 PROCEDURE
Model Inventory for the Cell

Identify the following structures of the cell on models and diagrams, using this unit and your textbook for reference. As you examine the anatomical models and diagrams, record the name of the model and the structures that you were able to identify on the model inventory in Table 4.2. When you have completed this activity, answer Check Your Understanding Questions 1 through 3 (p. 107).

1. Plasma membrane
   a. Phospholipid bilayer
   b. Integral proteins
   c. Peripheral proteins
   d. Carbohydrates
   e. Microvilli
2. Cytoskeleton
   a. Actin filaments
   b. Intermediate filaments
   c. Microtubules
   d. Cilia
   e. Flagella

3. Cytoplasmic organelles
   a. Ribosomes
   b. Peroxisomes
   c. Mitochondria
   d. Rough endoplasmic reticulum
   e. Smooth endoplasmic reticulum
   f. Golgi apparatus
   g. Lysosomes
   h. Centrioles

4. Nucleus
   a. Nuclear envelope
   b. Nuclear pores
   c. Chromatin
   d. Nucleolus

TABLE **4.2** Cellular Structures Model Inventory

Model/Diagram	Structures Identified

2 | **PROCEDURE**
Time to Draw

In the space provided, draw, color, and label one of the cell models that you examined. In addition, write the function of each organelle that you label.

Examining Cellular Diversity with Microscopy

The structure of different cell types can vary drastically. Cells differ not only in size and shape but also in the types and prevalence of organelles in the cell. In this activity, you will examine prepared microscope slides of red blood cells, sperm cells, and skeletal muscle cells. Use the techniques you learned in Unit 3: Begin your observation on low power, and advance to high power for each slide. Note that sperm cells can be difficult to find, so an oil-immersion lens is helpful for finding the tiny cells. In the space provided, draw, color, and label the cellular structures and organelles that you see on each slide. You may wish to look at Figures 5.9 (p. 130) for red blood cells, 5.10A (p. 136) for skeletal muscle, and 27.16 (p. 734) for sperm cells.

HINTS & TIPS

How to Draw Useful Micrograph Diagrams

You don't need to be a great artist to draw useful micrograph diagrams. Following are some tips for producing effective drawings that can help you learn the material and study for practical exams.

- ℹ First, look at a diagram of the cell or tissue in this book or your textbook to get oriented and get an idea of what you should look for in the field of view.

- ℹ Make note of the image's magnification. As always, start on low power, then advance to higher-powered objectives as needed. You should aim for a magnification about the same as the magnification in the diagram.

- ℹ Use a pencil to reproduce, as closely as possible, what you see in the field of view. This doesn't have to be a work of art, but you should take care to draw the shape of the cells, the way the cells are organized, and the components of the extracellular matrix. You may draw in the circles in this manual or on a piece of white paper for larger diagrams.

- ℹ Use colored pencils to add color to your drawing, referencing the slide as a guide. Color is a critical component, particularly for study purposes. Some slides will have uniquely colored stains or staining patterns, and studying the colored images can prove quite helpful. In addition, the slides that your lab uses might have different stains than the images in your book. In these cases, it is useful to have a drawing with those specific stain colors.

- ℹ The final step is to label your drawing. Use your lab manual, textbook, and other resources as a guide to ensure that your labels are accurate.

1 Red Blood Cells

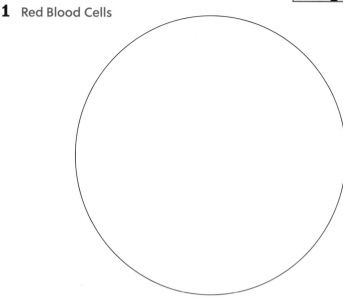

2 Sperm Cells

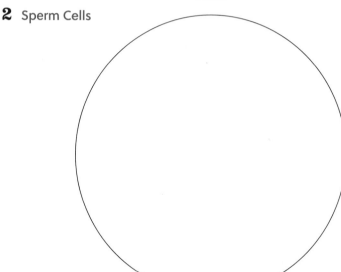

3 Skeletal Muscle Cells

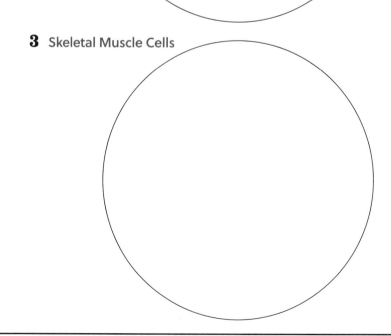

EXERCISE
4-2

MATERIALS

☐ 100 mL beakers (2)
☐ Food coloring
☐ Hot water
☐ Ice water
☐ Agar-filled petri dishes (4)
☐ 0.1 M potassium permanganate
☐ 0.1 M methylene blue
☐ 1.0 M methylene blue
☐ 0.1 M Congo red
☐ Ruler

Diffusion

Diffusion is defined as the movement of solute particles from a high solute concentration to a low solute concentration until a state of equilibrium is reached (Fig. 4.6). When equilibrium is reached, net diffusion stops, although particles continue moving. Diffusion is a **passive process**—one that requires no net input of energy by a cell—because diffusion is driven by a **concentration gradient**. A concentration gradient is defined as a situation in which two connected areas have different concentrations of a solute. Figure 4.6 illustrates a concentration gradient in the panels "Time 1" and "Time 2." Equilibrium is illustrated in "Time 3."

The rate at which diffusion takes place depends upon several factors, including the steepness of the concentration gradient, the temperature, and the size of the particles. Generally, smaller particle size, steeper concentration gradients, and higher temperatures will increase the rate of diffusion.

Diffusion occurs all around us and is very easy to see in action (Fig. 4.7). You'll observe it in this exercise while examining the effects of temperature, concentration, and particle size on the rate of diffusion. When you have completed both procedures, answer Check Your Understanding Question 4 (p. 107).

4

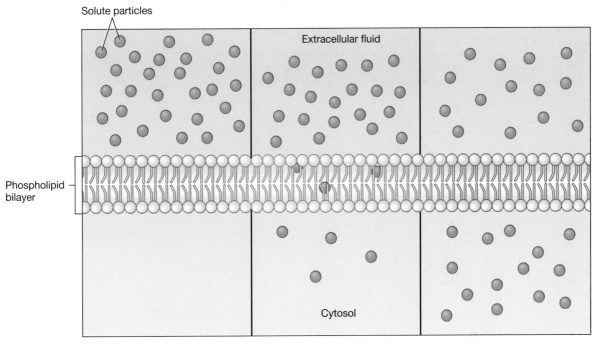

Solute particles

Extracellular fluid

Phospholipid bilayer

Cytosol

Time 1: Steep concentration gradient   **Time 2:** Diffusion begins   **Time 3:** Equilibrium

FIGURE **4.6** Diffusion across a plasma membrane.

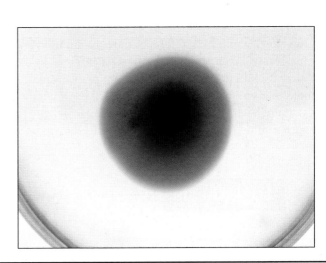

FIGURE **4.7** Example of diffusion seen with potassium permanganate dye in agar. Dye diffuses outward over time from a high concentration to a low concentration.

PROCEDURE

Measuring the Effect of Temperature on Diffusion Rate

The first variable you will test is the effect of temperature on the rate at which diffusion takes place. The setup here is very simple, and requires only food coloring and water at two different temperatures.

Hypothesis: How will temperature affect the rate of the diffusion?

1. Obtain two 100 mL glass beakers. Label one beaker "cold" and the other "hot." Fill the "cold" beaker with ice water (take care not to get ice in the beaker, though), and fill the "hot" beaker with water that has been heated.

2. Add two drops of food coloring to each beaker.

3. Observe the beakers from the side and measure with a ruler the distance that the dye spreads every minute for 5 minutes. Record your results in Table 4.3.

4. Interpret your results. What effect does temperature have on the rate of diffusion?

TABLE **4.3** Diffusion Results for Food Coloring in Water

Time	Distance of Dye Diffusion: Cold Water	Distance of Dye Diffusion: Hot Water
1 minute		
2 minutes		
3 minutes		
4 minutes		
5 minutes		

5. Compare your results to your hypothesis.

PROCEDURE

Measuring the Effect of Concentration and Particle Size on the Rate of Diffusion

Now you'll explore the effects of the concentration and particle size on diffusion rate. You will compare the effects of particle size by comparing three dyes of different molecular weights: potassium permanganate, which has the lowest molecular weight; methylene blue, which has a middle molecular weight; and Congo red, which has the highest molecular weight. To compare the effect of concentration, you will be using two different concentrations of methylene blue.

⚠ SAFETY NOTE

Safety glasses, gloves, and lab coats are required. *Use caution with the dyes, as they will stain clothes and irritate and stain skin.*

Hypothesis: How will molecular weight and concentration affect the rate of diffusion?

1 Obtain four agar-filled petri dishes. Label the plates 1, 2, 3, and 4. Mark a spot in the center of each dish. (If agar-filled dishes are not available, obtain empty petri dishes and fill each dish about half-full with corn syrup.)

2 Place a drop of 0.1 M potassium permanganate (molecular weight = 158 g/mol) in the center of Dish 1. Use a ruler to measure the distance the drop diffuses every 30 seconds for 2 minutes. Record these data in Table 4.4.

3 Place a drop of 0.1 M methylene blue (molecular weight = 374 g/mol) in the center of Dish 2. Use a ruler to measure the distance the drop diffuses every 30 seconds for 2 minutes. Record these data in Table 4.4.

4 Place a drop of 1.0 M methylene blue (molecular weight = 374 g/mol) in the center of Dish 3. Use a ruler to measure the distance the drop diffuses every 30 seconds for 2 minutes. Record these data in Table 4.4.

5 Place a drop of 0.1 M Congo red (molecular weight = 697 g/mol) in the center of Dish 4. Use a ruler to measure the distance the drop diffuses every 30 seconds for 2 minutes. Record these data in Table 4.4.

TABLE **4.4** Diffusion Results for Dyes in Agar

| Time | Distance of Diffusion | | | |
	Dish 1 0.1 Potassium Permanganate	Dish 2 0.1 M Methylene Blue	Dish 3 1.0 M Methylene Blue	Dish 4 0.1 M Congo Red
30 seconds				
60 seconds				
90 seconds				
120 seconds				

6 Interpret your results:

a Which dye diffused the fastest? _____

b Which dye diffused the slowest? _____

c What effect does particle size have on the rate of diffusion? _____

d What effect does concentration have on the rate of diffusion? _____

7 Compare your results to your hypothesis.

_____

_____

MATERIALS

- ☐ Animal or human blood cells
- ☐ Glass slides: blank (3)
- ☐ Coverslips
- ☐ Dropper
- ☐ Wooden applicator stick
- ☐ 5% dextrose in water solution
- ☐ Deionized water
- ☐ 25% NaCl in water solution
- ☐ Lens paper/paper towel
- ☐ Light microscope with 40x objective
- ☐ Permanent marker

For alternate procedure:
- ☐ Pieces of potato cut into equal sizes
- ☐ 400 mL beakers (3)
- ☐ Calipers
- ☐ Wax marker

Osmosis and Tonicity

Diffusion refers to the movement of solute, while the passive process called **osmosis** (oz-MOH-sis) refers to the movement of *solvent*. Specifically, osmosis is the movement of solvent from a solution with a lower solute concentration to a solution with a higher solute concentration (Fig. 4.8). In biological systems, the solvent is generally water, and that is the solvent we will discuss here.

A key feature of osmosis is that it occurs only through a *selectively permeable membrane*; in this case, the membrane allows the solvent to cross it but not the solute particles. For this reason, the solvent crosses the membrane and moves to the more concentrated solution, diluting it until both solutions have approximately the same concentration.

We can compare the solute concentration of two solutions—for example, the cytosol and the extracellular fluid (ECF)—with the concept of **tonicity**. Tonicity describes one solution's ability to cause osmosis relative to another. The ECF surrounding a cell can have three variations in tonicity:

- **Isotonic.** An **isotonic** (aye-soh-TAHN-ik; *iso-* = "same") ECF has the same solute concentration as the cytosol. As both solutions have the same solute concentration, both have an equal ability to cause osmosis. As a result, there is no net movement of water into or out of a cell in an isotonic solution (Fig. 4.9A). Solutions given by intravenous (IV) administration are almost always isotonic, and include 0.9% NaCl solution and 5% dextrose in water.

- **Hypotonic.** A **hypotonic** (hy-poh-TAHN-ik; *hypo-* = "below") ECF has a lower solute concentration than the cytosol. This means that the cytosol has more solute particles, and has a greater ability to cause osmosis than the ECF. For this reason, water will move into the cell by osmosis. This may cause the cell to swell and burst (Fig. 4.9B). Examples of hypotonic solutions include 0.45% NaCl, most sports drinks, and pure water. Hypotonic solutions are given as IV fluids when a patient has certain types of dehydration. Pure water, however, is never given as an IV fluid—the solution is far too hypotonic, and could lead to death of the patient.

- **Hypertonic.** A **hypertonic** (hy-per-TAHN-ik; *hyper-* = "above") ECF has a higher solute concentration than the cytosol, giving it a greater ability to cause osmosis. This causes the ECF to pull water molecules out of the cytosol by osmosis. The cell may shrivel or crenate as it loses water to the ECF (Fig. 4.9C). Hypertonic solutions include 3% NaCl and 10% dextrose in water. Such solutions are only ever given by IV under very specific conditions.

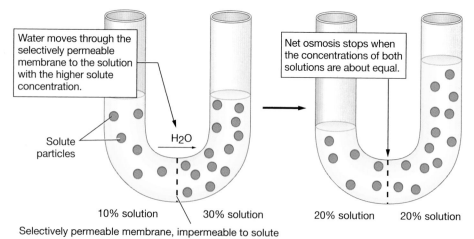

Water moves through the selectively permeable membrane to the solution with the higher solute concentration.

Net osmosis stops when the concentrations of both solutions are about equal.

Solute particles

H2O

10% solution   30% solution   20% solution   20% solution

Selectively permeable membrane, impermeable to solute

FIGURE **4.8** Osmosis.

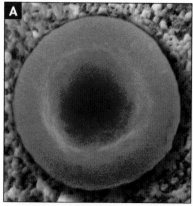
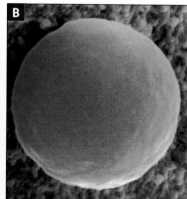
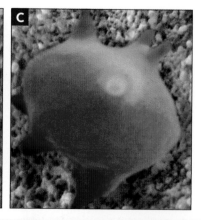

A   B   C

FIGURE **4.9** Effects of solutions of different tonicities on cells: (**A**) isotonic solution; (**B**) hypotonic solution; (**C**) hypertonic solution.

The following experiment will allow you to watch osmosis in action by placing cells—in this case, red blood cells or *erythrocytes*—into solutions of different tonicity. If your lab doesn't have access to blood products, skip down to the alternate procedure. When you have completed the activities, answer Check Your Understanding Questions 5 and 6 (p. 108).

1 PROCEDURE
Watching Osmosis in Action, Blood Version

Hypothesis: How will the different tonicities affect the blood cells?

1 Obtain three blank slides, and number them 1, 2, and 3 with a permanent marker.

2 Place one small drop of animal blood on each slide with a dropper. Take care to keep your droplet fairly small; otherwise you won't be able to see individual cells.

3 Gently spread the droplet around the center of the slide with a wooden applicator stick, and place a coverslip on it.

4 On Slide 1, place a drop of 5% dextrose solution on one side of the coverslip. On the other side of the coverslip, hold a piece of lens paper or a paper towel. The lens paper will draw the fluid under the coverslip.

5 Observe the cells under the microscope on high power.

6 Repeat the procedure by placing the 25% NaCl solution on Slide 2 and distilled water on Slide 3.

7 Draw and describe what you see with each slide. Then, move on to Procedure 3 to interpret your results.

⚠ SAFETY NOTE

Safety glasses and gloves are required!

Slide 1

Description:

Slide 2

Description:

_____

_____

Slide 3

Description:

_____

_____

2   PROCEDURE

Alternate: Watching Osmosis in Action, Potato Version

Hypothesis: How will the different tonicities affect the potato slices?

_____

_____

1. Obtain three pieces of potato of equal size. Mark them as 1, 2, and 3 with a permanent marker.

2. Measure the length and width of each piece of potato with calipers. Record these data in Table 4.5.

3. Obtain three 400-mL beakers and label them as 1, 2, and 3 with a wax marker.

4. Fill Beaker 1 about half-full with distilled water; fill Beaker 2 about half-full with 5% dextrose; and fill Beaker 3 about half-full with 25% NaCl.

5. Place each piece of potato in its corresponding numbered beaker, and leave them in the solutions undisturbed for one hour.

6. After an hour has passed, remove the potato pieces and measure their length and width with calipers. Record these data in Table 4.5. After you have recorded your data, move on to Procedure 3.

TABLE **4.5** Results for Potato Osmosis Experiment

Sample	Sample Contents	Length Before	Width Before	Length After	Width After
1	Distilled water				
2	5% dextrose				
3	25% NaCl				

3 **PROCEDURE**

Interpreting Your Results

Now that you've performed one of the osmosis experiments, you can interpret your data.

1 Which solution was hypotonic? Explain your reasoning.

2 Which solution was isotonic? Explain your reasoning.

3 Which solution was hypertonic? Explain your reasoning.

4 Compare your results to your hypothesis.

MATERIALS

☐ Anatomical models and
   diagrams:
   ▪ cell
   ▪ mitosis
☐ Slides: mitosis
☐ Light microscope
☐ Colored pencils

Mitosis and the Cell Cycle

Many cells go through a continual cycle of growth and replication called the **cell cycle**. The cell cycle consists of four phases (Fig. 4.10):

1. G_1 is the initial growth phase during which the cell grows, develops, and carries out activities that are specific to that cell type. Some cells are *amitotic*, meaning that they never divide, remaining in G_1 indefinitely. These cells are said to be in phase G_0 (pronounced "G not") of the cell cycle. Most adult neurons (nerve cells) are in G_0, as are multinucleated skeletal muscle cells and mature bone cells.

2. **S phase** is the period during which the cell's DNA is replicated. In this case, the "S" stands for "synthesis" because another copy of the DNA is synthesized.

3. G_2 is the second growth phase during which the cell makes its final preparations for division.

4. **M phase** is the phase during which the cell, sometimes called the *mother cell*, undergoes the process of **mitosis** (my-TOH-sis) and divides its replicated DNA among two identical **daughter cells**. Also occurring during M phase is the process of **cytokinesis** (sy-toh-kin-EE-sis; *kine-* = "movement"), during which the mother cell's cytoplasm is distributed between the two daughter cells. Each daughter cell has the same exact genetic and structural characteristics as the original mother cell.

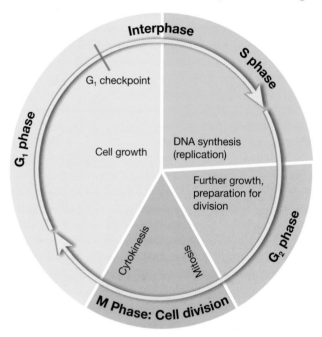

FIGURE **4.10** Cell cycle.

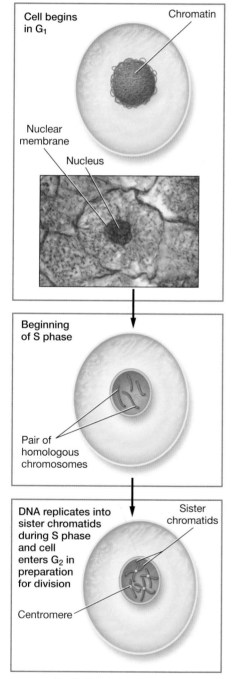

FIGURE **4.11** Cell interphase.

The portions of the cycle from G_1–G_2, when the cell is not dividing, are collectively called **interphase**, which is shown in Figure 4.11. In G_1, the cell has only a single copy of its DNA. As the cell enters S phase, DNA replication occurs. Human cells have 23 pairs of **homologous chromosomes** (KROH-moh-sohmz): one set from the mother, and one set from the father. After the DNA is replicated, each homologous chromosome exists in a set of "identical twins" called **sister chromatids**. Note that, in Figure 4.11, we show only two pairs of homologous chromosomes for simplicity. Note also that the DNA through all of interphase is still in the form of chromatin and you can't see individual chromosomes or sister chromatids—we have shown them here in the illustration for teaching purposes only.

When S phase has completed, the cell enters G_2, and when G_2 is finished, mitosis begins. Mitosis proceeds in the four general stages shown in Figure 4.12.

1. **Prophase.** During **prophase**, the nuclear membrane starts to degenerate, and the chromatin condenses into individual **chromosomes**. Also during this stage, we see a structure called the **mitotic spindle** organizing around the centrioles, which begin migrating to the opposite poles of the cell. By the end of late prophase, the centrioles have reached the opposite poles of the cell. Microtubules called spindle fibers emanate from each side of the mitotic spindle

and attach to a structure known as the **centromere** (SIN-troh-meer) that joins the two sister chromatids—one spindle fiber attaches to each side of the centromere.

2. **Metaphase.** In **metaphase,** we see the sister chromatids, which are attached to the spindle fibers, line up along the equator of the cell.

3. **Anaphase.** During **anaphase,** we see the spindle fibers shorten, which pulls the centromeres apart, and the sister chromatids migrate toward the opposite poles of the cell. In addition, **cytokinesis** begins, and the cell elongates.

4. **Telophase.** In the final phase of mitosis, **telophase** (TEL-oh-fayz), a divot called a **cleavage furrow** (Fig 4.13) forms between the two cells. As the cleavage furrow progressively narrows, the cell is pinched into two identical daughter cells and cytokinesis is completed. In addition, during this stage, the nuclear membranes begin to reassemble, the mitotic spindle becomes less visible, and the DNA returns to its chromatin form.

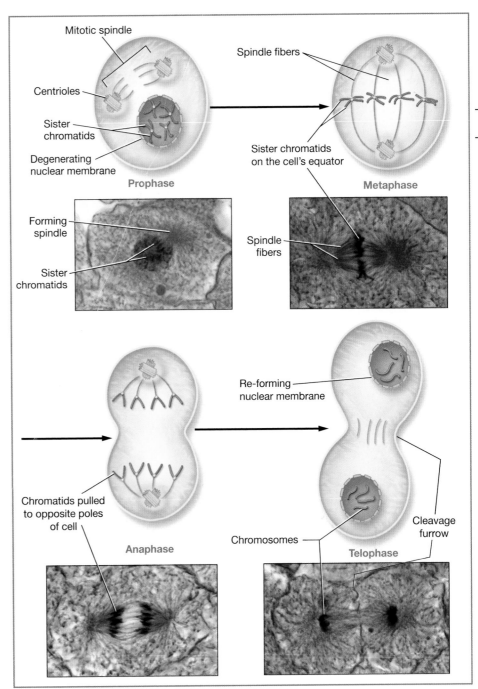

FIGURE **4.12** Cell during the stages of mitosis.

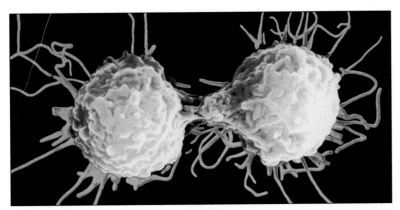

FIGURE **4.13** White blood cell in the telophase stage of mitosis.

1 PROCEDURE

Identifying Structures of Cell Division

Identify the following structures associated with mitosis on cell models and diagrams. Check off each structure as you identify it.

1. Mitotic spindle
   a. Centrioles
   b. Microtubules (spindle fibers)

2. Nucleus
   a. Nucleolus
   b. Nuclear membrane

3. Chromosomes
   a. Sister chromatids
   b. Centromere

2 PROCEDURE

Modeling Mitosis

Arrange models of the cell cycle and mitosis in the proper order.

1. Interphase
2. Mitosis
   a. Prophase
   b. Metaphase
   c. Anaphase
   d. Telophase

3 PROCEDURE

Examining the Cell Cycle with Microscopy

Using the highest-power objective, examine the five phases of the cell cycle on prepared whitefish mitosis slides. Note that you may not be able to find every stage of the cell cycle on one slide, so you might have to use multiple slides.

Draw and describe what the cell looks like during each phase of the cell cycle, and label your drawings with as many of the structures of cell division (see pp. 98–99) as you can see in each cell. Use your Pre-Lab Exercises and Figures 4.11 and 4.12 for reference. When you have completed the activities, answer Check Your Understanding Question 7 (p. 108).

1 Interphase

Description:

2 Mitosis

   α Prophase

      Description:

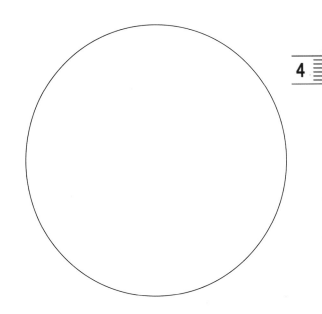

_____

_____

_____

_____

_____

_____

_____

_____

   b Metaphase

      Description:

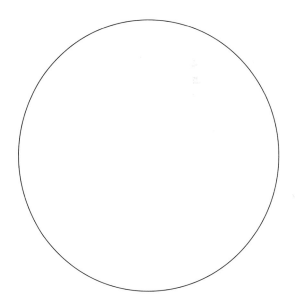

_____

_____

_____

_____

_____

_____

_____

_____

_____

c Anaphase

Description:

_____

_____

_____

_____

_____

_____

_____

_____

_____

d Telophase

Description:

_____

_____

_____

_____

_____

_____

_____

_____

Name _____

Section _____   Date_____

Check Your Recall

1 Label the following parts of the plasma membrane and cell on Figure 4.14.

❑ Centrioles   ❑ Integral protein   ❑ Nuclear envelope   ❑ Phospholipid bilayer
❑ Cholesterol   ❑ Lysosome   ❑ Nucleolus   ❑ Smooth endoplasmic
❑ Golgi apparatus   ❑ Mitochondrion   ❑ Peripheral protein   reticulum

A

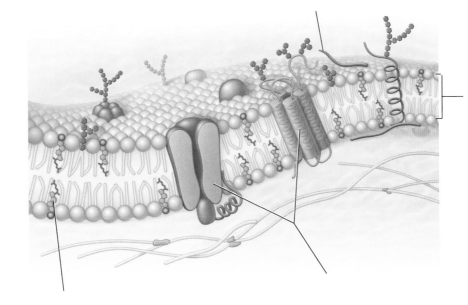

B

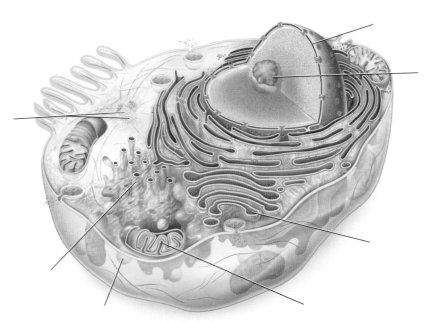

FIGURE **4.14** The cell: (**A**) plasma membrane; (**B**) generalized cell.

2 Which type of organelle contains its own DNA and ribosomes?

a. Rough endoplasmic reticulum.

b. Mitochondria.

c. Lysosomes.

d. Golgi apparatus.

3 Why do phospholipids form a bilayer in the plasma membrane?

_____

_____

4 Osmosis refers to the movement of _____, and diffusion refers to the movement of _____.

a. solvent; solvent

b. solute; solute

c. solvent; solute

d. solute; solvent

5 *True/False:* Mark the following statements as true (T) or false (F). If the statement is false, correct it to make it a true statement.

_____ a. In osmosis, solvent moves from an area of low solute concentration to an area of high solute concentration.

_____ b. In diffusion, larger particles have higher kinetic energy and so diffuse faster.

_____ c. A steeper concentration gradient increases the rate at which diffusion takes place.

_____ d. In diffusion, solvent moves from an area of high solute concentration to an area of low solute concentration.

6 *Matching:* Match the following organelles and cell structures with the correct definitions.

_____ Ribosomes

_____ Golgi apparatus

_____ Rough ER

_____ Chromatin

_____ Smooth ER

_____ Cilia

_____ Nucleolus

_____ Microtubule

_____ Microvilli

_____ Actin filaments

A. Series of membrane-enclosed sacs with ribosomes on the surface

B. A ball-like mass of tightly coiled DNA and proteins

C. Projections of the folded plasma membrane

D. The "birthplace" of ribosomes in the cell

E. Hair-like extensions from the plasma membrane that propel substances past the cell

F. Part of the cytoskeleton located along the plasma membrane and in microvilli that helps maintain the cell's shape

G. Granular organelles that are the sites of protein synthesis

H. Stack of flattened sacs that modifies and sorts proteins

I. Cytoskeletal filament found in cilia and flagella

J. Series of membrane-enclosed sacs that detoxify substances and synthesize lipids

7 *Fill in the blanks:* A cell placed in a hypotonic solution will _____, whereas a cell placed in a hypertonic solution will _____.

8 What happens during G_1 phase of the cell cycle?
   a. The cell divides.
   b. The cell undergoes its final preparation for division.
   c. The cell undergoes its initial growth phase.
   d. The cell replicates its DNA.

9 *Fill in the blank:* The cell in Figure 4.15 is in the _____ stage of mitosis.

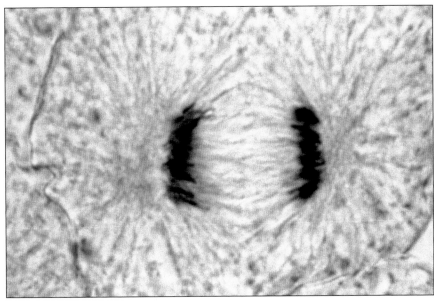

FIGURE **4.15** Dividing cell.

10 Which of the following correctly describes the function of the mitotic spindle?
   a. The spindle fibers pull sister chromatids apart during mitosis.
   b. The spindle fibers separate the cell during mitosis.
   c. The spindle fibers condense DNA into chromosomes.
   d. The spindle fibers separate DNA helices during DNA replication.

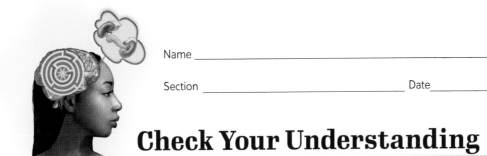

Name _____

Section _____ Date_____

Check Your Understanding

Critical Thinking and Application Questions

1 A condition known as *Zellweger syndrome* is characterized by a lack of functional peroxisomes. Given the functions of peroxisomes, what functions would affected cells be unable to perform?

_____

_____

_____

_____

2 There are many products on the market that claim to "detoxify the liver." However, the cells of the liver have a very high concentration of smooth endoplasmic reticulum. Given this information, does the liver need to be "detoxified"? What do you make of the claims of these products? Explain your reasoning.

_____

_____

_____

_____

3 As erythrocytes (red blood cells) mature, they gradually lose their nuclei and most other organelles. What processes are mature erythrocytes unable to carry out due to a lack of:

a Nucleus _____

b Mitochondria _____

c Lysosomes _____

d Centrioles _____

4 You perform an experiment in which you release two gases into the air from opposite sides of the room: one that smells like roses and one that smells like lemons. The rose gas was stored at a temperature of 0°C, is in a 10% concentration, and its particles have a molecular weight of 12.5 g/mol. The lemon gas was stored at a temperature of 100°C, is in a concentration of 12%, and has a molecular weight of 8.5 g/mol. Your lab partner is seated at an equal distance from each gas. Which gas will your lab partner smell first, and why?

_____

_____

_____

5 In 2007, a 28-year-old woman died after taking part in a radio station's water-drinking contest. Her cause of death was ruled as *water intoxication*. Explain why consuming such a large quantity of a hypotonic solution such as water in a very short period of time could result in death.

_____

_____

_____

_____

6 A popular product marketed as a cure for most diseases consists of nothing but cabbage, water, and several tablespoons of salt, making a very hypertonic solution. The marketer of this product claims that salt is "all natural" and could not possibly harm a user. If your friend wanted to try this product, what would you tell her about hypertonic solutions and their effects on cells?

_____

_____

_____

_____

7 The anticancer drug cytarabine interacts with DNA in such a way as to prevent DNA replication. Which phase of the cell cycle would this affect? Are there any cell populations that would not be affected by this drug? Explain.

_____

_____

_____

_____

Histology

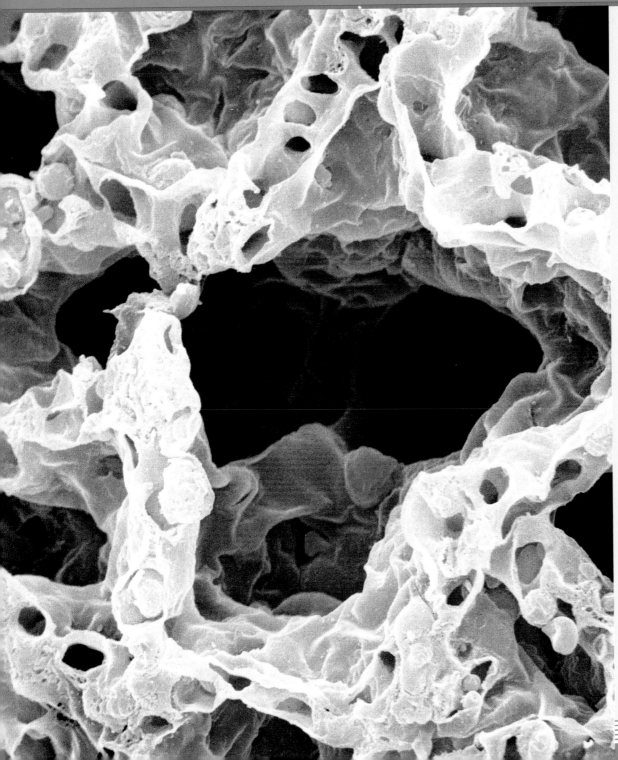

When you have completed this unit, you should be able to:

1 Describe the basic components of all tissues.

2 Identify epithelial tissues by number of layers and cell shape.

3 Identify and describe connective tissues.

4 Identify and describe muscle and nervous tissues.

5 Relate tissue structure to tissue function, and describe how organs are formed from two or more tissue types.

PRE-LAB EXERCISES

Complete the following exercises prior to coming to lab, using your lab manual and textbook for reference.

PRE-LAB

5-1 Key Terms

You should be familiar with the following terms before coming to lab.

Term	Definition

Extracellular Matrix

Ground substance

Collagen fiber

Elastic fiber

Reticular fiber

Epithelial Tissue

Simple epithelial tissue

Stratified epithelial tissue

Pseudostratified epithelial tissue

Squamous cell

Cuboidal cell

Columnar cell

Basement membrane

Connective Tissue

Loose connective tissue _____

_____

Dense connective tissue _____

_____

_____

Cartilage _____

_____

Bone _____

_____

Blood _____

_____

Muscle Tissue

Striated _____

_____

Skeletal muscle tissue _____

_____

Cardiac muscle tissue _____

_____

Smooth muscle tissue _____

_____

Nervous Tissue

Neuron _____

_____

Neuroglial cell _____

_____

EXERCISES

In the histology labs, we explore the third level of organization—tissues. A **tissue** is defined as a collection of cells and the surrounding material, called the **extracellular matrix** (**ECM**; *extra-* = "outside"). Together, the cells and ECM unite to perform a common function.

ECM consists of two components: **ground substance** and protein fibers (Fig. 5.1). Ground substance is a gelatinous material that contains water, ions, nutrients, and large polysaccharides, as well as *proteoglycans*, which are polysaccharides bound to a protein core. Notice in Figure 5.1 that thousands of proteoglycans come together to form huge structures called *proteoglycan aggregates* that resemble bottle brushes. The polysaccharides, proteoglycans, and proteoglycan aggregates trap water in the ECM and make it firmer, which helps a tissue resist compression.

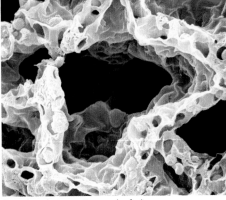
Scanning electron micrograph of a lung.

Protein fibers are found within ground substance. The three types of protein fiber include:

1. **Collagen fibers.** Cells make many different types of **collagen fibers** (known as type I, type II, type III, etc.), which are composed of multiple entwining strands of the thick protein **collagen** (KAHL-eh-jen; *colla-* = "glue"). Imagine collagen fibers as the steel cables of a tissue—just as steel cables give a structure the ability to withstand tension, collagen fibers give a tissue tensile strength (i.e., the ability to resist stretching forces).

2. **Elastic fibers.** Cells may produce another type of fiber called **elastic fibers,** which are composed of the protein **elastin.** These protein strands perform the opposite function of collagen fibers—collagen fibers resist stretch, while elastic fibers allow a tissue to be stretched, which is a property known as *distensibility*. Elastic fibers also give a tissue the property of *elasticity*, meaning that the tissue returns to its original shape and size when the stretching force is removed.

3. **Reticular fibers.** The final fiber type made by cells is thin **reticular fibers** (reh-TIK-yoo-luhr; *reticul-* = "netlike"). These fibers were long thought to be a unique fiber type, but are now understood to be a special type of collagen fiber composed of collagen proteins. The thin structure of reticular fibers allows them to interweave to form "nets" that support blood vessels, nerves, and other structures.

The exercises in this unit introduce you to the four basic types of tissue: epithelial tissue, connective tissue, muscle tissue, and nervous tissue (Fig. 5.2). All four of these tissue types are composed of cells, which are specialized for each tissue type, and

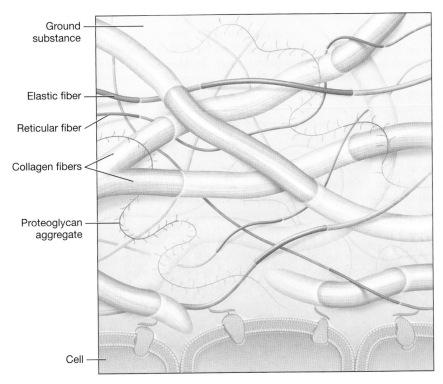

Ground substance

Elastic fiber

Reticular fiber

Collagen fibers

Proteoglycan aggregate

Cell

FIGURE **5.1** Composition of extracellular matrix.

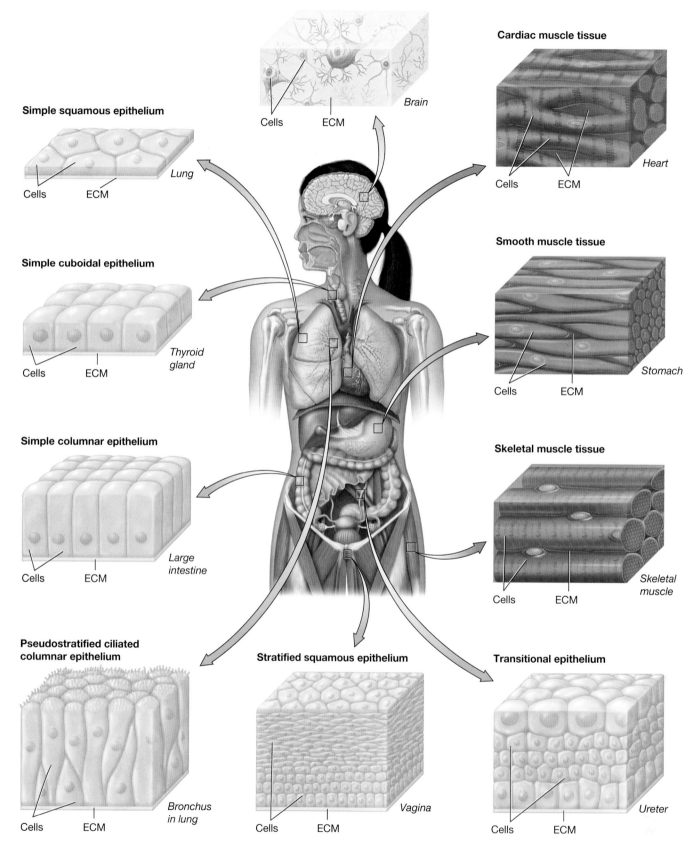

Epithelial tissues: Cover and line all internal and external body surfaces and glands

Nervous tissue: Receives and transmits stimuli

Muscle tissues: Contract and generate tension

Simple squamous epithelium

Cells ECM *Lung*

Simple cuboidal epithelium

Cells ECM *Thyroid gland*

Simple columnar epithelium

Cells ECM *Large intestine*

Pseudostratified ciliated columnar epithelium

Cells ECM *Bronchus in lung*

Cells ECM *Brain*

Stratified squamous epithelium

Cells ECM *Vagina*

Cardiac muscle tissue

Cells ECM *Heart*

Smooth muscle tissue

Cells ECM *Stomach*

Skeletal muscle tissue

Cells ECM *Skeletal muscle*

Transitional epithelium

Cells ECM *Ureter*

FIGURE **5.2** The major tissue types and their locations in the body. (*continues*)

Connective tissues: Bind, support, and transport

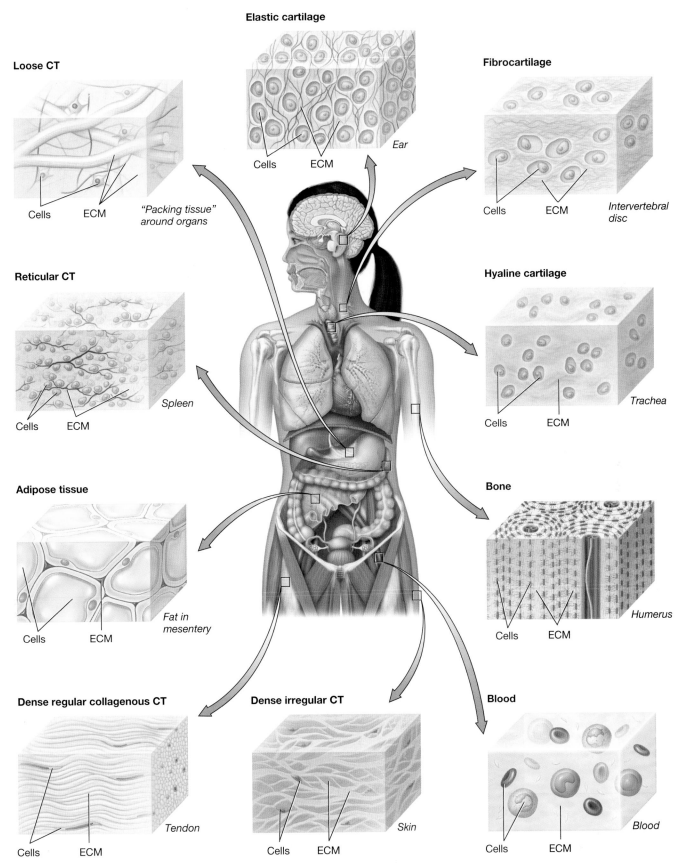

Elastic cartilage

Cells   ECM

Ear

Loose CT

Cells   ECM

"Packing tissue" around organs

Fibrocartilage

Cells   ECM

Intervertebral disc

Reticular CT

Cells   ECM

Spleen

Hyaline cartilage

Cells   ECM

Trachea

Adipose tissue

Cells   ECM

Fat in mesentery

Bone

Cells   ECM

Humerus

Dense regular collagenous CT

Cells   ECM

Tendon

Dense irregular CT

Cells   ECM

Skin

Blood

Cells   ECM

Blood

FIGURE **5.2** *(cont.)* The major tissue types and their locations in the body.

the surrounding ECM, which is largely produced by the cells themselves. As you can see in Figure 5.2, all tissues have ECM, although its prominence, composition, and location vary in the different tissue types.

Studying tissues sometimes proves intimidating and frustrating for beginning anatomy and physiology students. The subjects are abstract and unfamiliar and require use of a complicated tool—the microscope. The best way to approach this subject is to be systematic, and let your lab manual walk you through it step-by-step. If you get confused, don't panic. With the help of this book, your lab instructor, and a little patience, you can do it. Before you begin, you may wish to return to Unit 3 to review the box, "Hints and Tips: How to Approach Microscopy," which is shown on p. 73. Let's now begin our exploration of this fascinating level of organization, starting with epithelial tissues.

Let's now begin our exploration of this fascinating level of organization, starting with epithelial tissues.

MATERIALS

☐ Slides: epithelial tissues
☐ Light microscope
☐ Colored pencils

Epithelial Tissue

Epithelial tissues (ep-ih-THEE-lee-uhl; *epi-* = "on top") are our covering and lining tissues. They are found covering body surfaces, lining body passageways, lining body cavities, and forming glands. Epithelia contain mostly cells, called **epithelial cells**, with little visible ECM. In fact, the majority of their ECM is located underneath the cells in a thin layer called the **basal lamina** (BAY-zul LAM-in-uh; *basal* = "bottom;" *lamina* = "layer"). The basal lamina performs an important function: It effectively "glues" the epithelium in place. Within the basal lamina are collagen fibers that anchor to another layer of ECM, the *lamina reticularis*, produced by the connective tissues deep to the epithelium. Together, the basal lamina and lamina reticularis are called the **basement membrane**.

Epithelial tissues are all **avascular** (ay-VASS-kyu-lur; *a-* = "without," *vascul-* = "vessel"), which means that they have no blood vessels to supply them directly. As a result, epithelial cells must obtain oxygen and nutrients that have diffused up from blood vessels supplying deeper tissues. For this reason, epithelial tissues can be only a certain number of cell layers in thickness. If they are too thick, oxygen and nutrients will not reach the more superficial cells, and these cells will die.

The different types of epithelia are classified according to the number of layers of cells they have: **Simple epithelia** have only one layer of cells, and **stratified epithelia** (STRAT-ih-fy′d; *strat-* = "layer") have two or more cell layers. Epithelia are also classified by their predominant cell shape: **squamous** (SKWAY-muhs; *squam-* = "scaly") **cells** are flat; **cuboidal cells** are about as tall are they are wide; and **columnar cells** are taller than they are wide. These two criteria give us the following classes of epithelia (see Fig. 5.3):

1. **Simple epithelia:**

   a. **Simple squamous epithelium. Simple squamous epithelium,** shown in Figure 5.3A, consists of a single layer of flat cells with a centrally located, flattened nucleus. We often find simple squamous epithelium in places where substances have to cross the epithelium quickly, such as the air sacs of the lungs.

   b. **Simple cuboidal epithelium.** Note in Figure 5.3B that the cells of **simple cuboidal epithelium** are short and have a spherical, central nucleus. Simple cuboidal epithelium is found in the kidneys as well as lining certain respiratory passages and glands, such as the thyroid gland.

   c. **Simple columnar epithelium.** The cells of **simple columnar epithelium,** shown in Figure 5.3C, have spherical nuclei generally located near the base of the cell. These cells line certain respiratory passages and much of the digestive tract. The plasma membranes of simple columnar epithelial cells often contain cilia or are folded into microvilli.

   d. **Pseudostratified ciliated columnar epithelium. Pseudostratified** (SOO-doh-strat-ih-fy′d; *pseudo-* = "false") **epithelium,** seen in Figure 5.3D, looks as if it has many cell layers but actually has only one layer of cells. Notice in the figure that the nuclei of the cells are at different heights, which gives the epithelium the appearance of having many layers.

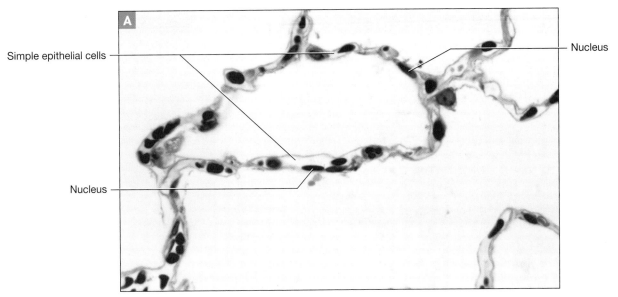

FIGURE **5.3** Simple epithelial tissues: (**A**) simple squamous epithelium from the lungs; (*continues*)

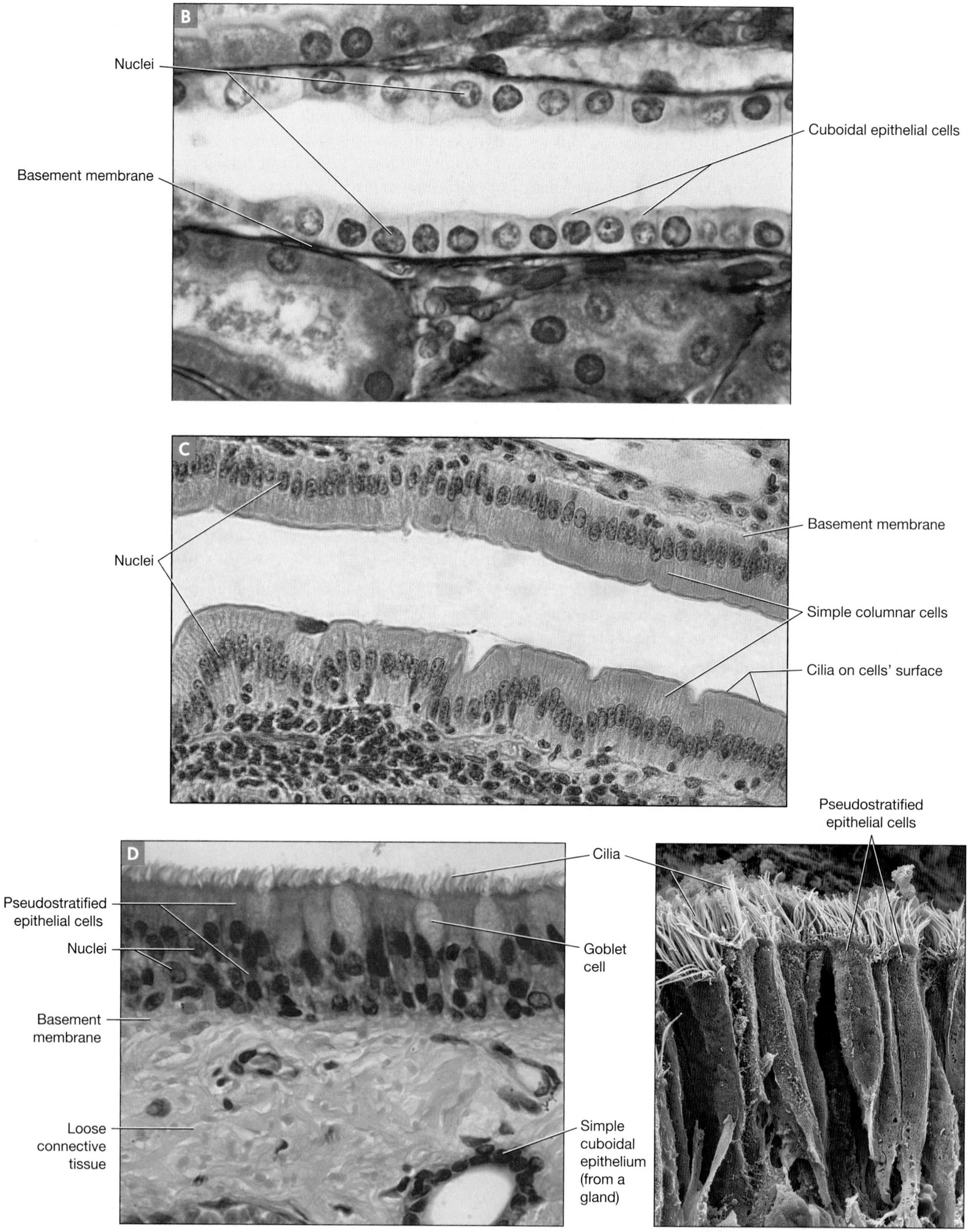

FIGURE **5.3** Simple epithelial tissues (*cont.*): (**B**) simple cuboidal epithelium from the kidney; (**C**) simple ciliated columnar epithelium from the uterine tube; (**D**) pseudostratified ciliated columnar epithelium from the trachea, light micrograph and scanning electron micrograph.

Labels in B:
Nuclei
Basement membrane
Cuboidal epithelial cells

Labels in C:
Nuclei
Basement membrane
Simple columnar cells
Cilia on cells' surface

Labels in D:
Pseudostratified epithelial cells
Nuclei
Basement membrane
Loose connective tissue
Cilia
Goblet cell
Simple cuboidal epithelium (from a gland)
Pseudostratified epithelial cells

However, the cells are all attached to the same basal lamina, and so exist in a single layer. This type of epithelium usually has cilia, and the cell shape is always columnar. It is found lining the nasal cavity and much of the respiratory tract, where it is often called *respiratory epithelium*.

2. Stratified epithelia:

   a. **Stratified squamous epithelium.** This type of epithelium consists of many layers of flattened cells and has two variants. The first, shown in Figure 5.4A, is **stratified squamous keratinized epithelium,** which consists of epithelial cells called **keratinocytes** (kehr-ah-TIN-oh-syt′z) that produce the protein **keratin** (KEHR-ah-tin). The more superficial flaky-looking cells are dead because they are too far away from the blood supply in the deeper tissues and, as a result, they harden and die. Stratified squamous keratinized epithelial cells resist mechanical stresses and so are found in the superficial layer of the skin where the body is subject to multiple environmental stresses. **Stratified squamous nonkeratinized epithelium** (Fig. 5.4B) contains no keratin and is located in places subject to lesser degrees of mechanical stress, such as the oral cavity, the pharynx (throat), the anus, and the vagina. This type of epithelium is not as thick and so the superficial cells are alive. As you can see, this gives them a much different appearance than the superficial cells of keratinized epithelium.

   b. **Stratified cuboidal epithelium** and **stratified columnar epithelium.** Both of these types of epithelium are rare in the human body (Fig. 5.4C shows stratified cuboidal epithelium only) and are found lining the ducts of certain glands.

   c. **Transitional epithelium. Transitional epithelium,** shown in Figure 5.4D, is stratified but is not classified by its shape because its cells can change shape. Typically, the apical or surface cells are dome-shaped, but when the tissue is stretched, they flatten and are squamous in appearance. Transitional epithelium is found lining the urinary bladder and ureters, and, for this reason, is also sometimes known as *urinary epithelium*.

HINTS & TIPS

Histology: Don't Panic

There's one mantra you always need to repeat before you place a slide on the stage: *Don't panic.* Histology really isn't as hard as it seems. Remember that everything that you see on a slide, no matter how disorganized or confusing the slide may look, is either cells or ECM. These are easy to tell apart. If you're looking at something that has a dark purple nucleus, it's a cell. If it doesn't, it's ECM. So right there, you've got a starting point.

Now, let's review the basics of microscopy that we talked about in Unit 3, as a good understanding of the basics makes histology much easier. So, first recall how to approach any slide: Examine the slide with the naked eye, place the slide on the stage with the specimen directly over the condenser (light source), and then begin to scan the slide on low power. Once you have found the structures or general area that you need, advance progressively to higher power to see details, and use the fine adjustment knob to get the image in better focus. Use the figures in this manual as a guide—if your slide looks nothing like the tissue in the figure, scroll around the slide and keep looking. But don't rely completely on the figures here, because the slides that your lab uses may be prepared with different stains or taken from different tissues.

As mentioned before, once you find the general area of the slide that you need, what you are seeing is nothing more than cells and ECM. So, first identify the cells, which are the things with dark purple nuclei. Sometimes these will be nice and round, other times they will be kind of flat, and other times they will just look like purple dots. But no matter their shape, nothing else in the tissue looks like this, so when you find something with a nucleus, you've found a cell.

Everything around the cell, no matter how haphazard it may be arranged, be it purple straight lines, pink wavy lines, light purple gel, or all of the above, is just ECM. The "lines" are simply protein fibers, and the "gel" is merely ground substance.

If you keep all this information in mind, and above all, don't panic, you can use the appearance and distribution of the cells and the makeup of the ECM to determine what type of tissue you are seeing.

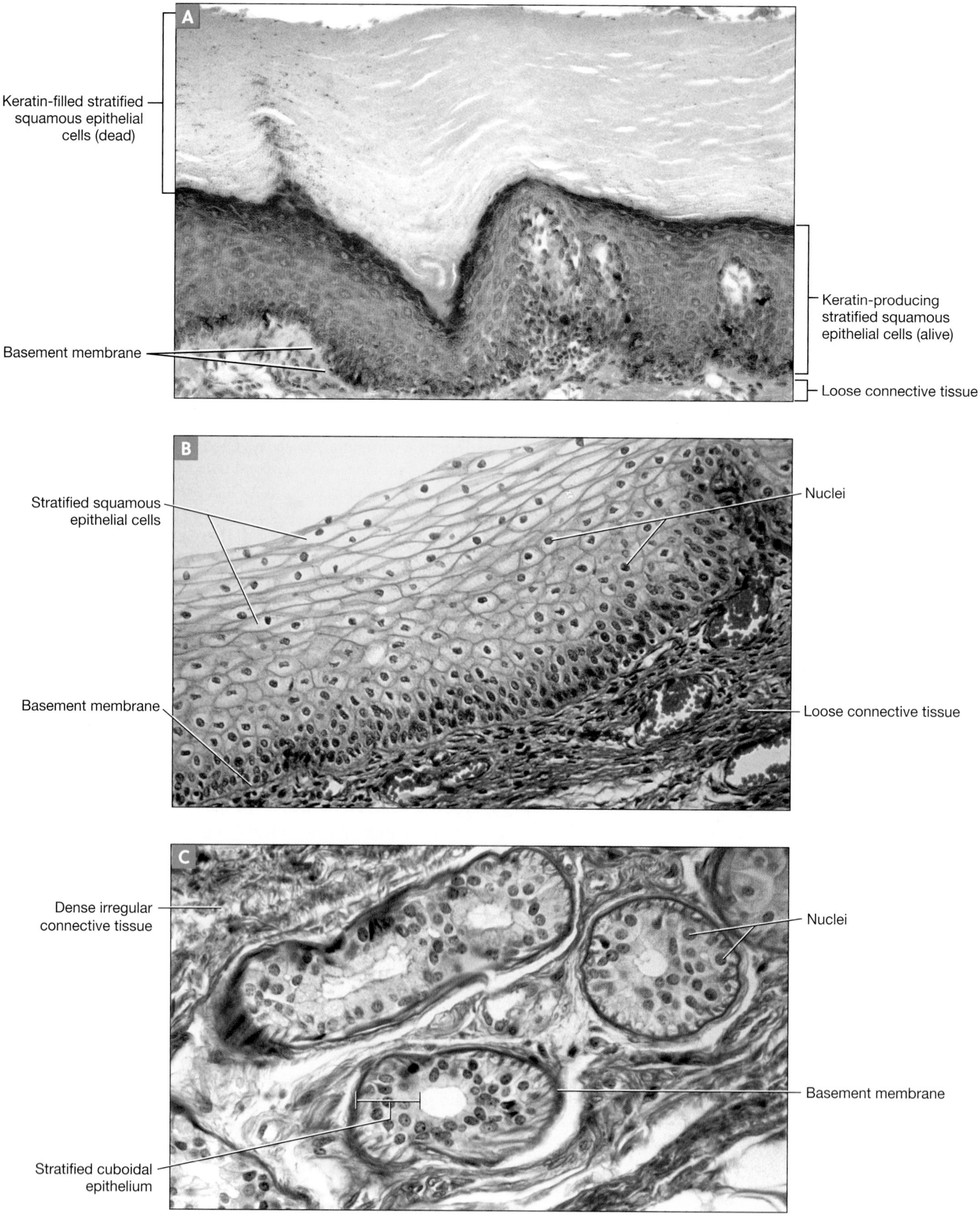

Keratin-filled stratified squamous epithelial cells (dead)

Basement membrane

Keratin-producing stratified squamous epithelial cells (alive)

Loose connective tissue

Stratified squamous epithelial cells

Nuclei

Basement membrane

Loose connective tissue

Dense irregular connective tissue

Nuclei

Basement membrane

Stratified cuboidal epithelium

FIGURE 5.4 Stratified epithelial tissues: (A) stratified squamous keratinized epithelium from the skin; (B) stratified squamous nonkeratinized epithelium from the vagina; (C) stratified cuboidal epithelium from a sweat gland; (continues)

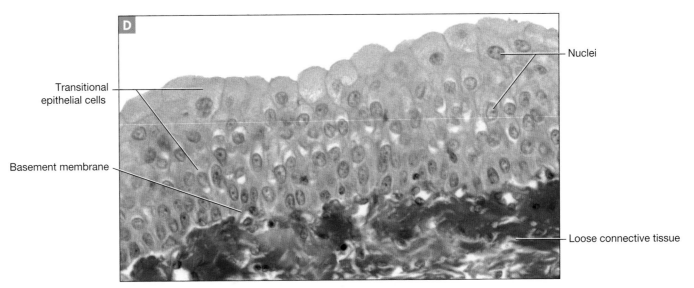

Transitional epithelial cells

Basement membrane

Nuclei

Loose connective tissue

FIGURE **5.4** Stratified epithelial tissues (*cont.*): (**D**) transitional epithelium from the urinary bladder.

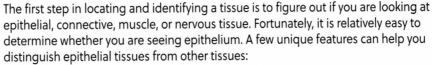

HINTS & TIPS

Identifying Epithelial Tissue

The first step in locating and identifying a tissue is to figure out if you are looking at epithelial, connective, muscle, or nervous tissue. Fortunately, it is relatively easy to determine whether you are seeing epithelium. A few unique features can help you distinguish epithelial tissues from other tissues:

ⓘ Epithelial tissues are all avascular, so you won't see any blood vessels in epithelium.

ⓘ Epithelial tissues are typically on the outer edge of the slide or, at least, on the outer edge of the tissue. Keep in mind that most slides have several tissues in each section. To find the epithelial tissue, often you need to scroll to one end of the slide or the other.

ⓘ Epithelial tissues consist mostly of cells. As we have established, everything in a tissue is either cells or ECM. In the case of epithelium, most ECM is restricted to a thin layer deep to the cells. So, you will be looking for cells—structures with dark purple nuclei—that are tightly packed together.

Examining Epithelial Tissues with Microscopy

Examine prepared slides of the following epithelial tissues. Use colored pencils to draw what you see under the microscope, and label your drawings with the terms from Figures 5.3 and 5.4. Then (a) describe what you see, and (b) give examples of locations in the body where this tissue is found. When you have completed the exercise, answer Check Your Understanding Questions 1 and 2 (p. 143).

5

1 Simple Squamous Epithelium

a _____

_____

_____

b _____

_____

_____

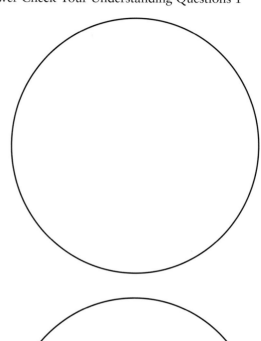

2 Simple Cuboidal Epithelium

a _____

_____

_____

b _____

_____

_____

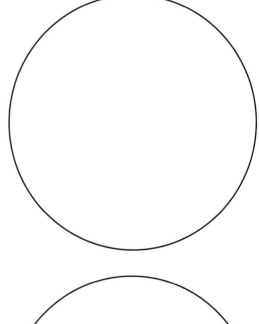

3 Simple Columnar Epithelium

a _____

_____

_____

b _____

_____

_____

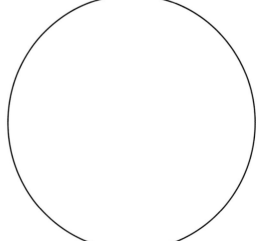

4 Pseudostratified Ciliated Columnar Epithelium

a _____

_____

_____

b _____

_____

_____

5

5 Stratified Squamous Keratinized Epithelium

a _____

_____

_____

b _____

_____

_____

6 Stratified Squamous Nonkeratinized Epithelium

a _____

_____

_____

b _____

_____

_____

7 Stratified Cuboidal or Columnar Epithelium

a _____

_____

_____

b _____

_____

_____

8 Transitional Epithelium

a _____

_____

_____

b _____

_____

_____

MATERIALS

❑ Slides: connective tissues
❑ Light microscope
❑ Colored pencils

Connective Tissue

Connective tissues are found throughout the body. They have a variety of functions, most of which serve to *connect*, as their name implies. All connective tissues stem from a common embryonic tissue called **mesenchyme** (MEZ-en-ky′m). Connective tissues are distinguished easily from epithelial tissues by the prominence of their extracellular matrices. Typically, connective tissues contain few cells and have an extensive ECM.

The four general types of connective tissue (CT) are as follows:

1. **Connective tissue proper. Connective tissue proper**, the most widely distributed class of connective tissue in the body, consists of scattered cells called **fibroblasts** (FY-broh-blastz) that secrete an extensive ECM filled with many types of protein fibers. This tissue is highly vascular with an extensive blood supply. The subclasses of CT proper include the following:

   ■ **Loose (areolar) CT.** You can see in Figure 5.5A that the primary element in **loose CT** is ground substance, which gives it a "loose" appearance on a slide. All three types of protein fibers are scattered in loose CT ground substance, although the slide is stained for only collagen and elastic fibers. Loose CT is found as part of the basement membrane and in the walls of hollow organs, where it helps to "glue" together the tissue layers of these organs.

   ■ **Reticular CT.** As you can guess by the name, **reticular CT** consists of many reticular fibers produced by cells called **reticular cells** (Fig. 5.5B). It is located in the spleen and lymph nodes, where the fine reticular fibers interweave to form "nets" that trap pathogens and foreign cells. Reticular CT also is located around blood vessels and nerves, where it forms supportive networks.

   ■ **Adipose tissue.** Notice in Figure 5.5C that **adipose tissue** (Ă-dih-pohs; *adip-* = "fat") has a much different appearance than the other types of CT proper. It consists mostly of huge cells called **adipocytes** (ĂD-ih-poh-syt′z) with collagen fibers in the ECM. Each adipocyte contains a large lipid droplet that occupies most of its cytoplasm. The nucleus and other organelles are barely visible, because they are pushed to the periphery of the cell against the plasma membrane. Adipose tissue is distributed widely throughout the body under the skin and around organs.

   ■ **Dense regular collagenous CT.** The difference between loose and dense CT is obvious in Figure 5.6A. **Dense regular collagenous CT** consists primarily of collagen fibers arranged in parallel bundles with little ground substance and few cells. It is exceptionally strong and makes up structures that require tensile strength in a single plane, such as tendons and ligaments.

   ■ **Dense irregular CT.** Like dense regular collagenous CT, dense *irregular* CT consists of bundles of collagen fibers. Notice in Figure 5.6B, however, that these collagen bundles are arranged in an irregular, haphazard fashion without a consistent pattern. You can see the difference clearly in the scanning electron micrographs of the two tissues. Like dense regular

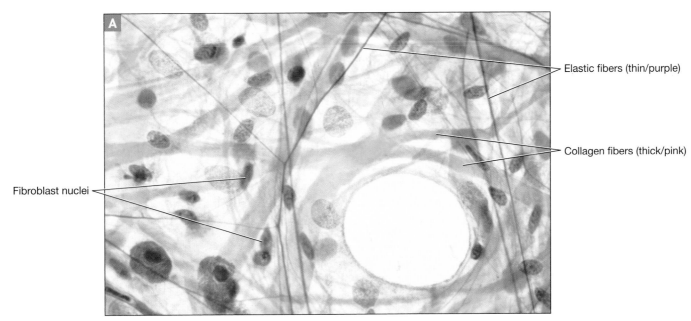

Elastic fibers (thin/purple)

Collagen fibers (thick/pink)

Fibroblast nuclei

FIGURE **5.5** Loose connective tissues: (**A**) loose (areolar) CT; *(continues)*

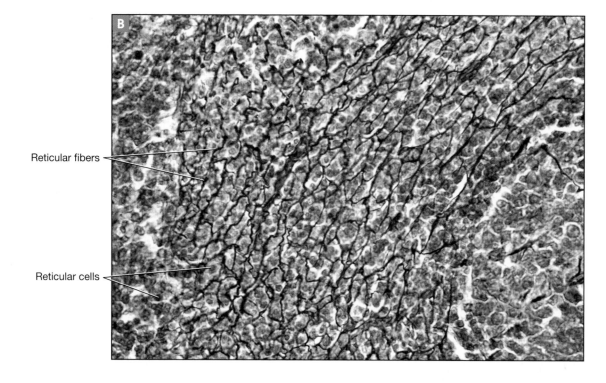

Reticular fibers

Reticular cells

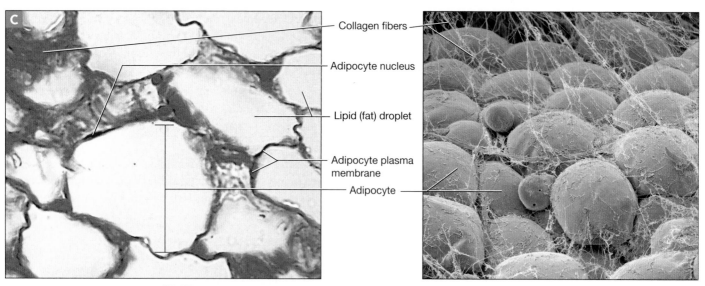

Collagen fibers

Adipocyte nucleus

Lipid (fat) droplet

Adipocyte plasma membrane

Adipocyte

FIGURE **5.5** Loose connective tissues (*cont.*): (**B**) reticular CT from the spleen; (**C**) adipose tissue, light micrograph and SEM.

collagenous CT, dense irregular CT also is quite strong. The arrangement of its collagen bundles makes it well-suited to support structures that require tensile strength in multiple planes, such as the dermis of the skin and joint and organ capsules.

- **Dense regular elastic CT. Dense regular elastic CT** contains elastic fibers arranged in parallel bundles (Fig. 5.6C). We find dense regular elastic CT in organs that need to be both distensible and elastic. A good example of such organs are large blood vessels, which are subject to pressure changes and so must be able to change size with each heartbeat. We also find this tissue type in certain ligaments, which allows them to be supportive without tearing when stretched.

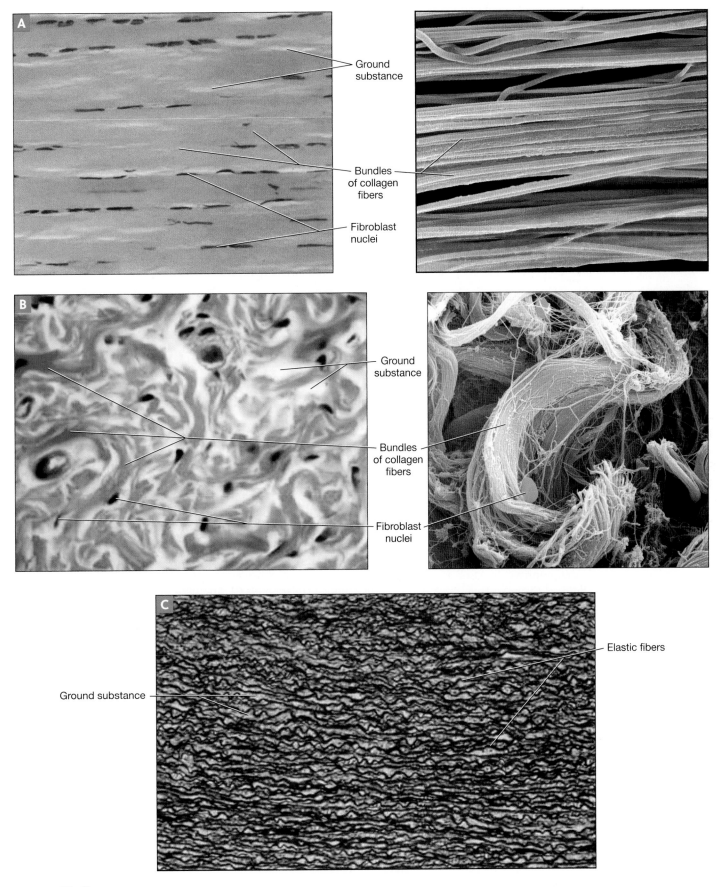

FIGURE 5.6 Dense connective tissues: (A) dense regular collagenous CT from a tendon, light micrograph and SEM; (B) dense irregular CT from the dermis, light micrograph and SEM; (C) dense elastic CT from the aorta.

2. **Cartilage.** **Cartilage** is a tough but flexible tissue that is resistant to tension, twisting, and compressive forces. It consists of cells called **chondrocytes** (KAHN-droh-syt'z; *chondr-* = "cartilage"), which are embedded in the ECM in cavities called **lacunae** (lah-KOO-nee). Cartilage is notable among the connective tissues for being avascular. Each of the three types of cartilage has a different ECM composition.

- **Hyaline cartilage.** Notice in **Figure 5.7A** that **hyaline cartilage** (HY-ah-lin; *hyalin-* = "glass") contains mostly chondrocytes scattered in ground substance with few visible protein fibers. This gives hyaline cartilage a smooth, glassy appearance and makes it an ideal tissue to cover the ends of bones where they form joints with another bone. The smooth texture of hyaline cartilage provides a nearly frictionless surface on which bones can articulate. Hyaline cartilage also is found connecting the ribs to the sternum, lining certain respiratory passages, and forming the framework for the nose.

- **Fibrocartilage.** As you can see in **Figure 5.7B**, **fibrocartilage** is named appropriately because its ECM is full of protein fibers (mostly collagen). This makes fibrocartilage tough and extremely strong but not very smooth (think of the surface of fibrocartilage like a flannel sheet, with the cotton fibers representing the protein fibers). For this reason, fibrocartilage does not form articular cartilage, but it does reinforce ligaments and form *articular discs*, tough structures that improve the fit of two bones. In addition, fibrocartilage is found in intervertebral discs, structures between two vertebrae that help to support the weight of the vertebral column and absorb shock.

- **Elastic cartilage.** The final type of cartilage, **elastic cartilage,** is shown in **Figure 5.7C.** Its ECM is filled with elastic fibers that allow it to stretch and recoil. Elastic cartilage is found in the ear and in the epiglottis.

HINTS & TIPS

Identifying Connective Tissue

Connective tissue really isn't as confusing as it seems. If you approach these slides systematically, use the figures in this manual as a guide, and, of course, don't panic, you will find they are surprisingly simple. Remember, everything in the field of view is only one of two things: cells or ECM.

The following points will help you to identify the various connective tissues and differentiate them from other tissue types:

🛈 Usually, in connective tissue, you will see a large amount of space between the cells because they aren't packed tightly together (adipose tissue is an exception). Remember to look for the nucleus to find the cells.

🛈 You will often see a lot of straight or wavy lines running through a connective tissue section. These are just protein fibers. Many types of CT can be distinguished by the types of fibers they contain:

- Reticular fibers are the thinnest fibers, and they require a special stain to be visible. As you saw in **Figure 5.5B** (p. 126), this stain makes reticular fibers brownish-black. In general, only reticular tissue is prepared with this stain, so if you see brownish-black reticular fibers, you know you are looking at reticular tissue.

- Collagen fibers are thick fibers that usually stain pink or light purple. Look for collagen fibers in fibrocartilage, dense regular collagenous CT, dense irregular CT, and loose CT. The arrangement of the collagen fibers can tell you even more about the tissue. Are the fibers arranged haphazardly (basically, does your slide look like an undefined mess)? Then it's loose CT. Are they arranged in straight rows? Then it's dense regular collagenous CT. Are there small, wavy bundles of collagen? Then it's dense irregular CT.

- Elastic fibers are thinner than collagen fibers, and may have a wavy appearance. Their color ranges from purple-black to blue, depending on the stain used. Look for them in dense elastic CT, elastic cartilage, and loose CT. Dense regular elastic CT and elastic cartilage are easy to tell apart. Are there many visible cells among the elastic fibers? Then it's elastic cartilage. Is it almost exclusively fibers with few, if any, cells? Then it's dense regular elastic CT.

🛈 Cartilage is easy to differentiate from CT proper by looking at the shape of the cells. Fibroblasts are generally small and flat, and often appear as just purple dots. Chondrocytes are also fairly small, but they sit in lacunae, which creates a clear space around the cells. This makes the cells much easier to see and makes them appear to be bigger.

🛈 Blood and bone are perhaps the two easiest tissues you will examine in this lab. They should look much like they do in **Figures 5.8** and **5.9** (p. 130), and no other tissues resemble them.

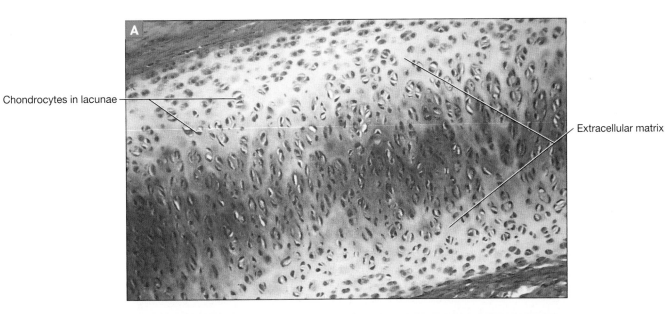

Chondrocytes in lacunae

Extracellular matrix

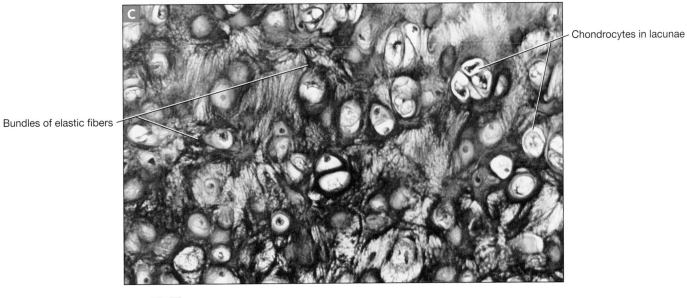

Chondrocytes in lacunae

Bundles of collagen fibers

Bundles of elastic fibers

Chondrocytes in lacunae

FIGURE **5.7** Cartilaginous connective tissues: (**A**) hyaline cartilage from a joint; (**B**) fibrocartilage from an articular disc; (**C**) elastic cartilage from the ear.

3. **Bone.** Bone tissue, also called **osseous tissue** (AHS-see-us; *os-* = "bone"), consists of bone cells called **osteocytes** (AHS-tee-oh-syt′z) encased in an ECM that contains collagen fibers and calcium hydroxyapatite crystals. Note in Figure 5.8 that the ECM is arranged in concentric layers called **lamellae** (lah-MELL-ee; *lam-* = "thin plate"), with the osteocytes sandwiched between them. This structure makes bone one of the hardest tissues in the body and very resistant to mechanical stresses.

4. **Blood.** Blood (Fig. 5.9) consists of a liquid ECM called **plasma**, within which we find cells called **erythrocytes**, or red blood cells (eh-RITH-roh-syt′z; *erythr-* = "red") and **leukocytes** or white blood cells (LOO-koh-syt′z; *leuk-* = "white"), and cellular fragments called **platelets**. Its main role is to transport oxygen, nutrients, electrolytes, wastes, and many other substances through the body. Note that blood features the only cell type in the body that lacks a nucleus: the mature erythrocyte.

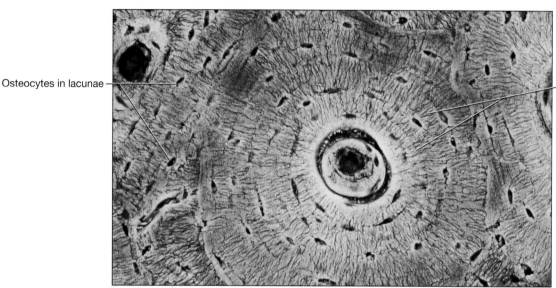

Osteocytes in lacunae

Lamellae containing collagen fibers and calcium salts in the extracellular matrix

FIGURE **5.8** Bone tissue.

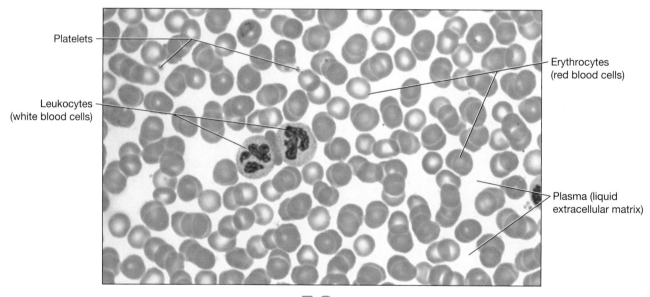

Platelets

Leukocytes (white blood cells)

Erythrocytes (red blood cells)

Plasma (liquid extracellular matrix)

FIGURE **5.9** Blood.

View prepared slides of each type of connective tissue proper. Use colored pencils to draw pictures of what you see under the microscope, and label your drawings with the terms from Figures 5.5 and 5.6 (pp. 126–127). Then (a) describe what you see, and (b) give examples of locations in the body where this tissue is found. When you have completed the exercise, answer Check Your Understanding Question 3 (p. 143).

1 Loose (Areolar) CT

a _____

b _____

2 Reticular CT

a _____

b _____

3 Adipose Tissue

a _____

b _____

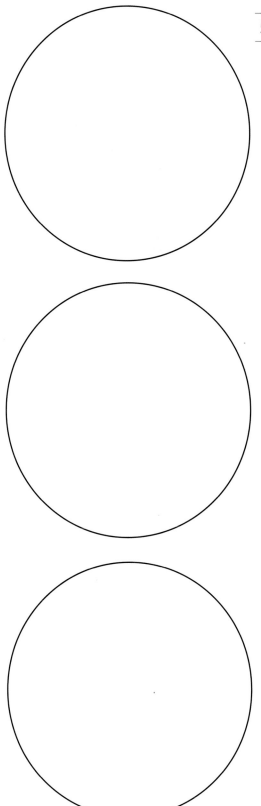

4 Dense Regular Collagenous CT

a _____

_____

_____

b _____

_____

_____

5 Dense Irregular CT

a _____

_____

_____

b _____

_____

_____

6 Dense Regular Elastic CT

a _____

_____

_____

b _____

_____

_____

View prepared slides of the three types of cartilage. Use colored pencils to draw pictures of what you see under the microscope, and label your drawings with the terms from Figure 5.7 (p. 129). Then (a) describe what you see, and (b) give examples of locations in the body where this tissue is found.

1 **Hyaline Cartilage**

a _____

_____

_____

b _____

_____

_____

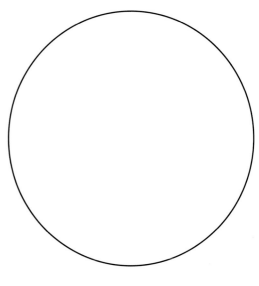

2 **Fibrocartilage**

a _____

_____

_____

b _____

_____

_____

3 **Elastic Cartilage**

a _____

_____

_____

b _____

_____

_____

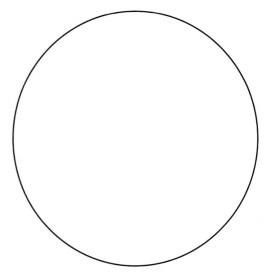

3 PROCEDURE

Examining Bone and Blood with Microscopy

View prepared slides of bone and blood. Use colored pencils to draw pictures of what you see under the microscope, and label your drawings with the terms in Figures 5.8 and 5.9 (p. 130). Then (a) describe what you see, and (b) give examples of locations in the body where this tissue is found.

1 Bone

a ______________________________

____

____

b ______________________________

____

____

2 Blood

a ______________________________

____

____

b ______________________________

____

____

EXERCISE 5-3

MATERIALS

❑ Slides: muscle tissues
❑ Light microscope
❑ Colored pencils

Muscle Tissue

Muscle tissue is located in skeletal muscles, in the walls of hollow organs, in the heart, and in other locations such as the iris of the eye. It consists of muscle cells, sometimes called **myocytes** (MY-oh-syt'z; *my-* = "muscle") or **muscle fibers**, and a small amount of ECM called the **endomysium** (in-doh-MY-see-um; *endo-* = "within"). The endomysium is rich with collagen fibers that support the muscle cells and bind them together. Note that the endomysium blends with connective tissue surrounding groups of muscle fibers and is often called connective tissue as a result. As you can see in Figures 5.10A–C, myocytes aren't shaped like the cells of epithelial or connective tissues. This makes muscle tissue easy to tell apart from most other tissue types.

There are three types of muscle tissue:

1. **Skeletal muscle tissue.** The muscle fibers of **skeletal muscle tissue** are long, tubular, and **striated** (STRY-ayt-ed; striped) in appearance (Fig. 5.10A). The striations result from the arrangement of proteins within the muscle fiber called **myofilaments**. Skeletal muscle fibers are formed from the fusion of cells called **myoblasts,** and thus have multiple nuclei. This type of muscle tissue is *voluntary*, which means that its contraction is under conscious control. For this reason, it has a close relationship with the nervous system and nervous tissue, because skeletal muscle fibers must be stimulated by a nerve cell to contract.

2. **Cardiac muscle tissue.** The myocytes of **cardiac muscle tissue** (KAR-dee-ak; *card-* = "heart"), located in the heart, are short, wide, striated, and tend to be branching (Fig. 5.10B). Cardiac myocytes typically have only one nucleus, but some may have two or more. Adjacent cardiac myocytes are linked by specialized junctions called **intercalated discs** (in-TER-kuh-lay-t'd; *inter-* = "between") that contain desmosomes and gap junctions. Intercalated discs link all cardiac myocytes physically and electrically so that the heart may contract as a unit. Cardiac muscle tissue is *involuntary* and *autorhythmic*, meaning that it requires no outside stimulus from the nervous system to contract. (Note, however, that the nervous system can influence the rate and force of cardiac muscle contraction.)

3. **Smooth muscle tissue.** The myocytes of **smooth muscle tissue** are flat with a single nucleus in the center of the cell (Fig. 5.10C). The arrangement of myofilaments within smooth muscle fibers differs from that of skeletal and cardiac muscle fibers, and, as a result, these cells lack noticeable striations (hence the name *smooth* muscle). Smooth muscle lines all hollow organs and is found in the skin, the eyes, and surrounding many glands. Like cardiac muscle tissue, smooth muscle tissue is involuntary. However, although there are populations of smooth muscle cells that are autorhythmic, much of our smooth muscle requires stimulation from the nervous system to contract.

We revisit each type of muscle tissue in later units in this book.

HINTS & TIPS

Identifying Muscle Tissue

The three types of muscle tissue aren't that difficult to tell apart from one another. The only two that might give you troubles are skeletal and cardiac muscle tissues, but if you remember that cardiac muscle tissue has intercalated discs, you shouldn't have any problems. However, sometimes students mistake skeletal or smooth muscle tissue for an entirely different tissue type: dense regular collagenous CT.

Take a look back to Figure 5.6A (p. 127). Notice how the collagen bundles are arranged in a way that almost looks like the tubular skeletal muscle fibers? And notice also how the nuclei of the fibroblasts have the same shape and arrangement as those of smooth muscle cells? Both of these situations can cause students to sometimes mix up these tissue types, so careful examination is needed to prevent these mistakes:

ℹ️ Look closely at the "tubes" to see whether they have striations running through them. If there are striations, as in Figure 5.10A, the section is skeletal muscle tissue.

ℹ️ If there are no striations, look more closely at the nuclei.

- Advance to a higher-power objective lens and look for plasma membranes or boundaries around each nucleus, which you can see in Figure 5.10D. If you can find plasma membranes around the nuclei, you are looking at smooth muscle tissue.

- If you can't see any boundaries around the nuclei, and the space between the nuclei looks slightly fuzzy rather than well-defined, you're probably looking at dense regular collagenous CT.

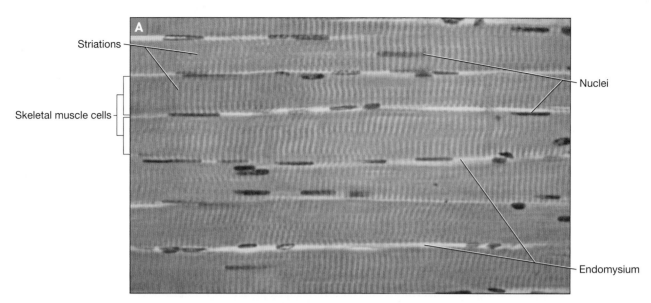

Striations

Skeletal muscle cells

Nuclei

Endomysium

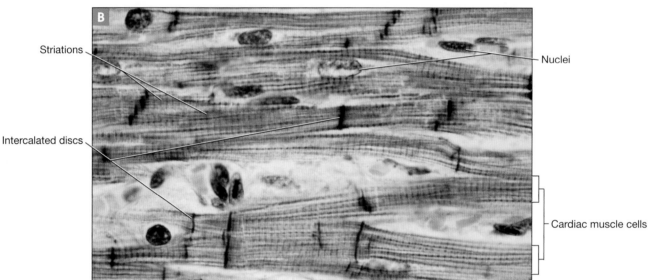

Striations

Intercalated discs

Nuclei

Cardiac muscle cells

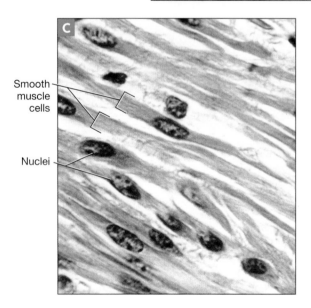

Smooth muscle cells

Nuclei

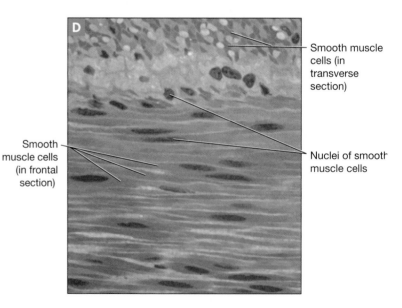

Smooth muscle cells (in transverse section)

Smooth muscle cells (in frontal section)

Nuclei of smooth muscle cells

FIGURE **5.10** Muscle tissue: (**A**) skeletal muscle tissue; (**B**) cardiac muscle tissue; (**C**) teased smooth muscle cells; (**D**) smooth muscle cells in an organ.

1 PROCEDURE

Examining Muscle Tissue with Microscopy

View prepared slides of skeletal, smooth, and cardiac muscle tissue. Use colored pencils to draw what you see under the microscope, and label your drawing with the terms from Figure 5.10. Record your observations of each slide in Table 5.1. When you have completed the microscope slides, answer Check Your Understanding Question 4 (p. 143).

1 Skeletal Muscle

a _____

_____

_____

b _____

_____

_____

5

2 Cardiac Muscle

a _____

_____

_____

b _____

_____

_____

3 Smooth Muscle

a _____

_____

_____

b _____

_____

_____

TABLE **5.1** Characteristics of Muscle Tissues

Muscle Tissue Type	Striated or Nonstriated	One or Multiple Nuclei	Size, Shape, and Special Features of Cells	Location in the Body
Skeletal muscle				
Cardiac muscle				
Smooth muscle				

5

MATERIALS

☐ Slide: nervous tissue
☐ Light microscope
☐ Colored pencils

Nervous Tissue

Nervous tissue (Fig. 5.11) is the primary component of the brain, the spinal cord, and the peripheral nerves. It consists of a unique ECM (rich in collagen fibers) and two main cell types:

1. **Neurons.** The **neurons** (NOOR-ahnz) are responsible for sending and receiving messages within the nervous system. On your slide, they are the larger of the two cell types. The large, central portion of the neuron is called the **cell body.** Within the cell body, we find the nucleus and many of the neuron's organelles, including clusters of rough endoplasmic reticulum called **Nissl bodies.** Most neurons contain two types of long armlike processes extending from the cell body: (1) the **dendrites** (DEN-dryt′z), which receive messages from other neurons, and (2) the **axon** (AX-ahn), which sends messages to other neurons, muscle cells, or gland cells.

2. **Neuroglial cells.** The smaller and more numerous cells around the neurons are the **neuroglial cells** (noor-oh-GLEE-uhl). The six different types of neuroglial cells vary significantly in shape and appearance. Neuroglial cells in general perform functions that support the neurons or the ECM in some way.

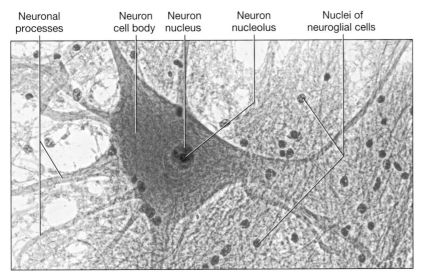

Neuronal processes | Neuron cell body | Neuron nucleus | Neuron nucleolus | Nuclei of neuroglial cells

FIGURE **5.11** Nervous tissue.

---

1 **PROCEDURE**

Examining Nervous Tissue with Microscopy

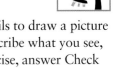

View a prepared slide of nervous tissue (the slide might be called a "motor neuron smear"). Use colored pencils to draw a picture of what you see under the microscope, and label your drawing with the terms from Figure 5.11. Then (a) describe what you see, and (b) give examples of locations in the body where this tissue is found. When you have completed the exercise, answer Check Your Understanding Question 5 (p. 144).

1 Nervous Tissue

a _____

_____

_____

b _____

_____

_____

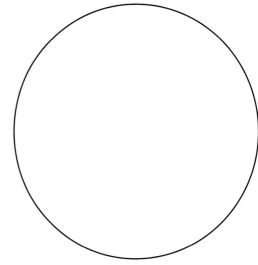

Organology

All organs consist of two or more tissues that must work together to enable the organ to function properly. The study of the tissues that make up the body's organs is called **organology**. Most organs are made of layers of tissues stacked upon one another and "glued" together by proteins and other compounds in the ground substance. This exercise introduces you to organology, a topic we explore repeatedly in the remainder of this lab manual.

1 PROCEDURE

Determining the Tissue Types of Organs

Following are illustrations of two organs: a joint and the esophagus (Figs. 5.12 and 5.13). Tissue sections from each organ have been taken, and your task is to identify each tissue. Be specific about which type of muscle, epithelial tissue, and connective tissue you identify in the organ. When you have completed the procedure, answer Check Your Understanding Question 6 (p. 144).

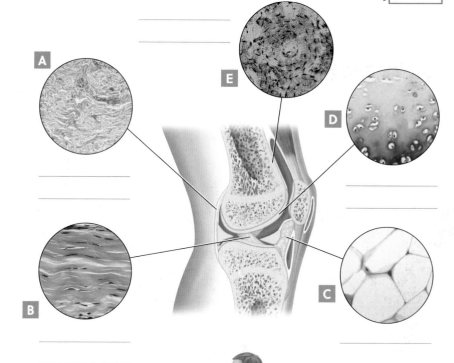

FIGURE **5.12** Tissues making up a joint.

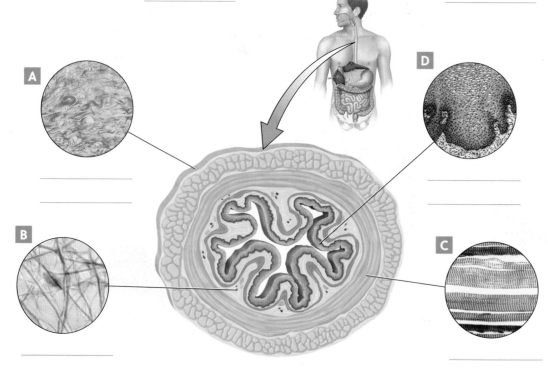

FIGURE **5.13** Tissues making up the esophagus.

Check Your Recall

UNIT
5
REVIEW

1 Identify each of the following tissues in Figure 5.14.

a _____ e _____

b _____ f _____

c _____ g _____

d _____ h _____

FIGURE **5.14** Unknown tissues for Question 1.

2 What is the definition of the term "tissue"?

_____

3 An epithelial tissue that has two or more layers of rectangular cells would be classified as

a. stratified squamous epithelium.

b. simple cuboidal epithelium.

c. stratified columnar epithelium.

d. simple columnar epithelium.

4 *Circle all that apply.* Which of the following statements about transitional epithelium is/are true?

a. Transitional epithelium is found lining organs of the urinary system.

b. The apical cells of transitional epithelium can change shape.

c. The apical cells of transitional epithelium contain cilia.

d. Transitional epithelium is stratified but not classified by the shape of its cells.

5 *True/False:* Mark the following statements concerning connective tissue proper and cartilage as true (T) or false (F). If the statement is false, correct it to make it a true statement.

_____ Fibroblasts contain a large lipid droplet in their cytoplasm.

_____ Collagen fibers are the primary element in dense regular collagenous connective tissue.

_____ Bundles of collagen fibers are arranged parallel to one another in dense elastic connective tissue.

_____ The primary element in loose connective tissue is ground substance.

_____ The ECM of fibrocartilage is filled with protein fibers.

6 Which of the following types of tissue has a liquid ECM?

a. Bone tissue.

b. Loose connective tissue.

c. Adipose tissue.

d. Blood.

7 *Circle all that apply.* Which of the following characteristics apply to smooth muscle tissue?

a. Striated.

b. Nonstriated.

c. Multinucleate.

d. Uninucleate.

e. Contains intercalated discs.

f. Voluntary.

g. Involuntary.

8 Why does skeletal muscle tissue have a close relationship with nervous tissue?

_____

_____

9 *Fill in the blanks:* Nervous tissue is composed of _____ and two types of cells:

_____ and _____ .

10 *Matching:* Match the tissue type with its location in the body.

_____ Simple cuboidal epithelium

_____ Pseudostratified ciliated columnar epithelium

_____ Dense elastic CT

_____ Stratified squamous keratinized epithelium

_____ Elastic cartilage

_____ Smooth muscle

_____ Dense irregular CT

_____ Fibrocartilage

A. Ear and the epiglottis

B. Articular discs and intervertebral discs

C. Thyroid gland, kidneys, and certain respiratory passages

D. In the skin, in the eye, surrounding many glands, and lining hollow organs

E. Large blood vessels (that are under high pressure) and certain ligaments

F. Joint and organ capsules and the dermis of the skin

G. Nasal cavity and larger respiratory passages

H. Epidermis of the skin

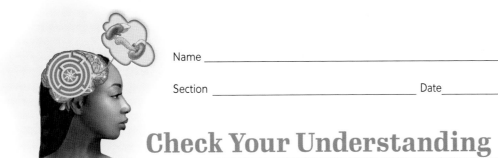

Name _____

Section _____ Date _____

UNIT

5

REVIEW

Check Your Understanding

Critical Thinking and Application Questions

1 Predict what might happen if stratified squamous keratinized and nonkeratinized epithelium were replaced in the body with simple squamous epithelium. Explain your reasoning.

2 In the condition *primary ciliary dyskinesia*, the cilia lining epithelia are not able to move. Explain why this disease would lead to recurrent respiratory infections.

3 *Ehlers-Danlos syndrome* is a disorder characterized by defects in collagen proteins or related proteins that support collagen fibers. Predict the potential consequences of Ehlers-Danlos syndrome to connective tissues, considering the function of collagen fibers.

4 Explain why, in the event of severe nervous system injury, cardiac muscle tissue often continues to function, but skeletal muscle tissue and some smooth muscle tissue does not.

5 Ehlers-Danlos syndrome is considered a *collagenopathy*, or a disorder of collagen fibers. Collagenopathies are generally classed as a "connective tissue disorder." Will collagenopathies affect other tissue types, as well? Explain.

6 A hypothetical organ has the following functional requirements: (1) the ability to brush substances past its cells; (2) the ability to contract in an involuntary and autorhythmic fashion; and (3) the ability to be flexible but also tough. The organ needs one tissue to carry out each of these requirements, and it also needs one tissue to "glue" all other tissues together. What are the four tissues that will make up this hypothetical organ? Justify your choices.

Integumentary System

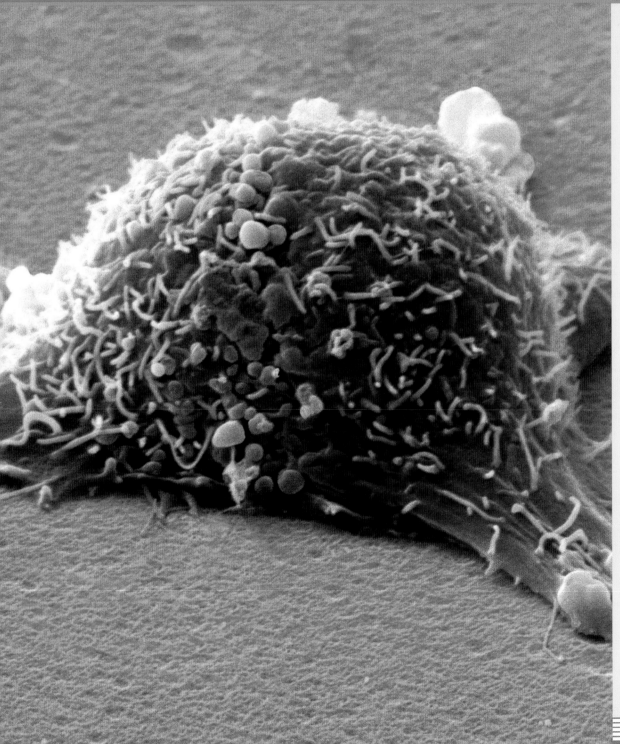

When you have completed this unit, you should be able to:

1 Identify structures of the integumentary system.

2 Describe the gross and microscopic structure of thick and thin skin.

3 Map the distribution of touch receptors on different areas of the body.

Name ______________________ Section __________ Date __________

PRE-LAB EXERCISES

Complete the following exercises prior to coming to lab, using your lab manual and textbook for reference.

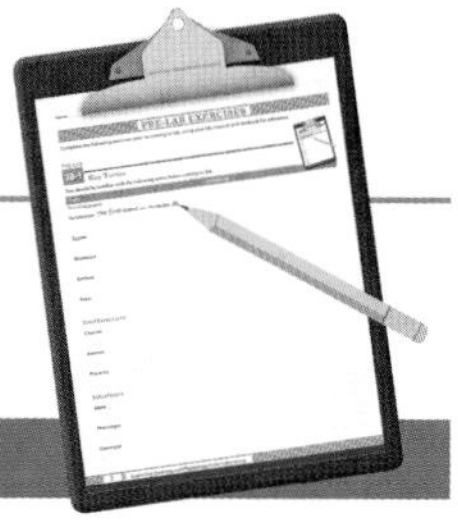

PRE-LAB

6-1 Key Terms

6

You should be familiar with the following terms before coming to lab.

Term	Definition
Structures of the Epidermis	
Epidermis	
Keratinocyte	
Melanocyte	
Melanin	
Tactile discs	
Basement membrane	
Thick skin	
Thin skin	
Structures of the Dermis	
Dermis	
Dermal papillae	
Tactile corpuscle	
Lamellated corpuscle	
Arrector pili muscle	

Accessory Structures and Other Structures

Hypodermis _____

Sweat gland _____

Sebaceous gland _____

Hair follicle _____

Nails _____

PRE-LAB

6-2 Skin Anatomy

Color the structures of the skin in Figure 6.1, and label them with the terms from Exercise 6-1 (p. 149). Use your text and Exercise 6-1 in this unit for reference.

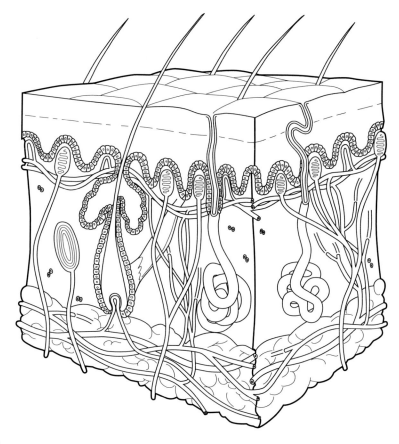

FIGURE **6.1** Skin section.

Hair and Nail Anatomy

Color the structures of the hair and nail in Figure 6.2, and label them with the terms from Exercise 6-1 (p. 149). Use your text and Exercise 6-1 in this unit for reference.

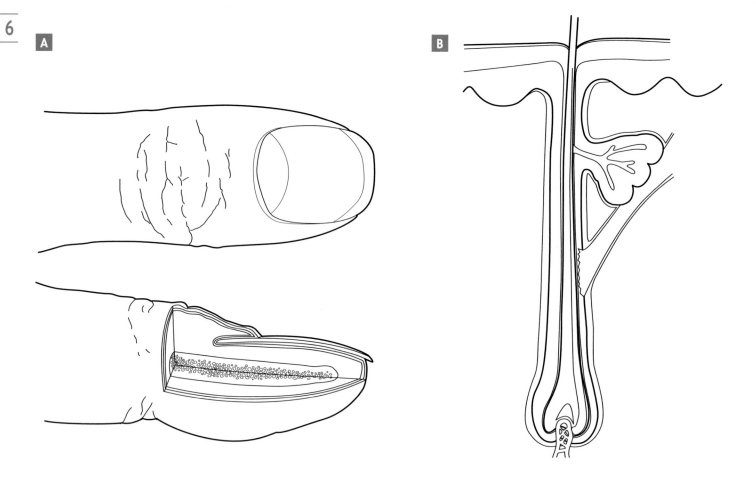

FIGURE **6.2** Accessory structures of the skin: (**A**) nail anatomy; (**B**) hair structure.

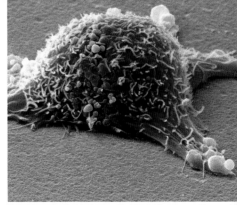

EXERCISES

A lthough the skin is the largest organ in the body, most people don't realize that it's actually an organ. Like all organs, the skin or **integument** (in-TEG-yoo-ment; *integ-* = "to cover") is composed of several tissue types, including epithelial tissue, connective tissue, muscle tissue, and nervous tissue. In the following exercises, you will examine the tissues of this organ, along with the other structures of the integumentary system, and apply your knowledge of skin anatomy to perform fingerprinting procedures.

Scanning electron micrograph of a melanoma cell.

EXERCISE 6-1

MATERIALS

❑ Anatomical models and diagrams: skin
❑ Colored pencils

Skin Anatomy and Accessory Structures

The **integumentary system** (in-teg'-yoo-MEN-tuh-ree) is composed of the skin and its **accessory structures**: the *hair*, *glands*, and *nails*. The skin is composed of two general tissue layers: the superficial *epidermis* and the deep *dermis*. The tissue beneath the dermis, called the **hypodermis** (hy-poh-DER-miss; *hypo-* = "beneath") or the *subcutaneous tissue*, connects the skin to the underlying tissues and is not considered part of the integument. The hypodermis is richly supplied with blood vessels.

The **epidermis** (ep-ih-DER-miss; *epi-* = "on top;" *derm-* = "skin") contains layers (or *strata*) of stratified squamous keratinized epithelium. The predominant cell type found in the epidermis is the keratin-producing **keratinocyte** (kehr-ah-TIN-oh-sy't). Keratin is a hard protein that protects the skin from mechanical and environmental stresses. From superficial to deep, the layers of the epidermis are as follows (Fig. 6.3):

1. **Stratum corneum.** The superficial layer of cells, called the **stratum corneum** (STRAT-um KOHR-nee-um; *strat-* = "layer"), is composed of dead keratinocytes. Under microscopic examination, the keratinocytes of the stratum corneum bear little resemblance to living cells and have a dry, flaky appearance. These cells typically appear dark purple or hot pink, which is due to the accumulation of keratin in their cytosol.

2. **Stratum lucidum.** The **stratum lucidum** (LOO-sid-um; *lucid-* = "clear") is a single layer of translucent, dead keratinocytes found only in the skin of the palms and the soles of the feet.

3. **Stratum granulosum.** The third layer of keratinocytes is the **stratum granulosum** (gran-yoo-LOH-sum). Here the superficial keratinocytes are dead, but the deeper cells are alive. This layer is named for the cells' cytoplasmic granules. Some of the granules contain keratin; others, called **lamellar granules**, contain a lipid-based substance. We can work out the function of this lipid-based substance from our previous knowledge of polar and non-polar substances.

Are lipids polar or nonpolar?

Is water polar or nonpolar?

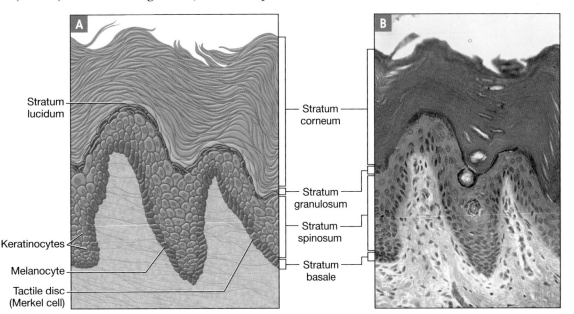

FIGURE **6.3** Layers of the epidermis: (**A**) illustration; (**B**) photomicrograph.

Do water and lipids interact? Why or why not?

What effect will the lipids have on water placed on the skin?

4. **Stratum spinosum.** The first actively metabolizing cells are encountered in the fourth cell layer, the **stratum spinosum** (spin-OH-sum). In this layer, we find the pigment **melanin** (MEL-uh-nin; *melan-* = "black"), which protects keratinocytes from UV light and prevents overproduction of vitamin D.

5. **Stratum basale.** The deep **stratum basale** (bay-SAY-lee; *bas-* = "bottom") consists of a single row of actively dividing keratinocytes. Here we also find **melanocytes** (mel-AN-oh-syt′z), which produce melanin, and sensory receptor cells called **tactile discs** (also known as *Merkel cells*), which discriminate light touch and texture.

Why does the epidermis have so many dead cells? Again, we can use our previous knowledge to figure this out.

The epidermis is composed of what type of tissue?

Are these types of tissue supplied with blood vessels?

From where do these tissues receive oxygen and nutrients?

What is deep to the epidermis?

So, from where does the epidermis receive oxygen and nutrients?

The preceding answers explain why there are so many dead cells in the epidermis. Only the cells of the deeper parts of the stratum granulosum, the stratum spinosum, and the stratum basale are close enough to the blood supply in the dermis to get adequate oxygen and nutrients for survival. For this reason, as the cells migrate farther away from the blood supply, they begin to die.

Immediately deep to the stratum basale of the epidermis is the **basement membrane**, which consists of the basal lamina, composed of ECM produced by keratinocytes, and the reticular lamina, composed of ECM produced by the dermis. The basement membrane holds the epidermis in place with collagen fibers and molecular "glue" that prevents it from separating from the dermis.

Deep to the epidermis is the **dermis**, which is composed of highly vascular connective tissue. It consists of two layers (Fig. 6.4):

1. **Papillary layer.** The superficial **papillary layer** is composed of loose connective tissue. It contains fingerlike projections called the **dermal papillae** (pah-PILL-ee) that project into the epidermis, which you can see in Figure 6.4. The dermal papillae contain touch receptors called **tactile corpuscles** (kohr-PUS-ulz) that detect fine touch. In addition, we find capillary loops that provide blood supply to the avascular epidermis.

2. **Reticular layer.** The thick **reticular layer** is composed of dense irregular connective tissue. It houses structures such as **sweat glands**, oil-producing *sebaceous glands* (seh-BAY-shuhs), blood vessels, and pressure receptors called **lamellated corpuscles**. Also within the reticular layer, we find numerous *free nerve endings* that transmit pain sensations, which is why it hurts when you cut yourself down to the dermis.

Let's move on to accessory structures of the integumentary system. First are its sebaceous glands and sweat glands. **Sebaceous glands** are exocrine glands that secrete **sebum** (SEE-bum; oil). Notice in Figure 6.4 that sebaceous glands are associated with hairs, and indeed they release sebum directly into a hair follicle. **Sweat glands** are also exocrine glands; however, notice that they secrete their product, *sweat*, through a **sweat duct**. There are two types of sweat glands. The type shown in Figure 6.4, the *eccrine sweat gland*, is found all over the body. This type of gland releases sweat onto the surface of the skin through a small **sweat pore**. The other type, the *apocrine sweat gland*, is found in the axillae and genital region. This type releases sweat into a hair follicle, similar to how a sebaceous gland releases sebum into a hair follicle.

Both hair and nails are also accessory structures of the integumentary system (Fig. 6.5). A **hair** consists of two basic parts: (a) the long, slender **shaft** composed of dead keratinocytes that projects from the skin's surface, and (b) the **hair root** embedded in the dermis (Fig. 6.5A). The base of the root is indented by a projection from the dermis called the **hair papilla**; the papilla and

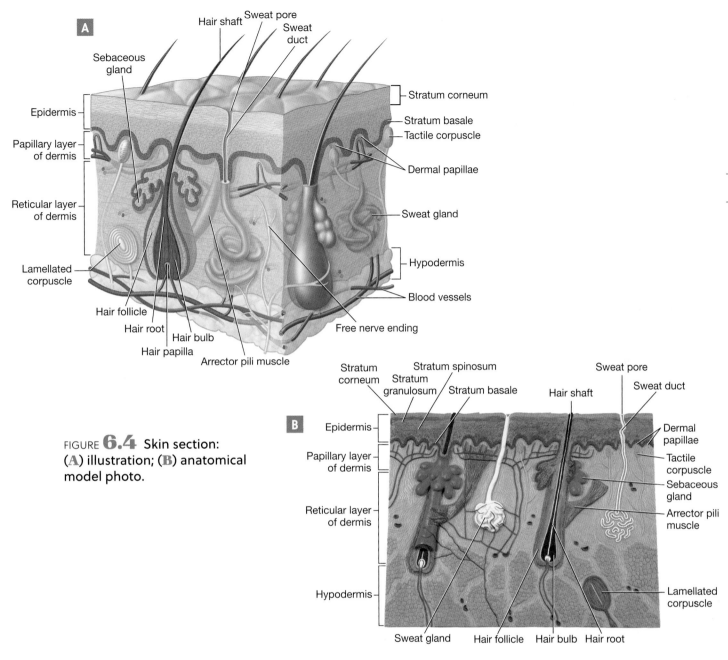

FIGURE **6.4** Skin section:
(**A**) illustration; (**B**) anatomical
model photo.

root together are known as the **hair bulb**. Surrounding the papilla is a group of rapidly dividing cells called the **hair matrix**—it is from the hair matrix that a hair grows.

The hair is embedded in a sheath known as the **hair follicle**. The inner lining of the hair follicle is epithelium that is continuous with the epidermis, and the outer lining is dermal connective tissue. A band of smooth muscle called an **arrector pili muscle** (ah-REK-tohr PIL-aye) attaches to this dermal sheath, and can pull the hair into an upright or erect position when it contracts.

Like hairs, **nails** are composed primarily of dead keratinocytes (Fig. 6.5B). A nail consists of a flat **nail plate** surrounded by folds of skin on all three sides, which are known as **nail folds**. Those on the sides of the nails are **lateral nail folds**, and the one at the base is the **proximal nail fold**. The stratum corneum of the proximal nail fold grows over the nail plate to form a thin structure called the **eponychium** (ep-oh-NIK-ee-um) or *cuticle*. Often, near the eponychium, we find a thickened area of the nail plate, the **lunula** (LOON-yoo-luh), which generally has a half-moon shape (note that many nails lack a lunula). Deep to the proximal nail fold is a group of actively dividing cells collectively known as the **nail matrix**. Just as hair grows from the hair matrix, nail growth occurs from the nail matrix. At the distal end of the nail, a thickened area of epithelium underlies the free edge of the nail plate. This epithelium is known as the **hyponychium** (hy-poh-NIK-ee-um; *hypo-* = "below").

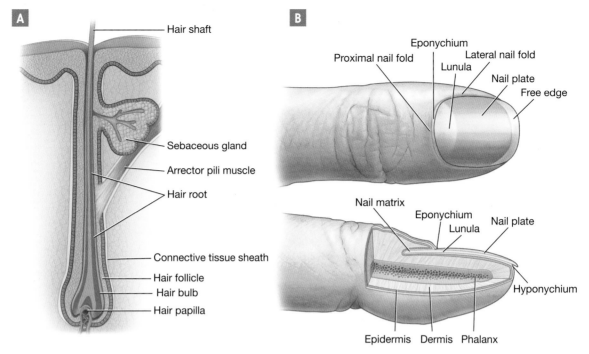

FIGURE **6.5** Accessory structures of the skin: (**A**) hair structure; (**B**) nail anatomy.

1 PROCEDURE
Model Inventory for the Integumentary System

Identify the following structures of the integumentary system on models and diagrams, using your textbook and this unit for reference. As you examine the anatomical models and diagrams, record the name of the model and the structures you were able to identify on the model inventory in Table 6.1. When you have completed this activity, answer Check Your Understanding Questions 1 through 3 (p. 163).

Structures of the Skin

1. Epidermal layers
   a. Stratum corneum
   b. Stratum lucidum
   c. Stratum granulosum
   d. Stratum spinosum
   e. Stratum basale
2. Dermis
   a. Papillary layer
      (1) Dermal papillae
      (2) Tactile corpuscle
   b. Reticular layer
      (1) Lamellated corpuscle
3. Blood vessels

Accessory Structures and Other Structures

1. Sebaceous gland
2. Sweat gland
   a. Sweat duct
   b. Sweat pore
3. Hair
   a. Hair shaft
   b. Hair root
   c. Hair papilla
   d. Hair bulb
   e. Hair follicle
   f. Arrector pili muscle
4. Nail
   a. Nail plate
   b. Nail fold (proximal and lateral)
   c. Eponychium
   d. Lunula
   e. Nail matrix
5. Hypodermis

TABLE **6.1** Model Inventory for the Integumentary System

Model/Diagram	Structures Identified

2 PROCEDURE
Time to Draw

In the space provided, draw, color, and label one of the skin models that you examined. In addition, write the main function of each structure that you label.

MATERIALS

❑ Light microscope
❑ Slides:
  ▪ thick skin
  ▪ thin skin
❑ Colored pencils

6

Histology of Integument

In this exercise, we will examine prepared slides of skin and hair. The skin sections are taken from different regions of the body so we can compare and contrast two types of skin: (a) **thick skin**, found on the palmar surfaces of the hands and the plantar surfaces of the feet, and (b) **thin skin**, found everywhere else (Fig. 6.6).

Before moving on, review the basics of microscopy from Units 3 and 5. Remember to follow a step-by-step approach when examining the slides: Look at the slide with the naked eye first, then begin your examination on low power, and advance to higher power to see more details.

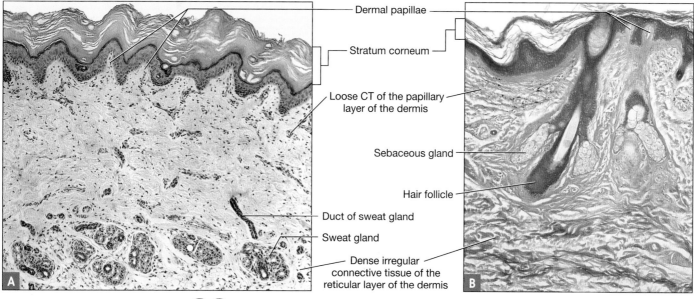
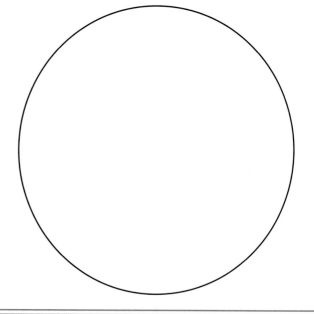
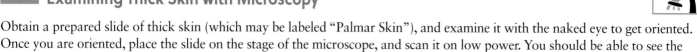

Labels: Dermal papillae · Stratum corneum · Loose CT of the papillary layer of the dermis · Sebaceous gland · Hair follicle · Duct of sweat gland · Sweat gland · Dense irregular connective tissue of the reticular layer of the dermis

FIGURE **6.6** Skin, photomicrographs: (**A**) thick skin; (**B**) thin skin.

---

1 | **PROCEDURE**
Examining Thick Skin with Microscopy

Obtain a prepared slide of thick skin (which may be labeled "Palmar Skin"), and examine it with the naked eye to get oriented. Once you are oriented, place the slide on the stage of the microscope, and scan it on low power. You should be able to see the epidermis with its superficial layers of dead cells and the dermis with its pink clusters of collagen bundles that make up the dense irregular connective tissue. Compare it to Figure 6.6A to make sure that you are looking at the right slide and the right magnification. Advance to higher power to see the cells and associated structures in greater detail.

Use your colored pencils to draw what you see in the field of view (you will be able to see the most structures on low power). Label your drawing with the following terms, using Figure 6.6A for reference. Note that you may not be able to see all structures in a single field of view. When you have completed your drawing, fill in the appropriate column of Table 6.2.

- ▪ Epidermis
  - ▪ Stratum corneum
  - ▪ Stratum lucidum
  - ▪ Stratum granulosum
  - ▪ Stratum spinosum
  - ▪ Stratum basale
- ▪ Dermis
  - ▪ Dermal papillae
  - ▪ Collagen bundles
  - ▪ Sweat gland

PROCEDURE
Examining Thin Skin with Microscopy

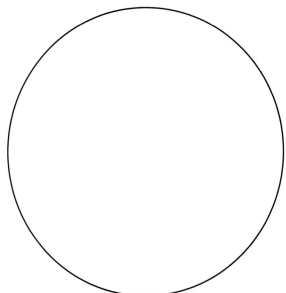

Obtain a prepared slide of thin skin (which may be labeled "Scalp Skin"). As before, examine the slide with the naked eye, then scan the slide on low power, advancing to higher power as needed to see the structures more closely. Compare what you see in your field of view to Figure 6.6B to ensure that you are looking at the correct region of the slide.

Use your colored pencils to draw what you see in the field of view (you will be able to see the most structures on low power). Label your drawing with the following terms, using Figure 6.6B for reference. Note that you may not be able to see all structures in a single field of view. When you have completed your drawing, fill in the remainder of Table 6.2, and answer Check Your Understanding Question 4 (p. 164).

- Epidermis
  - Stratum corneum
  - Stratum granulosum
  - Stratum spinosum
  - Stratum basale
- Dermis
  - Dermal papillae
  - Collagen bundles
- Hair follicle
- Sebaceous gland
- Sweat gland
- Arrector pili muscle

TABLE **6.2** Characteristics of Thick and Thin Skin

Characteristic	Thick Skin	Thin Skin
Thickness of stratum corneum		
Hair follicles present?		
Sebaceous glands present?		
Stratum lucidum present?		
Arrector pili muscles present?		

3 PROCEDURE

Examining Hair with Microscopy

Obtain a prepared slide of a sectioned hair. As before, examine the slide with the naked eye, then scan the slide on low power, advancing to higher power as needed to see the structures more closely. Compare what you see in your field of view to Figure 6.7 to ensure that you are looking at the correct region of the slide.

Use your colored pencils to draw what you see in the field of view (you will be able to see the most structures on low power). Label your drawing with the following terms, using Figure 6.7 for reference.

■ Cortex

■ Medulla

■ Hair papilla

■ Matrix

■ Hair follicle

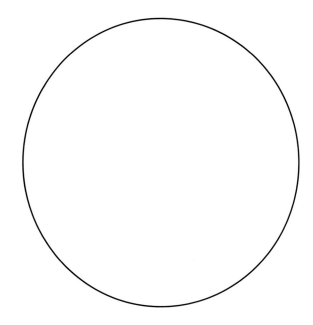

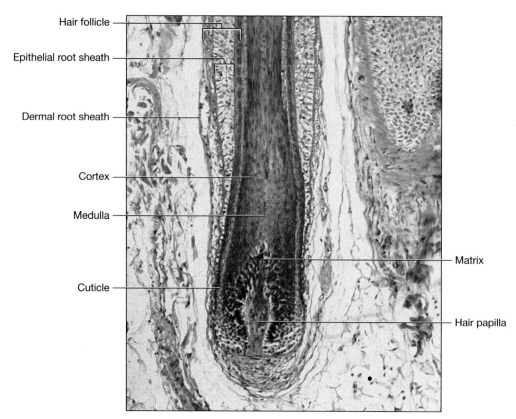

FIGURE **6.7** Light micrograph of a sectioned hair.

MATERIALS

- [ ] Sandpaper in five different grits
- [ ] Gloves (latex or nitrile)
- [ ] Samples of different items: piece of sponge, rock, eraser, sandpaper, etc.

Touch Receptor Distribution

The two types of sensory receptors in the skin that detect fine touch and texture are called **tactile corpuscles** and **tactile discs**. The distribution of these receptors in different parts of the body is not equal—some areas have a high density of receptors, and others have a very low density. The following two procedures will demonstrate the function of these receptors and their unequal distribution. When you have completed the activity, answer Check Your Understanding Questions 5 and 6 (p. 164).

6

1 PROCEDURE
Comparing the Textures of Sandpaper Samples

> **Hypothesis:** How will wearing a glove affect the ability to detect textures?

1 Obtain five samples of sandpaper of different textures or "grits." Ensure that the grit is written on the back of each sample.

2 While your partner's eyes are closed, arrange the pieces in random order. Have your partner feel each piece and attempt to arrange the pieces from roughest to smoothest.

3 When your partner has completed the task, look at the back of each sample to check how well your partner did, and record the results here:

4 Have your partner put on a latex (or nitrile) glove. While your partner's eyes are closed, arrange the pieces in random order. Repeat the procedure, having your partner feel each piece and attempt to arrange the pieces from roughest to smoothest.

5 When your partner has completed the task, look at the back of each sample to check how well your partner did, and record the results here:

6 Compare your results to your hypothesis.

Hypothesis: Where will the density of touch receptors be highest?

6

1 Obtain six samples of substances with different textures. Ensure that your partner doesn't see what samples you selected.

2 While your partner's eyes are closed, have your partner feel each of three samples with one finger and attempt to identify each one. Record the number of correct guesses: _____

3 While your partner's eyes are still closed, place each of the other three samples on your partner's posterior shoulder or posterior forearm.

4 Have your partner attempt to identify each sample placed on the posterior shoulder or posterior forearm. Record the number of correct guesses: _____

5 Compare your results to your hypothesis.

EXERCISE 6-4

MATERIALS

- ☐ Glass slide: blank (one per person)
- ☐ Ink pad
- ☐ Fingerprint card (one per person)
- ☐ Dusting powder
- ☐ Dusting brush
- ☐ Fingerprint lifting tape
- ☐ Gloves (latex or nitrile)

Fingerprinting

Specific patterns in the epidermis are seen in thick skin where the dermal papillae are folded into **dermal ridges**. These dermal ridges indent the overlying epidermis to create **epidermal ridges**, which increase gripping ability. They also lead to the characteristic patterns of finger, toe, palm, and footprints. The patterns of the epidermal ridges are unique to each individual, even identical twins.

Sweat pores open at the top of the epidermal ridges, which causes us to leave behind a thin film when we touch surfaces. This film can be detected in a variety of ways, most commonly using a powder that binds to it.

Fingerprinting was not a widely accepted means of identification in the United States until 1902, when the New York Civil Service began collecting and using fingerprints. Prior to this, fingerprints had been studied widely and even were used to solve a murder case in Argentina in 1892.

Fingerprints can be broadly classified into three ridge flow patterns: loop, arch, and whorl (Fig. 6.8). Once the ridge flow pattern has been identified, the characteristics of the ridges, also called *Galton points*, are examined (Figs. 6.9 and 6.10). In professional laboratories, the fingerprint is analyzed further on the basis of minute details, or "points," in the fingerprint. Most of this is done currently with the help of computers.

In this procedure, you will be playing the role of detective, searching for a "thief" among your group members (which may end up being you). Your group will determine the thief's identity by analyzing the ridge flow patterns and ridge characteristics of the fingerprints of your group members. When you have completed the activity, answer Check Your Understanding Question 7 (p. 164).

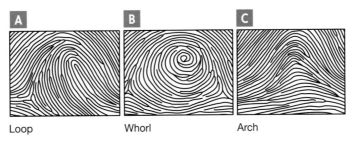

Loop   Whorl   Arch

FIGURE **6.8** The three basic patterns of fingerprints: (**A**) loop; (**B**) whorl; (**C**) arch.

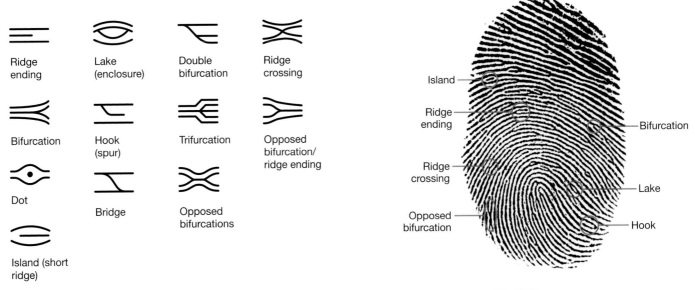

FIGURE **6.9** Fingerprinting: Galton points.

FIGURE **6.10** Fingerprinting: a sample loop fingerprint.

Analyzing Fingerprints

1 Obtain one blank glass slide, and handle it by the edges as you clean it off with a paper towel and water.

2 When the slide is clean and dry, use three different fingers to place three large fingerprints somewhere on one side of the slide.

3 After placing the fingerprints on the slide, put on gloves, and use the marker located at your table to write your initials on the upper right-hand corner of the slide.

4 Assemble into groups of a minimum of four people. Bring the slides for the entire group to your instructor, and your instructor will pick one slide from the group, cover the initials in the corner, and designate that person as the "thief." The thief is one of your group members, so you are all suspects.

5 Fingerprint each member of the group (using the ink and cards provided):

   a Obtain a blank fingerprinting card or a blank sheet of paper.

   b Roll each finger individually on the ink pad from right to left. Be certain not to get excessive ink on your fingers.

   c Roll each finger individually on the fingerprinting card slowly from left to right.

6 When all the fingerprinting is completed, put on a pair of latex (or nitrile) gloves.

7 Use a dusting brush to lightly sweep some dusting powder onto the slide containing the thief's fingerprints. Use the dusting powder *sparingly*, because too much powder will obscure your prints. Brush away the excess dusting powder. (You can tap the slide on its side to help with this.)

8 Place a piece of fingerprint lifting tape on the fingerprints that have appeared. Pat the tape into place firmly, and remove it slowly. Place the tape on a blank sheet of white paper for comparison.

9 With the help of Figures 6.8 and 6.9, identify the thief by comparing the fingerprints lifted from the slide with the fingerprints taken from the suspects. Be careful not to tell the other members of your group which fingers you used. Remember— you don't want to be caught!

Who is the thief from your table?

How did you arrive at this conclusion?

Check Your Recall

1 Label the following parts of the skin on Figure 6.11.

- ❏ Arrector pili muscle
- ❏ Dermis: papillary layer
- ❏ Dermis: reticular layer
- ❏ Epidermis
- ❏ Hair bulb
- ❏ Hair follicle
- ❏ Lamellated corpuscle
- ❏ Sebaceous gland
- ❏ Stratum basale
- ❏ Stratum corneum
- ❏ Sweat duct
- ❏ Tactile corpuscle

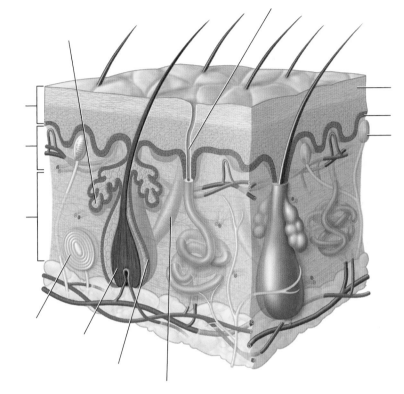

FIGURE **6.11** Skin section.

2 The pigment that accumulates in the cells of the stratum spinosum is

a. actin.

b. melanin.

c. keratin.

d. collagen.

3 The protein that accumulates in the dead cells of the stratum corneum is

a. actin.

b. melanin.

c. keratin.

d. collagen.

4 In which layer of the epidermis are tactile discs found?

a. Stratum corneum.

b. Stratum granulosum.

c. Stratum basale.

d. Stratum lucidum.

e. Stratum spinosum.

5 Why are the living cells of the epidermis limited to the deeper layers?

_____

_____

_____

6 _Matching:_ Match the following terms with the correct description.

_____ Stratum basale

_____ Lunula

_____ Lamellated corpuscle

_____ Hair matrix

_____ Dermal papillae

_____ Hair root

_____ Stratum corneum

_____ Eponychium

A. Projections of the dermis that indent the epidermis
B. A thin growth of the stratum corneum over the proximal nail plate
C. Area of actively dividing cells from which a hair grows
D. Portion of the hair that is embedded in the dermis
E. Pressure receptor in the dermis
F. Deepest layer of the epidermis
G. Thickened area of the proximal nail plate shaped like a half-moon
H. Superficial layer of the epidermis

7 Is the skin section illustrated in Figure 6.11 showing thin skin or thick skin? Explain all the ways you can make this determination.

_____

_____

_____

8 _True/False:_ Mark the following questions as true (T) or false (F). If the statement is false, correct it to make it a true statement.

_____ a. An arrector pili muscle is composed of smooth muscle tissue.

_____ b. The dividing cells of a hair are located in the hair follicle.

_____ c. Both hairs and nails are composed primarily of actively dividing keratinocytes.

_____ d. A hair follicle is composed of epithelium.

9 _Fill in the blanks:_ _____ corpuscles in the dermis detect pressure, whereas

_____ corpuscles in the dermis detect fine touch.

10 Eccrine sweat is released into a _____ , and apocrine sweat is released into a _____ .
a. a duct; a hair follicle
b. a hair follicle; a hair follicle
c. a duct; a duct
d. a hair follicle; a duct

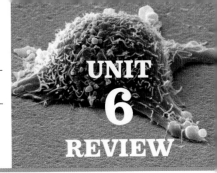

Check Your Understanding

Critical Thinking and Application Questions

1 You wear a pair of ill-fitting shoes and develop a blister, which occurs when the epidermis and dermis have become separated.

a As the blister heals, you notice that the blister's "roof"—which is composed entirely of epidermis—consists only of dead skin. Why did the epidermis of the blister die?

b While removing the dead epidermis, you notice that the blister is filled with clear fluid, but no blood. Why wouldn't you find blood in an epidermal injury?

2 The condition *epidermolysis bullosa* is characterized by repeated blister formation resulting from only minor trauma. Several forms of the disease are caused by mutations in genes coding for keratin proteins. Why would defective keratin lead to an inability to resist mechanical stresses?

3 Many types of cancer chemotherapy drugs work by attacking cells that divide actively and rapidly. What effects would you expect such drugs to have on hair and nails? Why?

4 Many medications can be given *transdermally*, meaning they can be applied topically to the skin and be absorbed into the bloodstream. Why can these medications be applied nearly anywhere on the body except the palms of the hands and the soles of the feet?

6

5 You develop calluses, which are thickenings of the epidermis, on the tips of your thumbs from texting too much. You notice that with these calluses, you have developed difficulty discerning textures with your fingertips. Explain this, considering the results of Procedure 1 in Exercise 6-3.

6 Interpret your results of Procedure 2 in Exercise 6-3. Were your partner's results more accurate with the fingertips or the posterior shoulder/forearm area? What does this tell you about the distribution of tactile discs and tactile corpuscles?

7 An online fingerprinting kit advertises that the fingerprinting powder detects "oil" left behind by fingertips. Is this accurate? Why or why not?

Introduction to the Skeletal System

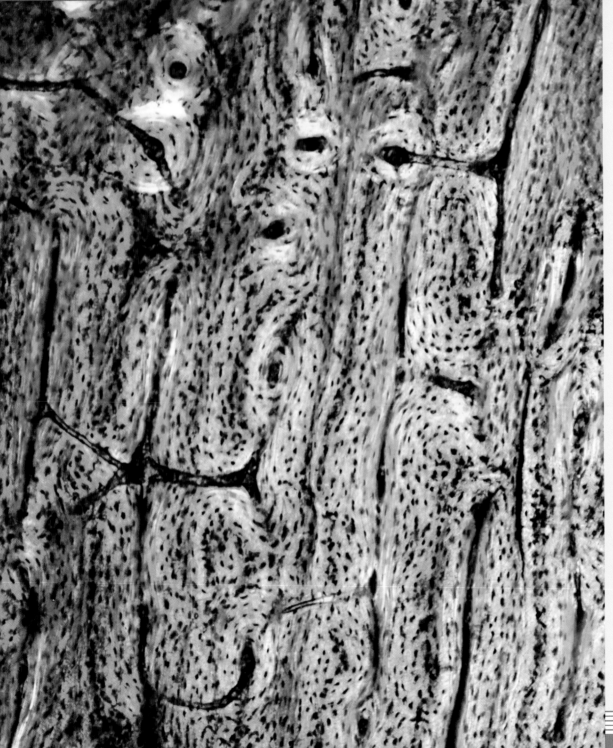

PRE-LAB EXERCISES

Complete the following exercises prior to coming to lab, using your lab manual and textbook for reference.

PRE-LAB

7-1 Key Terms

You should be familiar with the following terms before coming to lab.

Term	Definition

Types of Bone Tissue

Compact bone _____

_____

Spongy bone _____

_____

Microscopic Anatomy of Bone

Osteon _____

Concentric lamellae _____

Central canal _____

Perforating canal _____

Lacunae _____

Canaliculi _____

Periosteum _____

Endosteum _____

Trabeculae _____

Osteocytes _____

Osteoclasts _____

Osteoblasts _____

Bone Shapes

Long bone _____

Short bone _____

Flat bone _____

Irregular bone _____

Structures of Long Bones

Diaphysis _____

Epiphysis _____

Epiphyseal plate _____

Medullary cavity _____

Red bone marrow _____

Yellow bone marrow _____

PRE-LAB

7-2 Microscopic Anatomy of Compact Bone —————————

Color the microscopic anatomy of compact bone tissue in Figure 7.1, and label it with the terms from Exercise 7-1 (p. 171). Use your text and Exercise 7-1 in this unit for reference.

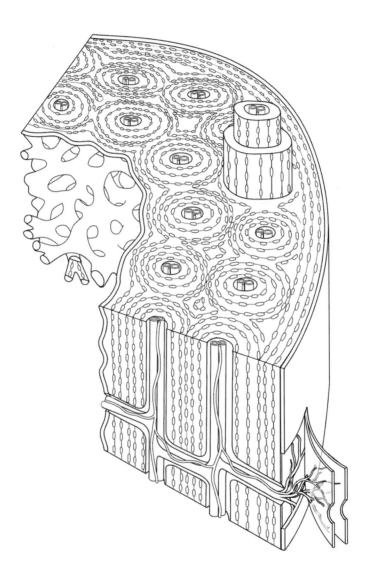

FIGURE **7.1** Microscopic anatomy of compact bone tissue.

Color the structures of a long bone (the femur) in Figure 7.2, and label them with the terms from Exercise 7-4 (p. 178). Use your text and Exercise 7-4 in this unit for reference.

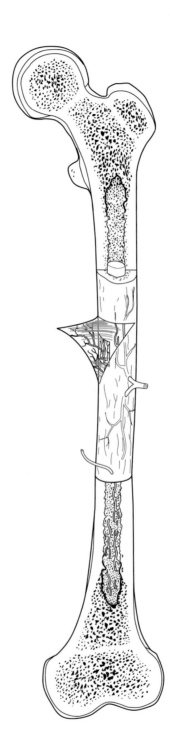

FIGURE **7.2** Adult long bone: the femur.

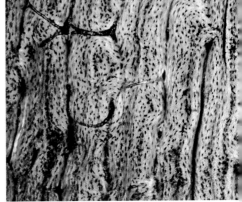

EXERCISES

he **skeletal system** consists of the bones and their cartilages. At first it might seem odd that a set of bones makes up an organ system, but remember that each bone is an organ. A bone consists of many tissue types, including osseous tissue, dense irregular connective tissue, and adipose tissue. The following exercises will introduce you to these complex organs and the histology of osseous tissue.

7

Microscopic Anatomy of Bone

The most superficial tissue of a bone is called the **periosteum** (pehr-ee-AH-stee-um; *peri-* = "around;" *oste-* = "bone;" Fig. 7.3). The outer layer of the periosteum is composed of dense irregular connective tissue richly supplied with blood vessels and nerves. Extensions of the collagen fibers from this layer, called **perforating fibers**, anchor the periosteum to the bone.

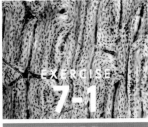

EXERCISE 7-1

MATERIALS

❏ Anatomical models and diagrams: osteon
❏ Slide: compact bone
❏ Light microscope
❏ Colored pencils

FIGURE **7.3** Microscopic anatomy of compact bone tissue: (**A**) illustration; (**B**) anatomical model photograph.

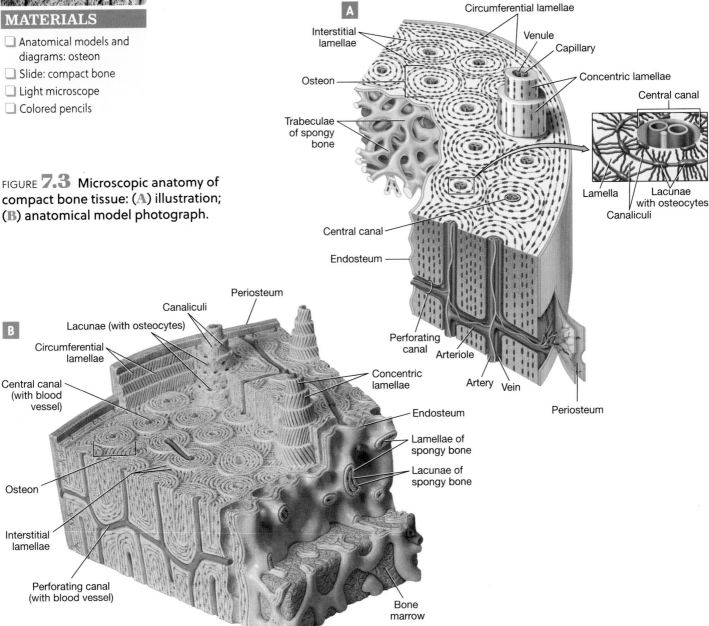

The innermost layer of the periosteum contains **osteogenic cells** (ah-stee-oh-JEN-ik; *-genic* = "generating/creating"), or *osteoprogenitor cells*, that can become cells called **osteoblasts** (AH-stee-oh-blasts; *-blast* = "immature cell"). Osteoblasts are "builder" cells that secrete bone extracellular matrix (ECM). Also within this layer are cells known as **osteoclasts** (AH-stee-oh-klasts; *-clasia* = "break down"). These are the "breakdown" cells, as they secrete enzymes that catalyze the digestion of bone ECM.

A balance between osteoblast and osteoclast activity is critical for bone health. Osteoclasts must degrade old and damaged bone, and osteoblasts must build new, healthy bone. These cells also play an important role in maintaining calcium ion homeostasis—the blood calcium ion concentration is lowered by osteoblast activity, whereas it is raised by osteoclast activity.

Deep to the periosteum, we find **osseous tissue**, a specialized connective tissue composed of a hardened ECM and different types of bone cells. The two general forms of osseous tissue are compact bone and spongy bone. **Compact bone** is hard, dense bone tissue found immediately deep to the periosteum. Its hardness comes from its structure, which consists of repeating, densely packed subunits called **osteons** (AHS-tee-ahnz; Figs. 7.3 and 7.4). Osteons have several features, including the following:

1. **Central canal**. Running down the center of each osteon is a **central canal**. Each central canal contains blood vessels and nerves and is lined with a connective tissue membrane called **endosteum** (in-DAH-stee-um; *endo-* = "within"). Like the periosteum, the endosteum has an inner layer of osteoblasts, which secrete bone ECM, and osteoclasts, which degrade bone.

2. **Lamellae**. Surrounding the central canal are rings of bone ECM called **lamellae** (lah-MELL-ee; *lamell-* = "thin plate"). The lamellae give compact bone a great deal of strength, much like a tree's rings. The lamellae in osteons are known as **concentric lamellae** due to the way they encircle the osteon. However, osteons are constantly remodeled, with osteoclasts breaking down old bone and osteoblasts building new bone. This leaves parts of old lamellae behind as new ones are built. These old lamellae, which are known as **interstitial lamellae**, are located between osteons.

3. **Lacunae**. Situated between the lamellae are small cavities called **lacunae** (lah-KOO-nee). Lacunae contain mature osteoblasts called **osteocytes**, which monitor and maintain the bone ECM. Neighboring lacunae and osteocytes are connected to each other by tiny canals called **canaliculi** (kan-ah-LIK-yoo-lee).

4. **Perforating canals**. The **perforating canals** run perpendicular to the lamellae and carry blood vessels deep into the bone from the periosteum. Like the central canals, perforating canals are lined by endosteum.

Notice in Figure 7.3 that there are additional lamellae lining the outside and inside of the compact bone. These are called **circumferential lamellae**, and are laid down by osteoblasts in the periosteum and endosteum. They give the compact bone additional strength.

Spongy bone is found on the inside of a bone deep to compact bone, and as its name implies, it somewhat resembles a sponge. It consists of a latticework-type structure with tiny bone spicules called **trabeculae** (trah-BEK-yoo-lee; *trab-* = "beam;" Fig. 7.5) that are lined with endosteum. The latticework-structure of spongy bone allows it to house another important tissue, the **bone marrow**. The two types of bone marrow are **red bone marrow**, which produces blood cells, and **yellow bone marrow**, which is composed primarily of adipose tissue.

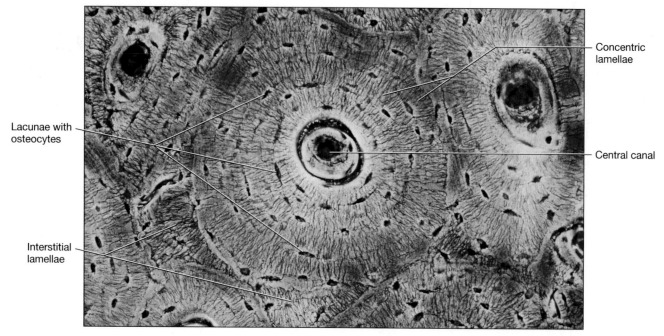

FIGURE **7.4** Compact bone, light micrograph.

As you can see in Figure 7.5, trabeculae are composed of lamellae but are not organized into osteons. For this reason, spongy bone lacks the hardness of compact bone. Between the lamellae are osteocytes in lacunae, and they are connected by canaliculi, as in compact bone.

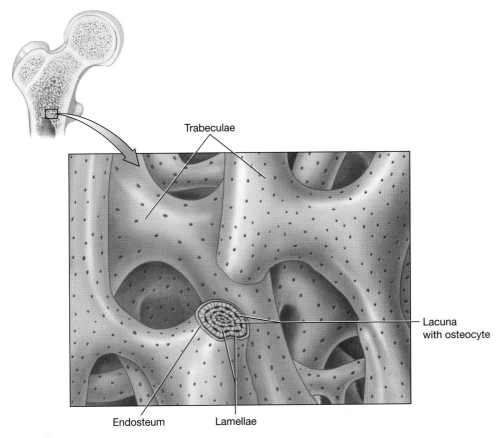

FIGURE **7.5** Microscopic anatomy of spongy bone tissue.

1 PROCEDURE

Model Inventory for Compact and Spongy Bone

Identify the following structures of compact and spongy bone on models and diagrams, using your textbook and this unit for reference. As you examine the anatomical models and diagrams, record the name of the model and the structures you were able to identify on the model inventory in Table 7.1. When you have completed the activity, answer Check Your Understanding Questions 1 through 3 (p. 183).

Compact Bone Structures
1. Periosteum
2. Perforating fibers
3. Osteons
  a. Central canal
  b. Endosteum
  c. Lamellae
    (1) Concentric lamellae
    (2) Interstitial lamellae
  d. Lacunae
  e. Osteocyte
  f. Canaliculi
  g. Perforating canal
4. Circumferential lamellae

Spongy Bone Structures
1. Trabeculae
2. Endosteum
3. Red bone marrow
4. Yellow bone marrow
5. Lamellae
6. Osteocytes
7. Lacunae
8. Canaliculi

TABLE **7.1** Model Inventory for Osseous Tissue

Model/Diagram	Structures Identified

2 PROCEDURE
Examining Bone Tissue with Microscopy

View a prepared slide of compact bone. The structures on the slide should look similar to the osteon models you viewed in lab earlier and Figure 7.4.

Use colored pencils to draw what you see under the microscope, and label your drawing with the compact bone structures from Procedure 1.

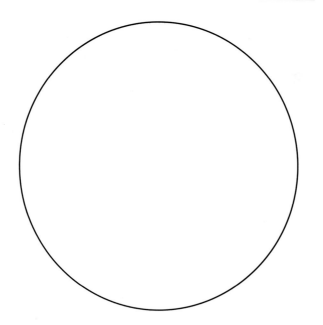

EXERCISE 7-2

MATERIALS

- ☐ Piece of normal bone (1)
- ☐ Piece of oven-heated bone (1)
- ☐ Piece of bone soaked in nitric acid (1)
- ☐ Plastic or metal tray

Chemical Components of Bone Tissue

The ECM of osseous tissue is made of two main chemical components:

1. The **organic component** consists of ground substance and protein fibers such as **collagen fibers**. The organic matrix provides a supportive network that gives the bone *tensile strength* (the ability to withstand stretching and twisting forces). Tensile strength is very important to bone function, as it prevents bones from breaking when muscles pull on them.

2. The **inorganic component** consists mostly of calcium salts in the form of calcium hydroxyapatite crystals. The inorganic component provides the bone with *compressional strength* (the ability to withstand compressive forces). Compressional strength is similarly important to bone function, as it allows bones to bear weight without breaking.

1 PROCEDURE

Examining the Chemical Components of Bone

In this procedure, you will compare the effects of removing different chemical components of bone. One sample has been heated in an oven. This destroys the organic component of the bone, leaving behind only the calcium hydroxyapatite crystals. The other sample has been treated with nitric acid to destroy the bone's inorganic component, leaving behind mostly ground substance and collagen fibers (Fig. 7.6). You will compare these two bone samples to an untreated bone to see how each component of the ECM contributes to the function of osseous tissue. When you have completed the activity, answer Check Your Understanding Question 4 (pp. 183–184).

> ⚠ **SAFETY NOTE**
>
> Safety glasses and gloves are required!

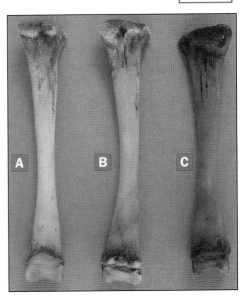

FIGURE **7.6** Three samples of bone: (**A**) untreated; (**B**) heated; (**C**) soaked in nitric acid.

Hypothesis: Which bone do you think will be strongest? Weakest?

1 Obtain and place three pieces of bone on a tray, including

  a. one piece of untreated bone;

  b. one piece of bone that has been baked in an oven for a minimum of two hours; and

  c. one piece of bone that has been soaked in nitric acid.

2 Place the three pieces of bone side by side. Describe their appearance. Do they look different from one another?

3 Squeeze each bone between your fingers, twist each sample between your fingers, and tap each sample on the tray. What happens to

  a the untreated bone? _____

  b the heated bone? _____

  c the bone treated with nitric acid? _____

4 Compare your results to your hypothesis.

MATERIALS

☐ Bones, disarticulated
☐ Skeleton, articulated

Bone Markings and Bone Shapes

When you examine a skeleton closely, you'll notice that few bones have smooth, flat surfaces. Instead, most bones contain depressions, openings, and projections. These features, collectively known as **bone markings**, perform numerous functions: *depressions* provide pathways along which blood vessels and nerves travel, or allow two bones to come together to form a joint; *openings* house and protect structures such as blood vessels and special sensory organs; and *projections* provide points of attachment for ligaments and tendons. The major types of bone markings are defined in Table 7.2.

Another thing you might notice about the skeleton is the variety of ways that the bones are shaped. As shown in Figure 7.7, there are four general shapes of bones:

1. **Long bones** are longer than they are wide. They include the bones of the upper and lower limbs, excluding the ankle and wrist bones.

HINTS & TIPS

Bone Shape, Not Length

Note that long bones are not named for their length but rather for their shape. Many long bones actually are quite short in length, such as the phalanges (the bones of the fingers and the toes). Be careful when identifying bone shapes to look at the overall shape of the bone rather than its size.

TABLE **7.2** Bone Markings

Bone Marking	Description
Depressions	
Facet	Shallow indented surface where two bones meet to form a joint
Fossa	Deeper indented surface in a bone; usually allows a rounded surface of another bone to fit inside of it
Fovea	Shallow pit; often the site for the attachment of a ligament
Groove	Long, typically shallow depression that usually allows a nerve or blood vessel to travel along the bone's surface
Sulcus	Another name for a groove
Openings	
Canal	Passageway through a bone
Fissure	Slit within a bone or between bones
Foramen	Hole in a bone through which a structure such as a nerve or blood vessel passes
Meatus	Another name for a canal
Projections	
Condyle	Round end of a bone that fits into a fossa or facet of another bone at a joint
Crest	Ridge along a bone; generally a site of muscle attachment
Epicondyle	Small projection usually proximal to a condyle; generally the site of muscle attachment
Head	Rounded end of the bone that fits into a fossa to form a joint
Line	Ridge along a bone where a muscle attaches
Process	Any bony projection; generally the site of muscle attachment
Protuberance	An outgrowth from a bone due to repetitive pull from a muscle
Trochanter	Large bony projection to which muscles attach; only examples are in the femur (thigh bone)
Tubercle	Small rounded projection where muscles attach
Tuberosity	A larger, more prominent tubercle

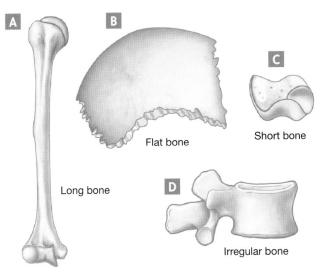

FIGURE **7.7** The four shapes of bones: (**A**) long bone; (**B**) flat bone; (**C**) short bone; (**D**) irregular bone.

Long bone

Flat bone

Short bone

Irregular bone

2. **Flat bones** are shaped exactly as they're named—they are flat. Flat bones include the ribs, the sternum, certain skull bones, and the hip bones.

3. **Short bones** are about as long as they are wide. The bones of the wrist and the ankle are short bones.

4. **Irregular bones** are those whose shape doesn't fit into any of the other classes. Irregular bones include the vertebrae, the sacrum, and certain bones of the skull, such as the sphenoid bone.

Note that there are two other classes of bones: sesamoid bones and sutural bones. **Sesamoid bones** (*sesam-* = "sesame") are roughly oval-shaped bones located within tendons, somewhat resembling the sesame seeds after which they are named. The sesamoid bone with which you are most likely familiar is the patella, or the kneecap. **Sutural bones** (SOO-tchur-uhl; *sutur-* = "sew") are small bones located between the flat bones of the skull. You will likely see sutural bones when you study the skull in the next unit.

1 PROCEDURE
Identifying Bone Shapes and Markings

Obtain a set of disarticulated bones, and classify them according to their shape. Identify examples of long bones, short bones, flat bones, and irregular bones, and record them in Table 7.3. Then, closely examine each bone and identify examples of bone markings on the bone. You may wish to use the figures in your text or Unit 8 (p. 185) to help you identify the disarticulated bones and their markings.

TABLE **7.3** Examples of Bone Shapes and Markings

Bone	Shape	Marking(s) on the Bone

MATERIALS

❑ Long bone, sectioned
❑ X-rays, if available
❑ Light microscope
❑ Slide: epiphyseal plate
❑ Colored pencils

Anatomy of Long Bones

All long bones share common structures and parts, illustrated in Figure 7.8 with the example of the femur. The **diaphysis** (dy-Ă-fih-sis; *dia-* = "through;" *-physis* = "growth") is the shaft of the long bone. As you can see in the figure, it consists of a thick collar of compact bone surrounding a hollow area called the **medullary cavity** (MED-yoo-lehr-ee; *medulla* = "marrow"). This collar of compact bone makes long bones quite strong. The medullary cavity has sparse trabeculae and generally is filled with yellow bone marrow in adult bones.

The ends of a long bone are called the **proximal** and **distal epiphyses** (eh-PIF-ih-seez; *sing.* = "epiphysis," eh-PIF-ih-sis; "growth on top"). Each epiphysis contains a shell of compact bone surrounding the inner spongy bone. The spongy bone within the epiphyses contains either red or yellow bone marrow. The end of each epiphysis is covered with **articular cartilage** (generally composed of hyaline cartilage), which allows two bones in a joint to move around one another with minimal friction.

At certain epiphysis-diaphysis junctions, you will note a thin, calcified line called the **epiphyseal line** (eh-PIF-ih-seel). This structure is the remnant of the **epiphyseal plate**, a band of hyaline cartilage from which long bones grow in length in children and young adults (Fig. 7.9A) As you can see in Figure 7.9B, there are five regions of an epiphyseal plate:

1. **Zone of reserve cartilage.** The first zone, or the one closest to the epiphysis, is called the **zone of reserve cartilage**. As its name implies, this zone contains a reserve of chondrocytes that can divide if needed.

2. **Zone of proliferation.** The next region is the **zone of proliferation**. Again, as suggested by its name, it consists of actively dividing (proliferating) chondrocytes.

3. **Zone of hypertrophy and maturation.** In the **zone of hypertrophy and maturation**, the dividing chondrocytes begin to enlarge in their lacunae as they mature.

4. **Zone of calcification.** Chondrocytes in the **zone of calcification** begin to die. As they die, they accumulate calcium salt deposits and harden.

5. **Zone of ossification.** The last zone, which abuts the diaphysis, is the **zone of ossification**. It contains calcified chondrocytes and osteoblasts, which blend with the diaphyseal bone.

When longitudinal growth ceases, the chondrocytes of the epiphyseal plate die and are replaced by calcified bone tissue.

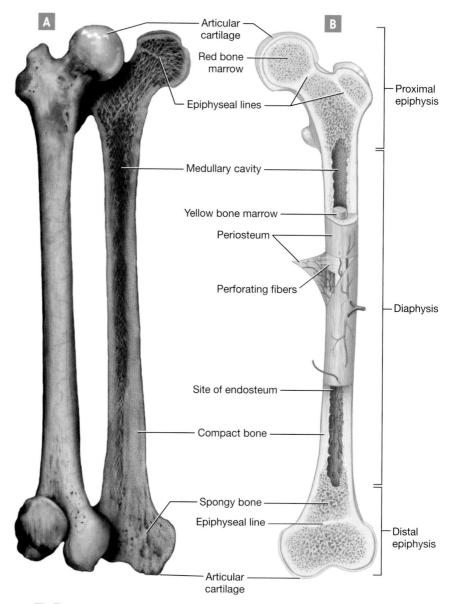

FIGURE **7.8** Adult long bone, the femur: (**A**) photograph; (**B**) illustration.

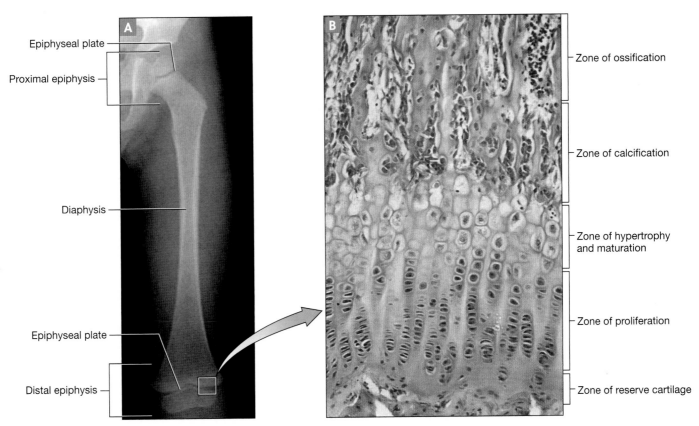

FIGURE **7.9** Epiphyseal plate: (**A**) x-ray of a child's femur; (**B**) light micrograph of the epiphyseal plate.

1	**PROCEDURE**

Identifying Structures of a Long Bone

Identify the following structures of long bones on specimens and x-rays (if available). Check off each structure as you identify it.

- ❑ Diaphysis
- ❑ Compact bone
- ❑ Medullary cavity
- ❑ Yellow bone marrow
- ❑ Proximal epiphysis
- ❑ Distal epiphysis
- ❑ Spongy bone
- ❑ Red bone marrow
- ❑ Articular cartilage
- ❑ Epiphyseal line
- ❑ Epiphyseal plate (may be visible only on x-ray)

2 PROCEDURE
Examining the Epiphyseal Plate with Microscopy

View a prepared slide of an epiphyseal plate. The structures on the slide should look similar to what you see in Figure 7.9.

Use colored pencils to draw what you see under the microscope, and label your drawing with the zones of the epiphyseal plate. When you have completed the activity, answer Check Your Understanding Question 5 (p. 184).

3 PROCEDURE
Time to Draw

In the space provided, draw, color, and label one of the long bone sections or diagrams that you examined. In addition, write the main function of each structure that you label.

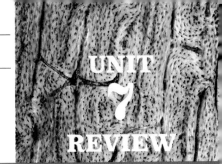

Check Your Recall

1 Label the following parts of compact bone on Figure 7.10.
- ❏ Canaliculi
- ❏ Central canal
- ❏ Circumferential lamellae
- ❏ Endosteum
- ❏ Interstitial lamellae
- ❏ Lacunae with osteocytes
- ❏ Osteon
- ❏ Perforating canal
- ❏ Periosteum
- ❏ Trabeculae of spongy bone

FIGURE **7.10** Microscopic anatomy of compact bone tissue.

2 *True/False:* Mark the following statements as true (T) or false (F). If the statement is false, correct it to make it a true statement.

_____ The endosteum contains osteoblasts and osteocytes.

_____ Osteocytes secrete bone matrix.

_____ Spongy bone is the inner bone, which is deep to compact bone.

_____ Spongy bone is composed of spicules called trabeculae.

_____ Compact bone houses red and yellow bone marrow.

_____ Concentric lamellae form the "rings" of bone matrix of an osteon.

3 The organic component of the ECM of osseous tissue is composed of _____ and gives the

bone _____.
- a. collagen fibers; compressional strength
- b. calcium hydroxyapatite crystals; compressional strength
- c. collagen fibers; tensile strength
- d. calcium hydroxyapatite crystals; tensile strength

4 Osteoclasts are located in _____ and function to _____.

   a. lacunae; maintain and monitor the bone ECM

   b. the periosteum; maintain and monitor the bone ECM

   c. lacunae; break down bone matrix

   d. the periosteum; build bone matrix

   e. the periosteum; break down bone matrix

5 *Circle all that apply.* **What is the general function of a bone depression?**

   a. It provides a pathway along which blood vessels or nerves travel.

   b. It provides a point of attachment for tendons or ligaments.

   c. It houses or protects structures such as blood vessels or sensory organs.

   d. It allows two bones to come together to form a joint.

6 Examples of long bones include

   a. the phalanges (bones of the fingers).

   b. the sternum.

   c. ankle bones.

   d. Both a and b are correct.

   e. Both a and c are correct.

7 Short bones are

   a. named for their length.

   b. about as long as they are wide.

   c. irregular in shape.

   d. longer than they are wide.

8 Label the following parts of a long bone on Figure 7.11.

   ❏ Articular cartilage

   ❏ Diaphysis

   ❏ Distal epiphysis

   ❏ Epiphyseal line

   ❏ Medullary cavity

   ❏ Perforating fibers

   ❏ Periosteum

   ❏ Proximal epiphysis

   ❏ Red bone marrow

   ❏ Yellow bone marrow

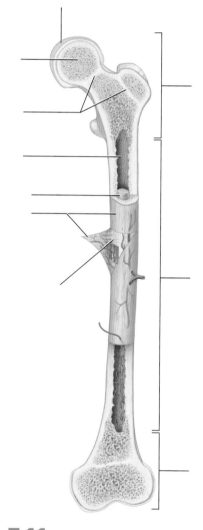

FIGURE **7.11** Adult long bone: the femur.

9 The epiphyseal plate is

   a. the structure from which long bones grow in length.

   b. a remnant of the structure from which long bones grow in length.

   c. composed of yellow bone marrow.

   d. found lining the surface of the epiphysis.

10 In the zone of proliferation of the epiphyseal plate,

   a. chondrocytes are actively dividing.

   b. chondrocytes are maintained in a reserve to divide if needed.

   c. chondrocytes begin to enlarge in their lacunae as they mature.

   d. chondrocytes are calcified and abut the diaphysis with osteoblasts.

Check Your Understanding

Critical Thinking and Application Questions

1 *Fibrous dysplasia* is a condition in which normal bone tissue is replaced with dense irregular connective tissue. Predict the consequences of this condition on bone health, and explain your reasoning.

2 A *carcinoma* is a cancer of epithelium, and a *sarcoma* is a cancer of connective tissue. Are bone tumors carcinomas or sarcomas? Explain.

3 The condition *osteopetrosis* is characterized by defective osteoclasts and a resulting decrease in osteoclast activity. This causes osteoblasts to lay down excessive bone with abnormal osteon structure. Interestingly, this disease increases the risk for fractures. Why do you think osteopetrosis would increase fracture risk?

4 *Malnutrition* is a condition resulting from a diet deficient in calories, macronutrients such as protein and carbo-hydrates, and/or vitamins and minerals. Malnutrition is associated with many different bone diseases due to its effect on the bone extracellular matrix.

a Predict the effect on bone health of a diet deficient in minerals such as calcium salts. Of the three bone samples you tested in Exercise 7-2, which one would most resemble a diet deficient in calcium salts? Explain.

b Predict the effect on bone health of a diet deficient in protein. Of the three bone samples you tested in Exercise 7-2, which one would most resemble a diet deficient in protein? Explain.

c Vitamin D is required for the absorption and deposition of calcium ions. Vitamin C is required for the synthesis of the protein collagen. Predict the effect on bone health of a diet deficient in vitamins D and C.

5 A common fracture seen in children is a fracture of the epiphyseal plate.

a Why do you think the epiphyseal plate fractures more easily than other parts of a bone?

b Some epiphyseal plate fractures are compression fractures, meaning the plate has been crushed. Predict the long-term potential consequences of such a fracture.

Skeletal System

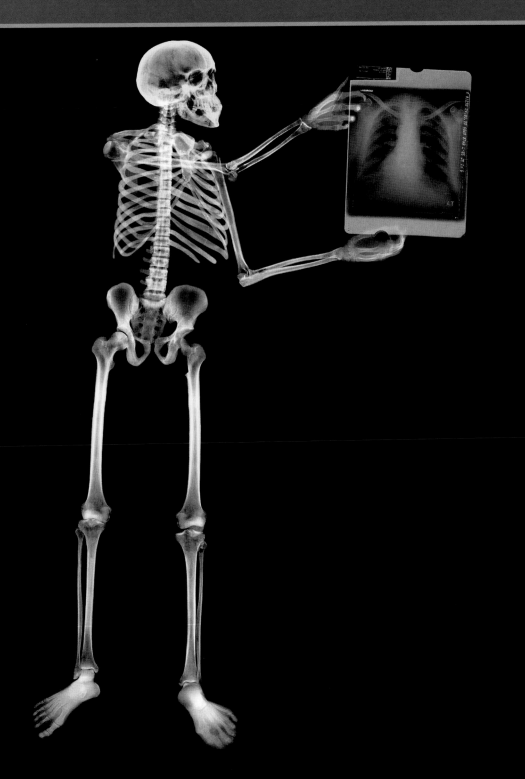

When you have completed this unit, you should be able to:

1 Identify bones and markings of the axial skeleton.

2 Identify bones and markings of the appendicular skeleton.

3 Build a skeleton using disarticulated bones.

PRE-LAB EXERCISES

Complete the following exercises prior to coming to lab, using your lab manual and textbook for reference.

PRE-LAB
8-1 Key Terms

You should be familiar with the following terms before coming to lab.

Term	Definition

Axial Skeleton

Cranial bones

Facial bones

Suture

Hyoid bone

Vertebrae

Ribs

Sternum

Appendicular Skeleton: Upper Limb and Pectoral Girdle

Pectoral girdle

Clavicle

Scapula

Humerus

Radius

Ulna

Carpals

Metacarpals

Phalanges

Appendicular Skeleton: Lower Limb and Pelvic Girdle

Pelvic girdle

Femur

Patella

Tibia

Fibula

Tarsals

Metatarsals

PRE-LAB

8-2 Bones of the Skull

Color the structures of the skull in Figure 8.1, and label them with the terms from Exercise 8-1 (p. 192). Use your text and Exercise 8-1 in this unit for reference.

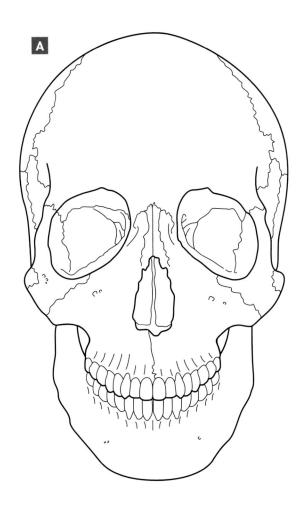

A

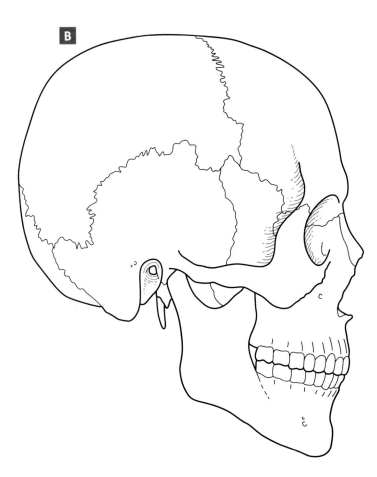

B

FIGURE **8.1** Skull: (**A**) anterior view; (**B**) lateral view; (*continues*)

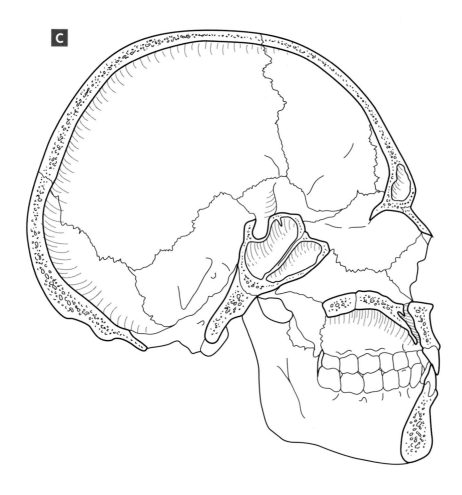

FIGURE **8.1** Skull (*cont.*): (**C**) midsagittal section.

8-3   Whole Skeleton

Color the structures of the skeleton in Figure 8.2, and label them with the terms from Exercises 8-1 to 8-3 (pp. 192–217). Use your text and Exercises 8-1 to 8-3 in this unit for reference.

A

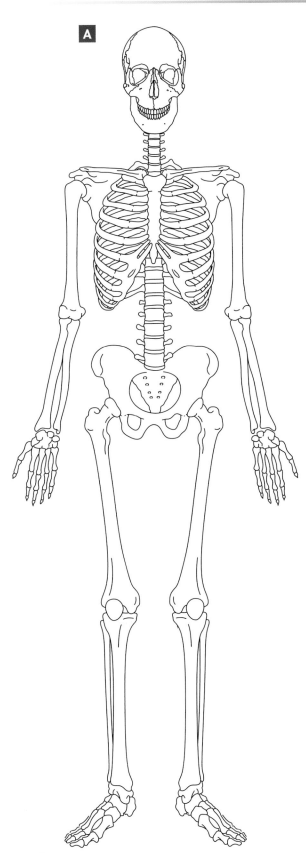

FIGURE **8.2** Skeleton: (**A**) anterior view; (*continues*)

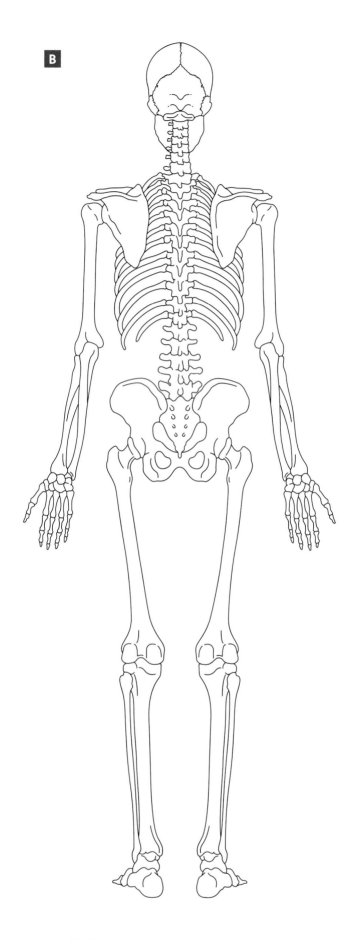

FIGURE **8.2** Skeleton (*cont.*): (**B**) posterior view.

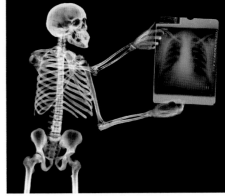

X-ray of a skeleton looking at an x-ray.

The **skeletal system** consists of the bones, the joints, and their associated cartilages. Its two divisions are the axial skeleton and the appendicular skeleton (Fig. 8.3). The **axial skeleton** is composed of the bones of the head, neck, and trunk—specifically, the cranial bones, the facial bones, the vertebral column, the hyoid bone, the sternum, and the ribs (shaded purple in Fig. 8.3). The **appendicular skeleton** (*append-* = "appendage") consists of the bones shaded "bone-colored" in Figure 8.3: those of the upper limbs, the lower limbs, the pectoral girdle (the bones forming the shoulder joint), and part of the pelvic girdle (the bones forming the pelvis and hip joint).

In this unit, we explore the anatomy of the bones and bone markings of the skeletal system, which serves as a foundation for later chapters. For example, the radial and ulnar arteries parallel the radius and the ulna, and the frontal, parietal, temporal, and occipital lobes of the brain are named for the cranial bones under which they are located.

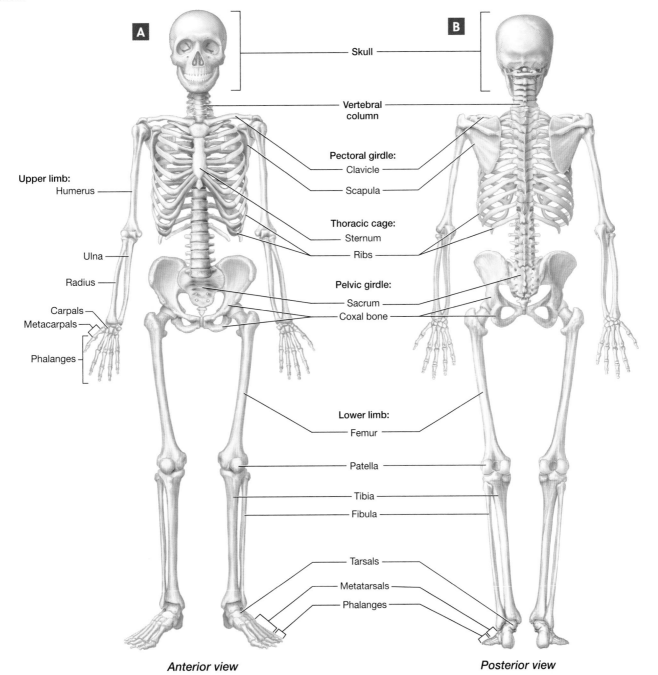

Anterior view *Posterior view*

FIGURE **8.3** The axial and appendicular skeletons: (**A**) anterior view; (**B**) posterior view.

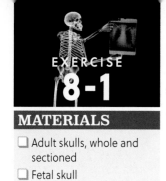

Anatomy of the Skull

The skull is composed of two classes of bones: the cranial bones and the facial bones (Figs. 8.4–8.10). The eight **cranial bones** (KRAY-nee-uhl; *cran-* = "skull") encase the brain and together form the **calvaria** (kal-VEHR-ee-uh; also known as the *cranial vault*; *calvaria* = "skull"). The calvaria consists of several of the cranial bones joined at immovable joints called **sutures** (SOO-tchurz; *sutur-* = "sew"). These bones also form the **cranial base**, which is made up of the **anterior, middle,** and **posterior cranial fossae**—indentations that support the brain (visible in Fig. 8.7). The cranial bones include the following:

1. Frontal bone;
2. Parietal bones (2);
3. Temporal bones (2);
4. Occipital bone;
5. Sphenoid bone; and
6. Ethmoid bone.

The 14 **facial bones** form the framework for the face, provide openings for ventilation and eating, and form cavities for the sense organs. Several of the facial bones are located deeper in the skull, and you will want to refer to several different figures (noted with each view) to best locate them and appreciate their structures. The facial bones include the:

1. Mandible;
2. Maxillae (2);
3. Lacrimal bones (2);
4. Nasal bones (2);
5. Vomer;
6. Inferior nasal conchae (2);
7. Palatine bones (2); and
8. Zygomatic bones (2).

What follows is a guide to which cranial and facial bones are visible in each view of the skull. At the end is a gallery featuring photographs of different views of the skull (see pp. 200–202 for Figs. 8.14.–8.18).

Anterior View (Fig. 8.4)

Cranial Bones

1. The **frontal bone** (*frons* = "forehead") forms the anterior portion of the cranium, the superior part of the orbit (where the eyeball is housed), and the anterior cranial fossa. Here you can see the smooth area between the eyes called the **glabella** (*glab-* = "smooth"). Over the anterior ridge of the orbit, an area known as the **supraorbital margin** (*supra-* = "above"), are two small holes called the **supraorbital foramina.**

2. The paired **parietal bones** (puh-RY-ih-tuhl; *pariet-* = "wall") form the superior and part of the lateral walls of the cranium. They are visible on the lateral sides of the anterior view.

3. The paired **temporal bones** form the lateral walls of the cranium. Like the parietal bones, they are visible on the lateral sides of the anterior view.

4. The posterior cranial bone is the **occipital bone** (ahk-SIP-ih-tuhl; *occiput* = "back of the head"). It is not visible in the anterior view.

5. The butterfly-shaped **sphenoid bone** (SFEE-noyd; *sphen-* = "wedge") is posterior to the frontal bone on the interior part of the skull. In Figure 8.4, note the **superior orbital fissure**, which is a slit between the greater and lesser wings through which nerves pass.

6. The complex **ethmoid bone** is the deepest cranial bone. From the anterior view, it is partially visible in the medial wall of the orbit.

Facial Bones

1. The **mandible**, or the lower jaw bone, consists of a central **body** and two "arms" called the **mandibular rami** (RAY-mee; *ramus* = "branch"). As you can see in the figure, the lower teeth are attached to the mandibular body along a border called the **alveolar margin** (al-vee-OH-luhr; *alveolus* = "small cavity"). On each side of the lateral mandibular body, we find a small hole called the **mental foramen** (*mentus* = "chin").

2. The two fused **maxillae** (mak-SILL-ee) are the upper jaw bones. They form the inferior wall of the orbit, part of the lateral wall of the nasal cavity, and part of the superior wall of the oral cavity. Inside the orbit, where the maxilla meets the sphenoid bone, we find a slit known as the **inferior orbital fissure**, which serves as a passageway for nerves and blood vessels. Just inferior to the orbit is a small hole called the **infraorbital foramen** (*infra-* = "below"). Laterally, the maxillae have projections called **zygomatic processes** that form part of the cheekbone. Like the mandible, the maxillae also have an alveolar margin along which the upper teeth are attached.

3. The tiny **lacrimal bones** (LAK-ruh-muhl; *lacrima* = "tear") are visible in the medial part of the orbit, where they form part of the structure that drains tears produced by the lacrimal gland of the eye.

4. The two **nasal bones** form the anterior framework of the bridge of the nose.

5. The single **vomer** (VOH-muhr) forms the inferior portion of the bony nasal septum. It is visible in the midline of the nasal cavity.

6. The small **inferior nasal conchae** form part of the lateral walls of the nasal cavity.

7. The two **palatine bones** (PAL-uh-ty'n) form the posterior part of the hard palate and the posterolateral walls of the nasal cavity. They are not visible in the anterior view.

8. The two **zygomatic bones** (zy-goh-MAT-ik) form the bulk of the cheek and a significant portion of the "cheekbone" or zygomatic arch.

The orbit and the nasal cavity are complicated structures with contributions from several bones. The **orbit** is formed by parts of seven bones: the frontal bone, maxilla, sphenoid bone, ethmoid bone, lacrimal bone, zygomatic bone, and a tiny piece of the palatine bone. The **nasal cavity** is formed by parts of six bones: the ethmoid bone, maxillae, palatine bones, inferior nasal conchae, sphenoid bone, and vomer (see Figs. 8.4 and 8.8).

8

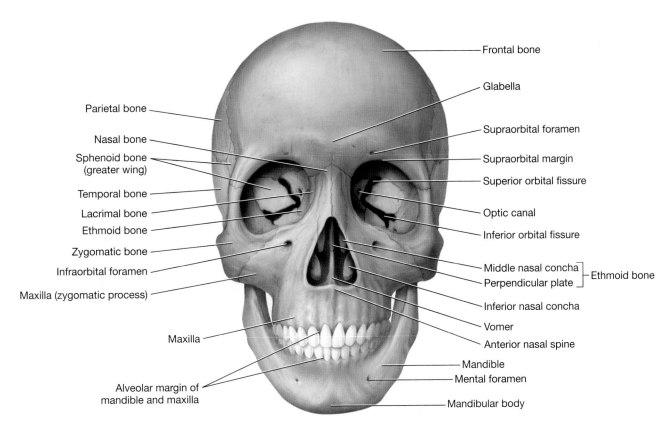

FIGURE **8.4** Anterior view of the skull.

Lateral View (Fig. 8.5)

Cranial Bones

1. The frontal, ethmoid, and sphenoid bones are visible in this view.

2. Here you can see that the parietal bones articulate with one another and many other cranial bones at sutures: They meet the frontal bone at the **coronal suture** (*corona* = "crown"); they meet the occipital bone at the **lambdoid suture** (LAM-doyd); and they meet the temporal bones at the **squamous sutures**.

3. Notice that each temporal bone has a complex shape with four general regions.

   a. The flat **squamous region** is the temporal bone's most lateral portion. As its name implies, it is largely flat; however, it does contain a projection called the **zygomatic process** that forms part of the *zygomatic arch* or cheekbone. Just inferior to the zygomatic process is an indentation, the **mandibular fossa**, which forms the *temporomandibular joint*—or the jaw joint—with the mandible.

   b. The temporal bone's inferior region is called the **tympanic region** (tim-PAN-ik; *tympan-* = "drum"). It houses the **external acoustic (auditory) meatus**, an opening to the *external auditory canal*, which leads to the middle and inner ear. Also in this region is a needlelike projection called the **styloid process** (STY-loyd; *stylus* = "pen"). Posterior to the tympanic region is the **mastoid region**, which contains the large **mastoid process**. Inside the mastoid process are numerous tiny sinuses known as *mastoid air cells*.

   c. The temporal bone's fourth region, the *petrous region*, is seen in Figure 8.6 and is discussed with that view.

Facial Bones

1. Notice that just lateral to the mental foramina, the mandibular rami turn superiorly at the **mandibular angle**. Their superior ends have two processes separated by the **mandibular notch**: an anterior process called the **coronoid process** (*coron-* = "hooked") and a posterior process called the **mandibular condyle**. The mandibular condyle fits into the mandibular fossa in the temporal bone to form the **temporomandibular joint**, or **TMJ**.

2. The maxillae, zygomatic bones, and nasal bones are visible in this view. The lacrimal bones are best seen from this view, where you can see the inferior indentation called the *lacrimal fossa*.

3. The inferior nasal conchae, vomer, and palatine bones are not visible here.

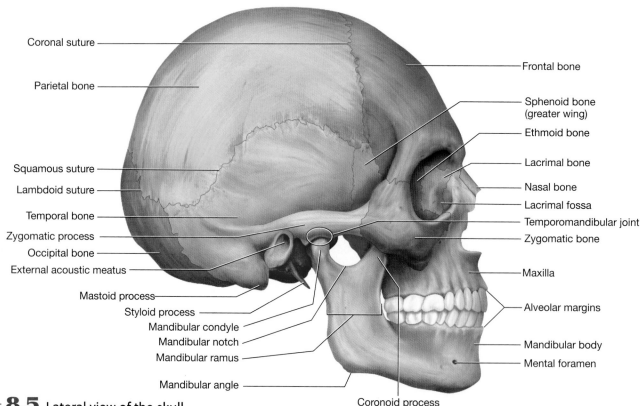

FIGURE **8.5** Lateral view of the skull.

Internal View (Fig. 8.6)

Cranial Bones

1. In the frontal bone, we can see the indentation known as the anterior cranial fossa.

2. In the middle of the frontal bone is the superior surface of the ethmoid bone, which is called the **cribriform plate** (KRIB-rih-form; *cribrum* = "sieve"). The cribriform plate forms the roof of the nasal cavity and part of the base of the cranial cavity. It has small holes, called **olfactory foramina** (*olfact-* = "smell"), through which olfactory nerves pass. It also has a superior projection, called the **crista galli** (KRIS-tah GAL-ee; "rooster's comb"), to which certain membranes around the brain attach.

3. Posterior to the frontal bone is the sphenoid bone. Centrally, the sphenoid bone consists of the **body**, the superior surface of which features two canals called the **optic canals** (*opt-* = "vision") through which the nerves for vision pass. Also in the body we find a saddlelike formation called the **sella turcica** (SELL-uh TUR-sih-kuh; "Turk's saddle") that houses the pituitary gland. Extending from the body are three sets of "wings":

   a. The small **lesser wings** are the superior and most anterior set.

   b. The larger **greater wings** are the inferior and posterior set. As you can see in the figure, each greater wing has three prominent sets of foramina: the anterior **foramen rotundum**, the middle **foramen ovale** (oh-VAL-ay), and the posterior **foramen spinosum** (a mnemonic that might help you remember this is "Rigatoni Over Spaghetti"). On the anterior side, the greater wings form the posterior portion of the orbit.

   c. The inferior set of wings, the *pterygoid processes*, are discussed with the inferior view.

4. Internally, the temporal bone is shaped like a mountain ridge and is accordingly called the **petrous region** (*petr-* = "rocky"). Within this region, we find the middle cranial fossa. We also find several openings, including the **jugular foramen** (*jugular* = "neck") and the **internal acoustic meatus**.

5. The posterior bone is the occipital bone. We can see its most conspicuous feature in its base—a large hole called the **foramen magnum** ("large hole") through which the spinal cord passes. In addition, it features the posterior cranial fossa.

6. The parietal bones are visible on the lateral walls of the skull in this view.

Facial Bones

There are no facial bones visible in the internal view of the skull.

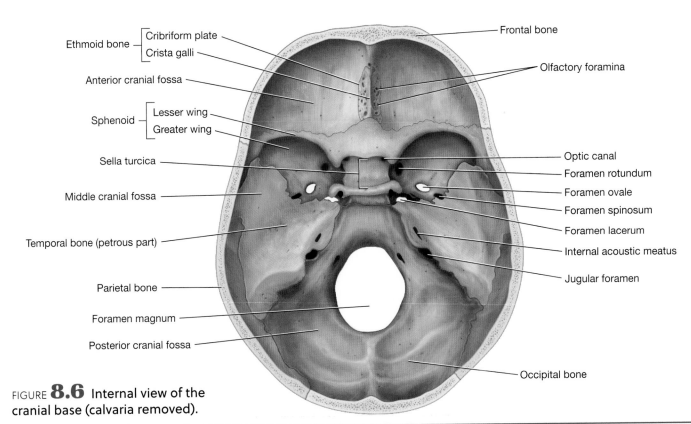

FIGURE **8.6** Internal view of the cranial base (calvaria removed).

Inferior View (Fig. 8.7)

Cranial Bones

1. The frontal and ethmoid bones are not visible in this view. Only tiny slivers of the parietal bones are visible near the lateral edges of the skull.

2. Here we can see two sets of the sphenoid bone's wings. Laterally are its greater wings. Medially are the inferior set of wings, which consists of the narrow **pterygoid processes** (TEHR-ih-goyd; *ptery-* = "wing"). The pterygoid processes form part of the posterior walls of the nasal and oral cavities.

3. In this view, we can see many features of the temporal bone's tympanic and mastoid regions, including the medial and anterior **foramen lacerum** (LAS-er-um), the middle **carotid canal**, and the posterior jugular foramen. Also featured are the mandibular fossa, styloid process, and mastoid process.

4. From the inferior view, we can see many important features of the occipital bone. Anterior and lateral to the foramen magnum are the two **occipital condyles**, which form a joint with the first cervical vertebra. Also visible are two prominent horizontal ridges on the occipital bone's posterior surface: the **superior** and **inferior nuchal lines** (NOO-kuhl). In the middle of the superior nuchal line, we find a bump called the **external occipital protuberance**.

Facial Bones

1. The mandible, lacrimal bones, nasal bones, and inferior nasal conchae are not visible in the inferior view.

2. In this view, you can see that the maxillae also form the anterior portion of the *hard palate* via their **palatine processes.** At the anterior edge of the palatine processes, where the two maxillae meet, is the **incisive fossa.**

3. Posterior to the palatine processes are the palatine bones, which make up the posterior quarter of the hard palate.

4. Along the midline, between the pterygoid processes of the sphenoid bones, the vomer is visible.

5. Just lateral to the maxillae, you can see the zygomatic bones forming part of the zygomatic arch.

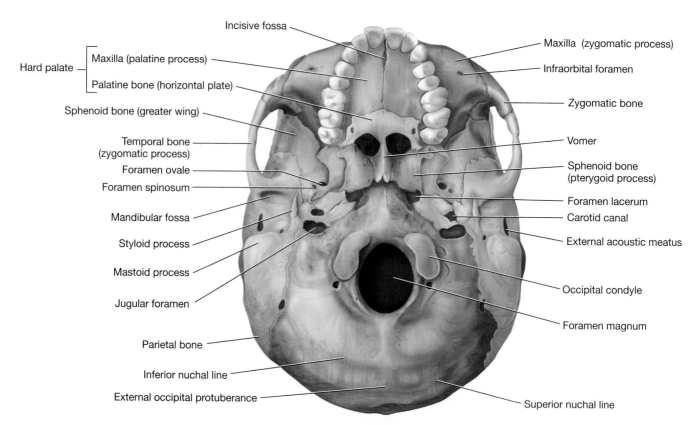

FIGURE **8.7** Inferior view of the skull (mandible removed).

Midsagittal Section (Fig. 8.8)

Cranial Bones

1. In the frontal bone, notice the hollow **frontal sinuses**, which are part of the **paranasal sinuses** (*para-* = "next to"), a group of bony cavities that surround the nasal cavity.

2. You can see three of the sutures where the parietal bones articulate with other cranial bones: the lambdoid suture, the squamous suture, and the coronal suture. They also articulate with one another at the *sagittal suture*, which is visible in later figures (see Figs. 8.9 and 8.10).

3. This view shows the petrous region of the temporal bone, and you can see clearly the internal acoustic meatus. In addition, the styloid process is visible.

4. Two features of the occipital bone to note in this view are the foramen magnum and the external occipital protuberance.

5. In the body of the sphenoid bone, notice the second paranasal sinus, the **sphenoid sinus**, which resides deep to the sella turcica. This is also a good view from which to appreciate the sphenoid bone's inferior set of wings—the narrow pterygoid processes.

6. This view shows the ethmoid bone's **perpendicular plate**, which forms the superior part of the bony nasal septum. You can also see its crista galli protruding into the cranial cavity.

Facial Bones

1. The body and ramus of the mandible are visible in this view, as is the mandibular condyle.

2. The maxilla and palatine bones can be seen making up the hard palate.

3. This section has the best view of the vomer—you can see how it makes up the inferior portion of the nasal septum.

4. A portion of one of the nasal bones is visible superficial to the perpendicular plate of the ethmoid bone.

5. The zygomatic bones, lacrimal bones, and inferior nasal conchae are not visible in this figure.

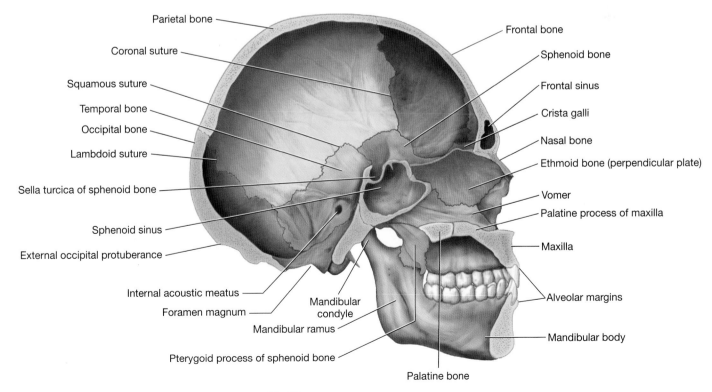

FIGURE **8.8** Midsagittal section of the skull.

Posterior View (Fig. 8.9) and Superior View (Fig. 8.10)

Cranial Bones

1. This is the best view for seeing the shape of the occipital bone and the way it articulates with the parietal bones. You can also see the superior and inferior nuchal lines and the external occipital protuberance. On its inferior side is the foramen magnum.

2. From the posterior view, you can appreciate the size and shape of the temporal bones' mastoid processes and styloid processes.

3. In the superior view, the frontal bone is visible on the anterior end, and the occipital bone is visible on the posterior end.

4. In both views, we can see the cranial sutures. Recall that the parietal bones articulate with one another and many other cranial bones at sutures. In Figures 8.9 and 8.10, you can see that they meet one another at the **sagittal suture**. You can also see their junctions with the occipital bone at the lambdoid suture (Figs. 8.9 and 8.10); with the temporal bones at the squamous sutures (Fig. 8.9); and with the frontal bone at the coronal suture (Fig. 8.10).

Facial Bones

Only the mandible and a small portion of the maxillae are visible from the posterior view; no facial bones are visible from the superior view.

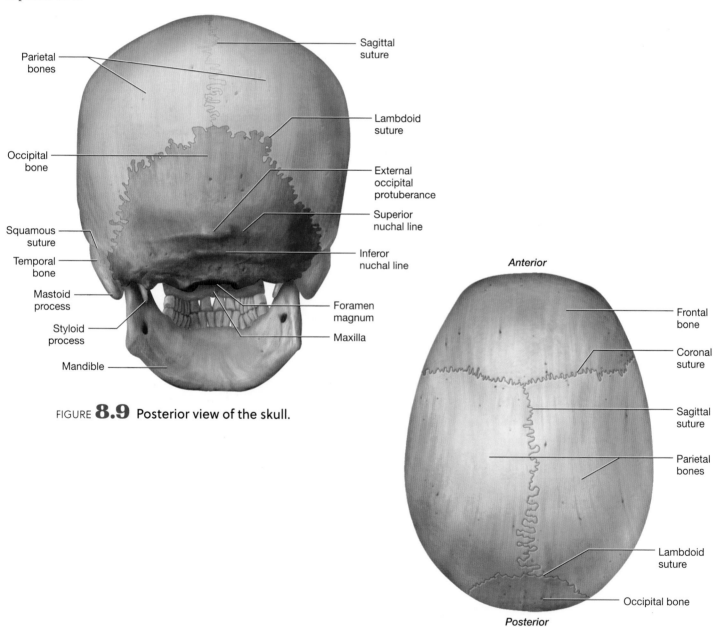

FIGURE **8.9** Posterior view of the skull.

FIGURE **8.10** Superior view of the calvaria.

View of the Ethmoid Bone (Fig. 8.11)

As the deepest cranial bone, the ethmoid bone is the most difficult one to see from standard views of the skull. For this reason, it is shown in a separate illustration, Figure 8.11.

1. Note the cribriform plate projecting from the ethmoid bone's superior surface, with its superior projection, the crista galli.

2. The lateral masses form the *orbital plate* and the walls of the nasal cavity. Notice how internally the lateral masses contain numerous cavities—this is the third set of paranasal sinuses, the **ethmoid sinuses**. Extending medially from the lateral masses are two projections into the nasal cavity: the **superior nasal conchae** and **middle nasal conchae** (KAHN-kee). Note that the superior nasal conchae are quite small and are usually difficult to see.

3. You can see here how the middle perpendicular plate forms the superior part of the bony nasal septum.

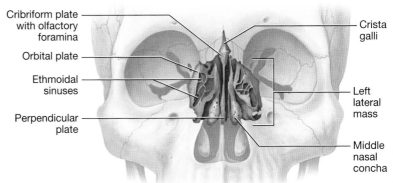

FIGURE **8.11** Ethmoid bone.

View of the Paranasal Sinuses (Fig. 8.12)

So far, we have seen three sets of paranasal sinuses: the frontal, sphenoid, and ethmoid sinuses. There is a fourth set we have yet to discuss: the large **maxillary sinuses**, which are located within the maxillae. Air from the nasal cavity enters the paranasal sinuses via small openings in the bones, and in the sinuses the air gets filtered, warmed, and humidified. The paranasal sinuses also decrease the weight of the skull and enhance voice resonance—which is evident from the change in your voice any time you have a sinus infection. Figure 8.12 illustrates all four sinuses so you can see how they relate to one another.

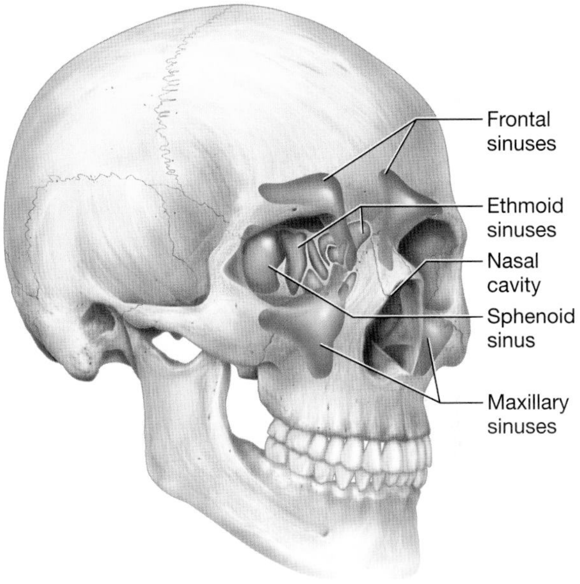

FIGURE **8.12** Paranasal sinuses.

Fetal Skull (Fig. 8.13)

The features we've been examining are found in an adult skull. However, as you can see in Figure 8.13, a fetal skull contains notable differences from an adult skull. In adults, the sutures are fused, but in the fetus, the sutures have not yet fused and are instead joined by fibrous membranes. This can be seen with the **frontal suture**, also known as the **metopic suture** (met-AHP-ik; *metop-* = "forehead"), which is where the two fetal frontal bones fuse. Where several sutures meet, we find large, membrane-covered areas called the **fontanels**, known to many as "soft spots." The two main fontanels are the **anterior fontanel**, where the sagittal and coronal sutures meet, and the **posterior fontanel**, where the sagittal and lambdoid sutures meet.

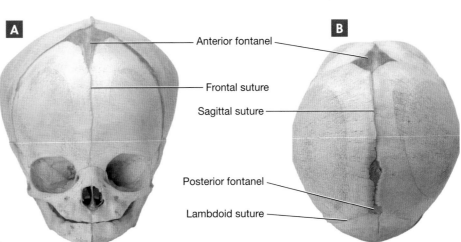

FIGURE **8.13** Fetal skull: **(A)** anterior view; **(B)** superior view.

Photo Gallery of the Skull

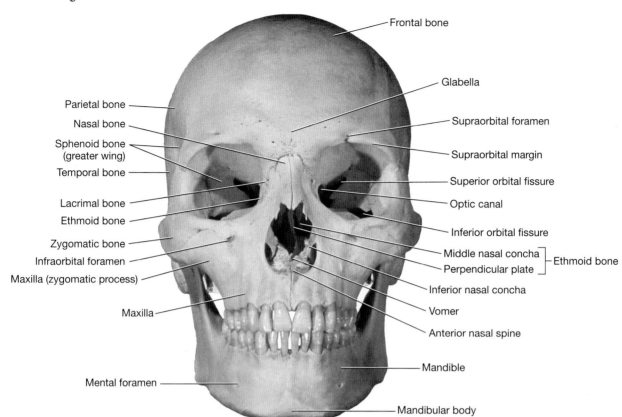

FIGURE **8.14** Anterior view of the skull, photograph.

Labels (Figure 8.14):
Frontal bone
Glabella
Parietal bone
Nasal bone
Supraorbital foramen
Sphenoid bone (greater wing)
Supraorbital margin
Temporal bone
Superior orbital fissure
Lacrimal bone
Optic canal
Ethmoid bone
Inferior orbital fissure
Zygomatic bone
Middle nasal concha — Ethmoid bone
Infraorbital foramen
Perpendicular plate — Ethmoid bone
Maxilla (zygomatic process)
Inferior nasal concha
Maxilla
Vomer
Anterior nasal spine
Mandible
Mental foramen
Mandibular body

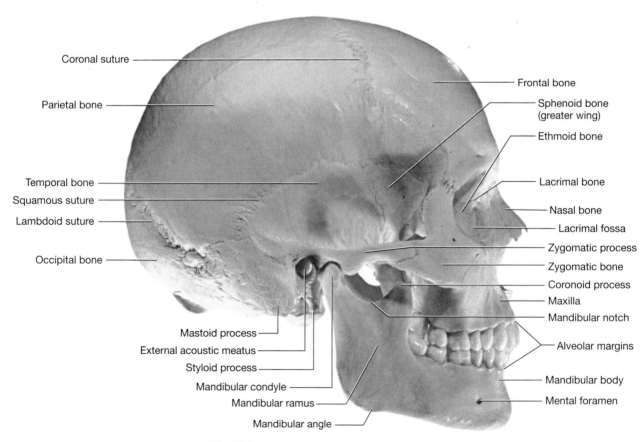

FIGURE **8.15** Lateral view of the skull, photograph.

Labels (Figure 8.15):
Coronal suture
Frontal bone
Parietal bone
Sphenoid bone (greater wing)
Ethmoid bone
Temporal bone
Lacrimal bone
Squamous suture
Nasal bone
Lambdoid suture
Lacrimal fossa
Zygomatic process
Occipital bone
Zygomatic bone
Coronoid process
Maxilla
Mandibular notch
Mastoid process
Alveolar margins
External acoustic meatus
Styloid process
Mandibular condyle
Mandibular body
Mandibular ramus
Mental foramen
Mandibular angle

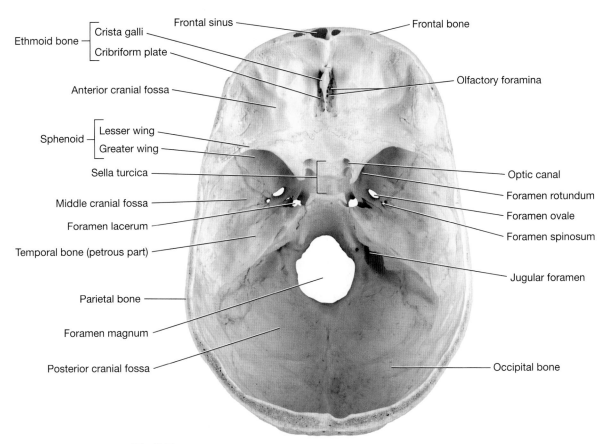

Ethmoid bone — Crista galli
Cribriform plate

Frontal sinus — Frontal bone

Anterior cranial fossa

Olfactory foramina

Sphenoid — Lesser wing
Greater wing

Sella turcica

Optic canal

Middle cranial fossa

Foramen rotundum

Foramen lacerum

Foramen ovale

Temporal bone (petrous part)

Foramen spinosum

Jugular foramen

Parietal bone

Foramen magnum

Posterior cranial fossa

Occipital bone

FIGURE **8.16** Internal view of the cranial base (calvaria removed), photograph.

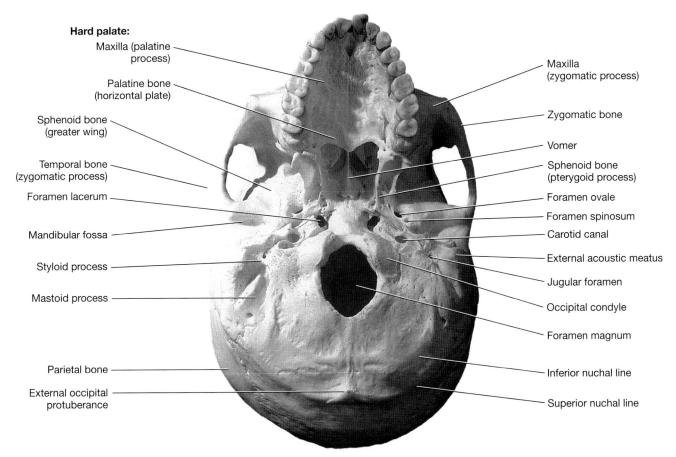

Hard palate:
Maxilla (palatine process)

Maxilla (zygomatic process)

Palatine bone (horizontal plate)

Zygomatic bone

Sphenoid bone (greater wing)

Vomer

Temporal bone (zygomatic process)

Sphenoid bone (pterygoid process)

Foramen lacerum

Foramen ovale

Mandibular fossa

Foramen spinosum

Styloid process

Carotid canal

Mastoid process

External acoustic meatus

Jugular foramen

Occipital condyle

Foramen magnum

Parietal bone

Inferior nuchal line

External occipital protuberance

Superior nuchal line

FIGURE **8.17** Inferior view of the skull (mandible removed), photograph.

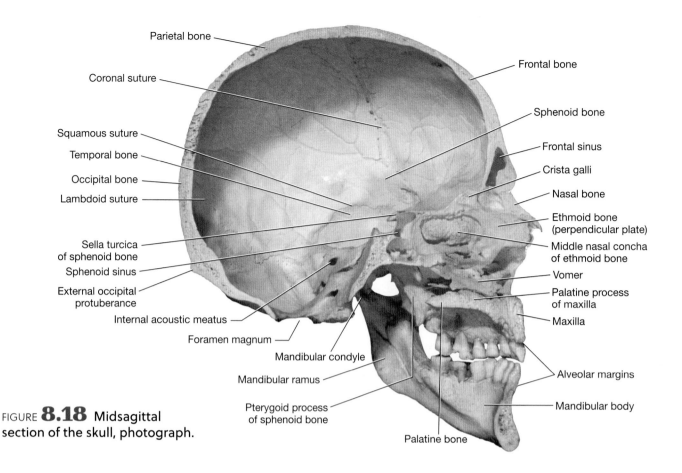

FIGURE **8.18** Midsagittal section of the skull, photograph.

Labels on figure:
Parietal bone
Coronal suture
Squamous suture
Temporal bone
Occipital bone
Lambdoid suture
Sella turcica of sphenoid bone
Sphenoid sinus
External occipital protuberance
Internal acoustic meatus
Foramen magnum
Mandibular condyle
Mandibular ramus
Pterygoid process of sphenoid bone
Palatine bone
Frontal bone
Sphenoid bone
Frontal sinus
Crista galli
Nasal bone
Ethmoid bone (perpendicular plate)
Middle nasal concha of ethmoid bone
Vomer
Palatine process of maxilla
Maxilla
Alveolar margins
Mandibular body

8

PROCEDURE

1 Cooperative Learning for the Skull

This exercise takes an approach called *cooperative learning*, in which you work with your lab partners to teach one another the bones and bone markings. The process may seem a bit confusing at first, but by the end of the first couple of rotations, it should move more quickly and smoothly. After you have completed the activity, answer Check Your Understanding Questions 1 through 3 (p. 231).

1 Assemble into teams of a minimum of four students; five is optimum.

2 Distribute a skull to each member of the team, and assign each student one of the following five groups of bones and bone markings (the specific structures of each bone are listed below and on the following page):

Group A: Calvaria, base, and structures of the frontal bone and parietal bones.

Group B: Temporal bone and occipital bone structures.

Group C: Ethmoid bone and sphenoid bone structures.

Group D: Mandible and maxillary bone structures.

Group E: Remainder of the facial bones, orbit, sutural bones, and anterior and posterior fontanels.

3 Spend approximately 3 minutes learning the assigned structures on your own. Explore each structure thoroughly. If there are canals and foramina, pass a pipe cleaner through the holes to see where they go.

4 Spend about 1 to 2 minutes teaching your assigned structures to your team. Then have each team member spend approximately 1 to 2 minutes teaching the team his or her assigned structures.

5 Rotate the assigned structures clockwise so each member has a new set of structures to learn and teach (the student who was assigned Group A will take Group B, and so on).

6 Repeat Steps 3 and 4, and then rotate the assigned structures again. Continue the process (it begins to speed up significantly at this point), repeating until each team member has taught each group of structures once.

By the end of this activity, each team member will have learned and presented each group of structures.

The following is a list of bones and bone markings of the skull that will be covered in this exercise.

Cranial Bones

Group A Structures

1. Calvaria
2. Base of cranial cavity
   a. Anterior cranial fossa
   b. Middle cranial fossa
   c. Posterior cranial fossa
3. Frontal bone
   a. Glabella
   b. Supraorbital foramen
   c. Frontal sinuses
4. Parietal bones
   a. Sagittal suture
   b. Coronal suture
   c. Lambdoid suture
   d. Squamous suture

Group B Structures

1. Temporal bones
   a. Zygomatic process
   b. Mandibular fossa
   c. External acoustic (auditory) meatus
   d. Styloid process
   e. Mastoid process with mastoid air cells
   f. Foramen lacerum
   g. Carotid canal
   h. Jugular foramen
   i. Internal acoustic meatus
2. Occipital bone
   a. Foramen magnum
   b. Occipital condyles
   c. Superior nuchal line
   d. Inferior nuchal line
   e. External occipital protuberance

Group C Structures

1. Sphenoid bone
   a. Body
   b. Optic canal
   c. Sphenoid sinus
   d. Sella turcica
   e. Lesser wings
   f. Greater wings
   g. Superior orbital fissure
   h. Foramen rotundum
   i. Foramen ovale
   j. Foramen spinosum
   k. Pterygoid processes
2. Ethmoid bone
   a. Cribriform plate
   b. Olfactory foramina
   c. Crista galli
   d. Lateral masses
   e. Ethmoid sinuses
   f. Superior and middle nasal conchae
   g. Perpendicular plate

Facial Bones and Other Structures

Group D Structures

1. Mandible
   a. Body of mandible
   b. Mandibular ramus
   c. Alveolar margin
   d. Mental foramen
   e. Mandibular angle
   f. Mandibular notch
   g. Coronoid process
   h. Mandibular condyle
   i. Temporomandibular joint
2. Maxillae
   a. Inferior orbital fissure
   b. Infraorbital foramen
   c. Palatine processes
   d. Maxillary sinuses
   e. Zygomatic processes
   f. Alveolar margin

Group E Structures

1. Lacrimal bones and lacrimal fossa
2. Nasal bones
3. Vomer
4. Inferior nasal conchae
5. Palatine bones
6. Zygomatic bones and zygomatic arch
7. Orbit
8. Nasal cavity
9. Frontal (metopic) suture
10. Anterior fontanel
11. Posterior fontanel

Your instructor may wish to omit certain structures included in these lists or add structures not included in the lists. List any additional structures in the space provided:

EXERCISE 8-2

MATERIALS

- ❏ Vertebral column, articulated
- ❏ Bones, disarticulated: vertebrae, sacrum, sternum, ribs, hyoid bone
- ❏ Skeleton, articulated

8

Remainder of the Axial Skeleton

Another key component of the axial skeleton is the **vertebral column**, which consists of 24 unfused vertebrae, the five fused vertebrae of the sacrum (SAY-krum), and the coccyx (KAHX-iks). If you view the vertebral column from the lateral side, as in Figure 8.19, you can see that there are spaces between the vertebrae called **intervertebral foramina** (*inter-* = "within" or "between"). In addition, the vertebral column has four curvatures: the concave **cervical** (*cerv-* = "neck") and **lumbar curvatures** (*lumb-* = "loin"), and the convex **thoracic** (*thorac-* = "chest") and **sacral curvatures**. The cervical and lumbar curvatures are particularly important to our ability to walk upright.

The 24 vertebrae consist of 7 cervical vertebrae, 12 thoracic vertebrae, and 5 lumbar vertebrae (remember this as "breakfast at 7, lunch at 12, dinner at 5"). Nearly all vertebrae share certain general features, which are visible in the typical cervical vertebra shown in Figures 8.20A and 8.20B. These features include a posterior **spinous process**, two lateral **transverse processes**, a central **vertebral foramen**, an anterior **vertebral body**, two **superior articular processes** (*artic-* = "joint") and **facets** (fuh-SETZ) that articulate with the vertebra above, and two inferior articular processes and facets that articulate with the vertebra below. In between each vertebral body is a fibrocartilage pad called an **intervertebral disc** that absorbs shock as the vertebral column moves. Extending from the vertebral body to the transverse processes on both sides are two short extensions known as **pedicles** (PED-ih-kullz), which—along with two posterior extensions, the **laminae** (LAM-ih-nee)—enclose the vertebral foramen.

The basic properties of each region of the vertebral column are as follows:

1. The seven **cervical vertebrae** are located in the neck (Fig. 8.20A–D). All cervical vertebrae have holes in their transverse processes called **transverse foramina**. These foramina permit the passage of blood vessels called the *vertebral artery* and *vein*.

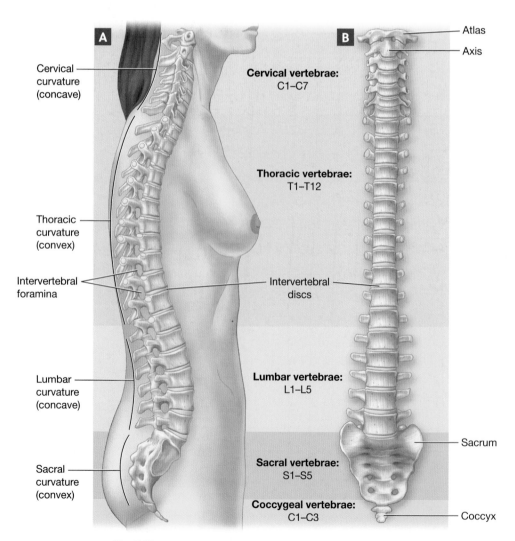

FIGURE **8.19** Vertebral column: (**A**) lateral view; (**B**) anterior view.

In addition, the spinous processes of cervical vertebrae are often forked. Two cervical vertebrae are named differently than the others because of their unique features:

a. **Atlas** (C1): The **atlas** is the first cervical vertebra, and it articulates with the occipital condyles of the occipital bone. It is easily identified because it has a large vertebral foramen, no body, and no spinous process (Fig. 8.20C).

b. **Axis** (C2): The **axis** is the second cervical vertebra. It is also easily identified by a superior projection called the **dens** (or the **odontoid process**; Fig. 8.20D). The dens fits up inside the atlas to form the *atlantoaxial joint*, which allows rotation of the head.

HINTS & TIPS

How to Tell the Different Vertebrae Apart

It's not uncommon to find yourself in a lab practical having to identify a single vertebra as being cervical, thoracic, or lumbar. Fortunately, they're really easy to tell apart if you remember a few key things.

ℹ Only cervical vertebrae have transverse foramina. So, if you see holes in the transverse processes of the vertebra, you know you're holding a cervical vertebra. From there, you might need to know whether you're holding the atlas (C1) or the axis (C2):
- Only the atlas lacks a vertebral body, which gives it a huge vertebral foramen.
- Only the axis has a superior projection—the dens. If you get confused as to which is the axis and which is the atlas, here's a simple visual analogy: Think about the dens as being a projection you could stick something like a DVD on top of, and the DVD would be able to spin on its axis.

ℹ Only thoracic vertebrae have costal facets. So, if you find yourself with a vertebra that lacks transverse foramina but has indentations (facets) on its body where it articulates with ribs, you've got a thoracic vertebra.

ℹ Lumbar vertebrae are easy to identify by their large, blocky shape, but they can also be identified by process of elimination. If there are no transverse foramina and no costal facets, you're left with only lumbar vertebrae. If the costal facets on your bones aren't well-defined and you're stuck between thoracic and lumbar, you can also use the giraffe/moose trick. The thoracic vertebra really does look like a giraffe and the lumbar like a "lumbering moose."

8

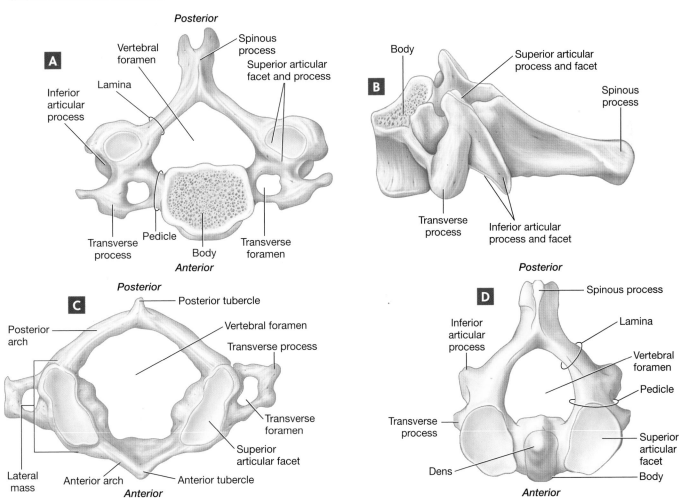

FIGURE **8.20** Cervical vertebrae: (**A**) typical cervical vertebra, superior view; (**B**) typical cervical vertebra, lateral view; (**C**) atlas (C1); (**D**) axis (C2).

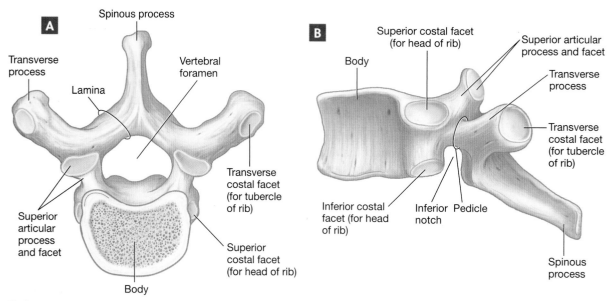

FIGURE **8.21** Thoracic vertebrae: (**A**) typical thoracic vertebra, superior view; (**B**) typical thoracic vertebra, lateral view.

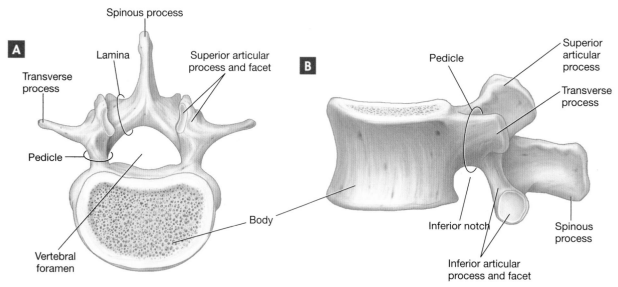

FIGURE **8.22** Lumbar vertebrae: (**A**) typical lumbar vertebra, superior view; (**B**) typical lumbar vertebra, lateral view.

2. The 12 **thoracic vertebrae** each articulate with a pair of ribs, and they share the following common features (Fig. 8.21):

   a. The spinous processes are thin and point inferiorly.

   b. They lack transverse foramina.

   c. Most have two *costal facets* that articulate with the ribs (there are 12 pairs of ribs). They also have *transverse costal facets* on their transverse processes that articulate with a part of the rib called the *tubercle*.

   d. All have approximately triangular vertebral foramina.

   e. If you look at a thoracic vertebra from the posterolateral side, it looks like a giraffe. Try it—it really does!

3. The five large **lumbar vertebrae** share the following common features (Fig. 8.22):

   a. All have a large, blocklike body.

   b. The spinous processes are thick and point posteriorly.

   c. They lack transverse foramina and costal facets.

   d. If you look at a lumbar vertebra from the posterolateral side, it looks like a moose.

4. The **sacrum** consists of five fused vertebrae (Fig. 8.23). It's a fun note that the word "sacrum" means "sacred bone," reflecting the belief that it was the residence of the soul. On the sacrum's superior surface, we find the **sacral promontory**, which is the

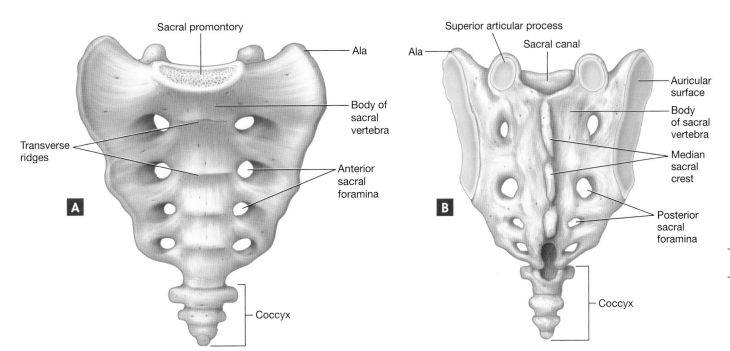

FIGURE **8.23** Sacrum: (**A**) anterior view; (**B**) posterior view

portion of the first sacral body that projects anteriorly into the pelvic cavity. Lateral to the sacral promontory are smooth regions known as the **alae** (AY-lee; *ala* = "wing"). Just posterior to the sacral promontory is the **sacral canal**, through which the inferior bundle of spinal nerve roots passes from the vertebral foramen of the fifth lumbar vertebra. You can see the fused spinous processes of the vertebrae on the sacrum's posterior side as the **median sacral crest**. Spinal nerves pass through holes called **anterior** and **posterior sacral foramina** that flank both sides of the sacral bodies. The lateral surfaces of the sacrum, known as the *auricular surfaces*, articulate with the hip bones to form the **sacroiliac joints** (say-kroh-ILL-ee-ak).

5. The **coccyx** consists of three to five (average: four) small, fused vertebrae that articulate superiorly with the sacrum.

The remainder of the axial skeleton consists of the bones of the thoracic cavity (the sternum and the ribs; Figs. 8.24 and 8.25) and the hyoid bone in the neck (Fig. 8.26). The **sternum** (*stern-* = "chest") is the central bone of the thorax. It is divided

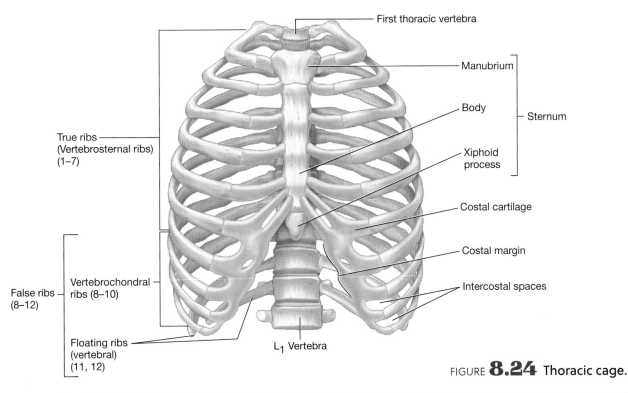

FIGURE **8.24** Thoracic cage.

into three parts: the superior **manubrium** (mah-NOO-bree-um), the middle **body**, and the inferior **xiphoid process** (ZY-foyd; *xiphos* = "sword"). It is the body of the sternum that you compress during the chest compressions of cardiopulmonary resuscitation (CPR), and the xiphoid process that you must take care not to break.

The 12 pairs of **ribs** enclose the thoracic cavity and protect its vital organs (note that men and women have the same number of ribs). The spaces between the ribs are known as **intercostal spaces** (*cost-* = "rib"), and they contain muscles, blood vessels, nerves, and lymphatic vessels. Ribs articulate anteriorly with the sternum via **costal cartilage**. They are classified according to the structure of their costal cartilage: ribs 1–7 are considered **true ribs** or **vertebrosternal ribs**, because they attach directly to the sternum by their own costal cartilage, whereas ribs 8–12 are classified as **false ribs**, because they lack this direct attachment to the sternum. However, ribs 8–10 do attach to the sternum via the cartilage of the true ribs and so they are called **vertebrochondral ribs**. Ribs 11–12 lack any attachment to the sternum, so they are often referred to as **floating ribs** or **vertebral ribs**. The medial border of the costal cartilage of the false ribs is known as the **costal margin**.

In Figure 8.25, you can see the rib's **superior** and **inferior facets** on the rib's posterior **head**. Here the rib straddles two thoracic vertebral bodies—the superior facet of the rib articulates with the inferior costal facet of the vertebra above, and the inferior facet of the rib articulates with the superior costal facet of the rib below. Lateral to the head, we find the **neck**, which contains a **tubercle** that articulates with a vertebra's transverse process. The rib curves around anteriorly at its **angle**, after which the main anterior portion becomes known as the **shaft**. On the shaft's interior surface is the **costal groove**, which is where blood vessels and nerves travel.

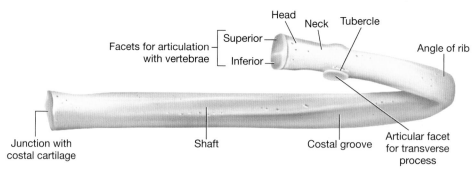

FIGURE **8.25** A rib, posterior view.

The **hyoid bone** (hy-OYD), shown in Figure 8.26, is located in the superior neck, where it is occasionally classified as a skull bone. Note, however, that it does not articulate with any skull bone, or any other bone, for that matter. It is held in place in the superior neck by muscles and ligaments, and it helps to form part of the framework for the larynx (LEHR-inks; voice box). It also serves as an attachment site for the muscles of the tongue and aids in swallowing. When a person is choked manually, the hyoid bone is often broken.

The bones and bone markings of the axial skeleton are listed with Exercise 8-3 (p. 209), where they will be included with another cooperative learning exercise.

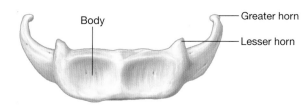

FIGURE **8.26** Hyoid bone.

EXERCISE
8-3

MATERIALS

☐ Bones, disarticulated
☐ Skeleton, articulated
☐ Pelvises, male and female

Anatomy of the Appendicular Skeleton

The bones of the appendicular skeleton can be divided into those of the pectoral girdle, the upper limb, the pelvic girdle, and the lower limb. Let's look at each individually.

Pectoral Girdle

The **pectoral girdle** (pek-TOHR-uhl; *pect-* = chest) consists of the two bones that frame the shoulder: the scapula and the clavicle (Fig. 8.27). The **scapula** (SKAP-yoo-luh; *scapul-* = "shoulder"), shown in Figure 8.28, is a roughly triangular-shaped bone with **superior, lateral,** and **medial borders**. The corners of the "triangle" are known as the **superior, lateral,** and **inferior angles**. The scapula's broad, flat surface is the **body**. On the anterior surface (Fig. 8.28A), the body has a broad indentation called the **subscapular fossa** (*sub-* = "below"). On its lateral surface (Fig. 8.28B) is a shallow depression called the **glenoid cavity** (*glen-* = "socket") that forms the shoulder joint with the humerus. From this side, you can also get a good view of its two superior projections: the anterior **coracoid process** (KOHR-ah-koyd) and the posterior **acromion** (ah-KROH-mee-ahn; *acrom-* = "highest"). The acromion joins with the lateral portion of the clavicle to form the **acromioclavicular** (ah-KROH-mee-oh-klah-VIK-yoo-lur; **AC**) joint. When we turn to the scapula's posterior surface (Fig. 8.28C), we find a prominent ridge called the **spine** (you can feel this under your skin as your "shoulder blade"). Superior and inferior to the scapular spine are two depressions: the **supraspinous** and **infraspinous fossae**.

The **clavicle** is a small S-shaped bone that spans between the acromion of the scapula at its lateral **acromial end** and the manubrium of the sternum at its medial **sternal end**. Note its "S" shape is best appreciated from the superior view shown in Figure 8.29, as the clavicle appears nearly straight from an anterior view. Functionally, the clavicle acts somewhat like a brace, holding the upper limb in place away from the body.

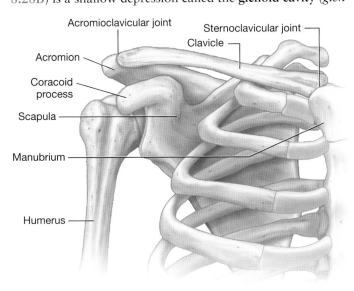

FIGURE **8.27** Pectoral girdle.

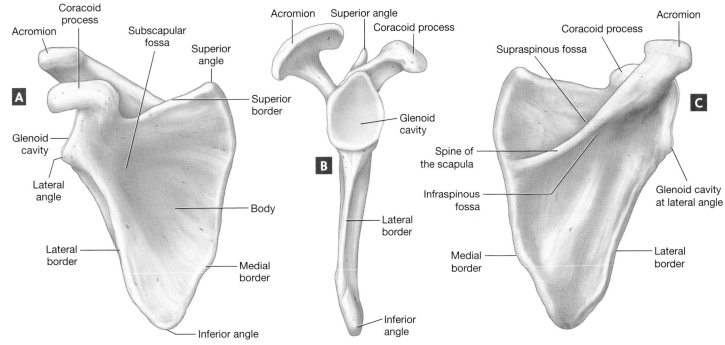

FIGURE **8.28** Right scapula: (**A**) anterior view; (**B**) lateral view; (**C**) posterior view.

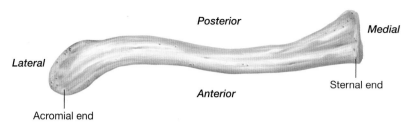

Posterior

Medial

Lateral

Sternal end

Anterior

Acromial end

FIGURE **8.29** Clavicle, superior view.

Upper Limb

The **upper limb** consists of the arm, the forearm, the wrist, and the hand. The only bone within the arm is the **humerus** (HYOO-mur-uhs; *humerus* = "upper arm"), a long bone that forms the shoulder joint with the scapula at its proximal end and the elbow joint with the ulna and radius at its distal end. The humerus has a number of features, including the following (Fig. 8.30):

- At its proximal end is a rounded **head** that fits into the glenoid cavity. Just lateral to the head is the **greater tubercle**, separated from the smaller **lesser tubercle** by the **intertubercular sulcus** (in-ter-too-BUR-kyoo-lur SUL-kuhs).

- The diaphysis of the humerus features a projection called the **deltoid tuberosity**, where the deltoid muscle attaches. On the posterior diaphysis we find another feature—the **radial groove**—which is an indentation along which the radial nerve travels.

- At the humerus' distal end, we find two small projections called the **medial** and **lateral epicondyles**. Distal to these are two larger condyles: the medial **trochlea** (TROH-klee-uh), which is shaped like a spool of thread, and the lateral **capitulum** (kah-PIT-yoo-lum; *capit-* = "head"), which is ball-shaped. Just proximal to the trochlea are indentations in the humerus where the ulna and radius articulate—the anterior **coronoid** and **radial fossae** and the posterior **olecranon fossa** (oh-LEK-ruh-nahn; *olec-* = "elbow").

The two forearm bones, shown in Figure 8.31, are the lateral **radius** (RAY-dee-uhs) and medial **ulna** (*ulna* = "elbow;" if you have a hard time remembering which is which, stand in anatomical position and take your radial pulse; the pulse is on the lateral side of the forearm, just like the radius). The ulna is wide proximally where it articulates with the humerus and thin

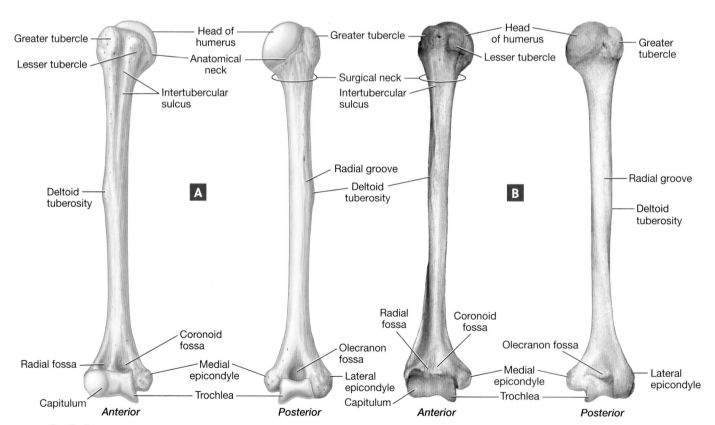

FIGURE **8.30** Right humerus: (**A**) illustration, anterior and posterior views; (**B**) photograph, anterior and posterior views.

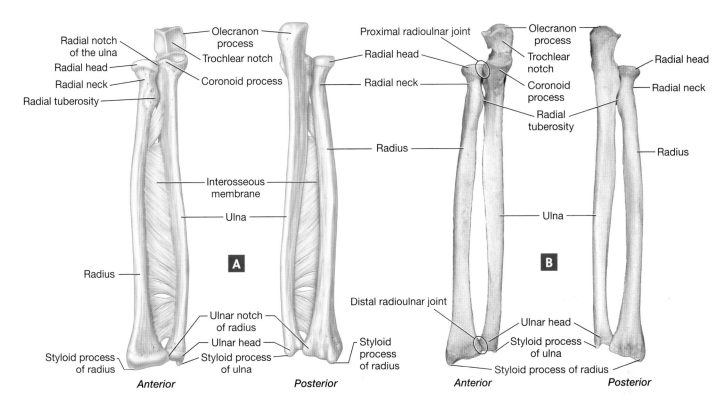

FIGURE **8.31** Right radius and ulna: (**A**) illustration, anterior and posterior views; (**B**) photograph, anterior and posterior views.

distally where it articulates with the bones of the wrist. Its proximal end has two processes—the large, posterior **olecranon process** and the smaller, anterior **coronoid process**—separated by a deep curve called the **trochlear notch**.

As its name implies, the trochlear notch fits around the trochlea of the humerus to form the elbow joint. The olecranon process is the actual "elbow bone," which you can feel on your posterior arm. The trochlear notch and the ulna's two processes form a "U" shape when the ulna is held on its side. This makes the ulna easy to differentiate from the radius (think "U" for "ulna").

The distal end of the ulna is known as the **ulnar head.** It articulates with one of the wrist (or *carpal*) bones that is known as the *lunate.* On its medial side, it has a small projection called the **styloid process** that is palpable through the skin.

The shape of the radius is opposite to that of the ulna: It is skinny proximally and wide distally. Proximally, it consists of a round, flattened **radial head** that articulates with the capitulum of the humerus to help form the elbow joint. Distal to the radial head, we find the **radial neck** and a projection called the **radial tuberosity**. At its most distal end, the radius articulates with several carpal bones. It also features a lateral **styloid process**, just as we found on the ulna.

Notice in Figure 8.31 that the radius and ulna also articulate with one another. On the ulna, just distal to the coronoid process, we find the **radial notch**, which is where the radius and ulna articulate at the **proximal radioulnar joint**. At the distal end of the radius is an indentation called the **ulnar notch** where the ulna fits into the radius. This joint is known as at the **distal radioulnar joint**. These joints are stabilized by the *interosseous membrane*, a band of dense regular collagenous connective tissue that joins the radius and ulna along their length.

The wrist is composed of eight short bones called **carpals** (KAR-pulz; *carp-* = "wrist"), which are arranged into two rows. The proximal row, from medial to lateral, consists of the *triquetrum, pisiform, lunate,* and *scaphoid* bones. The distal row, from medial to lateral, includes the *hamate, capitate, trapezoid,* and *trapezium* bones (Fig. 8.32; remember that the thumb is lateral because we are in anatomical position). The carpals articulate proximally with the radius and the ulna, and distally with the five long bones in the hand called the **metacarpals**. The metacarpals articulate distally with the fingers, which are formed from 14 long bones called **phalanges** (fuh-LAN-jeez). The second through fifth digits have three phalanges each (the *proximal, intermediate* [or *middle*], and *distal phalanges*); the thumb has only two (a *proximal* and a *distal phalanx*).

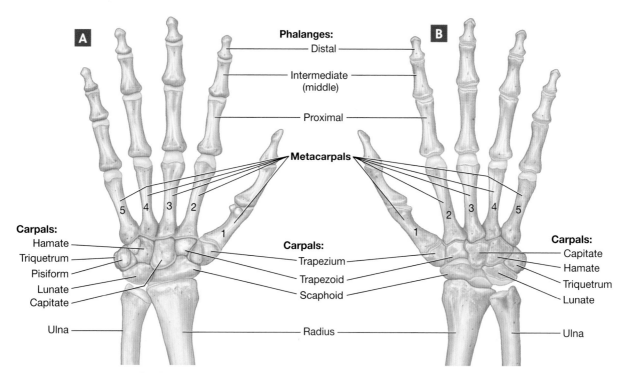

FIGURE **8.32** Right wrist and hand: (**A**) anterior view; (**B**) posterior view.

Pelvic Girdle

The **pelvis** (*pelvis* = "basin" or "bucket") connects the lower limbs to the trunk, supports the pelvic organs, and transmits the weight of the trunk to the legs. It is formed by the **pelvic girdle**, which itself is composed of two **coxal bones** (*cox-* = "hip;" Fig. 8.33), the sacrum and the coccyx. The coxal bones meet the sacrum at the two sacroiliac joints. The opening into the pelvis is known as the **pelvic inlet;** the ridge around the inlet is the **pelvic brim.** The pelvic inlet and brim separate what is known as the **greater pelvis** (colored green in the figure), which sits superior to the pelvic inlet, from the **lesser pelvis** (colored yellow in the figure), which sits inferior to it. As you can see in Figure 8.33B, we find the **pelvic outlet** at the inferior edge of the lesser pelvis.

Each coxal bone is also known as a **hemipelvis** (*hemi-* = "half"). Three fused bones—the ilium, the ischium, and the pubis—make up each coxal bone (Fig. 8.34). You can see in the lateral view the place where all three bones come together to form a deep socket. This socket, called the **acetabulum** (ă-seh-TAB-yoo-lum), forms the hip joint with the femur. Notice also that where the ischium and pubis meet there is a large hole called the **obturator foramen** (AHB-too-ray-tur). In a living person, this hole is covered with a membrane and allows only small blood vessels and nerves to pass through.

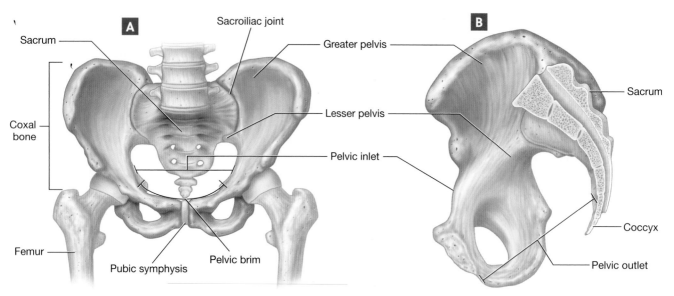

FIGURE **8.33** Pelvis: (**A**) anterior view; (**B**) midsagittal section.

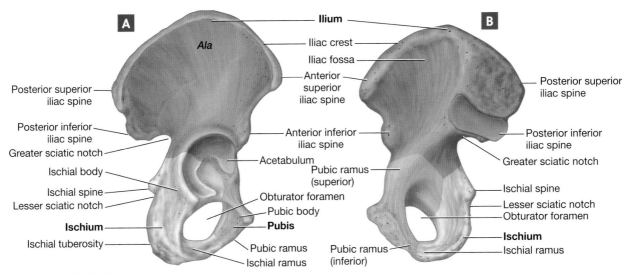

FIGURE **8.34** Hemipelvis: (**A**) right coxal bone, lateral view; (**B**) right coxal bone, medial view.

Let's look more closely at the three bones of the pelvic girdle and their features.

1. **Ilium.** The **ilium** (ILL-ee-um; *ilia-* = "flank") is the largest of the three bones. Its main portion is called the **body**, and its superior "wing" is called the **ala** (AY-luh). The medial side of the ala is concave; this indentation is called the **iliac fossa**. The ridge of the ala, called the **iliac crest**, is where you rest your hands when your hands are on your hips. At the anterior end of the crest, we find a projection called the **anterior superior iliac spine,** and, inferior to it, the smaller **anterior inferior iliac spine.** A similar but smaller **posterior superior iliac spine** is located posteriorly, with a corresponding **posterior inferior iliac spine.** The posterior ilium also features a notch called the **greater sciatic notch** (sy-Ă-tik; *sciat-* = "hip joint"), which allows the greater sciatic nerve to pass from the pelvis to the thigh.

2. **Ischium.** The **ischium** (ISS-kee-um; *ischi-* = "hip joint") makes up the posteroinferior pelvis. It contains three features on its posterior side: the superior **ischial spine**, the middle **lesser sciatic notch**, and the thick, inferior **ischial tuberosity.** The ischial tuberosities are the "butt bones": the bones that bear your weight when you sit down. On the ischium's anterior side, we find the **ischial ramus**, which articulates with the pubis.

3. **Pubis.** The anterior portion of the pelvis is formed by the **pubis** (PYOO-bis; *pub-* = "groin") or the **pubic bone.** The pubis consists of a **body** and two extensions called the **superior** and **inferior rami.** The bodies of the two pubic bones meet at a fibrocartilage pad called the **pubic symphysis** (SIM-fih-sis; *sym-* = "together;" *-physis* = "growth;" see Fig. 8.33). The angle that these bones form when they meet, called the **pubic arch,** can help to determine the sex of a skeleton (see the "Hints and Tips" box).

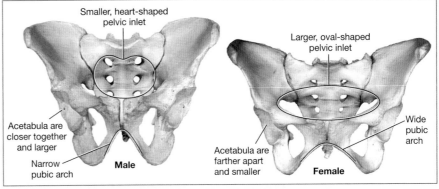

HINTS & TIPS

How to Determine Sex Based upon Pelvic Features

A skeleton's sex can be determined based upon the differences between the male and female pelvises. In general, the male and female pelvis can be distinguished by the features listed below and shown in the photos here:

Feature	Male Pelvis	Female Pelvis
Pelvic inlet shape	Narrower and heart-shaped	Wider and oval-shaped
Pubic arch	Narrow angle	Wide angle
Acetabulae	Closer together	Farther apart
Ischial tuberosities	Inverted	Everted
Coccyx	Curved anteriorly, less movable	Straighter, more movable

Pelvic bones, male and female

Lower Limb

The lower limb consists of the thigh, the **patella** or kneecap (puh-TEL-uh; "little plate"), the leg, the ankle, and the foot. The thigh contains only a single bone—the large, heavy **femur** (Fig. 8.35). Proximally, the femur articulates with the acetabulum at its rounded **head**. In the center of the femoral head, we find a pit called the **fovea capitis** (FOH-vee-uh CAP-ih-tiss). This is the point of attachment for a ligament that holds the femur in the acetabulum. Just distal to the femoral head is the **neck** of the femur, the weakest part of the femur and the most common location for it to fracture (note that when the femoral neck fractures, it is usually called a "broken hip," even though the hip itself doesn't fracture). Where the femoral neck meets the femoral shaft, we find two large prominences: the anterolateral **greater trochanter** (TROH-kan-tur) and the posteromedial **lesser trochanter**. Between the two trochanters on the anterior side is a ridge called the **intertrochanteric line** (in-ter-troh-kan-TEHR-ik), and on the posterior side is another ridge in the same location known as the **intertrochanteric crest**.

The femoral diaphysis is mostly smooth, save for a few features that mark the attachment points for specific muscles on the posterior side:

- The proximal **gluteal tuberosity** (GLOO-tee-uhl; *glut-* = "buttocks") is a rough projection that serves as the attachment spot for one of the gluteal muscles (the gluteus maximus muscle).
- The **linea aspera** (LIN-ee-ah ASS-per-ah) is a prominent line that runs along the femoral diaphysis. It serves as an attachment point for many muscles that move the femur.
- Near the femoral epiphysis, the linea aspera splits into the **medial** and **lateral supracondylar lines** (soo-prah-KAHN-duh-lar), where hamstring muscles attach to the femur.

Distally, the femur expands into two small projections, the **medial** and **lateral epicondyles** (ep-ih-KAHN-dyl'z), distal to which we find the large **medial** and **lateral condyles**, which form the knee joint with the largest bone of the leg—the tibia. On the posterior side of the femur is a depression between the two condyles, the **intercondylar fossa**.

The **tibia** (TIB-ee-uh) is the medial and larger of the two leg bones (Fig. 8.36). It is flattened proximally at its articular surface, the **tibial plateau**, where its **medial** and **lateral condyles** fit together with those of the femur. Between the medial and lateral condyles is a ridge called the *intercondylar eminence*. Just distal to the condyles on the tibia's anterior surface is a rough projection called the **tibial tuberosity**, which is where the patellar ligament inserts. Along the anterior tibial diaphysis is a sharpened ridge known as the **anterior crest**, which is commonly known as the "shin." At the tibia's distal epiphysis, it articulates with a tarsal bone called the *talus*, with which it forms the ankle joint. At its terminal end is a projection called the **medial malleolus** (mal-ee-OH-luhs), which you may think of as your "medial ankle bone."

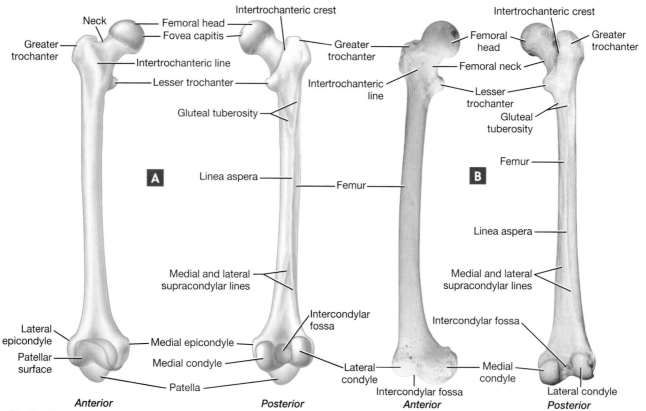

FIGURE **8.35** Right femur: (**A**) illustration, anterior and posterior views; (**B**) photograph, anterior and posterior views.

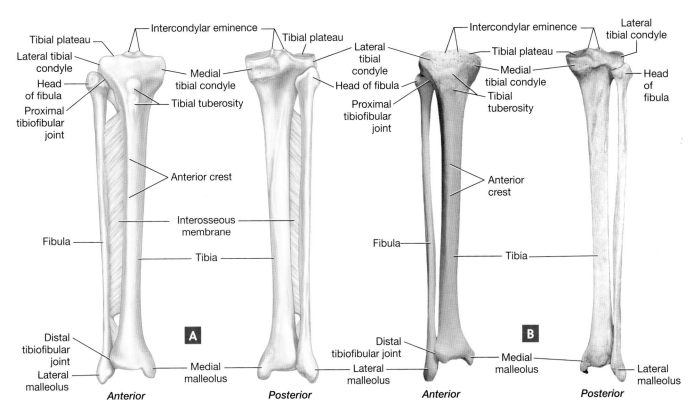

FIGURE **8.36** Right tibia and fibula: (**A**) illustration, anterior and posterior views; (**B**) photograph, anterior and posterior views.posterior views.

The other leg bone is the thin, lateral **fibula** (FIB-yoo-luh). The proximal fibular end is called the **head**, and its distal end is the **lateral malleolus** (which you may think of as your "lateral ankle bone"). The head has no articulation with the femur, but the lateral malleolus articulates with the talus to help form the ankle joint.

Notice in Figure 8.36 that the tibia and fibula articulate with one another just as the radius and ulna do. At the proximal end, we find the **proximal tibiofibular joint**, and, at the distal end, we find the **distal tibiofibular joint**. The two bones are also held together by a stabilizing interosseous membrane.

The ankle is composed of seven short bones called **tarsals** (TAHR-sulz; *tars-* = "ankle;" Fig. 8.37). The largest tarsal bone is the **calcaneus** (kal-KAYN-ee-uhs; *calcan-* = "heel"), or the heel bone. Resting on top of the calcaneus is the **talus** (TAY-luhs), which forms the ankle joint with the tibia and fibula. Distally, the talus articulates with a ship-shaped bone called the *navicular*. The remaining tarsals are, from medial to lateral, the *medial cuneiform*, *intermediate cuneiform*, *lateral cuneiform*, and *cuboid* bones. The tarsals articulate distally with the five long bones in the foot called **metatarsals** (met-uh-TAHR-sulz). Notice in

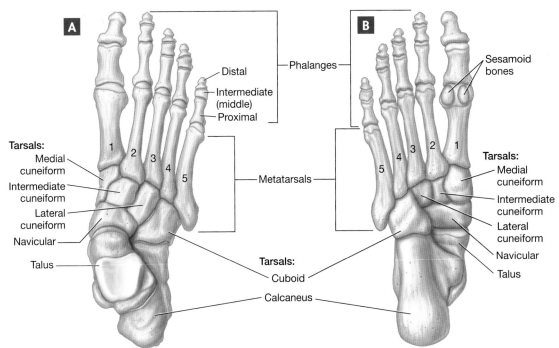

FIGURE **8.37** Right foot and ankle: (**A**) superior view; (**B**) inferior view.

Figure 8.37B that there are two small *sesamoid bones* at the head of the first metatarsal—these bones are found in a tendon located here. Like the bones of the fingers, the bones of the toes also consist of 14 **phalanges**. The second through fifth digits have three phalanges each (the *proximal, intermediate* [or *middle*], and *distal phalanges*); and the big toe or *hallux* has only two (a *proximal* and a *distal phalanx*).

1 PROCEDURE

Cooperative Learning for the Axial and Appendicular Skeletons

We will follow essentially the same procedure here as we did in Exercise 8-1, but with different groups of bones and bone markings. Note that this cooperative learning exercise includes the structures from Exercises 8-2 and 8-3. When you have completed this activity, answer Check Your Understanding Questions 4 through 6 (p. 232).

1 Assemble into teams with a minimum of four students; five is optimum.

2 Distribute a bone or set of bones to each member of the team, and assign each student one of the following five groups of bones and bone markings (the specific structures of each bone are listed on this page and page 217:

Group A: Cervical, thoracic, and lumbar vertebrae and vertebral markings; ribs and rib markings; sternum structures; the hyoid bone.

Group B: Scapula structures; clavicle structures; humerus structures.

Group C: Radius and ulna markings; carpals, metacarpals, and phalanges.

Group D: Ilium, ischium, and pubis structures; the difference between the male and female pelvises.

Group E: Femur, tibia, and fibula structures; tarsals, metatarsals, and phalanges.

3 Spend approximately 3 minutes learning the assigned structures on your own.

4 Spend about 1 to 2 minutes teaching your assigned structures to your team. Then have each team member spend approximately 1 to 2 minutes teaching the team his or her assigned structures.

5 Rotate the assigned structures clockwise so each member has a new set of structures to learn and teach (the student that was assigned Group A will take Group B, and so on).

6 Repeat Steps 3 and 4, and then rotate assigned structures again. Continue this process (it begins to speed up significantly at this point) until each team member has taught each group of structures once.

The following is a list of bone and bone markings of the axial and appendicular skeletons covered in this exercise.

Remaining Structures of the Axial Skeleton

Group A Structures

1. Vertebral column
   a. Intervertebral foramina
   b. Cervical curvature
   c. Lumbar curvature
   d. Thoracic curvature
   e. Sacral curvature
2. Vertebrae
   a. Spinous process
   b. Transverse processes
   c. Vertebral foramen
   d. Vertebral body
   e. Intervertebral disc
   f. Pedicle
   g. Lamina

3. Cervical vertebrae
   a. Transverse foramina
   b. Atlas
   c. Axis
   d. Dens
4. Thoracic vertebrae
   a. Costal (articular) facets
5. Lumbar vertebrae
6. Sacrum
   a. Sacral promontory
   b. Sacral canal
   c. Anterior sacral foramina
   d. Posterior sacral foramina
7. Coccyx

8. Sternum
   a. Manubrium
   b. Body
   c. Xiphoid process
9. Ribs
   a. Intercostal spaces
   b. Costal cartilage
   c. True (vertebrosternal) ribs
   d. False ribs
      (1) Vertebrochondral ribs
      (2) Floating ribs (vertebral ribs)
   e. Costal margin
   f. Head of rib
   g. Neck of rib
   h. Shaft of rib
10. Hyoid bone

Pectoral Girdle and Upper Limb

Group B Structures

1. Scapula
   a. Superior, lateral, and medial borders
   b. Superior, lateral, and inferior angles
   c. Subscapular fossa
   d. Glenoid cavity
   e. Coracoid process
   f. Acromion
   g. Spine
   h. Supraspinous fossa
   i. Infraspinous fossa
2. Clavicle
3. Humerus
   a. Head
   b. Greater tubercle
   c. Lesser tubercle
   d. Intertubercular sulcus
   e. Deltoid tuberosity
   f. Trochlea
   g. Capitulum
   h. Coronoid fossa
   i. Radial fossa
   j. Olecranon fossa

Group C Structures

1. Ulna
   a. Olecranon process
   b. Coronoid process
   c. Trochlear notch
   d. Ulnar head
   e. Styloid process
2. Radius
   a. Radial head
   b. Radial neck
   c. Radial tuberosity
   d. Styloid process
3. Carpals
   a. Triquetrum
   b. Pisiform
   c. Lunate
   d. Scaphoid
   e. Trapezium
   f. Trapezoid
   g. Capitate
   h. Hamate
4. Metacarpals
5. Phalanges

Pelvic Girdle and Lower Limb

Group D Structures

1. Pelvis
   a. Sacroiliac joints
   b. Pelvic inlet
   c. Pelvic brim
   d. Greater pelvis
   e. Lesser pelvis
   f. Pelvic outlet
2. Coxal bone (hemipelvis)
3. Acetabulum
4. Obturator foramen
5. Ilium
   a. Ala
   b. Iliac crest
   c. Anterior superior iliac spine
   d. Anterior inferior iliac spine
   e. Posterior superior iliac spine
   f. Greater sciatic notch
6. Ischium
   a. Ischial spine
   b. Lesser sciatic notch
   c. Ischial tuberosity
7. Pubis
   a. Body
   b. Superior and inferior rami
   c. Pubic symphysis
   d. Pubic arch
8. Male and female pelvises

Group E Structures

1. Femur
   a. Head
   b. Fovea capitis
   c. Neck
   d. Greater and lesser trochanters
   e. Intertrochanteric line and crest
   f. Gluteal tuberosity
   g. Linea aspera
   h. Medial and lateral condyles
   i. Intercondylar fossa
2. Patella
3. Tibia
   a. Tibial plateau
   b. Tibial tuberosity
   c. Anterior crest
   d. Medial malleolus
4. Fibula
   a. Head
   b. Lateral malleolus
5. Tarsals
   a. Calcaneus
   b. Talus
   c. Navicular
   d. Cuneiforms
   e. Cuboid
6. Metatarsals
7. Phalanges

Your instructor may wish to omit certain structures included in these lists or add structures not included in the lists. List any additional structures in the space provided:

8

EXERCISE 8-4

MATERIALS

❑ Bones in a box, disarticulated
❑ Skeleton, articulated
❑ Colored pencils

More Practice

On average, the human body contains 206 bones and thousands of bone markings, processes, fossae, and foraminae. The previous cooperative learning exercises gave you a solid foundation on which to build your knowledge of the skeleton—but a good foundation is just a start. A lot more work is needed to actually build a house on that foundation. This exercise contains activities to help you build that "house" and practice what you learned in Exercises 8-1 through 8-3.

1 PROCEDURE

Building a Skeleton

1 Obtain a set of disarticulated bones (real bones are best).

2 Assemble the bones into a full skeleton. (If you have an articulated vertebral column and rib cage, go ahead and use them.)

3 Be certain to keep your skeleton in anatomical position. Figure 8.38 gives an overall "big picture" view of the skeleton that you may use for reference.

4 Assemble the bones into a full skeleton.

2 PROCEDURE

Identifying Bones from Touch

Work with a lab partner to try to identify bones based only on feeling their shapes and bone markings.

1 Obtain a set of disarticulated bones and place them in a box.

2 Close your eyes, reach into the box, and grab a bone randomly. Attempt to identify it only by its feel.

3 If necessary, have your lab partner give you hints to help you determine the bone's identity.

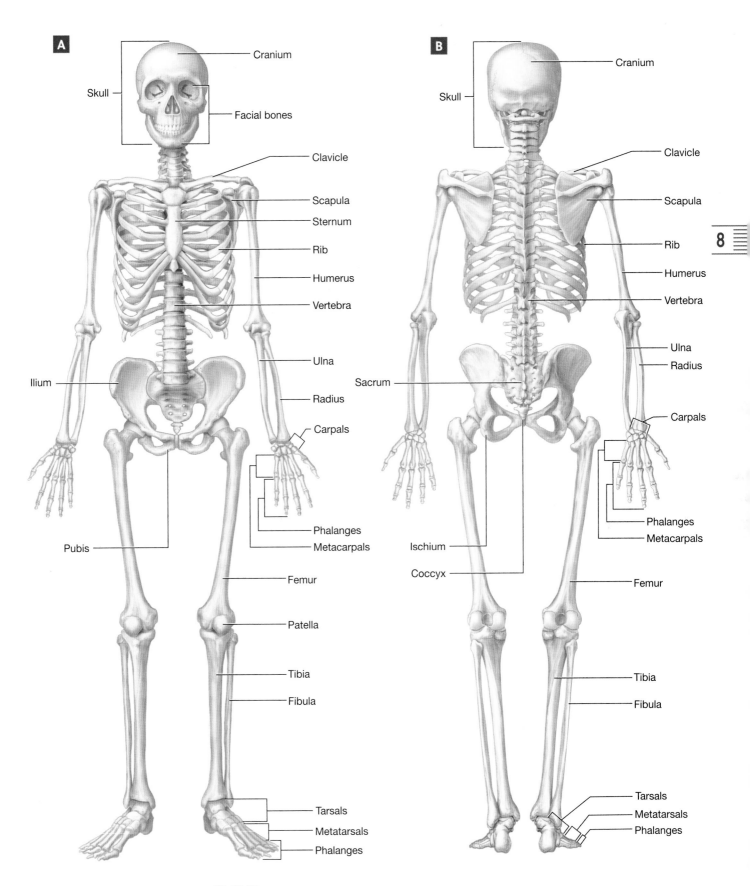

FIGURE **8.38** Skeleton: (**A**) anterior view; (**B**) posterior view.

PROCEDURE

Comparing Bones on the Right and Left Sides

Examine the following bones, and figure out how you can determine whether the bones are from the left or the right side of the body.

Femur: _____

_____

_____

_____

_____

Tibia: _____

_____

_____

_____

_____

Humerus: _____

_____

_____

_____

_____

Scapula: _____

_____

_____

_____

_____

PROCEDURE

Time to Draw

Remember from your previous drawing exercises that drawing even the crudest picture of an anatomical structure or physiological pathway engages multiple parts of the brain and greatly enhances memory. So, with that in mind: (1) draw a skull and a skeleton in the spaces provided; and (2) label and color your drawings.

These drawings are not meant to be works of art, so don't worry if you aren't even remotely skilled as an artist (however, if they turn out well, feel free to take them out of your lab book and put them on your refrigerator).

1 Skull: anterior view

2 Skull: lateral view

3 Skeleton: anterior view

8

Check Your Recall

1 Label the following bones in Figure 8.39.

❏ Carpals
❏ Clavicle
❏ Femur
❏ Fibula
❏ Humerus
❏ Ilium
❏ Metatarsals
❏ Mandible
❏ Radius
❏ Sacrum
❏ Tibia
❏ Ulna

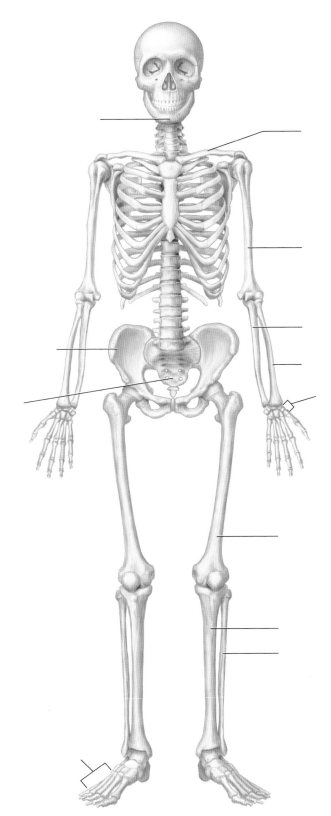

FIGURE **8.39** Anterior view of the skeleton.

2 Label the bones and markings of the skull in Figure 8.40.

- ❑ Coronal suture
- ❑ Cribriform plate
- ❑ Inferior nasal concha
- ❑ Lacrimal bone
- ❑ Occipital bone
- ❑ Palatine bone
- ❑ Parietal bone
- ❑ Perpendicular plate of ethmoid bone
- ❑ Pterygoid process
- ❑ Sella turcica
- ❑ Squamous suture
- ❑ Styloid process
- ❑ Temporomandibular joint
- ❑ Vomer
- ❑ Zygomatic bone

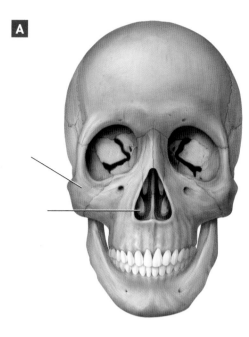

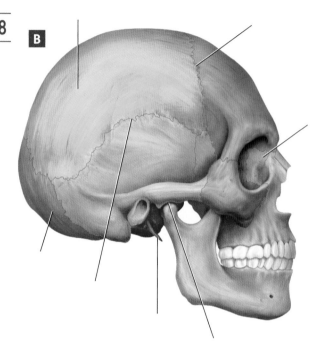

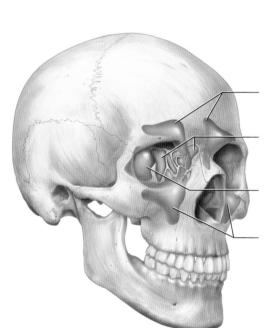

FIGURE **8.40** Skull: (**A**) anterior view; (**B**) lateral view; (**C**) midsagittal section.

3 Label the paranasal sinuses in Figure 8.41.

- ❑ Ethmoid sinuses
- ❑ Frontal sinuses
- ❑ Maxillary sinuses
- ❑ Sphenoid sinus

FIGURE **8.41** Paranasal sinuses.

8

4 Label the following parts of the vertebra and vertebral column in Figure 8.42.

❏ Atlas
❏ Axis
❏ Cervical curvature
❏ Coccyx
❏ Lamina
❏ Lumbar curvature
❏ Pedicle
❏ Spinous process
❏ Superior articular process (and facet)
❏ Thoracic vertebrae
❏ Transverse foramen
❏ Vertebral body
❏ Vertebral foramen

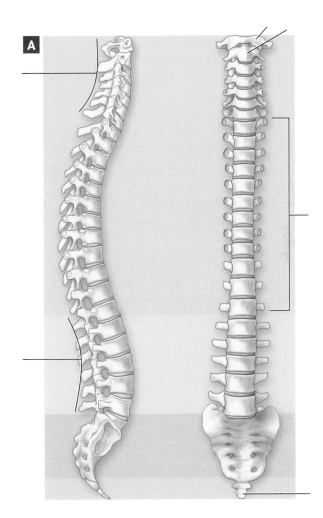

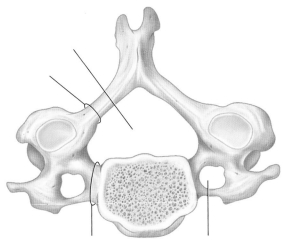

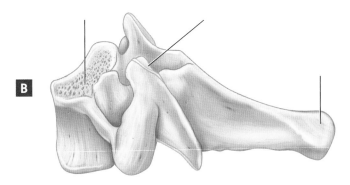

FIGURE **8.42** Vertebrae: (**A**) vertebral column; (**B**) a typical vertebra, superior and lateral views.

5 Label the following parts of the axial skeleton in Figure 8.43.

❑ Body of sternum
❑ Costal cartilage
❑ False ribs
❑ Floating ribs
❑ Manubrium
❑ True ribs
❑ Xiphoid process

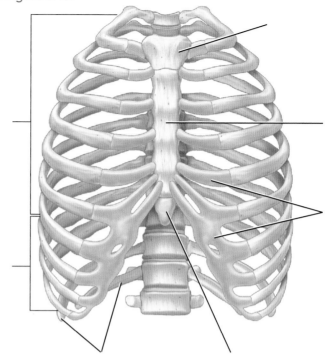

FIGURE **8.43** Thoracic cage.

6 Identify each of the following vertebrae in Figure 8.44 as being cervical, thoracic, lumbar, cervical-axis, or cervical-atlas. Additionally, explain how you arrived at this conclusion.

a _____

_____

_____

b _____

_____

c _____

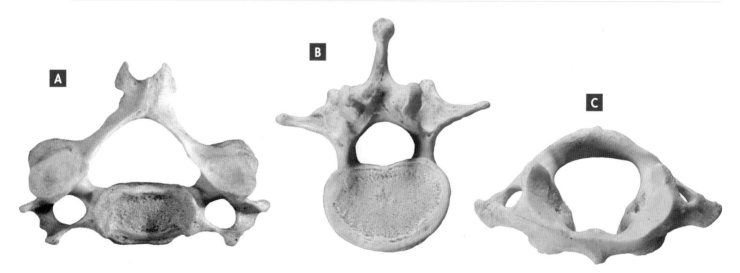

FIGURE **8.44** Vertebrae for identification: (**A**) Unknown Vertebra 1; (**B**) Unknown Vertebra 2; (**C**) Unknown Vertebra 3.

7 Label the following parts of the scapula in Figure 8.45.

❏ Acromion ❏ Inferior angle ❏ Spine of the scapula ❏ Supraspinous fossa
❏ Coracoid process ❏ Infraspinous fossa ❏ Subscapular fossa
❏ Glenoid cavity ❏ Medial border ❏ Superior angle

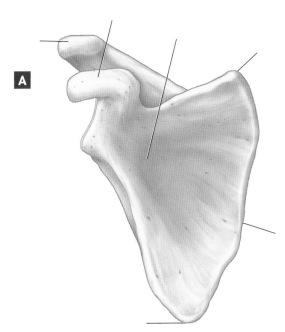
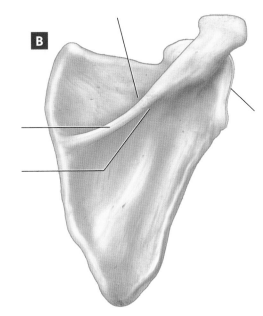

FIGURE **8.45** Scapula: (**A**) anterior view; (**B**) posterior view.

8 Label the following parts of the coxal bone (hemipelvis) in Figure 8.46.

❏ Acetabulum
❏ Ala
❏ Anterior superior iliac spine
❏ Greater sciatic notch
❏ Iliac crest
❏ Ischial ramus
❏ Ischial tuberosity
❏ Lesser sciatic notch
❏ Obturator foramen
❏ Posterior inferior iliac spine
❏ Pubic ramus

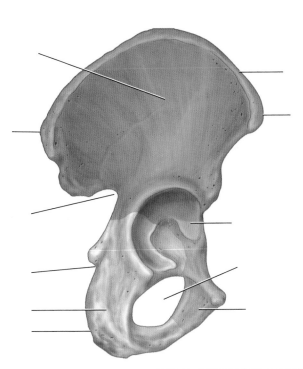

FIGURE **8.46** Right coxal bone, lateral view.

9 Label the following parts of the upper limb in Figure 8.47.

- ❏ Coronoid fossa
- ❏ Coronoid process
- ❏ Deltoid tuberosity
- ❏ Greater tubercle

- ❏ Humeral head
- ❏ Lesser tubercle
- ❏ Olecranon
- ❏ Olecranon fossa

- ❏ Radial neck
- ❏ Trochlea
- ❏ Trochlear notch
- ❏ Ulnar head

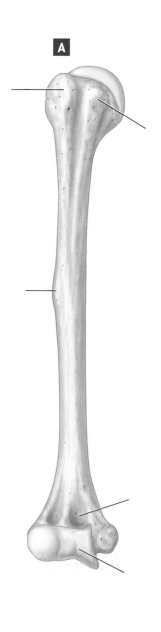

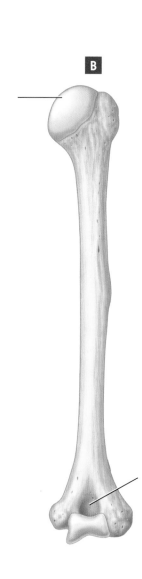

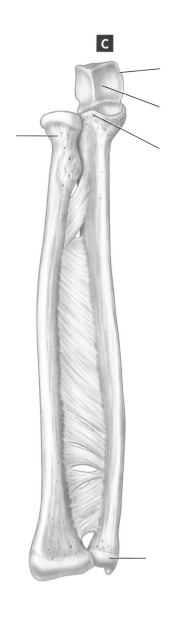

FIGURE **8.47** Upper limb: (**A**) arm, anterior view; (**B**) arm, posterior view; (**C**) forearm, anterior view.

10 Label the following parts of the lower limb in Figure 8.48.

- ❏ Calcaneus
- ❏ Femoral head
- ❏ Femoral neck
- ❏ Greater trochanter
- ❏ Intercondylar fossa
- ❏ Intertrochanteric crest
- ❏ Lateral malleolus
- ❏ Lesser trochanter
- ❏ Linea aspera
- ❏ Medial malleolus
- ❏ Phalanges
- ❏ Talus
- ❏ Tibial plateau
- ❏ Tibial tuberosity

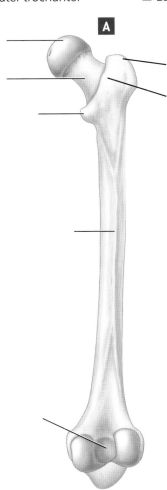

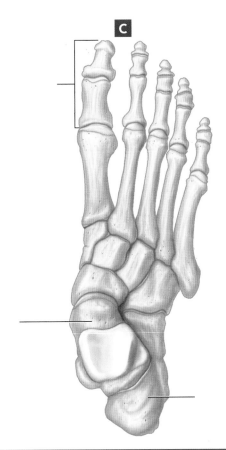

FIGURE **8.48** Lower limb: (**A**) thigh, posterior view; (**B**) leg, anterior view; (**C**) right foot, superior view.

Name _____

Section _____ Date_____

Check Your Understanding

Critical Thinking and Application Questions

1 A persistent urban legend states that hitting someone in the nose will "break off the nose bones" and cause the bones to enter the person's brain.

   a What are the actual "nose bones"? Given their anatomy, is it likely they could enter the brain if a person were struck in the nose?

   b A different version of the urban legend states that the bone forming the roof of the nasal cavity can enter the brain if struck. Although this is untrue, this bone may crack due to head trauma. What is this bone on the roof of the nasal cavity? Why might a crack in it cause problems in the cranial cavity?

2 The disease *osteopetrosis*, characterized by defective osteoclasts, can result in the growth of bone in such a way that it narrows canals and other openings in a bone. Why might this particularly cause problems in the skull?

3 Ava was in an auto accident during which she received a fracture of the cribriform plate. Five days after the injury, she reports back to her doctor with a stiff neck, a "blinding" headache, and a high fever. She is diagnosed with *bacterial meningitis*, a bacterial infection of the membranes around her brain. How does her cribriform plate fracture explain her meningitis diagnosis?

4 Julian was injured when he slipped on ice and fell. In the emergency department of the hospital, he reports that the right side of his chest hurts, especially when he breathes. What has likely happened? Why does it hurt when he breathes?

5 Julian also complains of right arm pain and an inability to move his elbow. An x-ray reveals that the elbow has been dislocated. What bones and bone structures, specifically, have dislocated from each other in this injury?

6 Jamie presents with foot pain after being stepped on by her pet cow, who weighs 1,500 pounds (Fig. 8.49).

   a Identify the bones in the x-ray.

   b Examine the x-ray and determine what is likely causing her pain.

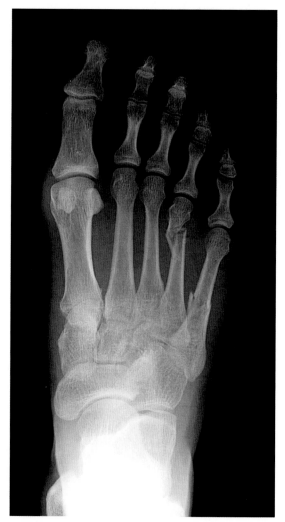

FIGURE **8.49** X-ray of the foot.

Lab Practical Practice Quiz 1

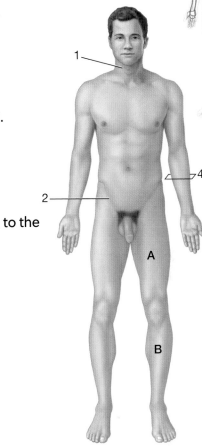

1 Number 1 is on the _____ region of Figure Q.1.1.
   a. inguinal
   b. axillary
   c. popliteal
   d. cervical

2 Number 2 is on the _____ region of Figure Q.1.1.
   a. gluteal
   b. tarsal
   c. inguinal
   d. femoral

3 The structure marked A on Figure Q.1.1 is _____ to the structure marked B.
   a. proximal
   b. superior
   c. medial
   d. distal
   e. inferior

4 The structure marked number 4 on Figure Q.1.1 is sectioned along

the _____ plane.
   a. midsagittal
   b. parasagittal
   c. frontal
   d. transverse

FIGURE **Q.1.1** Anterior view of the human body for Questions 1–4.

5 The cavity marked number 5 on Figure Q.1.2 is the _____ cavity.
   a. cranial
   b. pericardial
   c. pelvic
   d. vertebral

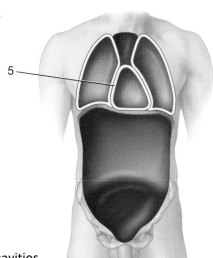

FIGURE **Q.1.2** The body cavities for Question 5.

6 The structure marked number 6 in Figure Q.1.3 is the
   a. nucleus.
   b. centriole.
   c. ribosome.
   d. Golgi apparatus.

7 The structure marked number 7 in Figure Q.1.3 is the
   a. rough endoplasmic reticulum.
   b. smooth endoplasmic reticulum.
   c. nuclear membrane.
   d. Golgi apparatus.

8 The stage of the cell cycle pictured in Figure Q.1.4 is
   a. anaphase.
   b. metaphase.
   c. telophase.
   d. interphase.

9 The tissue seen in Figure Q.1.5A is
   a. simple cuboidal epithelium.
   b. loose connective tissue.
   c. nervous tissue.
   d. pseudostratified ciliated columnar epithelium.

10 The tissue seen in Figure Q.1.5B is
   a. simple columnar epithelium.
   b. bone tissue.
   c. stratified squamous keratinized epithelium.
   d. hyaline cartilage.

11 The tissue seen in Figure Q.1.5C is
   a. dense regular collagenous connective tissue.
   b. loose connective tissue.
   c. fibrocartilage.
   d. stratified squamous epithelium.

FIGURE **Q.1.3** A generalized animal cell for Questions 6–7.

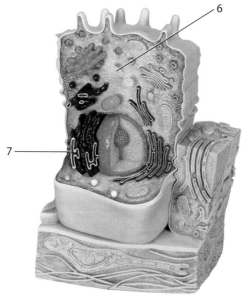

FIGURE **Q.1.4** A generalized cell in an unknown stage of the cell cycle for Question 8.

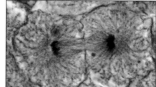

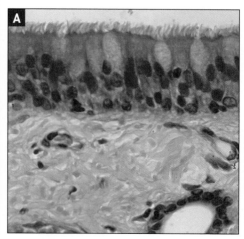

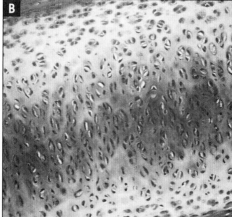

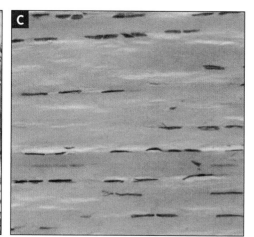

FIGURE **Q.1.5** Unknown tissues for Questions 9–11: (**A**) unknown tissue for Question 9; (**B**) unknown tissue for Question 10; (**C**) unknown tissue for Question 11.

12 The structure marked number 12 in Figure Q.1.6 is the
   a. stratum corneum.
   b. stratum basale.
   c. dermal papillae.
   d. sweat gland.

13 The structure marked number 13 in Figure Q.1.6 is the
   a. arrector pili muscle.
   b. sebaceous gland.
   c. sweat gland.
   d. hair follicle.

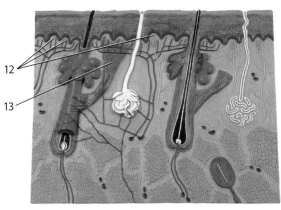

FIGURE **Q.1.6** A skin section for Questions 12–13.

14 The structure marked number 14 in Figure Q.1.7 is the
   a. diaphysis.
   b. epiphyseal line.
   c. medullary cavity.
   d. epiphysis.

15 The bone in Figure Q.1.7 is a _____ bone.
   a. short
   b. flat
   c. irregular
   d. long

16 The structure marked number 16 in Figure Q.1.8 is a/an
   a. lamella.
   b. canaliculus.
   c. lacuna.
   d. central canal.

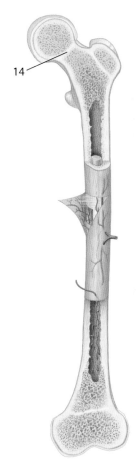

FIGURE **Q.1.7**
A sectioned bone for
Questions 14–15.

17 The structure housed in structure 17 of Figure Q.1.8 is/are
   a. the bone marrow.
   b. osteons.
   c. the periosteum.
   d. osteocytes.

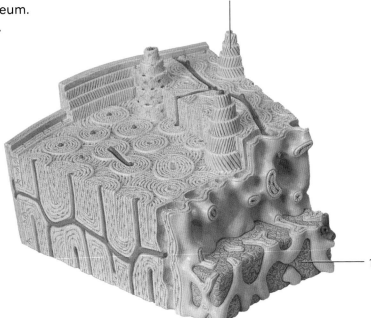

FIGURE **Q.1.8** Bone tissue section for Questions 16–17.

18 The bone marked number 18 in Figure Q.1.9 is the
  a. radius.
  b. ulna.
  c. tibia.
  d. fibula.

19 The bone marked number 19 in Figure Q.1.9 is the
  a. humerus.
  b. tibia.
  c. femur.
  d. ischium.

20 The bone marked number 20 in Figure Q.1.9 is the
  a. pubis.
  b. ilium.
  c. sternum.
  d. clavicle.

21 The bone marked number 21 in Figure Q.1.9 is the
  a. calcaneus.
  b. carpals.
  c. metatarsals.
  d. metacarpals.

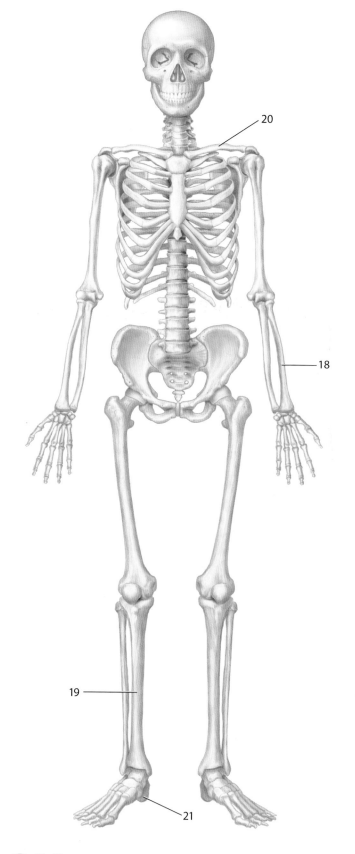

FIGURE **Q.1.9** Diagram of the skeleton for Questions 18–21.

22 The structure marked number 22 in Figure Q.1.10A is the
   a. greater trochanter.
   b. trochlea.
   c. humeral head.
   d. olecranon fossa.

23 The structure marked number 23 in Figure Q.1.10B is the
   a. olecranon.
   b. medial malleolus.
   c. lateral malleolus.
   d. glenoid cavity.

24 The structure labeled number 24 in Figure Q.1.10C is the
   a. coracoid process.
   b. xiphoid process.
   c. manubrium.
   d. acromion.

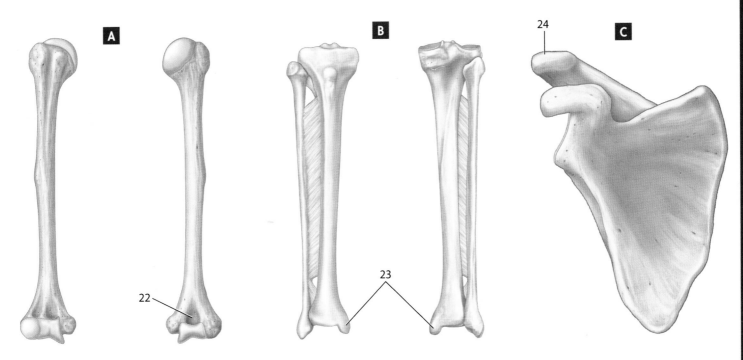

FIGURE **Q.1.10** Bones for Questions 22–24: (**A**) Unknown bone A; (**B**) Unknown bone B; (**C**) Unknown bone C.

25 The bone marked number 25 in Figure Q.1.11A is the

   a. frontal bone.
   b. parietal bone.
   c. ethmoid bone.
   d. temporal bone.

26 The bone marked number 26 in Figure Q.1.11B is the

   a. maxilla.
   b. sphenoid bone.
   c. occipital bone.
   d. zygomatic bone.

27 The bone structure marked number 27 in Figure Q.1.11B is the

   a. foramen magnum.
   b. occipital condyle.
   c. styloid process.
   d. mastoid process.

28 The structure marked number 28 in Figure Q.1.11B is the

   a. sella turcica.
   b. cribriform plate.
   c. vomer bone.
   d. nasal concha.

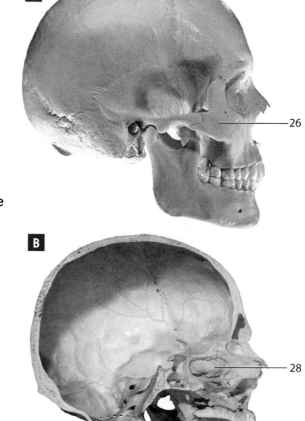

FIGURE **Q.1.11** Skulls for Questions 25–28: (**A**) lateral view of the skull; (**B**) midsagittal section of the skull.

29 The vertebra in Figure Q.1.12 is a/the

   a. cervical vertebra (C3–C7).
   b. axis (C2).
   c. thoracic vertebra.
   d. lumbar vertebra.
   e. atlas (C1).

30 The structure marked number 30 in Figure Q.1.12 is the

   a. spinous process.
   b. transverse process.
   c. vertebral foramen.
   d. pedicle.
   e. transverse foramen.

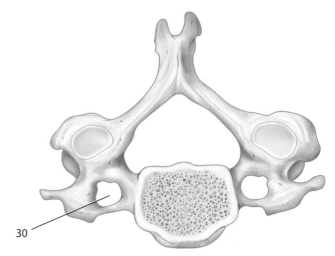

FIGURE **Q.1.12** Unknown vertebra for Questions 29–30.

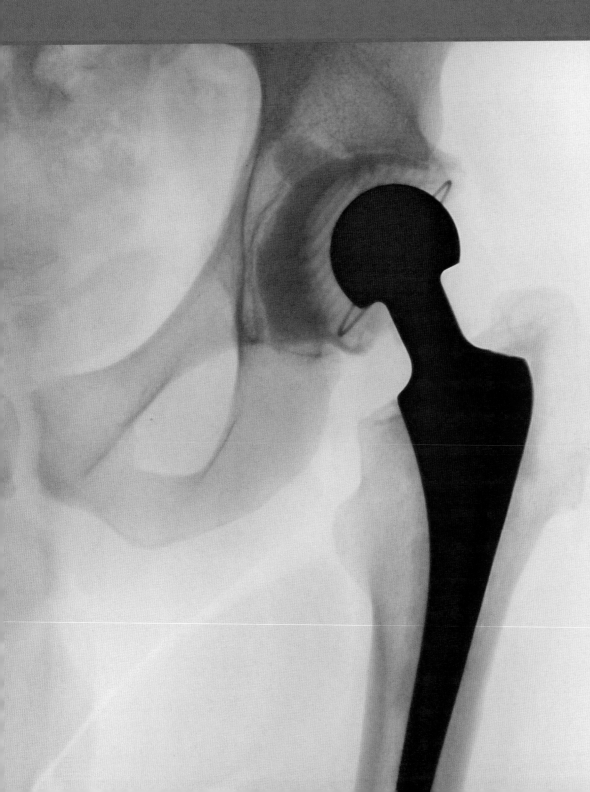

Articulations

When you have completed this unit, you should be able to:

1 Classify joints based upon structure and function.

2 Identify examples of the different types of joints.

3 Identify structures associated with synovial joints.

4 Classify synovial joints according to range of motion.

5 Demonstrate and describe motions allowed at synovial joints.

6 Identify structures of the knee and shoulder joints.

PRE-LAB EXERCISES

Complete the following exercises prior to coming to lab, using your lab manual and textbook for reference.

PRE-LAB

9-1 Key Terms

You should be familiar with the following terms before coming to lab.

Term	Definition

Classes of Joints by Function

Synarthrosis _____

_____

Amphiarthrosis _____

_____

Diarthrosis _____

_____

Classes of Joints by Structure

Fibrous _____

_____

Cartilaginous _____

_____

Synovial _____

_____

Classes of Synovial Joints by Structure

Plane _____

_____

Hinge _____

_____

Pivot _____

_____

Condyloid _____

_____

Saddle _____

_____

Ball-and-socket _____

_____

Name ______________________ Section ______________ Date ______________

Types of Movement in Synovial Joints

Flexion ______________________

____

Extension ______________________

____

Abduction ______________________

____

Adduction ______________________

____

Circumduction ______________________

____

Rotation ______________________

____

Inversion ______________________

____

Eversion ______________________

____

Plantarflexion ______________________

____

Dorsiflexion ______________________

____

Pronation ______________________

____

Supination ______________________

____

Elevation ______________________

____

Depression ______________________

____

Opposition ______________________

____

Anatomy of Synovial Joints

Color the structures of generalized synovial joints in Figure 9.1, and label them with the terms from Exercise 9-2 (p. 248). Use your text and Exercise 9-2 in this unit for reference.

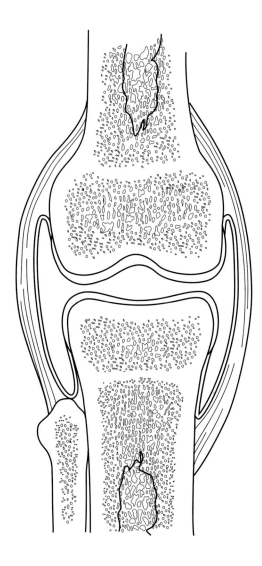

FIGURE **9.1** Generalized synovial joint.

PRE-LAB

9-3 The Knee Joint

Color the structures of the knee joint in Figure 9.2, and label them with the terms from Exercise 9-3 (p. 252). Use your text and Exercise 9-3 in this unit for reference.

A

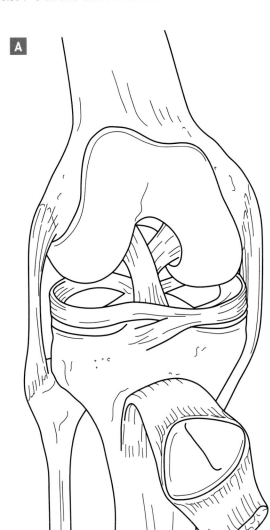

B

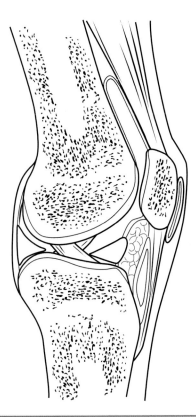

FIGURE **9.2** The right knee joint:
(**A**) anterior view; (**B**) midsagittal section.

Color the structures of the shoulder joint in Figure 9.3, and label them with the terms from Exercise 9-4 (p. 255). Use your text and Exercise 9-4 in this unit for reference.

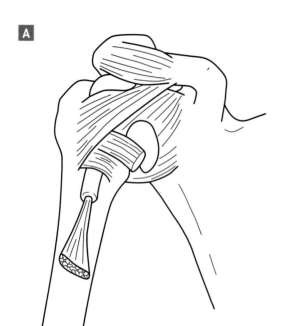

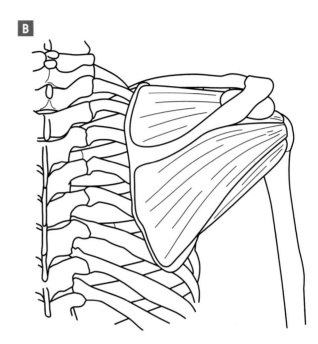

FIGURE **9.3** Shoulder joint: (**A**) anterior view of the joint capsule; (**B**) posterior view of the musculature.

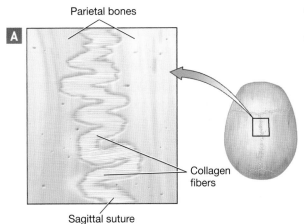

EXERCISES

Most bones in the body form **articulations**, or **joints**, with another bone. These articulations provide stability and allow you to perform the wide variety of motions involved in everyday movement. You probably don't realize just how many joints are articulating when you perform routine activities such as answering the phone, walking to the door, or holding a model in A&P lab. In the following exercises, you will identify and classify joints according to structure, function, and the amount of motion that they allow; examine the knee and shoulder joints; and determine which joints are involved in simple everyday movements.

X-ray of a loosened hip replacement.

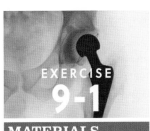

EXERCISE 9-1

MATERIALS

☐ Skeleton, articulated
☐ Skull

Classification of Joints

Joints are classified according to both their structure and their function. Functionally, joints are classified by the amount of motion that they allow. There are three functional classes of joints:

1. **Synarthroses** (sin-ar-THROH-seez; *syn-* = "together;" *arthr-* = "joint"), which are immovable joints;

2. **Amphiarthroses** (am-fee-ar-THROH-seez; *amphi-* = "both"), which are joints that allow some motion; and

3. **Diarthroses** (dy-ar-THROH-seez; *dia-* = "through"), which are freely movable joints.

Structurally, joints are classified by the type of connecting elements we find between the two bones. There are also three structural joint classes (Fig. 9.4):

1. **Fibrous joints. Fibrous joints** consist of bones joined by short collagen fibers. Most fibrous joints allow no motion and are synarthroses. Their main function is to provide stability between the bones. There are three subclasses of fibrous joints:

   a. **Sutures.** A **suture**, which you learned about in the previous unit, is a joint between two bones of the skull. The edges of the bones feature interlocking wavy ridges that are united by short collagen fibers—a construction that makes these joints very stable.

   b. **Gomphosis.** A **gomphosis** (gahm-FOH-sis; "bolt together") is located between a tooth and its alveolus in the mandible or maxilla. It is held in place by a fibrous membrane called the *periodontal ligament.*

   c. **Syndesmosis.** Syndesmoses (sin-dez-MOH-seez; "binding, fastening") are located between two parallel articulating bones such as the radius and ulna. The bones in a syndesmosis are joined by a long fibrous membrane called an interosseous membrane. There is some movement allowed between the bones in a syndesmosis, so these joints are classified as amphiarthroses.

2. **Cartilaginous joints. Cartilaginous joints**, as their name implies, consist of bones united by cartilage, which may be hyaline cartilage

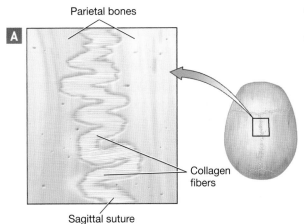

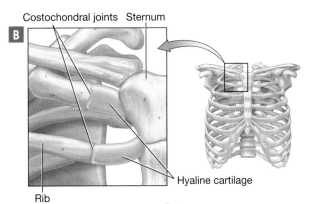

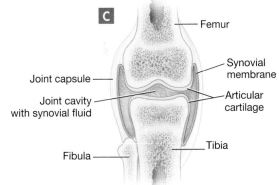

FIGURE **9.4** Structural classes of joints: **(A)** fibrous joint, shown in the skull; **(B)** cartilaginous joint; shown in the rib cage; **(C)** synovial joint, shown in the knee.

or fibrocartilage. Most cartilaginous joints in the body allow some motion and are amphiarthroses. The function of cartilaginous joints is also to provide stability, although most provide somewhat less stability than fibrous joints. There are two types of cartilaginous joints:

a. **Symphyses.** A common type of cartilaginous joint in the body is the **symphysis** (SIM-fih-sis; *sym-* = "together;" *-physis* = "growth"), in which the bones are joined by a tough cartilaginous pad. Examples include the intervertebral joints and the pubic symphysis.

b. **Synchondroses. Synchondroses** (sin-khan-DROH-seez) consist of bones joined by hyaline cartilage. The epiphyseal plate is an example of a synchondrosis that is a temporary joint. After the plate closes and becomes the epiphyseal line, the joint ceases to exist. Permanent synchondroses include the costochondral joints and the first sternocostal joint.

3. **Synovial joints. Synovial joints** (sih-NOH-vee-uhl) have a true joint cavity, which makes them diarthroses. The two bones are united by a **joint capsule** composed of dense irregular connective tissue that surrounds and encloses the joint cavity, which is filled with a liquid called *synovial fluid*. The function of synovial joints is to allow motion to occur between two bones, which makes synovial joints much less stable than either fibrous or cartilaginous joints. The subtypes of synovial joints include the following (Fig. 9.5):

a. **Plane.** The bones of **plane joints** have flat articular surfaces that allow the bones to glide past one another (Fig. 9.5A). There are several examples of plane joints in the body, including the intertarsal joints, the intercarpal joints, and the articulations between the superior and inferior articular processes of the vertebrae. These joints allow the least amount of motion of the synovial joints, which makes this the most stable class of synovial joints.

b. **Condyloid. Condyloid joints** consist of one bone that fits into the concave surface of another bone, such as the radiocarpal and metacarpophalangeal joints (Fig. 9.5B).

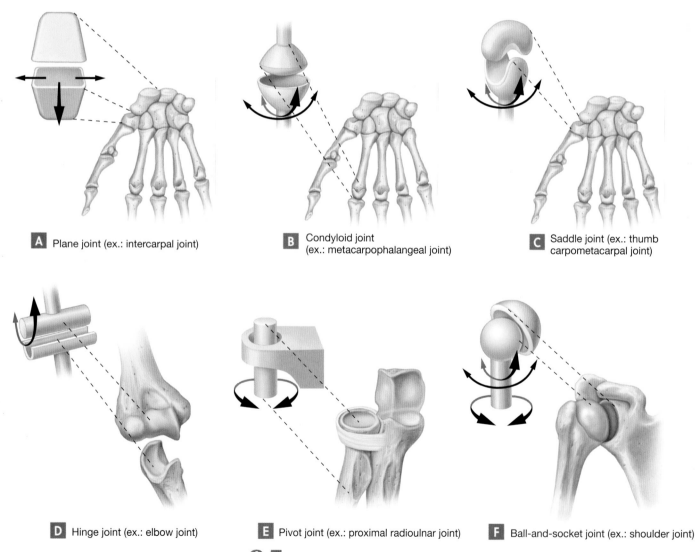

A	Plane joint (ex.: intercarpal joint)
B	Condyloid joint (ex.: metacarpophalangeal joint)
C	Saddle joint (ex.: thumb carpometacarpal joint)
D	Hinge joint (ex.: elbow joint)
E	Pivot joint (ex.: proximal radioulnar joint)
F	Ball-and-socket joint (ex.: shoulder joint)

FIGURE **9.5** Structural classes of synovial joints.

c. **Saddle.** Note in Figure 9.5C that **saddle joints** resemble their namesake. Functionally, they are similar to condyloid joints but permit a greater range of motion. An example of a saddle joint is the first carpometacarpal joint of the thumb.

d. **Hinge.** In a **hinge joint,** the bones fit together much like the hinge of a door (Fig. 9.5D). Generally, the convex articular surface of one bone fits into a concave articular surface of another bone. Examples of hinge joints include the elbow, knee, and interphalangeal joints.

e. **Pivot.** In a **pivot joint,** one bone rotates or "pivots" around another bone (Fig. 9.5E). Generally, pivot joints consist of one bone with a rounded projection that fits into a groove of another bone, as seen with the atlantoaxial and proximal radioulnar joints.

f. **Ball-and-socket.** **Ball-and-socket joints** are named for the rounded, ball-like end of one bone that fits into the concave "socket" of another bone (Fig. 9.5F). The only examples of ball-and-socket joints in the body are the shoulder and hip joints.

| 1 | **PROCEDURE** |

Classifying Joints by Structure and Function

9

Classify each joint listed in Table 9.1 by its structure. Then, examine the joint to determine its structural subcategory. Finally, manipulate the joint to determine its functional classification and how much motion is allowed at the joint. After you have completed the activity, answer Check Your Understanding Questions 1 and 2 (p. 263).

TABLE **9.1** Structural and Functional Classification of Joints

Joint	Structural Classification	Structural Subcategory	Functional Classification and Amount of Motion Allowed
Intervertebral joint			
Shoulder (glenohumeral) joint			
Intercarpal joint			
Coronal suture			
Costochondral joint			
Atlantoaxial joint			
Tooth in its alveolus			
Interphalangeal joint			

MATERIALS

❑ Skeleton, articulated
❑ Anatomical models and diagrams: knee joint

Synovial Joints

Synovial joints are freely movable joints in which the bones are separated by a **joint cavity**. Features common to synovial joints are the following:

- **Articular cartilage.** The articulating ends of the bones are covered with **articular cartilage**, which is usually hyaline cartilage. The cartilage provides a smooth, nearly frictionless surface for articulation. Damage to the articular cartilage leads to the common condition called *osteoarthritis*, which leads to joint pain, swelling, and stiffness.

- **Joint capsule.** As you just read, the **joint capsule** is made of dense irregular connective tissue. The irregularly arranged collagen fibers allow the capsule to resist pulling forces in many different planes, which provides strength and structural reinforcement for the joint. Internally, the joint capsule is lined by a thin layer of connective and epithelial tissue known as the **synovial membrane**. This membrane secretes **synovial fluid**, which fills the joint cavity, reducing friction and exchanging oxygen, nutrients, and wastes with the cells of articular cartilage.

- **Ligaments.** The bones in a synovial joint are held together by **ligaments**, cords of dense collagenous connective tissue, which further reinforce the joint. Some ligaments (called *extrinsic ligaments*) are within the joint cavity, whereas others (*intrinsic ligaments*) are embedded in the capsule (they are called "intrinsic" because they are an intrinsic part of the capsule).

- **Articular discs.** Also known as **menisci** (men-ISS-kee; *menisc-* = "crescent"), **articular discs** are fibrocartilage pads that improve the fit of two bones so as to prevent dislocation.

Synovial joints typically are surrounded by **tendons,** the collagenous cords that generally attach a muscle to a bone. Fluid-filled sacs called **bursae** (BURR-see; *burs-* = "bag") are often located between tendons and joints, and this also reduces friction. Specialized, elongated bursae are found around certain tendons that are subject to a great deal of friction; such bursae are known as **tendon sheaths**.

1 PROCEDURE
Identifying Structures of Synovial Joints

Identify the following structures on anatomical models. Check off each structure as you identify it. When you have completed the activity, answer Check Your Understanding Questions 3 and 4 (p. 263).

❑ Joint cavity
❑ Articular cartilage
❑ Joint capsule
❑ Synovial membrane

❑ Synovial fluid
❑ Ligaments
  ▪ Extrinsic
  ▪ Intrinsic

❑ Articular discs (menisci)
❑ Bursae
❑ Tendon with tendon sheath

Functional Classes of Synovial Joints

The range of motion of a synovial joint is described conventionally in terms of an invisible *axis* about which the bone moves. Synovial joints are classified according to the number of planes of motion in which the bones can move around this axis. In general, the more planes around which a bone can move, the less stable the joint is.

The classes are as follows:

1. **Nonaxial joints.** As implied by its name, a **nonaxial joint** does not move around an axis. Instead, the bones in a nonaxial joint simply glide past one another. Nonaxial joints include the plane joints, such as the vertebrocostal joints (located between a thoracic vertebra and a rib) and intercarpal joints.

2. **Uniaxial joints.** Joints that allow motion in one plane or direction around a single axis of motion are called **uniaxial joints**. A classic example is the elbow, which is a hinge joint that permits only flexion and extension.

3. **Biaxial joints.** Joints that allow motion in two planes around two axes of motion, such as flexion/extension and abduction/adduction, are called **biaxial joints.** Examples include the wrist and carpometacarpal joints, both of which are condyloid joints, and the carpometacarpal joint of the thumb, which is a saddle joint.

4. **Multiaxial joints.** The joints with the greatest range of motion are **multiaxial joints,** which allow motion in multiple planes around all three axes of motion. An example of a multiaxial joint is the ball-and-socket shoulder joint.

9

Motions of Synovial and Cartilaginous Joints

Each time you move your body in a seemingly routine fashion (such as walking or climbing stairs), you are producing motion at a tremendous number of joints. Many possible motions can occur at synovial and cartilaginous joints. These motions are defined in Table 9.2 and illustrated in Figure 9.6.

TABLE **9.2** Motions at Synovial and Cartilaginous Joints

Motion	Definition	Examples Where Motion Occurs
Flexion	A movement that decreases the angle between articulating bones	Hinge joints (knee, elbow), condyloid joints (wrist), saddle joints (thumb), and ball-and-socket joints (hip, shoulder); also occurs at the cartilaginous intervertebral joints
Extension	Movement that increases the angle between articulating bones	Hinge joints (knee, elbow), condyloid joints (wrist), saddle joints (thumb), and ball-and-socket joints (hip, shoulder); also occurs at the cartilaginous intervertebral joints
Abduction	Motion of a body part away from the body's midline (or the midline of another reference point)	Condyloid joints (wrist), saddle joints (thumb), and ball-and-socket joints (hip, shoulder)
Adduction	Motion of a body part toward the body's midline (or the midline of another reference point)	Condyloid joints (wrist), saddle joints (thumb), and ball-and-socket joints (hip, shoulder)
Circumduction	A conical movement that includes flexion-extension and abduction-adduction	Condyloid joints (wrist, metacarpophalangeal joints), ball-and-socket joints (hip, shoulder)
Rotation	A pivoting motion in which one bone rotates or twists around the bone's longitudinal axis	Pivot joints (atlantoaxial joint), ball-and-socket joints (hip, shoulder); also occurs at the cartilaginous intervertebral joints
Opposition	Movement of the thumb across the palm	Occurs only at the saddle joint of the thumb
Reposition	Movement of the thumb from an opposed position back to its anatomical position	Occurs only at the saddle joint of the thumb
Depression	Movement of a body part inferiorly	Temporomandibular joint (modified hinge); shoulder joint (ball-and-socket)
Elevation	Movement of a body part superiorly	Temporomandibular joint (modified hinge); shoulder joint (ball-and-socket)
Protraction	Movement of a body part anteriorly	Temporomandibular joint (modified hinge); shoulder joint (ball-and-socket)
Retraction	Movement of a body part posteriorly	Temporomandibular joint (modified hinge); shoulder joint (ball-and-socket)
Dorsiflexion	Motion in which the angle between the foot and the leg decreases	Occurs only at the joints of the ankle, foot, and toes
Plantarflexion	Motion in which the angle between the foot and the leg increases (pointing the toe toward the ground)	Occurs only at the joints of the ankle, foot, and toes
Inversion	Movement of the plantar surface of the foot toward the body's midline	Occurs only at the joints of the ankle and foot
Eversion	Movement of the plantar surface of the foot away from the body's midline	Occurs only at the joints of the ankle and foot
Pronation	A rotational motion that turns the palm of the hand to face posteriorly (in anatomical position)	Occurs at the radioulnar pivot joint
Supination	A rotational motion that turns the palm of the hand to face anteriorly (in anatomical position)	Occurs at the radioulnar pivot joint

9

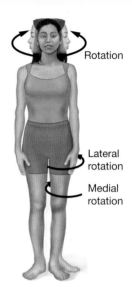

The Differences Between Rotation and Circumduction

Rotation and circumduction both involve circular motions, which causes them to be frequently confused. Try to imagine the two with something easy to envision—the Earth. In rotation, the bone is moves around its own axis, just as the Earth rotates on its own axis every 24 hours. In circumduction, the bone moves around something else, much as the Earth moves around the Sun.

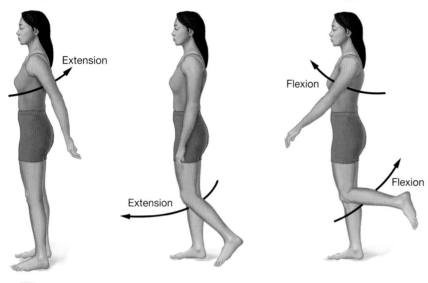

A Angular movements: extension and flexion at the shoulder and knee

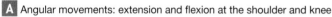

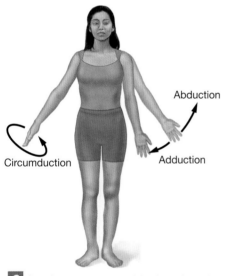

C Angular movements: adduction, abduction, and circumduction of the upper limb at the shoulder

B Rotation of the head, neck, and lower limb

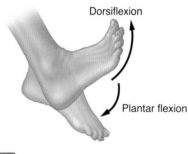

D Dorsiflexion and plantar flexion

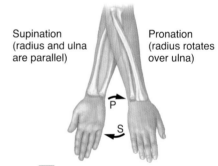

E Pronation (P) and supination (S)

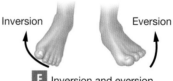

F Inversion and eversion

G Opposition and reposition

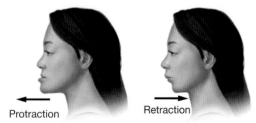

H Protraction and retraction

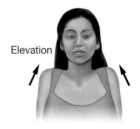

I Elevation and depression

FIGURE **9.6** Motions of synovial and cartilaginous joints.

2

PROCEDURE

Classifying Synovial Joints

For each of the following joints, first list the joint's structural classification in Table 9.3. Then, obtain an articulated skeleton so you can manipulate each joint and determine whether the joint is nonaxial, uniaxial, biaxial, or multiaxial. Also, note which motions are allowed at the joint. When you have completed the activity, answer Check Your Understanding Question 5 (p. 264).

TABLE **9.3** Classification of Synovial Joints

Joint	Structural Classification	Range of Motion (Nonaxial, Uniaxial, Biaxial, or Multiaxial)	Motions Allowed at Joint
Shoulder joint			
Intercarpal joint			
Proximal radioulnar joint			
Radiocarpal joint			
Thumb carpometacarpal joint			
Interphalangeal joint			
Knee joint			
Atlantoaxial joint			
Hip joint			

9

EXERCISE 9-3

MATERIALS

- ❑ Anatomical models and diagrams: knee joint
- ❑ Colored pencils

Knee Joint Structure and Function

The **knee joint**, illustrated in Figure 9.7, is a modified hinge joint made up of the medial and lateral femoral condyles and the tibial plateau. As with all synovial joints, the joint cavity is surrounded by a joint capsule. The capsule is stabilized by numerous ligaments, including intrinsic ligaments (which are part of the joint capsule) and extrinsic ligaments. Four important extrinsic ligaments include the following:

1. **Anterior cruciate ligament (ACL).** The **anterior cruciate ligament** (KROO-shee-iht; *cruci-* = "cross"), or **ACL**, extends from the anterior tibial plateau to the posterior part of the lateral femoral condyle. Its function is to prevent hyperextension of the knee.

2. **Posterior cruciate ligament (PCL).** The **posterior cruciate ligament**, or **PCL**, extends from the posterior tibial plateau to the anterior part of the medial femoral condyle. It crosses under the ACL, and the two, together, form an "X." The PCL prevents posterior displacement of the tibia on the femur (i.e., it stops the tibia from sliding backward on the femur).

3. **Tibial collateral ligament.** The **tibial collateral ligament**, also known as the *medial collateral ligament (MCL)*, extends from the medial tibia to the medial femur. It resists stresses that pull the tibia laterally on the femur.

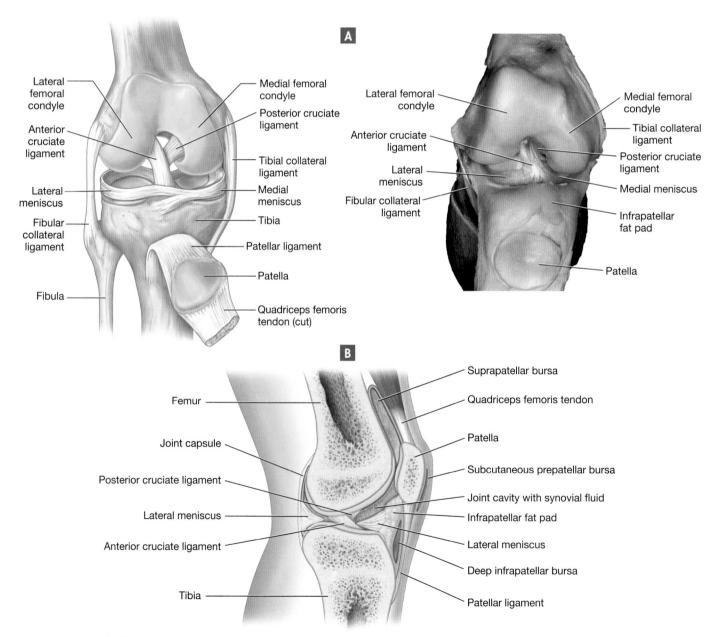

FIGURE **9.7** Right knee joint: (**A**) anterior view, illustration and photograph; (**B**) midsagittal section.

4. **Fibular collateral ligament.** The **fibular collateral ligament**, also known as the *lateral collateral ligament (LCL)*, extends from the lateral fibula to the lateral femur. It resists stresses that pull the tibia medially on the femur.

Two other important supportive structures of the knee joint are the **medial** and **lateral menisci**. These half-moon-shaped articular discs are located on the outer edges of the tibial plateau, and they help to improve the fit of the tibia and femur. The tibial collateral ligament attaches to the medial meniscus, a fact that becomes apparent when the tibial collateral ligament is injured, as the medial meniscus is often injured along with it.

As you can see in Figure 9.7B, anterior to the joint capsule, we find the **patella**, a sesamoid bone located within the quadriceps femoris tendon. The structure that attaches the patella to the tibia is the **patellar ligament.** There are a number of bursae concentrated around the patella, as it generates a great deal of friction over the femur during motion. For this reason, these bursae can become inflamed as a result of repetitive activities or simply "overdoing" it.

1 PROCEDURE
Identifying Structures of the Knee Joint

Identify the following structures of the knee joint on anatomical models or diagrams. Check off each structure as you identify it.

- ❏ Medial and lateral femoral condyles
- ❏ Tibial plateau
- ❏ Joint cavity
- ❏ Joint capsule
- ❏ Ligaments
  - ▪ Anterior cruciate ligament (ACL)

- ▪ Posterior cruciate ligament (PCL)
- ▪ Tibial collateral ligament
- ▪ Fibular collateral ligament
- ❏ Menisci
  - ▪ Medial meniscus
  - ▪ Lateral meniscus

- ❏ Patella
- ❏ Patellar ligament
- ❏ Quadriceps femoris tendon
- ❏ Patellar bursae
  - ▪ Deep infrapatellar bursa
  - ▪ Subcutaneous prepatellar bursa
  - ▪ Suprapatellar bursa

2 PROCEDURE
Time to Draw

In the space provided, draw, color, and label one of the knee joint models that you examined. In addition, write the function of each structure that you label.

PROCEDURE

3

Testing the Integrity of the ACL and PCL

One of the more common knee injuries is a torn ACL and/or PCL. To assess the integrity of the ACL and PCL, tests known as the **anterior drawer** and **posterior drawer**, respectively, are performed. A normal result of both tests is a minimum amount of motion when the tibia is moved anteriorly and posteriorly. When you have completed the tests, answer Check Your Understanding Question 6 (p. 264).

1 Have your partner sit with the knees bent at 90° and relaxed.

2 Grasp your partner's leg with both hands around the proximal tibia and fibula.

3 Gently pull the leg anteriorly, being careful not to extend the knee joint.

Amount of motion: _____

Which ligament was being assessed (ACL or PCL)? _____

4 Now, gently push the leg posteriorly. Be careful not to flex the knee joint.

Amount of motion: _____

Which ligament was being assessed (ACL or PCL)? _____

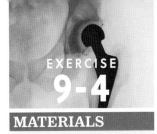

MATERIALS

❑ Anatomical models and diagrams: shoulder joint

Anatomy of the Shoulder Joint

The **shoulder joint**, more properly called the **glenohumeral joint** (glen'-oh-HYOO-mur-uhl), is a multiaxial joint that consists of the head of the humerus and the *glenoid cavity* of the scapula (Figs. 9.8 and 9.9). Like the knee joint, the shoulder is supported by a number of surrounding structures, including the following:

- **Glenoid labrum.** The **glenoid labrum** (GLEN-oyd LAY-brum; *glen-* = "socket;" *labrum* = "lip") is a fibrocartilaginous ring along on the rim of the glenoid cavity that improves the fit of the humeral head in the glenoid cavity (Fig. 9.8A).

- **Ligaments.** The shoulder joint has a much greater range of motion than the knee, and, as a result, its joint capsule is thinner and weaker and its ligaments are fewer in number. One ligament is the **coracohumeral ligament** (kohr'-uh-koh-HYOO-muhr-uhl), located in the anterior articular capsule between the humeral head and the coracoid process (Fig. 9.8B). Another is the **coracoacromial ligament**, located between the acromion and the coracoid process. In addition, three **glenohumeral ligaments** may be found reinforcing the anterior joint capsule.

- **Biceps brachii tendon.** Another stabilizing force comes from the tendon of the *biceps brachii muscle*, found in the anterior arm. This tendon passes through the articular capsule of the shoulder joint on its way to its attachment point on the scapula.

9

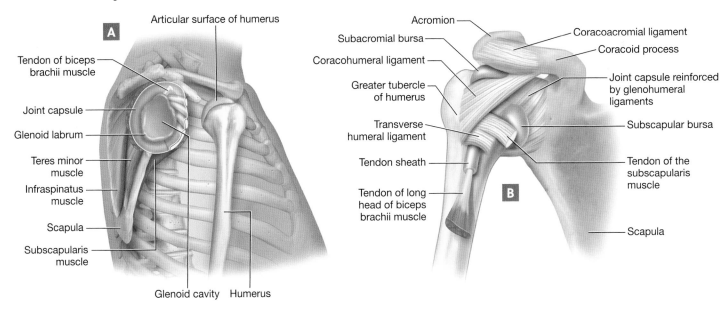

FIGURE **9.8** Right shoulder joint capsule: (**A**) lateral view; (**B**) anterior view.

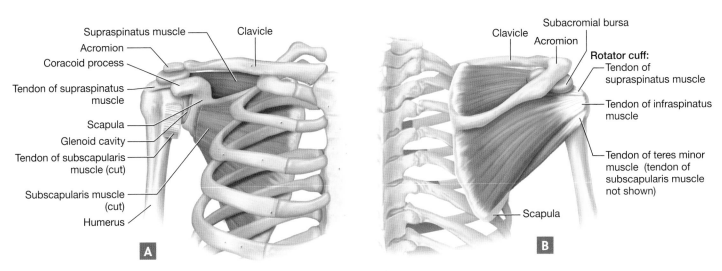

FIGURE **9.9** Right shoulder joint musculature of the rotator cuff: (**A**) anterior view; (**B**) posterior view.

- **Rotator cuff.** One of the major stabilizing forces of the shoulder joint is a group of four muscles and their tendons—the supraspinatus, infraspinatus, teres minor, and subscapularis muscles—collectively called the **rotator cuff** (Figs. 9.9A and B). One of the most common injuries of the shoulder joint is a rotator cuff tear, which may be caused by an injury or repetitive circumduction as occurs with certain sports as well as activities such as painting and carpentry.

Several bursae and tendon sheaths are found around the shoulder joint, including the tendon sheath of the biceps brachii muscle; the **subscapular bursa**, located deep to the subscapularis muscle; and the large **subacromial bursa**, located between the humeral head and the acromion. The subacromial bursa is frequently inflamed with overuse injuries.

1 PROCEDURE
Identifying Structures of the Shoulder Joint

Identify the following structures of the shoulder joint on anatomical models or fresh specimens. Check off each structure as you identify it. When you have completed the activity, answer Check Your Understanding Question 7 (p. 264).

❑ Humeral head

❑ Glenoid cavity
- Glenoid labrum

❑ Ligaments
- Coracoacromial ligament
- Coracohumeral ligament
- Glenohumeral ligaments

❑ Biceps brachii tendon

❑ Tendons of rotator cuff muscles
- Supraspinatus tendon
- Infraspinatus tendon
- Teres minor tendon
- Subscapularis tendon

❑ Bursae
- Subacromial bursa
- Subscapular bursa

❑ Joint capsule

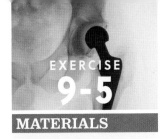

EXERCISE
9-5

MATERIALS

None required

The Big Picture of Movement at Synovial and Cartilaginous Joints

In the following procedure, you will put together the pieces of everything you've learned in order to see the big picture of joint movement. You will perform four common movements: walking up the stairs, doing jumping jacks, and jumping rope. You will determine which joints you are moving with each action, and then which motions are occurring at each joint.

---

1 **PROCEDURE**

Identifying Joint Motions of Common Movements

Team up with a partner, and have your partner perform each of the following actions. Watch carefully as the actions are performed and list the joints that are in motion. Some of the joints, such as the hip joint and knee joint, will be obvious. Others, such as the radioulnar joint, the fingers and toes, and the intervertebral joints, are less obvious and easily overlooked. (**Note:** Ask your instructor whether you should use the technical name or the common name for each joint—for example, glenohumeral versus shoulder joint).

After you have listed the joints being used, determine which motions are occurring at each joint. Keep in mind the type and the range of motion of each joint as you answer each question.

1 **Walking down stairs**

Joints moving: Motions occurring:

_____   _____
_____   _____
_____   _____
_____   _____
_____   _____
_____   _____
_____   _____
_____   _____

2 **Performing a push-up**

Joints moving: Motions occurring:

_____   _____
_____   _____
_____   _____
_____   _____
_____   _____
_____   _____
_____   _____

3 Throwing a baseball

Joints moving:

Motions occurring:

4 Performing a lunge

Joints moving:

Motions occurring:

Check Your Recall

1 A synarthrosis is defined as a

   a. joint that allows no motion.

   b. joint that is freely movable.

   c. joint with multiple axes of motion.

   d. joint that allows some motion.

2 The main function of a cartilaginous joint is to

   a. allow motion to occur between two bones.

   b. provide stability between two bones.

   c. unite two bones with dense irregular connective tissue.

   d. allow some motion while still providing stability between two bones.

   e. unite two bones with a synovial cavity.

3 How does a synovial joint differ from cartilaginous and fibrous joints?

   a. In a synovial joint, the ends of the articulating bones are covered in dense irregular connective tissue.

   b. In a synovial joint, the articulating bones are united by a fibrocartilage pad.

   c. In a synovial joint, the articulating bones are united by collagen fibers.

   d. In a synovial joint, the articulating bones are separated by a fluid-filled joint cavity.

4 Which of the following describes a plane joint correctly?

   a. One bone fits into a concave articular surface of another bone.

   b. One bone rotates around another bone.

   c. The flat articular surfaces of two bones glide past one another.

   d. The rounded, ball-like end of one bone fits into a concave depression of another bone.

5 *True/False:* Mark the following statements as true (T) or false (F). If the statement is false, correct it to make it a true statement.

   _____ a. Articular discs improve the fit of two bones.

   _____ b. Bursae are collagenous cords that generally connect a muscle to a bone.

   _____ c. The joint capsule of a synovial joint is lined with a serous membrane.

   _____ d. Articular cartilage provides a smooth, nearly frictionless surface for articulation.

   _____ e. Tendon sheaths are specialized, elongated bursae that surround tendons subject to a great deal of friction.

6 An example of a biaxial joint is the

   a. vertebrocostal joint.

   b. hip joint.

   c. wrist joint.

   d. intercarpal joint.

7 Which of the following correctly describes a condyloid joint?

   a. One bone fits into a concave articular surface of another bone.

   b. One bone rotates around another bone.

   c. The flat articular surfaces of two bones glide past one another.

   d. The rounded, ball-like end of one bone fits into a concave depression of another bone.

8 Label the following parts of the knee joint in Figure 9.10.

❏ Anterior cruciate ligament

❏ Fibular collateral ligament

❏ Joint cavity

❏ Lateral meniscus

❏ Medial meniscus

❏ Quadriceps femoris tendon

❏ Patellar ligament

❏ Posterior cruciate ligament

❏ Subcutaneous prepatellar bursa

❏ Tibial collateral ligament

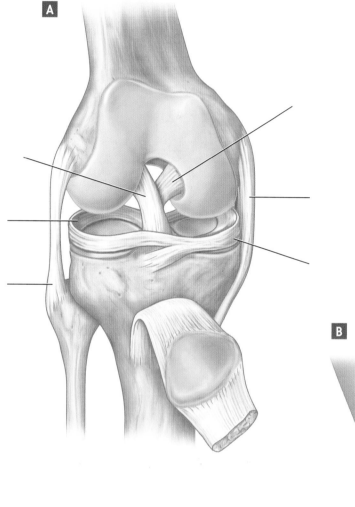

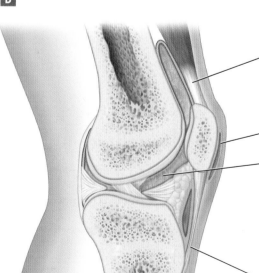

FIGURE **9.10** Knee joint: (**A**) anterior view; (**B**) midsagittal section.

9 Label the following parts of the shoulder joint in Figure 9.11.

❏ Biceps brachii tendon
❏ Coracoacromial ligament
❏ Glenoid cavity

❏ Infraspinatus tendon
❏ Subacromial bursa
❏ Subscapular bursa

❏ Subscapularis tendon
❏ Teres minor tendon

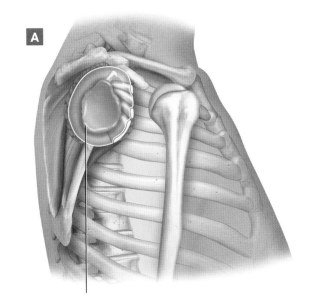

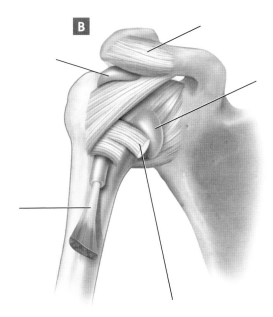

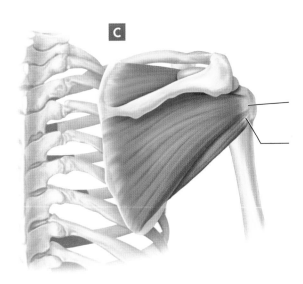

FIGURE **9.11** Right shoulder joint: (**A**) lateral view; (**B**) anterior view; (**C**) posterior view.

10 *Matching:* Match the following terms with the correct description.

_____ Rotation

_____ Adduction

_____ Pronation

_____ Opposition

_____ Plantarflexion

_____ Circumduction

_____ Inversion

_____ Abduction

_____ Dorsiflexion

_____ Protraction

A. Movement of the plantar surface of the foot toward the body's midline

B. Movement of a body part anteriorly

C. Turning the palm to face posteriorly

D. Increasing the angle between the foot and the leg

E. Movement of a body part away from the midline

F. Movement of a body part toward the midline

G. Movement of the ankle that decreases the angle between the foot and leg

H. Movement in a circle

I. Movement around a central axis

J. Movement of the thumb across the palm

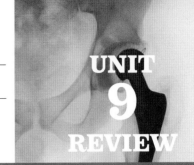

Check Your Understanding

Critical Thinking and Application Questions

1 How would the function of fibrous and cartilaginous joints be changed if they had joint cavities? Explain.

2 Could a synovial joint perform its functions if it were a synarthrosis? Explain your reasoning.

3 Diseases known as *collagenopathies* affect the structure and function of collagen fibers.

   a Explain why a common feature of collagenopathies is hypermobility (excessive motion) of synovial joints.

   b Could collagenopathies affect fibrous and cartilaginous joints? Explain.

4 The amount of synovial fluid produced by the synovial membrane tends to decrease as we age. Predict the consequences of inadequate synovial fluid.

5 Why do you think a metacarpophalangeal joint is more likely to dislocate than an intercarpal joint?

_____

_____

_____

_____

6 Joaquin is playing football when he is tackled from the lateral side. He feels a "pop" in his knee, and immediately goes down. A trainer examines Joaquin's knee, and finds that the tibia is able to move too far laterally on the femur. In addition, the anterior drawer test is positive. What has likely happened to Joaquin's knee? Explain.

_____

_____

_____

_____

7 Softball pitchers throw the ball in a winding motion at the shoulder joint.

a Is this an example of rotation or circumduction? _____

b Could this motion be performed by nonaxial or uniaxial joints? Explain. _____

_____

c Why do you think performing this motion is associated with a high risk of injury? _____

_____

_____

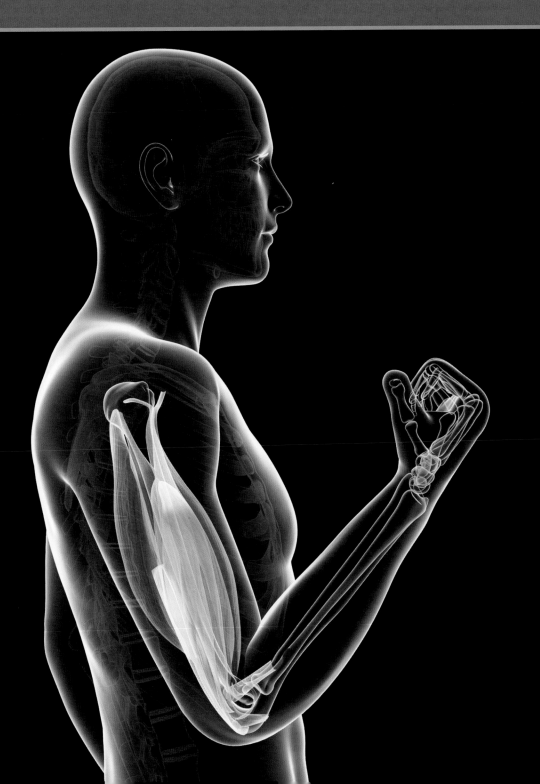

Muscular System: The Gross Anatomy of Muscles

When you have completed this unit, you should be able to:

1 Identify muscles of the upper and lower limbs, trunk, head, and neck on anatomical models.

2 Describe the origin, insertion, and action of selected muscles.

3 Describe the muscle actions required to perform common motions.

PRE-LAB EXERCISES

Complete the following exercises prior to coming to lab, using your lab manual and textbook for reference.

PRE-LAB

10-1 Key Terms

You should be familiar with the following terms before coming to lab. Please note that the individual skeletal muscles are covered in Table 10.1 (pp. 266–267).

Term	Definition
General Terms	
Origin	
Insertion	
Muscle action	

PRE-LAB

10-2 Muscle Origins, Insertions, and Actions

Complete Table 10.1 with the origins, insertions, and *main* actions for the listed muscles. You may notice in your textbook that the origin and insertion of a muscle often are extensive. For example, the latissimus dorsi muscle originates from T7–L5, the lower three or four ribs, the inferior angle of the scapula, and the thoracolumbar fascia. This obviously is quite a bit to write and to remember, so I suggest shortening it to something that makes sense to you (e.g., "inferior back and scapula"). You also will notice that most muscles have more than one action, which you may wish to simplify as well. If your instructor prefers that you learn the more technical version, learning a simplified version first may be helpful.

TABLE **10.1** Selected Muscle Origins, Insertions, and Actions

Muscle	Origin	Insertion	Action(s)
Muscles of the Head and Neck			
Orbicularis oculi m.			
Orbicularis oris m.			
Masseter m.			
Sternocleidomastoid m.			
Trapezius m.			

(continues)

TABLE **10.1** Selected Muscle Origins, Insertions, and Actions *(cont.)*

Muscle	Origin	Insertion	Action(s)
Muscles of the Thorax, Abdomen, and Back			
Rectus abdominis m.			
External oblique m.			
Internal oblique m.			
Erector spinae m. group			
Deltoid m.			
Pectoralis major m.			
Latissimus dorsi m.			
Muscles of the Upper Limb			
Biceps brachii m.			
Triceps brachii m.			
Brachialis m.			
Brachioradialis m.			
Muscles of the Lower Limb			
Iliopsoas m.			
Gluteus maximus m.			
Gluteus medius m.			
Sartorius m.			
Quadriceps femoris m. group			
Adductor m. group			
Biceps femoris m.			
Semitendinosus m.			
Semimembranosus m.			
Gastrocnemius m.			
Tibialis anterior m.			

10

Color the muscles in Figure 10.1, and label them with the terms from Exercise 10-1 (p. 271). Use your text and Exercise 10-1 in this unit for reference.

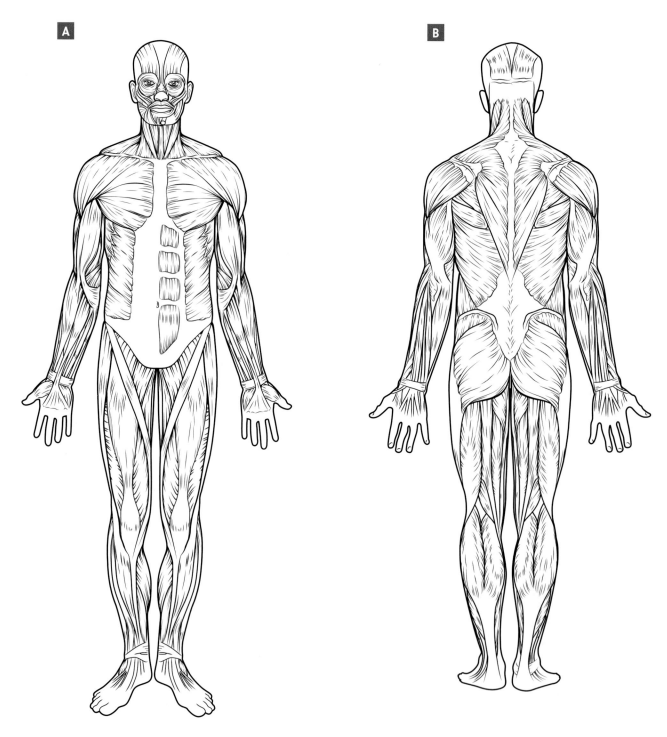

FIGURE **10.1** Human musculature: (**A**) anterior view; (**B**) posterior view; *(continues)*

C

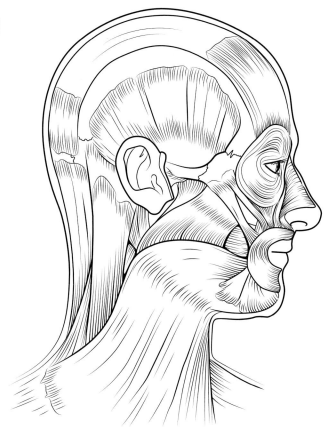

D

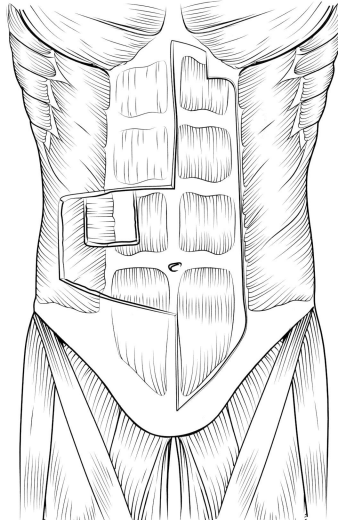

FIGURE **10.1** Human musculature (*cont.*):
(C) lateral view of the head and neck;
(D) abdominal muscles; (*continues*)

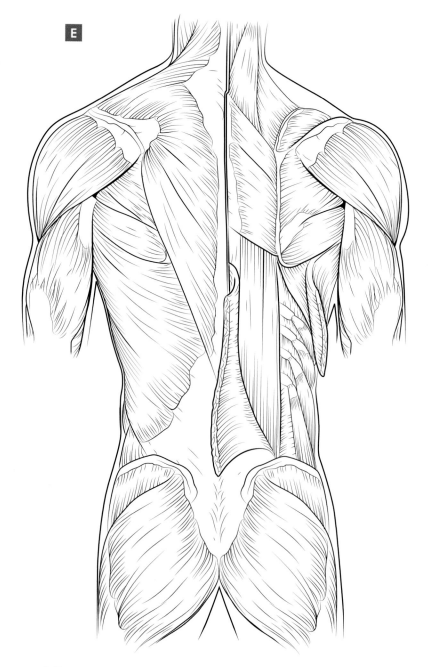

FIGURE **10.1** Human musculature (*cont.*): (**E**) posterior view of the torso.

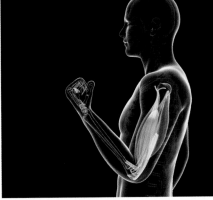

Flexed biceps brachii muscle.

EXERCISES

The human body has nearly 700 skeletal muscles that range dramatically in size and shape from the large trapezius muscle to the tiny corrugator supercilii muscle. Luckily for you, we will be learning only about 70 muscles rather than the full 700. A muscle usually has two main attachment points. First is its **origin**, which generally is the body part that remains stationary, and second is its **insertion**, which, in most cases, is the part that the muscle moves. We are most familiar with muscles that insert into and move bones. Many muscles, however, insert into structures other than bones. Examples include the diaphragm, which inserts into its own central tendon, and the muscles of facial expression, which insert into skin or other muscles.

The exercises in this unit help you become familiar with the main muscle groups and their component muscles. The first exercise introduces you to muscle anatomy. The second exercise focuses on muscle origins and insertions, and the third and final exercise explores muscle actions.

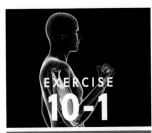

EXERCISE 10-1

MATERIALS

☐ Anatomical muscle models and diagrams:
- upper limb
- lower limb
- trunk
- head
- neck

Skeletal Muscle Anatomy

In this exercise, we divide skeletal muscles into muscle groups that have similar functions. For example, we classify the latissimus dorsi muscle with the muscles of the upper limb, rather than the muscles of the back or trunk, because it moves the upper limb. We will use the following groupings of skeletal muscles in this unit: muscles that move the head, neck, and face; muscles that move the trunk; muscles that move the scapula; muscles that move the arm; muscles that move the forearm, hand, and fingers; muscles that move the thigh and leg; and muscles that move the foot and toes.

Muscles That Move the Head, Neck, and Face

We can subdivide the muscles that move the head, neck, and face into the muscles of facial expression, the muscles of mastication, and the muscles that move the head and neck. The muscles of facial expression control the various facial expressions humans are capable of making, and they all insert into skin or other muscles (Figs. 10.2 and 10.3). One of the largest muscles of facial expression is the *epicranius muscle* (eh-pih-KRAY-nee-uhs), which elevates the eyebrows and skin of the forehead. The muscle has two parts, the **frontalis** (frun-TAL-iss; *fron-* = "forehead") and **occipitalis** (ahk-sip-ih-TAL-iss; *occipit-* = "back of the head") **muscles,** which are connected by a sheet of connective tissue called the *epicranial aponeurosis* (ap-oh-noo-ROH-sis). Just inferior to the frontalis muscle are the two circular **orbicularis oculi muscles** (ohr-bik-yoo-LEHR-iss AHK-yoo-lye; *orb* = "circle;" *ocul-* = "eye"). Their circular structure enables them to close and squint the eyes.

Other muscles of facial expression move the lips and skin around the mouth:

- The most obvious muscle around the mouth is the circular **orbicularis oris muscle** (OHR-iss; *or-* = "mouth"), which purses the lips.

- Under the skin of the cheeks, we find the **buccinator muscle** (BUK-sin-ay-tur; *bucc-* = "cheek"). It pulls the cheeks inward to produce sucking and whistling movements.

Epicranial aponeurosis

Frontalis muscle

Orbicularis oculi muscle

Orbicularis oris muscle

Platysma muscle

Zygomaticus minor muscle

Zygomaticus major muscle

Buccinator muscle

Risorius muscle

FIGURE **10.2** Facial musculature, anterior view.

- Covering the superficial surface of the neck is the broad, flat **platysma muscle** (plah-TIZ-muh; *platysm-* = "flat plate"). It depresses the mandible (opens the jaw) and tightens the skin of the neck.

- Three muscles are involved in smiling: The **zygomaticus major** and **minor muscles** (zy-goh-MAT-ih-kuhs) pull the corners of the mouth superiorly and laterally during smiling while the **risorius muscle** (ry-ZOHR-ee-uhs; *risus* = "laugh") pulls the corners of the mouth nearly directly laterally to produce a closed-mouth smile or smirk.

The **muscles of mastication**, another group of muscles found in the head, are involved in *mastication*, or chewing (Fig. 10.3). They include the thick **masseter muscle** (MASS-uh-tur), located over the lateral mandible, and the fan-shaped **temporalis muscle** (tem-pur-AL-iss), located over the temporal bone.

Several muscles move the head, including the diamond-shaped **trapezius muscle** (trah-PEE-zee-uhs) on the back, which holds the head upright and hyperextends the head and the neck (best seen in Fig. 10.9A, p. 274). In the neck, we find the strap-like **sternocleidomastoid muscle** (stern-oh-kly-doh-MASS-toy'd; *stern-* = "sternum/chest;" *cleid-* = "clavicle"). When the two muscles contract together, they flex the head and neck. Acting individually, each muscle rotates the head toward the opposite side and flexes the head and neck laterally. On the posterior neck, two muscles called the **splenius capitis** (SPLEN-ee-uhs CAP-ih-tiss; *capit-* = "head") and **splenius cervicis muscles** (SUR-vih-sis; *cerv-* = "neck") extend and hyperextend the head and neck (Fig. 10.4).

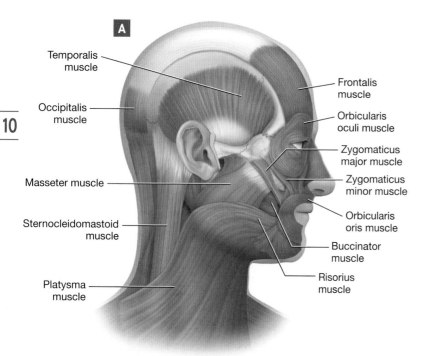

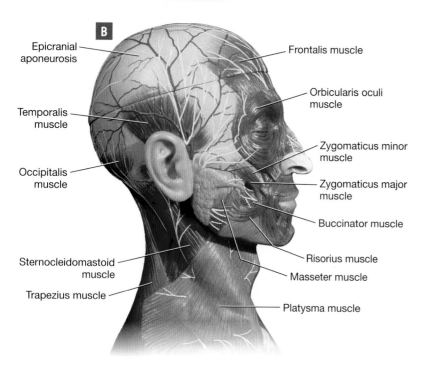

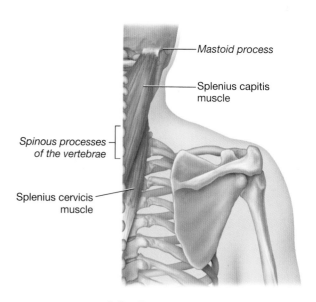

FIGURE **10.3** Muscles of the head and neck, lateral view: (**A**) illustration; (**B**) anatomical model photo.

FIGURE **10.4** Posterior view of the splenius muscles of the neck.

Muscles That Move the Trunk

The muscles that move the trunk include the muscles of the thorax, muscles of the abdominal wall, and postural muscles of the back.

1. The muscles of the thorax are generally involved in the muscle movements that produce ventilation: the **external** and **internal intercostal muscles** are located between the ribs and are involved in both inspiration and expiration, respectively (Fig. 10.5); the dome-shaped **diaphragm muscle** (DY-uh-fram) produces the movements necessary for inspiration; and the small **pectoralis minor muscle** (PEK-tohr-AL-iss; *pect-* = "chest") draws the scapula anteriorly and the rib cage superiorly during forced inspiration and expiration (Fig. 10.6).

2. The abdominal muscles move the trunk and increase intra-abdominal pressure (Figs. 10.7 and 10.8). The

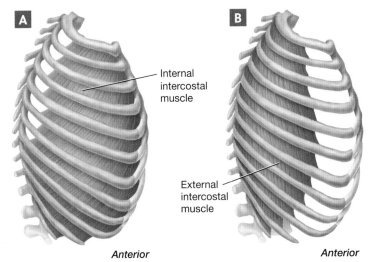

Anterior   Anterior

FIGURE **10.5** Lateral view of the intercostal muscles: (**A**) internal intercostal muscles; (**B**) external intercostal muscles.

10

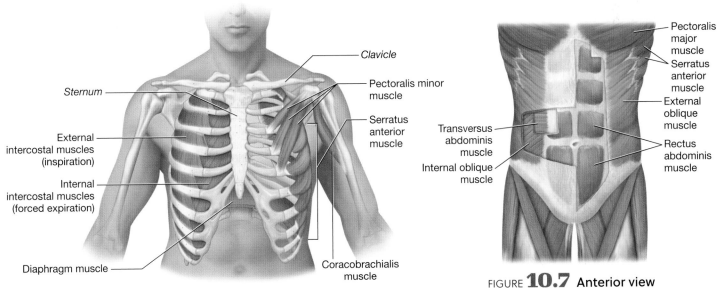

FIGURE **10.6** Deep muscles of the anterior thorax.

FIGURE **10.7** Anterior view of the abdominal muscles.

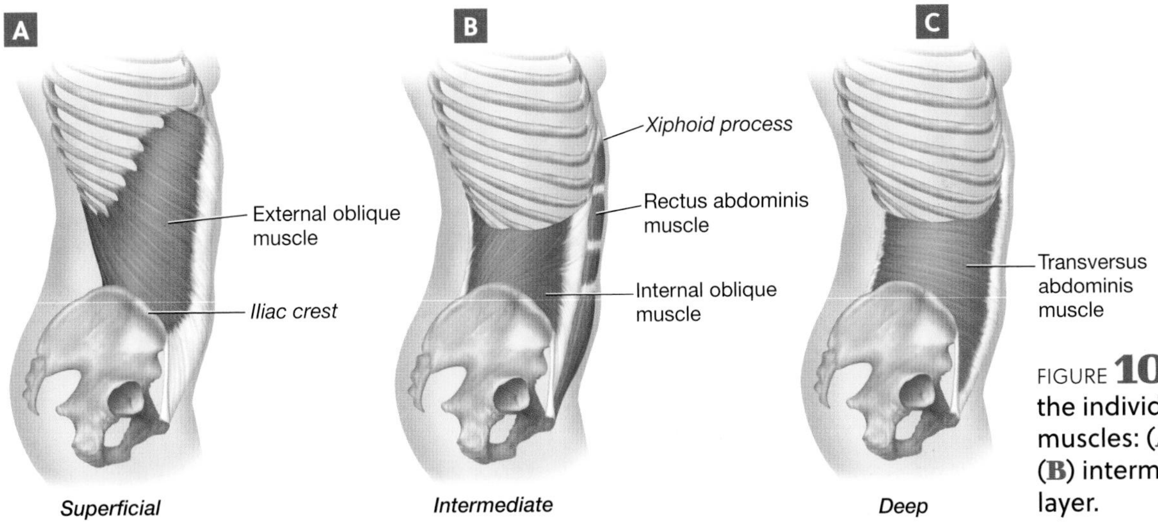

FIGURE **10.8** Lateral view of the individual abdominal muscles: (**A**) superficial layer; (**B**) intermediate layer; (**C**) deep layer.

rectus abdominis muscle (ab-DAHM-in-iss; *rect-* = "straight") is the central and superficial muscle that flexes the trunk. It is covered by a thick layer of connective tissue called the *rectus sheath*. On the lateral torso, we find the **external** and **internal oblique muscles,** which rotate and laterally flex the trunk. Deep to all three muscles, the **transversus abdominis muscle** (*trans-* = "across") squeezes the abdominal contents like a belt to increase intra-abdominal pressure.

3. The postural muscles of the back ensure that we remain upright. Most of these postural muscles also extend the back. One of the main postural muscles is a group known collectively as the **erector spinae muscle** (eh-REK-tohr SPY-nee). The three components of the erector spinae muscle include the lateral **iliocostalis** (ill-ee-oh-kahst-AL-iss), the middle **longissimus** (lahn-JISS-ih-muhs), and the medial **spinalis muscles** (spy-NAL-iss; Fig. 10.9). Another postural muscle group is the *trans-versospinal group*, which runs along the vertebral column and includes the *multifidus* and *semispinalis muscles*. A final postural muscle is the deep *quadratus lumborum muscle* in the lumbar region of the back.

Muscles That Move the Scapula

The **serratus anterior muscle** (ser-AY-tuhs; *serra-* = "saw"), named for its resemblance to a saw or knife, is located on the lateral thorax. It pulls the scapula anteriorly, protracting it (as in when throwing a punch) and rotating it superiorly (as in when doing a bench press; see Figs. 10.6 and 10.7). On the posterior neck and back is the trapezius muscle. Due to its multiple insertions on the scapula, the trapezius muscle has several actions, including elevation, retraction, and protraction. Deep to the trapezius muscle is the **levator scapulae muscle.** True to its name, this muscle elevates the scapula. Also deep to the trapezius muscle are the **rhomboid major** and **rhomboid minor muscles,** both of which retract the scapula (see Fig. 10.9).

Muscles That Move the Arm

As you learned in the articulations unit, the shoulder joint has the greatest range of motion of any joint in the body. For this reason, there are many muscles acting on it, both to move the arm and to stabilize the joint. Some of these muscles include:

- The posterior **latissimus dorsi muscle** (lah-TISS-ih-muhs DOHR-sye; *latissimus* = "broadest;" *dors-* = "back") is the prime muscle of arm extension, and it also adducts and rotates the arm. It is assisted in its actions by the **teres major muscle** on the posterior scapula (Fig. 10.9).

- The **pectoralis major muscle,** or "chest muscle," is the prime muscle of arm flexion, and it also adducts the arm (Fig. 10.10). It is assisted by the *coracobrachialis muscle* on the proximal humerus.

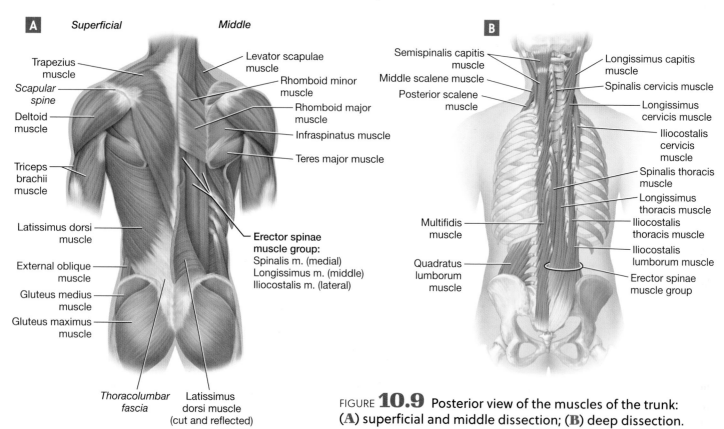

FIGURE **10.9** Posterior view of the muscles of the trunk: **(A)** superficial and middle dissection; **(B)** deep dissection.

- The **deltoid muscle** (*delt-* = "triangular") is the prime abductor of the arm, and assists in both flexion and extension (Fig. 10.10).

- The **rotator cuff muscles**, visible in Figure 10.11, reinforce the capsule of the shoulder joint to prevent dislocation of the humerus from the scapula. They include the **infraspinatus muscle** (in-frah-spy-NAY-tuhs), which is inferior to the scapular spine; **teres minor muscle** (TEHR-eez), which is superior to the teres major muscle; the **supraspinatus muscle** (soo-prah-spy-NAY-tuhs), which is superior to the scapular spine; and the **subscapularis muscle**, which is on the anterior surface of the scapula (sub-skap-yoo-LEHR-uhs; see Fig. 9.9A, p. 255).

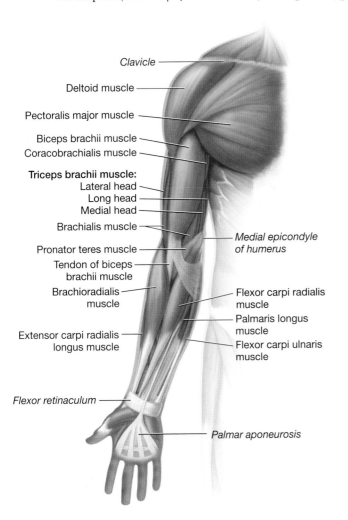

FIGURE **10.10** Anterior view of the muscles of the right upper limb.

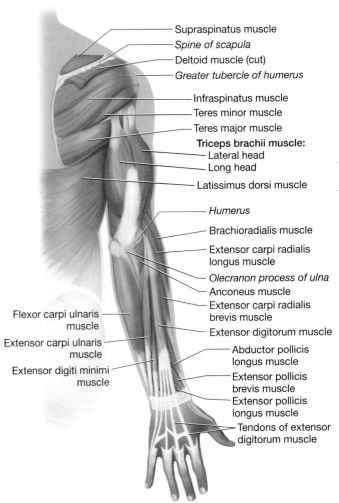

FIGURE **10.11** Posterior view of the muscles of the right upper limb.

Muscles That Move the Forearm, Hand, and Fingers

The four main muscles that move the forearm are the anterior **biceps brachii** (BY-seps BRAY-kee-aye; *biceps* = "two headed;" *brach-* = "arm"), the anterior and deep **brachialis** (bray-kee-AL-iss), the anterior and lateral **brachioradialis** (bray-kee-oh-ray-dee-AL-iss), and the posterior **triceps brachii muscles** (*triceps* = "three headed;" Figs. 10.10 and 10.11). The first three muscles flex the forearm, while the triceps brachii muscle extends the forearm.

The remainder of the muscles of the upper limb act on the hand at the wrist, the hand itself (the *intrinsic hand muscles*), and/or the digits. Muscles that flex the hand, located on the anterior forearm, are the **flexor carpi radialis** (KARP-aye ray-dee-AL-iss), **flexor carpi ulnaris** (uhl-NEHR-iss), **flexor digitorum superficialis**, and **flexor digitorum profundus muscles** (*profund-* = "deep;" Fig. 10.12). As implied by their names, the flexor digitorum superficialis and flexor digitorum profundus muscles also flex the digits. Muscles that extend the hand, located on the posterior forearm, are the **extensor carpi radialis longus, extensor digitorum**, and **extensor carpi ulnaris muscles** (Fig. 10.13). The extensor digitorum also extends the digits. Other muscles that move the hand and digits are labeled in Figures 10.12 and 10.13 for your reference. Figure 10.14 presents a view of an anatomical muscle model of the left upper limb, also for your reference.

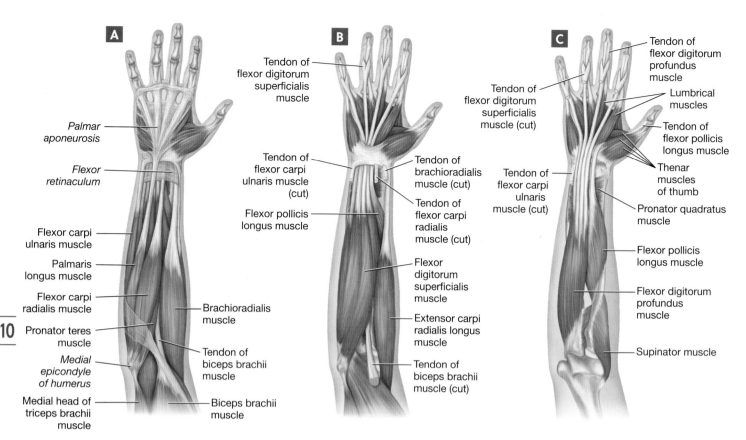

FIGURE **10.12** Anterior view of the muscles of the right forearm: (**A**) superficial muscles; (**B**) intermediate muscles; (**C**) deep muscles.

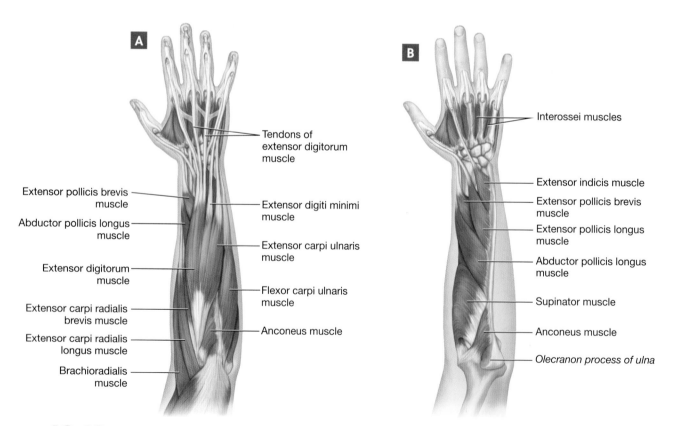

FIGURE **10.13** Posterior view of the muscles of the right forearm: (**A**) superficial muscles; (**B**) deep muscles.

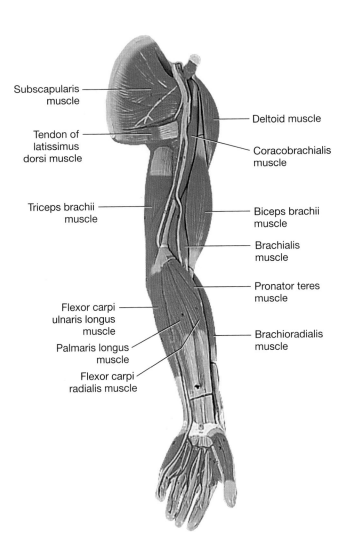

FIGURE **10.14** Anteromedial view of the muscles of the left upper limb, anatomical model photo.

Labels for Figure 10.14:
- Subscapularis muscle
- Tendon of latissimus dorsi muscle
- Triceps brachii muscle
- Flexor carpi ulnaris longus muscle
- Palmaris longus muscle
- Flexor carpi radialis muscle
- Deltoid muscle
- Coracobrachialis muscle
- Biceps brachii muscle
- Brachialis muscle
- Pronator teres muscle
- Brachioradialis muscle

Muscles that Move the Thigh and Leg

We can divide muscles that move only the thigh into three groups:

- The *gluteal muscles* consist of three muscles on the posterior pelvis. The large, superficial **gluteus maximus muscle** (GLOO-tee-uhs; *glut-* = "buttock") is the prime extensor of the thigh (Fig. 10.15). The **gluteus medius muscle** (MEE-dee-uhs), which is deep to the gluteus maximus muscle, is a major abductor of the thigh. The small, deep *gluteus minimus muscle* assists the gluteus medius muscle in its actions. (Other deep muscles of the gluteal region are illustrated in Fig. 10.15 for your reference.)

- As implied by their names, the muscles in the *adductor group*, located on the medial femur, are the prime adductors of the thigh (Fig. 10.16). This group includes the superior **adductor brevis** (*brevis* = "short"), the inferior **adductor longus**, and the deep, broad **adductor magnus muscles** (*magnus* = "large").

- The **iliopsoas muscle** (ill-ee-oh-SOH-uhs) is composed of two parts—the *iliacus muscle* (ill-ee-AK-uhs), originating from the iliac fossa of the ilium, and the *psoas major muscle* (SOH-uhs), originating from the lumbar vertebrae (Fig. 10.17). The two muscles come together to form the iliopsoas muscle, which inserts via a common tendon into the lesser trochanter of the femur. The iliopsoas muscle is the prime flexor of the thigh and is assisted by the **pectineus muscle** (pek-TIN-ee-uhs) in the proximal thigh.

10

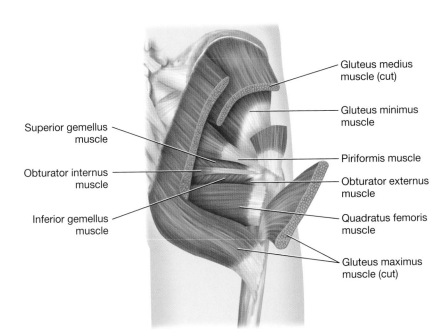

FIGURE **10.15** Deeper muscles of the gluteal region.

Labels for Figure 10.15:
- Superior gemellus muscle
- Obturator internus muscle
- Inferior gemellus muscle
- Gluteus medius muscle (cut)
- Gluteus minimus muscle
- Piriformis muscle
- Obturator externus muscle
- Quadratus femoris muscle
- Gluteus maximus muscle (cut)

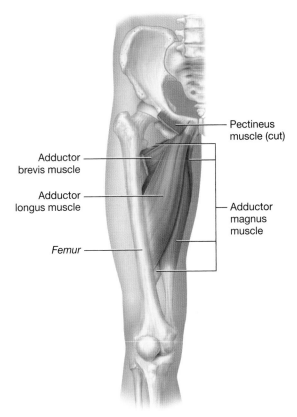

FIGURE **10.16** Muscles of the adductor muscle group.

Labels for Figure 10.16:
- Adductor brevis muscle
- Adductor longus muscle
- Femur
- Pectineus muscle (cut)
- Adductor magnus muscle

The remainder of the thigh muscles may move both the thigh and leg, or just the leg. One of the most prominent groups of thigh muscles is located in the anterior thigh: the **quadriceps femoris group** (*quadricep* = "four heads"). As implied by its name, it consists of four muscles, including the **rectus femoris, vastus medialis, vastus intermedius,** and **vastus lateralis muscles** (*vast-* = "broad"). These four muscles converge to form the common quadriceps femoris or patellar tendon, which envelops the patella. Distal to the patella, the tendon becomes the *patellar ligament,* and inserts into the tibial tuberosity. Note that the vastus intermedius muscle is deep to the rectus femoris muscle and so is not visible in Figure 10.17. The rectus femoris muscle both flexes the thigh and extends the leg, but the vastus group doesn't cross the hip joint and so only extends the leg.

Other prominent thigh muscles include the strap-like **sartorius muscle** (sar-TOHR-ee-uhs), which crosses from lateral to medial across the thigh, and the medial **gracilis muscle** (gruh-SILL-iss; *gracil-* = "slender"). Both these muscles have the dual action of flexing the hip and extending the leg. The sartorius muscle also laterally rotates the thigh (it pulls your leg and thigh into the position you assume when you're looking at something on the bottom of your shoe). The posterior thigh muscles include the three muscles of the **hamstrings group:** the lateral **biceps femoris** and the medial **semitendinosus** (sem-aye-ten-din-OH-suhs) and **semimembranosus** (sem-aye-mem-brah-NOH-suhs) **muscles** (Fig. 10.18). Notice in the figure that the superficial semitendinosus muscle is named for its long, narrow tendon. These three muscles both extend the thigh and flex the knee.

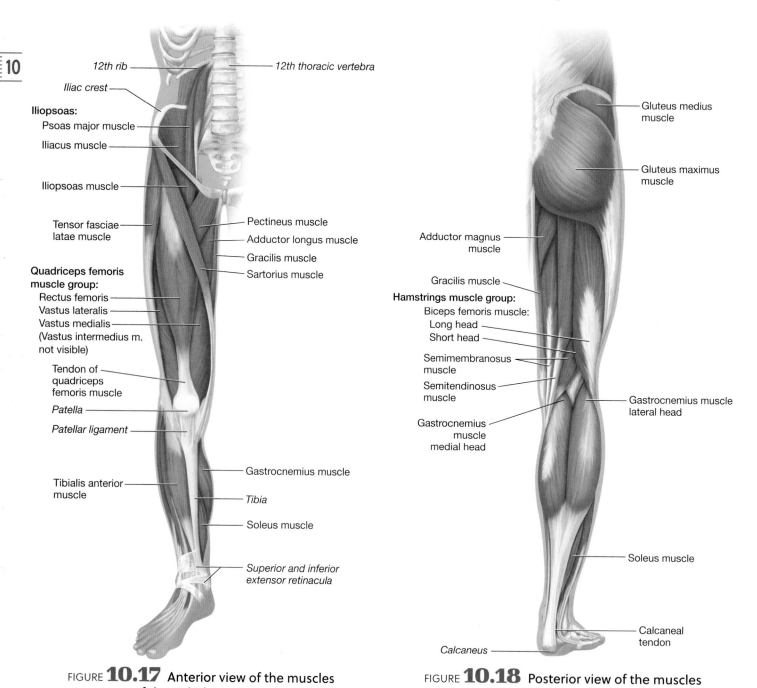

FIGURE **10.17** Anterior view of the muscles of the right lower limb.

FIGURE **10.18** Posterior view of the muscles of the right lower limb.

Muscles That Move the Foot and Toes

The most obvious muscle of the posterior leg is the large **gastrocnemius muscle** (gas-trahk-NEE-mee-uhs), also known as the "calf muscle," a two-headed muscle that originates from the distal femur. Just deep to the gastrocnemius muscle is the **soleus muscle** (SOHL-ee-uhs). Together, these two muscles insert into the posterior calcaneus via a common tendon called the **calcaneal tendon** (kal-KAY-nee-uhl), more commonly known as the *Achilles tendon*. The gastrocnemius and soleus muscles, also known as the *triceps surae muscle*, are the prime plantarflexors of the foot. The gastrocnemius also contributes to flexion of the leg, as it crosses the knee joint.

Deep to the gastrocnemius and soleus muscles, we find the **tibialis posterior muscle** (tib-ee-AL-is)—the main inverter of the foot—as well as the muscles that plantarflex the foot and the digits (Fig. 10.18). On the lateral leg, we find two muscles, the **fibularis longus** (fib-yoo-LEHR-iss) and **fibularis brevis muscles**, which are the main everters of the foot. Anteriorly on the leg, we find extensors such as the **extensor digitorum longus**, which extends the toes, and the **tibialis anterior**, which dorsiflexes the foot. These and other leg muscles are labeled in Figures 10.19 and 10.20 for reference purposes. Figure 10.21 provides photos of anatomical models of the lower limb and leg, also for your reference.

Figures 10.22 and 10.23 provide whole-body views of many of the muscles we have just discussed. Other muscles and anatomical landmarks are labeled to help orient you and for your reference.

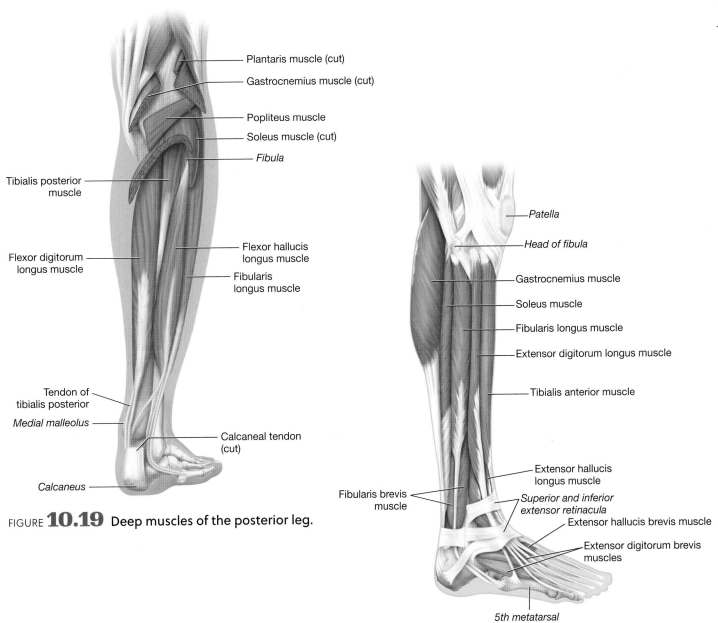

FIGURE **10.19** Deep muscles of the posterior leg.

FIGURE **10.20** Lateral view of muscles of the leg.

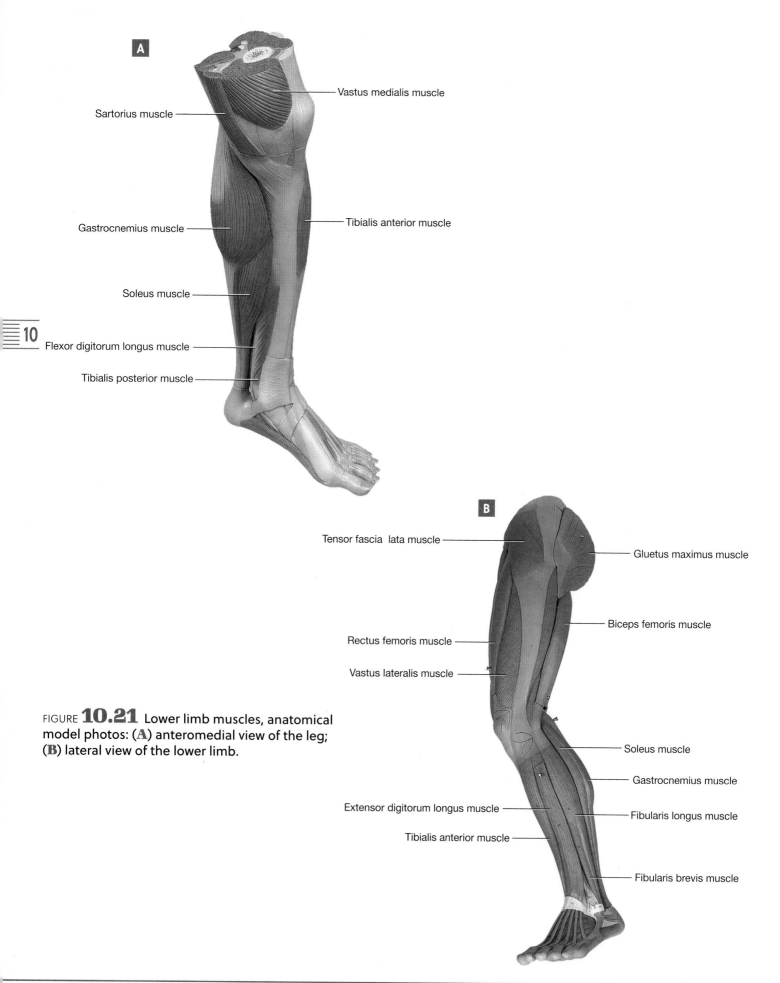

A

Sartorius muscle

Vastus medialis muscle

Gastrocnemius muscle

Tibialis anterior muscle

Soleus muscle

Flexor digitorum longus muscle

Tibialis posterior muscle

B

Tensor fascia lata muscle

Gluetus maximus muscle

Biceps femoris muscle

Rectus femoris muscle

Vastus lateralis muscle

Soleus muscle

Gastrocnemius muscle

Extensor digitorum longus muscle

Fibularis longus muscle

Tibialis anterior muscle

Fibularis brevis muscle

FIGURE **10.21** Lower limb muscles, anatomical model photos: (**A**) anteromedial view of the leg; (**B**) lateral view of the lower limb.

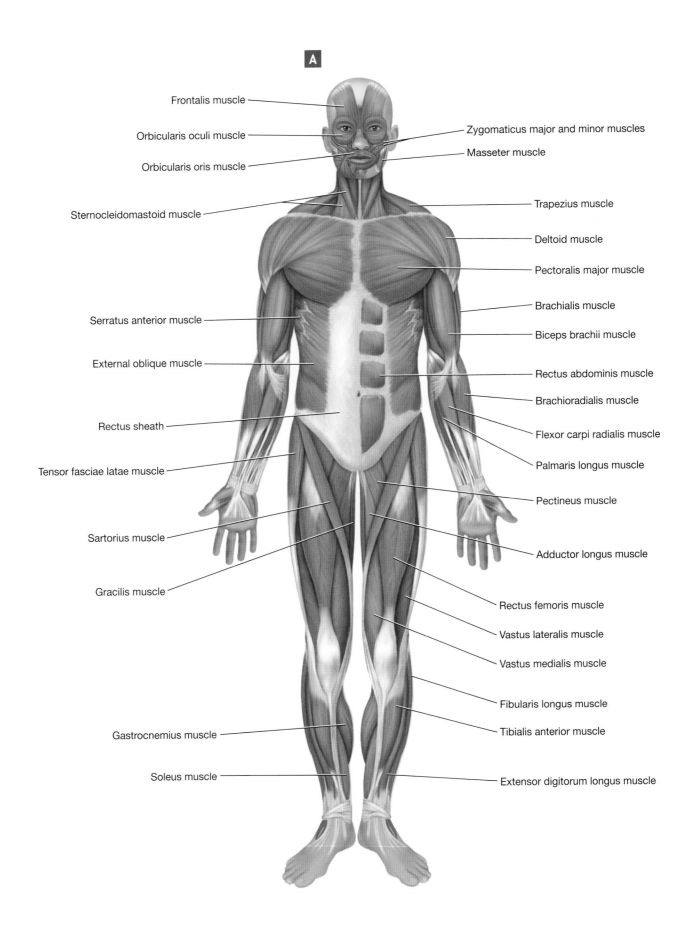

FIGURE **10.22** Anterior view of the muscles of the body: (**A**) illustration; *(continues)*

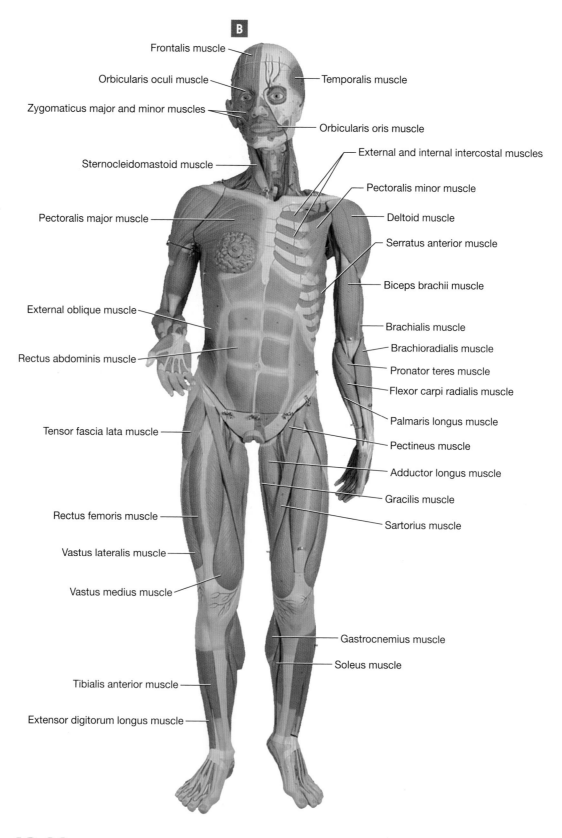

Frontalis muscle

Orbicularis oculi muscle

Zygomaticus major and minor muscles

Sternocleidomastoid muscle

Pectoralis major muscle

External oblique muscle

Rectus abdominis muscle

Tensor fascia lata muscle

Rectus femoris muscle

Vastus lateralis muscle

Vastus medius muscle

Tibialis anterior muscle

Extensor digitorum longus muscle

Temporalis muscle

Orbicularis oris muscle

External and internal intercostal muscles

Pectoralis minor muscle

Deltoid muscle

Serratus anterior muscle

Biceps brachii muscle

Brachialis muscle

Brachioradialis muscle

Pronator teres muscle

Flexor carpi radialis muscle

Palmaris longus muscle

Pectineus muscle

Adductor longus muscle

Gracilis muscle

Sartorius muscle

Gastrocnemius muscle

Soleus muscle

FIGURE **10.22** Anterior view of the muscles of the body (*cont.*): (**B**) anatomical model photo.

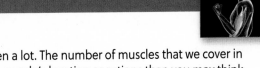

Muscle Names

What's in a name? When it comes to a skeletal muscle, there's often a lot. The number of muscles that we cover in this lab may seem intimidating, but it can be easier to figure out a muscle's location or actions than you may think. Many muscles have descriptive names, which you may have noticed from your reading of the preceding section. Some of the common features used in muscle names include the following:

ⓘ **Size.** Many muscle names include clues about their size. Some of these are obvious—*longus* describes a long muscle, and a pair of *major* and *minor* muscles describes a set in which one is larger and one is smaller. Others are a little less obvious, such as *brevis*, which means short (think "brief"), or *vastus*, which means wide (think "vast").

ⓘ **Location.** A great many muscles are named for their location. This can include directional terms, such as *lateralis*, *superficialis*, or *anterior*. It can also include regional terms such as *abdominis*, *cervicis* (neck), *brachii* (arm), and *costal* (rib). Finally, some of the terms that describe location use words or prefixes with which you're likely already familiar such as *sub-* (below) and *profundus* (deep—think "profound").

ⓘ **Appearance or shape.** Several muscles have names based on their appearance or shape. For example, the semitendinosus muscle has a very long tendon, and the rhomboid major and minor muscles are shaped like a rhombus. Similarly, the orbicularis oris and orbicularis oculi muscles are named for their circular structure, as "orb" means "sphere."

ⓘ **Points of origin.** Related to appearance is a muscle's number of points of origin, or "heads." We see this with muscles named *biceps*, *triceps*, and *quadriceps*, which mean "two-headed," "three-headed," and "four-headed," respectively.

ⓘ **Function.** Finally, the function of many muscles is revealed in their names. As you can imagine, an *extensor* has extension as a primary action, and an *adductor* has adduction as a primary action.

When you take all this into consideration, it's much easier to figure out the location, appearance, and, occasionally, function of complicated-sounding muscles. For example, if you are tasked with identifying the brachioradialis muscle, just from its name you can infer that it is a muscle that attaches to the arm (brachio-) and the radius (radialis). Similarly, the tibialis anterior muscle is clearly a muscle on the anterior tibia, and the iliocostalis muscle has attachments to the ilium and the ribs (*cost* = "ribs"). If we take a more complicated muscle name, such as the extensor carpi radialis longus muscle, we can say that it is a long muscle that originates from the radius, inserts into the carpals, and extends the hand at the wrist. See? It's not as difficult as you thought.

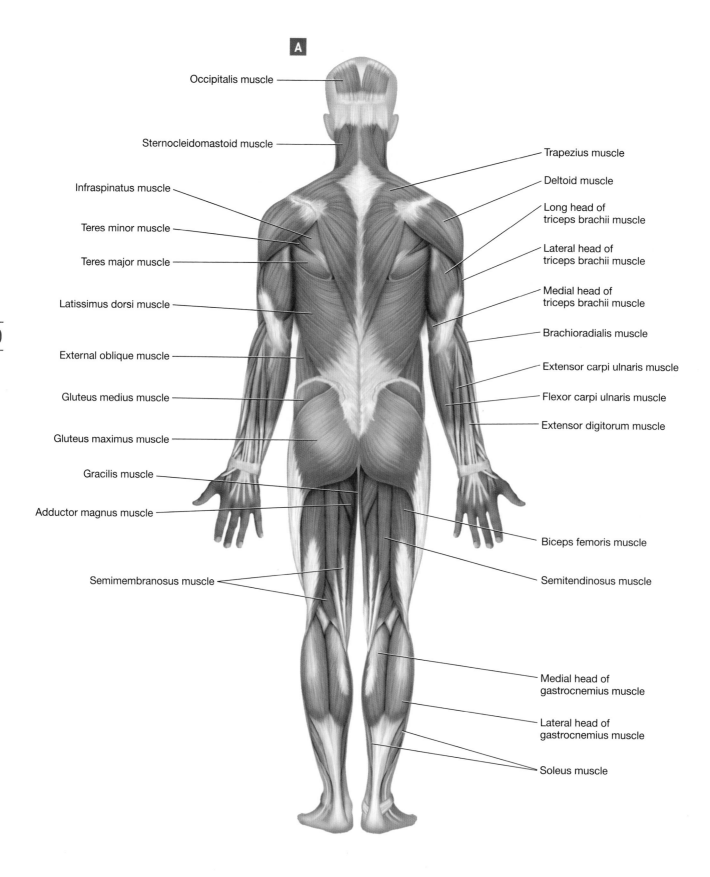

Occipitalis muscle

Sternocleidomastoid muscle

Infraspinatus muscle

Teres minor muscle

Teres major muscle

Latissimus dorsi muscle

External oblique muscle

Gluteus medius muscle

Gluteus maximus muscle

Gracilis muscle

Adductor magnus muscle

Semimembranosus muscle

Trapezius muscle

Deltoid muscle

Long head of
triceps brachii muscle

Lateral head of
triceps brachii muscle

Medial head of
triceps brachii muscle

Brachioradialis muscle

Extensor carpi ulnaris muscle

Flexor carpi ulnaris muscle

Extensor digitorum muscle

Biceps femoris muscle

Semitendinosus muscle

Medial head of
gastrocnemius muscle

Lateral head of
gastrocnemius muscle

Soleus muscle

FIGURE **10.23** Posterior view of the muscles of the body: (**A**) illustration; (*continues*)

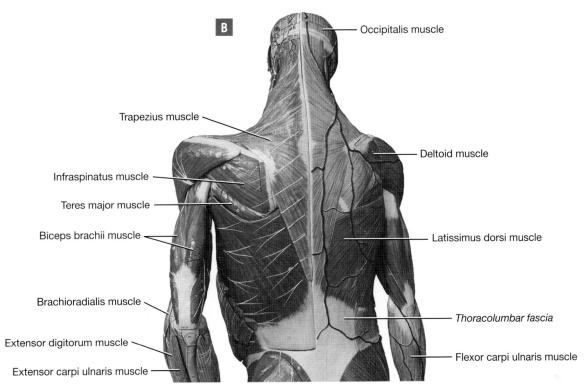

FIGURE **10.23** Posterior view of the muscles of the body (*cont.*): (**B**) anatomical model photo.

Labels (clockwise from top): Occipitalis muscle — Deltoid muscle — Latissimus dorsi muscle — Thoracolumbar fascia — Flexor carpi ulnaris muscle — Extensor carpi ulnaris muscle — Extensor digitorum muscle — Brachioradialis muscle — Biceps brachii muscle — Teres major muscle — Infraspinatus muscle — Trapezius muscle

1 PROCEDURE

Model Inventory for the Skeletal Muscles

Identify the following muscles on models and diagrams, using your textbook and this unit for reference. As you examine the anatomical models and diagrams, record the name of the model and the structures you were able to identify on the model inventory in Table 10.2. When you have completed the activity, answer Check Your Understanding Questions 1 through 3 (p. 297).

Muscles That Move the Head, Neck, and Face

1. Muscles of facial expression
   a. Frontalis m.
   b. Occipitalis m.
   c. Orbicularis oculi m.
   d. Orbicularis oris m.
   e. Buccinator m.
   f. Platysma m.
   g. Zygomaticus major and minor mm.
   h. Risorius m.
2. Muscles of mastication
   a. Masseter m.
   b. Temporalis m.
3. Muscles of head and neck
   a. Sternocleidomastoid m.
   b. Splenius capitis m.
   c. Splenius cervicis m.

Muscles That Move the Trunk

1. Muscles of the thorax
   a. External intercostal mm.
   b. Internal intercostal mm.
   c. Diaphragm m.
   d. Pectoralis minor m.
2. Muscles of the abdominal wall
   a. Rectus abdominis m.
   b. External oblique m.
   c. Internal oblique m.
   d. Transversus abdominis m.
3. Postural muscles of the back
   a. Erector spinae m.
      (1) Iliocostalis m.
      (2) Longissimus m.
      (3) Spinalis m.

Muscles That Move the Scapula

1. Serratus anterior m.
2. Trapezius m.
3. Levator scapulae m.
4. Rhomboid major and minor mm.

Muscles That Move the Arm

1. Latissimus dorsi m.
2. Teres major m.
3. Pectoralis major m.
4. Deltoid m.
5. Rotator cuff muscles
   a. Infraspinatus m.
   b. Teres minor m.
   c. Supraspinatus m.
   d. Subscapularis m.

Muscles That Move the Forearm, Hand, and Fingers

1. Muscles of the arm
   a. Biceps brachii m.
   b. Brachialis m.
   c. Brachioradialis m.
   d. Triceps brachii m.
2. Flexors of the forearm
   a. Flexor carpi radialis m.
   b. Flexor carpi ulnaris m.
   c. Flexor digitorum superficialis m.
   d. Flexor digitorum profundus m.
3. Extensors of the forearm
   a. Extensor carpi radialis longus m.
   b. Extensor digitorum m.
   c. Extensor carpi ulnaris m.

Muscles That Move the Thigh and Leg

1. Muscles that move the thigh only
   a. Gluteus maximus m.
   b. Gluteus medius m.
   c. Adductor brevis m.
   d. Adductor longus m.
   e. Adductor magnus m.
   f. Iliopsoas m.
   g. Pectineus m.
2. Muscles that move the thigh and the leg
   a. Quadriceps femoris group
      (1) Rectus femoris m.
      (2) Vastus medialis m.
      (3) Vastus intermedius m.
      (4) Vastus lateralis m.
   b. Sartorius m.
   c. Gracilis m.
   d. Hamstrings group
      (1) Biceps femoris m.
      (2) Semitendinosus m.
      (3) Semimembranosus m.

Muscles That Move the Foot and Toes

1. Gastrocnemius m.
2. Soleus m.
3. Tibialis posterior m.
4. Fibularis longus m.
5. Fibularis brevis m.
6. Extensor digitorum longus m.
7. Tibialis anterior m.

Your instructor may wish to omit certain muscles included above or add muscles not included in these lists. List any additional structures in the space provided:

TABLE **10.2** Model Inventory for Skeletal Muscles

Model/Diagram	Structures Identified

10

MATERIALS

❑ Skeletons, small
❑ Modeling clay in five
   colors

Muscle Origins, Insertions, and Actions

You can best understand a muscle's actions by first understanding its origin and insertion. As we discussed in the introduction to this unit, the **origin** of a muscle generally is the more stationary part, and the muscle typically **inserts** into the part that it moves. For example, you can see in Figure 10.24 that the biceps brachii muscle originates on the coracoid process of the scapula and crosses the elbow joint, where it inserts into the radial tuberosity. Notice also that the triceps brachii muscle originates from the humerus and the inferior scapula and crosses the elbow joint to insert into the olecranon process.

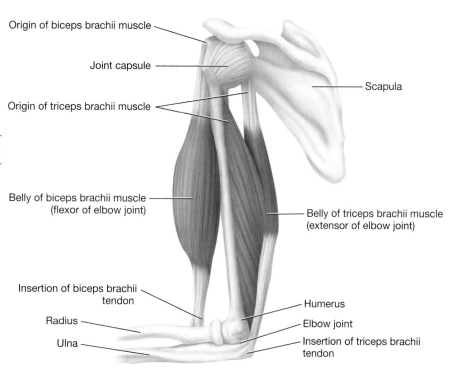

Origin of biceps brachii muscle

Joint capsule

Origin of triceps brachii muscle

Scapula

Belly of biceps brachii muscle
(flexor of elbow joint)

Belly of triceps brachii muscle
(extensor of elbow joint)

Insertion of biceps brachii
tendon

Radius

Ulna

Humerus

Elbow joint

Insertion of triceps brachii
tendon

After you determine a muscle's origin and insertion, figuring out its actions becomes easy. Let's examine the biceps brachii and triceps brachii muscles again. The biceps brachii muscle inserts into the radial tuberosity, so we know it will move the forearm. Given how it crosses the anterior elbow joint, we can conclude it will cause forearm *flexion* at the elbow joint. The triceps brachii muscle inserts into the olecranon process, so we know it also will move the forearm. Given how it crosses the posterior elbow joint, we can conclude that it will cause forearm *extension* at the elbow joint. Now, wasn't that easy? So, you don't need to actually memorize most muscle actions—all you need to do is look at a muscle's origin and insertion and use some basic logic to figure out its actions. We practice doing this in the next two procedures.

FIGURE **10.24** Origin and insertion of the biceps brachii and triceps brachii muscles, posterior view.

PROCEDURE 1

Building Muscles

In this procedure, you will use small skeletons and modeling clay to build specific muscle groups. This may sound easy, but there is a catch: You must determine the actions of the muscle by looking only at the origin and insertion of each muscle you build. Use Pre-Lab Exercise 10-3 (p. 268) as a guide to each muscle's origin and insertion. When you have finished the activity, answer Check Your Understanding Questions 4 and 5 (pp. 297–298).

1 Obtain a small skeleton and five colors of modeling clay.

2 Build the indicated muscles, using a different color of clay for each muscle. As you build, pay careful attention to the origin and insertion of each muscle.

3 Determine the primary actions for each muscle you have built by looking *only* at the origin and insertion. Record this information in Tables 10.3 through 10.5.

TABLE **10.3** Muscles and Actions for Group 1

Muscle	Actions
Biceps femoris m.	
Rectus femoris m.	
Gluteus medius m.	
Adductor m. group	

TABLE **10.4** Muscles and Actions for Group 2

Muscle	Actions
Biceps brachii m.	
Triceps brachii m.	
Deltoid m.	
Pectoralis major m.	

TABLE **10.5** Muscles and Actions for Group 3

Muscle	Actions
Gastrocnemius m.	
Tibialis anterior m.	
Rectus abdominis m.	
Trapezius m.	

PROCEDURE

Identifying Muscle Actions of Common Movements

This procedure should look familiar, because you did a similar procedure in Unit 9 (Articulations, p. 239). As before, you will be performing various activities to demonstrate which joints are moving with each activity. In this procedure, however, rather than focusing on the motions that occur at each joint, you will be determining *which muscles* are causing the motions at each joint. Following is an example:

Walking in Place

Part 1

First, list all motions occurring at each joint (as before, the joints are listed with their common names, and the lists are certainly *not* all-inclusive):

 10

- Vertebral column and neck: extension
- Shoulder: flexion/extension
- Elbow: flexion
- Hip: flexion/extension, abduction/adduction
- Knee: flexion/extension
- Ankle: dorsiflexion/plantarflexion, inversion/eversion

Part 2

Now, refer to Table 10.1 in Pre-Lab Exercise 10-2 (p. 266) to determine which muscles are causing each joint to move. Please note that these lists are far from complete. With nearly 700 muscles in the human body, a complete list could take all day!

- Vertebral column and neck
  - Extension: erector spinae and trapezius muscles
- Shoulder
  - Flexion: pectoralis major muscle
  - Extension: latissimus dorsi muscle
- Elbow
  - Flexion: biceps brachii, brachialis, and brachioradialis muscles
- Hip
  - Flexion: iliopsoas and sartorius muscles
  - Extension: biceps femoris, semitendinosus, semimembranosus, and gluteus maximus muscles
  - Abduction: tensor fasciae latae, sartorius, and gluteus medius muscles
  - Adduction: gracilis and adductor muscles
- Knee
  - Flexion: biceps femoris, semitendinosus, semimembranosus, and gastrocnemius muscles
  - Extension: rectus femoris, vastus medialis, vastus intermedius, and vastus lateralis muscles
- Ankle
  - Dorsiflexion: tibialis anterior muscle
  - Plantarflexion: gastrocnemius and soleus muscles
  - Inversion: tibialis anterior and tibialis posterior muscles
  - Eversion: fibularis brevis and fibularis longus muscles

OK, so now you're thinking, "Wow, that's a lot of work!" Following are a few hints that will make this task less daunting:

- You will notice that the following activities are the same as the activities from Exercise 9-5 (p. 257) in Unit 9. To save yourself some work, reference that exercise to complete Part 1 of this exercise.
- As before, perform the indicated activity. If you don't, you'll miss some things.

- Unless your instructor asks you to do otherwise, try to keep it simple. List only the main muscles for each action. For example, when listing the muscles to flex the hip, we easily could include 10 different muscles. To make it simpler, list only those muscles we discussed that flex the hip as their primary action (as in the example on this page).

Ready to give it a try? Determine the joints being moved for Part 1, and then determine the muscles moving the joints for Part 2. Refer to Unit 9 (p. 239) for help. When you have completed the activity, answer Check Your Understanding Question 6 (p. 298).

1 Walking down stairs

Part 1:

Part 2:

2 Performing a pushup

Part 1:

Part 2:

3 Throwing a baseball

Part 1:

Part 2:

4 Performing a lunge

Part 1:

Part 2:

Name _____

Section _____ Date _____

UNIT
10
REVIEW

Check Your Recall

1 Label the following muscles on Figure 10.25.

❏ Buccinator m.

❏ Masseter m.

❏ Occipitalis m.

❏ Orbicularis oculi m.

❏ Orbicularis oris m.

❏ Platysma m.

❏ Risorius m.

❏ Sternocleidomastoid m.

❏ Temporalis m.

❏ Zygomaticus minor m.

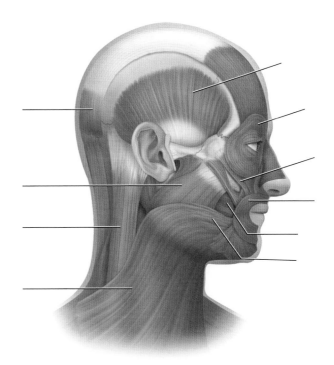

FIGURE **10.25** Facial musculature, lateral view.

2 Which of the following muscles extends the forearm at the elbow joint?

a. Brachioradialis m.

b. Triceps brachii m.

c. Biceps brachii m.

d. Brachialis m.

3 *Circle all that apply.* Which of the following muscles flex the forearm at the elbow joint?

a. Flexor digitorum superficialis m.

b. Triceps brachii m.

c. Brachioradialis m.

d. Brachialis m.

e. Flexor hallucis longus m.

f. Biceps brachii m.

4 Which of the following muscles flexes the thigh at the hip?

a. Iliopsoas m.

b. Biceps femoris m.

c. Vastus intermedius m.

d. Gluteus medius m.

5 What is the difference between a muscle's origin and insertion? What can you determine by knowing the origin and insertion?

6 Label the following muscles of Figure 10.26.

❑ External oblique m.
❑ Gluteus medius m.
❑ Iliocostalis m.
❑ Infraspinatus m.
❑ Internal oblique m.
❑ Latissimus dorsi m.
❑ Levator scapulae m.
❑ Longissimus m.
❑ Rectus abdominis m.
❑ Rhomboid major m.
❑ Serratus anterior m.
❑ Transversus abdominis m.
❑ Trapezius m.

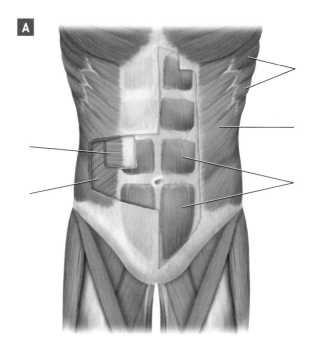

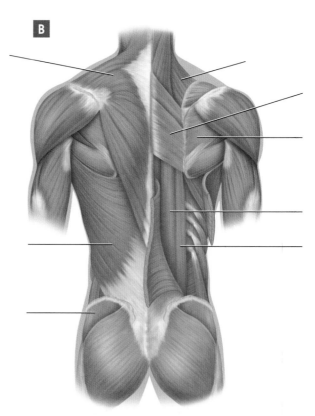

FIGURE **10.26** Muscles of the trunk: (**A**) anterior view; (**B**) posterior view.

7 Label the following muscles on Figure 10.27.

- ❑ Biceps brachii m.
- ❑ Brachialis m.
- ❑ Brachioradialis m.
- ❑ Deltoid m.

- ❑ Extensor digitorum m.
- ❑ Flexor carpi ulnaris m.
- ❑ Pectoralis major m.
- ❑ Supraspinatus m.

- ❑ Teres minor m.
- ❑ Triceps brachii m.

10

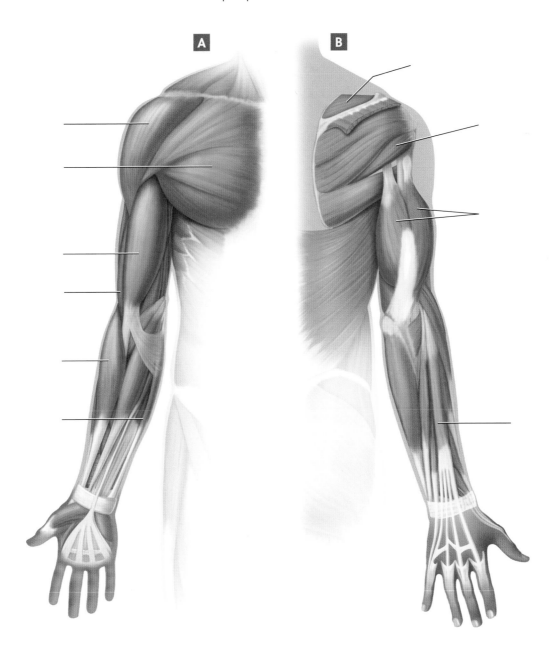

FIGURE **10.27** Muscles of the right upper limb: (**A**) anterior view; (**B**) posterior view.

8 What is the main action of the latissimus dorsi muscle?

    a. Extension of the arm at the shoulder joint.

    b. Rotation of the back.

    c. Extension of the back.

    d. Abduction of the arm at the shoulder joint.

9 Label the following muscles on Figure 10.28.

    ❏ Biceps femoris m.

    ❏ Gastrocnemius m.

    ❏ Gracilis m.

    ❏ Iliopsoas m.

    ❏ Pectineus m.

    ❏ Rectus femoris m.

    ❏ Sartorius m.

    ❏ Semimembranosus m.

    ❏ Semitendinosus m.

    ❏ Soleus m.

    ❏ Tibialis anterior m.

    ❏ Vastus lateralis m.

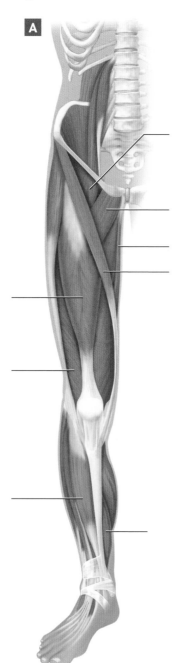
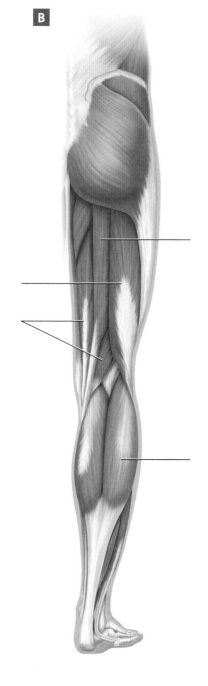

FIGURE **10.28** Muscles of the right lower limb: (**A**) anterior view; (**B**) posterior view.

10 What is the main action of the transversus abdominis muscle?

    a. Maintaining posture.

    b. Lateral flexion of the trunk.

    c. Compression of abdominal contents.

    d. Extension of the trunk.

Name _____

Section _____ Date_____

Check Your Understanding

Critical Thinking and Application Questions

1 Muscle strain, or "pulling a muscle," may result from overuse injuries or from trauma. Typically, muscle strain causes pain around the muscle with movement and with pressure. Predict which muscle or muscles may be strained if a patient complains of pain in each of the following locations:

a Anterior thigh _____

b Posterior forearm _____

c Scapula _____

d Gluteal region _____

e Posteromedial leg _____

f Cervical region of the back _____

2 A stroke, caused by a clot in a blood vessel of the brain, may lead to a loss of function of certain muscles. Which motions would an individual be unable to perform if the following muscles lost function?

a Orbicularis oris m. _____

b Trapezius m. _____

c Rectus femoris m. _____

3 Predict the location, appearance, and function of the *extensor carpi ulnaris* muscle by looking only at its name.

_____

_____

_____

4 The *adductor longus* muscle originates from the pubic bone of the pelvis and inserts into the medial femur. The *semimembranosus* muscle originates from the ischial tuberosity of the pelvis and inserts into the medial tibia.

a Predict the actions of each muscle from this information.

_____

_____

b How do their different origins and insertions explain their different actions?

_____

_____

5 The *soleus* muscle originates from the posterior tibia and fibula, and inserts into the posterior calcaneus.

    a Predict its action from this information. _____

    _____

    b Suppose the origin and insertion of the soleus m. switched. What would be its action now? _____

    _____

6 A soccer player falls and injures her right lower limb. Injuries to which lower limb muscles would most interfere with her ability to kick the ball?

_____

_____

_____

_____

10

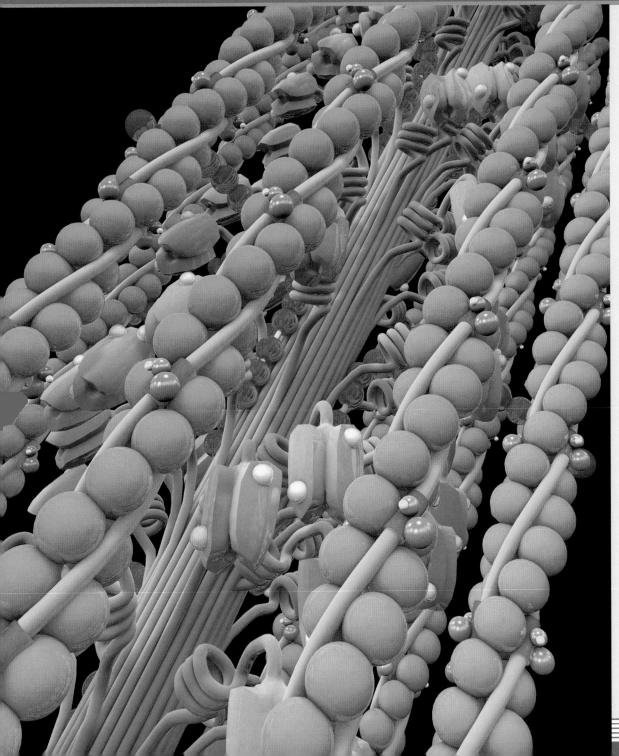

Muscle Tissue

When you have completed this unit, you should be able to:

1 Describe the microscopic anatomy of skeletal muscle fibers.

2 Identify structures of skeletal muscle fibers on anatomical models and microscope slides.

3 Identify structures associated with the neuromuscular junction on anatomical models and microscope slides.

4 Describe the mechanism of skeletal muscle contraction, including the roles of ATP and calcium ions.

5 Describe the length-tension relationship of skeletal muscle fibers.

6 Distinguish between smooth and cardiac muscle tissue.

Name _____   Section _____   Date _____

Complete the following exercises prior to coming to lab, using your lab manual and textbook for reference.

PRE-LAB

11-1 Key Terms

You should be familiar with the following terms before coming to lab.

Term	Definition

General Skeletal Muscle Structures

Epimysium _____

Fascicle _____

11 Perimysium _____

Muscle fiber _____

Endomysium _____

Structures of the Skeletal Muscle Fiber

Sarcolemma _____

T-tubule _____

Sarcoplasmic reticulum _____

Myofibril _____

Thick filament _____

Myosin _____

Thin filament _____

Actin _____

Elastic filament _____

Structures of the Neuromuscular Junction

Neuromuscular junction _____

Axon terminal _____

Acetylcholine _____

Motor end plate _____

Components of the Sarcomere

A band _____

I band _____

Z disc _____

Terms of Muscle Physiology

Action potential _____

Depolarization _____

Repolarization _____

Crossbridge cycle _____

Excitation-contraction coupling _____

Sliding filament mechanism _____

Length-tension relationship _____

Color the basic structures of skeletal muscles depicted in Figure 11.1, and label them with the terms from Exercise 11-1 (p. 305). Use your text and Exercise 11-1 in this unit for reference.

11

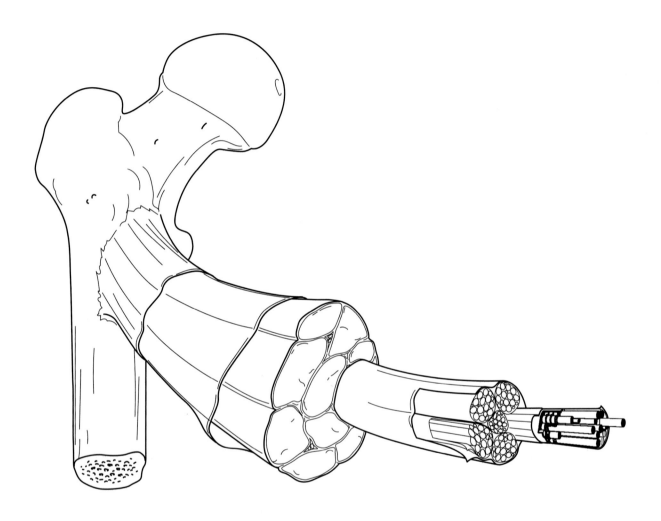

FIGURE **11.1** Skeletal muscle structural levels of organization.

PRE-LAB

11-3   Muscle Fiber Microanatomy

Color the microscopic anatomy of the skeletal muscle fiber and neuromuscular junction in Figures 11.2 and 11.3, and label them with the terms from Exercise 11-1 (p. 305). Use your text and Exercise 11-1 in this unit for reference.

A

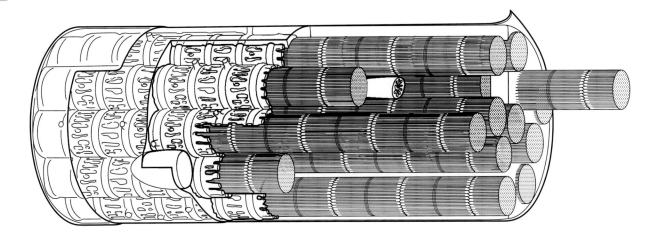

11

B

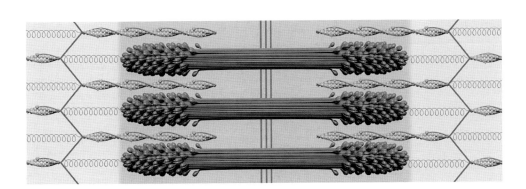

FIGURE **11.2** Skeletal muscle fiber: (**A**) myofibrils and organelles; (**B**) myofilaments.

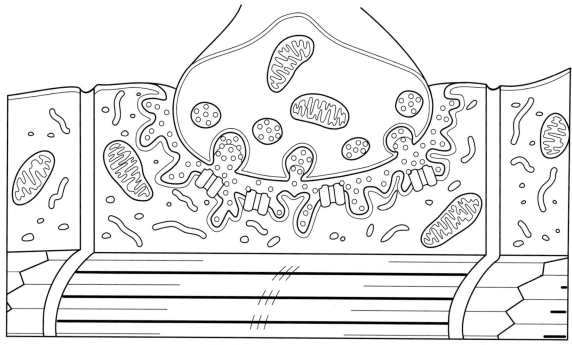

FIGURE **11.3** Neuromuscular junction.

11-4 Types of Muscle Tissue

You learned about the three types of muscle tissue in Exercise 5-3 (p. 135). Review the properties of each type of muscle tissue by filling in Table 11.1.

TABLE **11.1** The Three Types of Muscle Tissue

Muscle Type	Striated or Nonstriated	One or Multiple Nuclei	Size and Shape of Cells	Voluntary or Involuntary	Special Features
Cardiac muscle					
Skeletal muscle					
Smooth muscle					

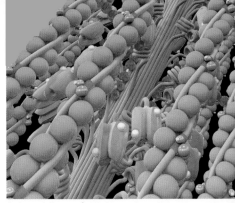
Actin-myosin muscle structure.

EXERCISES

This unit explores the structure and function of muscle tissue. There are three types of muscle tissue: *skeletal, cardiac,* and *smooth*. Although the three types differ in structure, they all share the same basic function—to generate a force called **tension**. In this unit, we focus on skeletal muscle tissue to build on what you learned in the previous unit. Although generally we study anatomy and physiology from the microscopic (chemical, cell, and tissue) level to the gross (organ and organ system) level, we do it backward with the muscular system. The reason for this is simply one of continuity— skeletal muscles as organs have a close structural and functional relationship with the skeleton and joints, and muscle tissue has a close structural and functional relationship with nervous tissue, our next topic.

You were already introduced to the basic structure and function of muscle tissue in Exercise 5-3 (p. 135). The first two exercises in this unit expand on these topics with an examination of the gross and microscopic structure of skeletal muscles and the nerve cells that supply them. In the third exercise, we apply what we learned about skeletal muscle structure to skeletal muscle physiology. In the final exercise, we examine the structure of smooth and cardiac muscle tissue to help you differentiate these tissue types on microscope slides.

EXERCISE 11-1

MATERIALS

❑ Anatomical models and diagrams:
  ▪ skeletal muscle
  ▪ skeletal muscle fiber
  ▪ neuromuscular junction
❑ Slides:
  ▪ skeletal muscle tissue
  ▪ neuromuscular junction
❑ Light microscope with oil-immersion objective
❑ Oil
❑ Colored pencils

Skeletal Muscle Anatomy and Microanatomy

Recall that skeletal muscle tissue is composed of skeletal muscle cells, also called **muscle fibers**. Individual skeletal muscle fibers are surrounded by their extracellular matrix, known as the **endomysium** (in-doh-MY-see-um; *endo-* = "within;" *my-* = "muscle"). (Note that the endomysium blends with surrounding connective tissue and so is often referred to as connective tissue itself.) Muscle fibers are arranged into groups called **fascicles** (FASS-ih-kullz; *fasc-* = "bundle;" Fig. 11.4). Each fascicle is surrounded by a connective tissue sheath called the **perimysium** (pehr-ih-MY-see-um; *peri-* = "around"). The muscle as a whole is covered by another connective tissue sheath called the **epimysium** (ep-ih-MY-see-um; *epi-* = "on top"), which holds the muscle together structurally, even during forceful contractions. The epimysium and perimysium merge near the end of a muscle to form *tendons* and *aponeuroses*, which connect the muscle to bones or soft tissue.

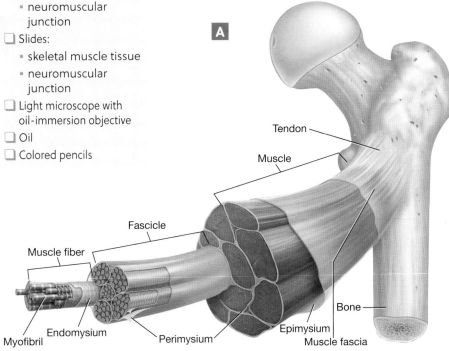

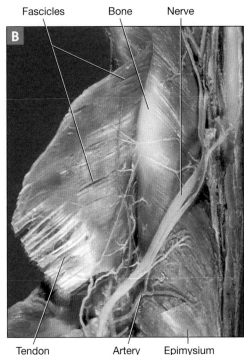

FIGURE **11.4** Overview of skeletal muscle structure: (**A**) skeletal muscle structural levels of organization; (**B**) dissected muscle.

The most superficial connective tissue around a skeletal muscle is thick **fascia** (FASH-uh), which separates individual muscles and binds them into groups.

As you can see in Figures 11.5 and 11.6, the long, multinucleated, cylindrical skeletal muscle fiber is quite different in appearance from the cells you are used to seeing. Due to these differences, we use different terms to describe some of a muscle fiber's structures. For example, the muscle fiber's plasma membrane is known as the **sarcolemma** (sar-koh-LEM-uh; *sarc-* = "flesh;" *lemma* = "sheath"), and its cytoplasm is called **sarcoplasm** (SAR-koh-plazm; Fig. 11.5A).

Small, cylindrical organelles called **myofibrils** (my-oh-FY-brillz) make up about 80% of the skeletal muscle fiber's sarcoplasm. Myofibrils are composed of subunits known as **myofilaments**, which themselves are composed of muscle proteins, including contractile,

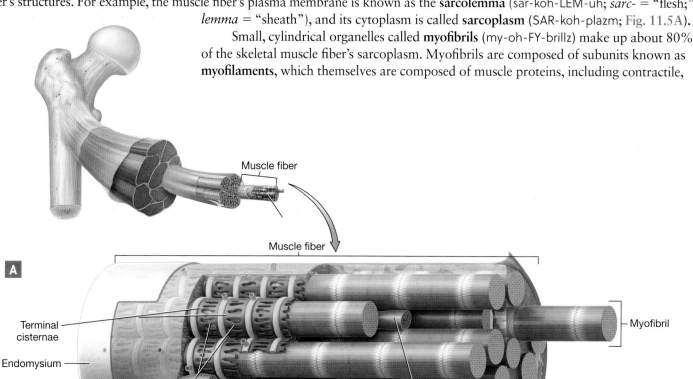

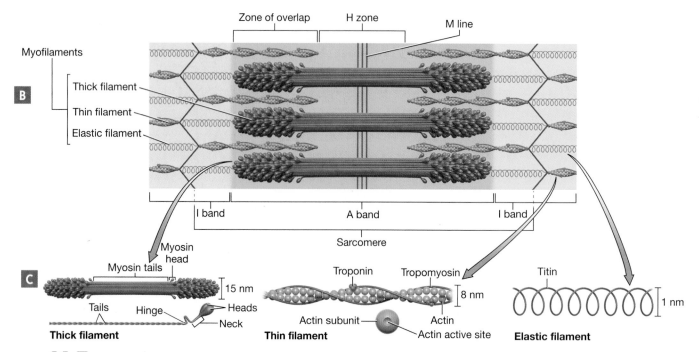

FIGURE **11.5** Skeletal muscle structure: (**A**) myofibrils and organelles; (**B**) myofilaments; (**C**) myofilament proteins.

structural, and/or regulatory proteins. Other organelles such as mitochondria are packed in between the myofibrils. Notice in the figure that myofibrils are wrapped by the weblike **sarcoplasmic reticulum** (sar-koh-PLAZ-mik reh-TIK-yoo-lum; **SR**), which is a modified smooth endoplasmic reticulum that stores calcium ions. Myofibrils are also wrapped by inward extensions of the sarcolemma known as **transverse tubules** or **T-tubules**. On either side of a T-tubule, the SR swells to form **terminal cisternae** (sis-TUR-nee; *cistern* = "reservoir"); a T-tubule and two terminal cisternae form a structure called a **triad**. These structures are important for coordinating electrical stimulation of the muscle fiber with release of calcium ions from the SR and initiation of a muscle contraction.

Tension generation—the actual muscle contraction—occurs at the level of the myofilaments. There are three types of myofilaments (**Figs. 11.5B** and **11.5C**):

1. **Thick filaments** are composed of many units of the contractile protein **myosin** (MY-oh-sin). Each myosin protein looks like two twisted golf clubs—the "handles" of the golf clubs are the *myosin tails*, and the "heads" of the golf clubs are—appropriately—the *myosin heads*.

2. **Thin filaments** are composed of the contractile protein **actin** (AK-tin; *actin* = "ray"). Each actin subunit is shaped somewhat like a bead, and the thin filament consists of multiple actin subunits arranged like beads on a string. Actin subunits contain a location called the *active site*, which binds to myosin heads during a contraction. Thin filaments also contain the regulatory proteins **troponin** (TROH-poh-nin; *trop-* = "turning") and **tropomyosin** (trohp-oh-MY-oh-sin), which are involved in turning a contraction "on" or "off."

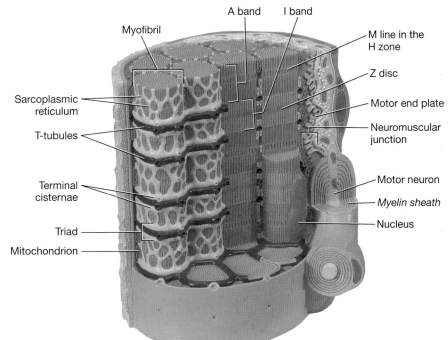

FIGURE **11.6** Skeletal muscle fiber, anatomical model photo.

3. **Elastic filaments** are composed of the spring-shaped structural protein **titin** (TY-tin). Titin is located at the core of the thick filament, where it structurally stabilizes the myofibril. Its spring-shape also gives the myofibril a critical property: elasticity, or the ability to recoil back to its original size when a stretching force is removed. Elastic filaments also resist excessive stretching.

The arrangement of myofilaments within the myofibrils is what gives skeletal muscle its characteristic **striated** (*stria-* = "streak") appearance that you can see in **Figures 11.5** and **11.6**. The dark regions of the striations, called **A bands**, are dark because this is where we find overlapping thick and thin filaments or thick filaments alone. The light regions, called **I bands**, appear light because they contain only thin filaments.

On closer inspection, there are more lines and bands than simply the A and I bands:

- In the middle of the A band is a lighter region called the **H zone**, where we find only thick filaments.
- Running down the middle of the H zone is the **M line**, which contains structural proteins that stabilize and support the thick filament.
- On either side of the H zone is an area where both thick and thin filaments are found in the A band; this area is known as the *zone of overlap*.
- In the middle of each I band is a dark line called the **Z disc**, which consists of structural proteins that support the thin filaments and stabilize the structure of the myofibril.

Although these terms might sound like alphabet soup, they are important, as they are used to define the fundamental unit of contraction: the **sarcomere** (SAR-koh-meer; *mere* = "part"). A sarcomere, defined as the space from one Z disc to the next Z disc, consists of a full A band and two half-I bands. This is the unit that generates tension during a contraction.

Model Inventory for Skeletal Muscle and Skeletal Muscle Fibers

Identify the following structures of skeletal muscle and skeletal muscle fibers on models and diagrams, using your textbook and this unit for reference. As you examine the anatomical models and diagrams, record the name of the model and the structures you were able to identify on the model inventory in Table 11.2. When you have finished the activity, answer Check Your Understanding Question 1 (p. 321).

Skeletal Muscle Anatomy

1. Muscle fiber
2. Endomysium
3. Fascicles
4. Connective tissue coverings
   a. Perimysium
   b. Epimysium
   c. Fascia

Muscle Fiber Microanatomy

1. Sarcolemma
2. Sarcoplasm
3. Myofibrils
4. Sarcoplasmic reticulum
5. T-tubules
6. Terminal cisternae
7. Triad
8. Myofilaments
   a. Thick filaments
   b. Thin filaments
   c. Elastic filaments
9. Sarcomere
   a. A band
   b. I band
   c. H zone
   d. M line
   e. Zone of overlap
   f. Z disc

11

TABLE **11.2** Model Inventory for Skeletal Muscle Anatomy and Microanatomy

Model/Diagram	Structures Identified

Examining Skeletal Muscle Tissue with Microscopy

View a prepared slide of skeletal muscle tissue. First, examine the slide with the low-power objective and advance to the high-power objective of your light microscope (see Fig. 11.7A for reference). Draw what you are able to see under the high-power objective, then color your drawing and label it with the terms listed. Then switch to an oil-immersion lens (your instructor may have one set up as a demonstration) and identify the structures of the sarcomere (see Fig. 11.7B for reference).

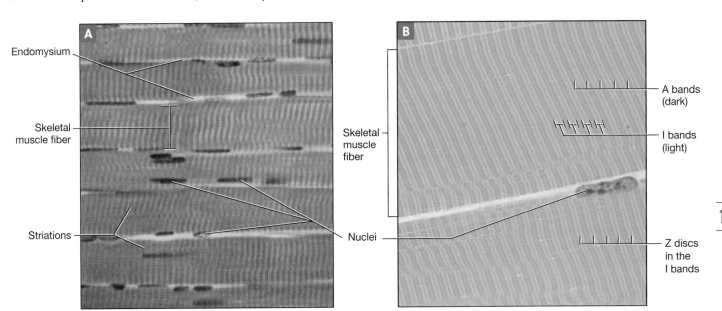

FIGURE **11.7** Skeletal muscle tissue, photomicrograph: (**A**) 40× objective; (**B**) 100× objective oil immersion.

1 High-Power (40×) Objective

- Striations
  - A band
  - I band
- Sarcolemma
- Nuclei
- Endomysium

2 Oil-Immersion Lens

- Sarcomere
- A band
- I band
- Z disc
- H zone
- M line

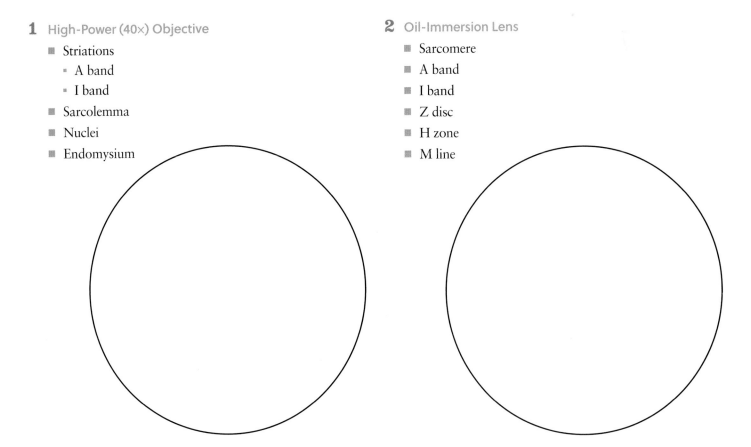

The Neuromuscular Junction

Skeletal muscle fibers are voluntary, which means that they contract under the conscious control of the nervous system. Each skeletal muscle fiber has a **motor neuron** that triggers it to contract. The place where the neuron meets the muscle fiber is called the **neuromuscular junction** (NMJ; Fig. 11.8). The neuromuscular junction consists of three parts:

1. **Axon terminal.** At its end, a motor neuron splits into many branches, each of which terminates in a swollen **axon terminal** (or *synaptic end bulb*) that communicates with one muscle fiber. An axon terminal has **synaptic vesicles** in its cytosol that contain the neurotransmitter **acetylcholine** (ah-SEE-til-koh-leen) or **ACh**.

2. **Synaptic cleft.** The axon terminal doesn't come into direct contact with the muscle fiber; instead, there is a space between the axon terminal and the muscle fiber called the **synaptic cleft.** Within the synaptic cleft is an extracellular gel that contains the enzyme **acetylcholinesterase** (ah-see-til-kohl-in-ESS-ter-ayz; AChE) that catalyzes the breakdown of ACh. This is necessary to terminate ACh stimulation of the muscle fiber.

3. **Motor end plate.** The **motor end plate** is a specialized, folded region of the sarcolemma that contains cation channels called **acetylcholine receptors** to which ACh binds. The binding of the ACh to these channels opens them, beginning the events that will eventually lead to a muscle contraction.

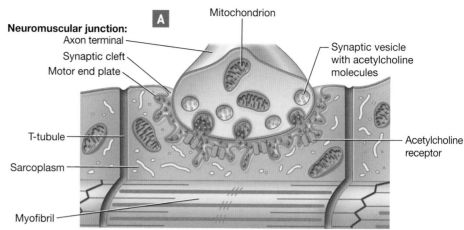

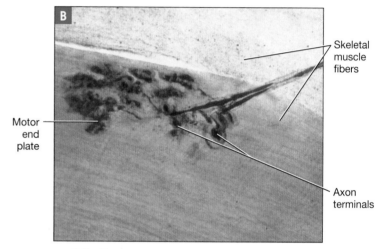

FIGURE **11.8** Neuromuscular junction: (**A**) illustration; (**B**) photomicrograph.

---

3 PROCEDURE
Model Inventory for the Neuromuscular Junction

Identify the following structures of the neuromuscular junction on models and diagrams, using your textbook and this unit for reference. As you examine the anatomical models and diagrams, record the name of the model and the structures you were able to identify on the model inventory in Table 11.2 (note that this is the model inventory you used for the muscle fiber anatomy). When you have finished the activity, answer Check Your Understanding Question 2 (p. 321).

1. Motor neuron
2. Axon terminal
3. Synaptic vesicles
4. Synaptic cleft
5. Motor end plate
6. Acetylcholine receptors

4 PROCEDURE

Examining the Neuromuscular Junction with Microscopy

Obtain a prepared slide of a neuromuscular junction. Use your colored pencils to draw what you see, and label your drawing with the following terms.

Neuromuscular Junction

- Motor neuron
- Axon terminal
- Skeletal muscle fiber
- Striations

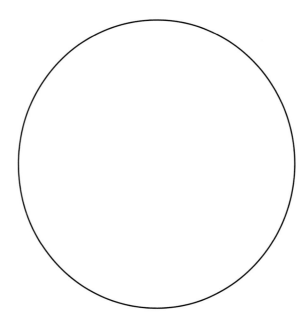

11

- Hand dynamometer
- Anatomical models and diagrams: muscle fiber contraction
- Colored pencils
- Glycerinated muscle, teased, in glycerol in a petri dish
- 0.25% ATP/0.05 M KCl/0.001 M MgCl solution
- 4× magnifying glass
- Glass slides: blank
- Glass needles or teasing needles
- Millimeter ruler
- Light microscope
- Dissecting microscope

11

Muscle Physiology

Skeletal muscle contraction begins when a skeletal muscle fiber is stimulated by a motor neuron, in a relationship known as **excitation–contraction coupling**. Notice in Figure 11.9 what happens when a nerve impulse, also called a **neuronal action potential**, reaches the axon terminal: ACh is released into the synaptic cleft by exocytosis of the synaptic vesicles and binds to its receptors on the motor end plate. This triggers a contraction.

To understand how excitation and contraction are coupled, we need to understand some basics about the branch of physiology known as *electrophysiology*. Two points are important to consider, which are shown in Figure 11.10:

- **A muscle fiber at rest has a resting membrane potential.** In a muscle fiber at rest, we find an unequal distribution of charged particles near the sarcolemma: There is a thin layer of negative ions in the sarcoplasm and a thin layer of positive ions in the extracellular fluid. This separation of charges is called an *electrical potential*, but note that, really, it's simply an *electrical gradient*—positive and negative ions are separated by a barrier. The difference in electrical potential across the sarcolemma is called the **membrane potential**; the potential at rest is called, appropriately, the **resting membrane potential**. The resting membrane potential in a skeletal muscle fiber is a negative number, generally about -90 millivolts (mV).

- **Sodium and potassium ions are unequally distributed across the sarcolemma.** We find another type of gradient across the membrane—a *concentration gradient*. Specifically, the concentration of sodium ions in the extracellular fluid is high, and the concentration in the sarcoplasm is low. The distribution of potassium ions is opposite—the concentration of potassium ions in the extracellular fluid is low, and the concentration in the sarcoplasm is high. This gradient is made by the ATP-consuming **sodium–potassium ion pump**, or **Na⁺/K⁺ ATPase**.

Understanding these two points allows us to understand the events of a muscle fiber **action potential**, which is a rapid, temporary change in the membrane potential from negative to positive and back to negative (Fig. 11.11). In the first stage of the action potential, the membrane potential moves from -90 mV to $+30$ mV—a change known as **depolarization**. The action potential finishes with a return of the membrane potential to the resting value of -90 mV—a change known as **repolarization**. Note that repolarization must occur, or the motor neuron cannot re-stimulate the muscle fiber. In addition, repolarization completes before the contraction actually takes place, which allows the neuron to re-stimulate the muscle fiber rapidly.

The action potential in skeletal muscle initiates when ACh binds to its cation channel receptors in the motor end plate. This event triggers the opening of sodium ion channels that are in the sarcolemma around the motor end plate. We can walk through the events of the action potential by using logic. Let's start with depolarization:

Is the resting membrane potential negative or positive?

_____

Where do we have more sodium ions—inside the cell or outside? _____

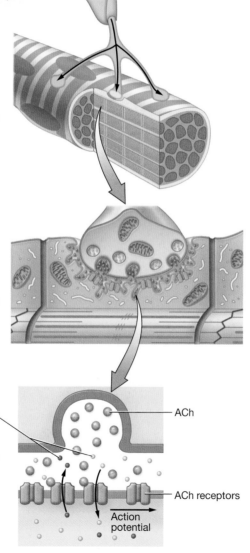

1. A neuronal action potential travels through the motor neuron to the axon terminals.

2. The action potential triggers release of acetylcholine from the synaptic vesicles by exocytosis.

3. Acetylcholine binds acetylcholine receptors in the motor end plate and triggers a muscle action potential.

Ions

ACh

ACh receptors

Action potential

FIGURE **11.9** Events at the neuromuscular junction.

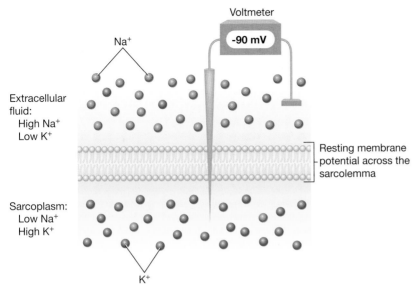

Voltmeter

-90 mV

Na⁺

Extracellular
fluid:
High Na⁺
Low K⁺

Resting membrane
potential across the
sarcolemma

Sarcoplasm:
Low Na⁺
High K⁺

K⁺

FIGURE **11.10** The resting membrane potential
and the distribution of sodium and potassium ions
across the sarcolemma.

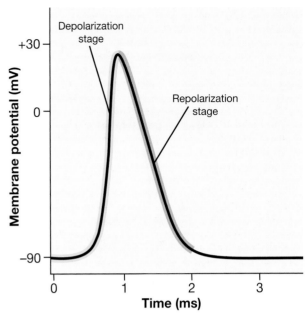

FIGURE **11.11** A skeletal muscle fiber
action potential.

So, when sodium ion channels in the sarcolemma open, will sodium ions diffuse into the sarcoplasm or out of it?

As the sarcoplasm gains positive charges, what will happen to the membrane potential?

After the initial depolarization, sodium ion channels close and potassium ion channels open, which begins repolarization. Again, let's use logic to figure out what happens during repolarization:

Where do we have more potassium ions—inside the cell or outside?

So, when potassium ion channels in the sarcolemma open, will potassium ions diffuse into the sarcoplasm or out of it?

As the sarcoplasm loses positive charges, what will happen to the membrane potential?

The depolarization that begins at the motor end plate is what leads to the skeletal muscle fiber contraction. The depolarization spreads—or *propagates*—through the sarcolemma and dives into the interior of the muscle fiber along the T-tubules. As the action potential spreads along the T-tubules, it passes calcium ion channels in the adjacent terminal cisternae. The depolarization triggers calcium ion channels to open, which allows calcium ions to leave the sarcoplasmic reticulum and flood the sarcoplasm.

This increase in calcium ion concentration is a key event in initiating a muscle contraction, and is directly how excitation and contraction are coupled. Before calcium ions enter the sarcoplasm, actin and myosin are prevented from interacting by the regulatory protein tropomyosin. When calcium ions enter, they bind to troponin, and this causes troponin to pull tropomyosin away from the actin-myosin binding site. This allows a contraction to begin.

A skeletal muscle fiber contracts by a process known as the **sliding filament mechanism**, in which the myosin heads of the thick filament pull the thin filament toward the M line of the sarcomere. As this occurs, the thick and thin filaments "slide" past one another. The key event of this mechanism is the **crossbridge cycle**, which consists of the following steps (Fig. 11.12):

1. **Myosin head is cocked by ATP hydrolysis.** Before the cycle starts, the myosin head is in its "relaxed" position and is unable to bind to the active site of actin. The first step of the cycle, then, is to put the myosin head into its upright, "cocked" position. This is accomplished using the energy from ATP hydrolysis. The leftover products of the reaction, ADP and the inorganic phosphate (abbreviated P_i), remain associated with the myosin head.

2. **An actin-myosin crossbridge forms.** The myosin head binds to the active site of an actin subunit, forming a **crossbridge**.

3. **A power stroke occurs.** P_i dissociates from the myosin head, and the myosin molecule moves forward into its relaxed position. As it moves, it pulls the thin filament with it toward the M line in a motion known as a **power stroke**. At the end of the power stroke, ADP leaves the myosin head.

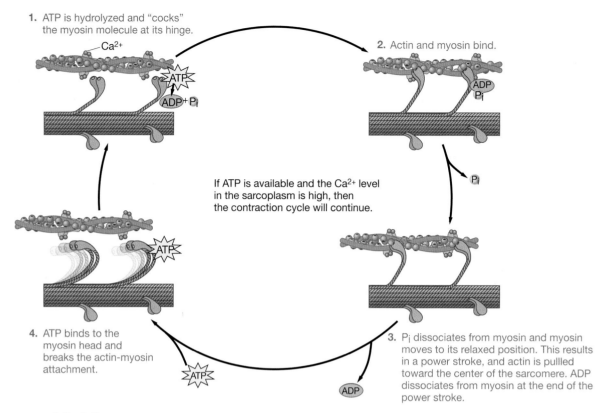

1. ATP is hydrolyzed and "cocks" the myosin molecule at its hinge.

Ca²⁺

ATP

ADP⁺ Pᵢ

2. Actin and myosin bind.

ADP
Pᵢ

If ATP is available and the Ca²⁺ level in the sarcoplasm is high, then the contraction cycle will continue.

Pᵢ

ATP

4. ATP binds to the myosin head and breaks the actin-myosin attachment.

ATP

3. Pᵢ dissociates from myosin and myosin moves to its relaxed position. This results in a power stroke, and actin is pulled toward the center of the sarcomere. ADP dissociates from myosin at the end of the power stroke.

ADP

FIGURE **11.12** Single crossbridge cycle showing the sliding filament mechanism of contraction.

4. **ATP breaks the actin-myosin attachment and re-cocks the myosin head.** After the power stroke, the actin and myosin are still attached, and they will remain attached until a new ATP molecule comes in and breaks that attachment. When that ATP molecule is hydrolyzed, the myosin head will be re-cocked, it will bind a new actin subunit, and another crossbridge cycle will begin. If no ATP is present, the actin will remain bound to myosin and the muscle fiber will remain in a contracted state.

This cycle will continue as long as ACh is in the synaptic cleft (provided that calcium ions and ATP are available). To terminate a contraction, (1) the neuron must stop releasing ACh and (2) the body must degrade the ACh in the synaptic cleft with reactions catalyzed by the enzyme acetylcholinesterase. When stimulation ceases, the calcium ions are pumped back into the SR, and troponin and tropomyosin move back into their original positions. At this point, actin and myosin can no longer bind, and the muscle fiber returns to its resting length.

1 PROCEDURE
Seeing Muscle Fiber Contraction in Action

Recently harvested muscle fibers, when stored properly, surprisingly retain their ability to contract under the correct conditions. This procedure uses *glycerinated muscle*, which is muscle tissue prepared in such a way that it removes all ions and ATP, and also disrupts the troponin/tropomyosin complex such that they no longer block the active sites of actin. For this reason, glycerinated muscle does not need calcium ions to contract.

However, the myosin heads in glycerinated muscle are in the relaxed position, and so they must be "cocked" by ATP hydrolysis in order for a contraction to occur. In this procedure, you will be supplying that ATP to see contractions of muscle fibers as they happen. When you have completed the activity, answer Check Your Understanding Questions 3 and 4 (pp. 321–322).

Hypothesis: How will adding ATP to muscle fibers affect their length?

1 Your instructor has placed pre-teased glycerinated skeletal muscle tissue into a petri dish under a dissecting microscope. Use a glass needle or a teasing needle to obtain a very thin thread of skeletal muscle tissue from this petri dish, and place it on a blank slide with a coverslip.

2 Examine your sample under a light microscope using the low-power objective and look for very small muscle threads. If your slide has large clumps and you are unable to see striations, get another sample and try again until you have smaller pieces and can see striations.

3 Prepare a second blank slide, and place a tiny drop of glycerol in the center of the slide with your needle. It is important not to use too much glycerol, or you will not see muscle contraction.

4 Use a glass needle or teasing needle to transfer three or more of the smallest threads to the glycerol on the second slide.

5 Using a 4× magnifying glass or your microscope, measure the length of the muscle fiber threads with a ruler in millimeters (mm). You may find it easier to use a magnifying glass.

Length of muscle fibers before contraction: _____ mm

6 Apply several drops of the 0.25% ATP/0.05 M KCl/0.001 M MgCl solution to the fibers on the slide.

7 Put the slide back on the microscope stage and observe it for 1 minute. Watch as the muscle fibers contract.

8 After 1 minute, remeasure the muscle fiber threads with a ruler in mm.

Length of muscle fibers after contraction: _____ mm

9 Compare your results to your hypothesis.

---

2 PROCEDURE
Measuring the Length-Tension Relationship

The amount of tension that can be generated during a contraction is influenced by the size of the zone of overlap of the thick and thin filaments when the muscle fiber is at rest, a principle known as the **length-tension relationship** (Fig. 11.13). The zone of overlap of the thick and thin filaments is determined by the resting length of the sarcomeres. When the muscle is stretched, the sarcomeres are longer and have a smaller zone of overlap. When the muscle is shortened, the sarcomeres are shorter and have a larger zone of overlap.

Notice in Figure 11.13 that the muscle fiber can generate the maximum amount of tension when its sarcomeres are at about 100 to 120% of their natural length. At this resting length, the zone of overlap is "just right" to generate maximum tension. Conversely, the amount of tension generated during a contraction diminishes greatly both when the muscle is overly stretched and when it is excessively shortened because the zone of overlap is not ideal. Not only does the amount of tension decrease, but the risk of injury *increases* when a muscle contraction occurs in a muscle that is overly stretched or shortened.

In this experiment, you will be measuring the ability of your digital flexor muscles to generate tension at different resting muscle lengths. You will take your measurements with an instrument called a **hand dynamometer** (dy-nuh-MAH-muh-tur;

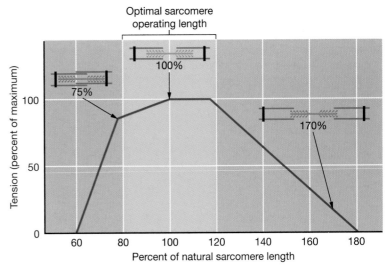

FIGURE **11.13** Length-tension relationship.

dyna- = "power"), which measures the force you apply when it is squeezed. When you have finished the experiment, answer Check Your Understanding Question 5 (p. 322).

> ## Hypothesis: In which position will tension be highest?

1 Position your forearm and hand as shown in Figure 11.14A, with your hand flexed at a 90° angle at the wrist.

2 Grip the dynamometer, and squeeze it with your maximum effort. Record in Table 11.3 the amount of force you generated.

3 Position your forearm and hand as shown in Figure 11.14B, with your hand extended at a 0° angle at the wrist.

4 Grip the dynamometer, and squeeze it with your maximum effort. Record in Table 11.3 the amount of force you generated.

5 Position your forearm and hand as shown in Figure 11.14C, with your hand hyperextended at a –90° angle at the wrist.

6 Grip the dynamometer, and squeeze it with your maximum effort. Record in Table 11.3 the amount of force you generated.

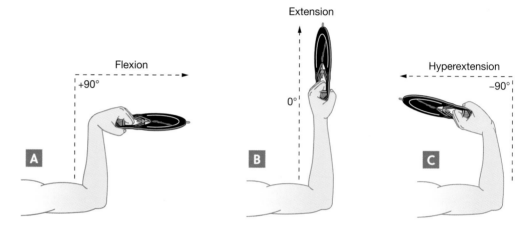

FIGURE **11.14** Hand positions for the dynamometer experiment: (**A**) flexed at 90°; (**B**) extended at 0°; (**C**) hyperextended at –90°.

7 Interpret your results:

  a In which hand position were the muscles' sarcomeres overly stretched?

  b In which hand position were the muscles' sarcomeres excessively shortened?

  c Which hand position yielded the most forceful contraction? Why?

8 Compare your results to your hypothesis.

TABLE **11.3** Results of Dynamometer Experiment

Hand Position	Amount of Force Generated
Flexed at 90°	
Extended at 0°	
Hyperextended at –90°	

MATERIALS

☐ Slides:
  • smooth muscle tissue
  • cardiac muscle tissue
☐ Light microscope
☐ Colored pencils

Smooth and Cardiac Muscle Tissues

Although smooth and cardiac muscle tissues differ from skeletal muscle tissue in many ways, all three share the same basic function—to generate tension. This functional similarity brings with it structural similarities, as well. Cardiac muscle tissue is structurally the most similar to skeletal muscle tissue. As you can see in Figure 11.15A, cardiac muscle tissue is also striated and consists of alternating A bands and I bands arranged into sarcomeres.

The two tissue types have notable differences, though. For one, the cells of cardiac muscle tissue, called **cardiac myocytes**, are branching, shorter than skeletal muscle fibers, and typically have only one or two nuclei. In addition, adjacent cardiac myocytes are joined by specialized structures called **intercalated discs** (in-TER-kuh-lay-t'd), which contain gap junctions and desmosomes. The intercalated discs connect all cardiac myocytes physically and electrically and allow the heart to contract as a unit. Finally, cardiac myocytes are involuntary and **autorhythmic**: They depolarize and contract without stimulation from the nervous system because of specialized cardiac myocytes called **pacemaker cells**.

Smooth muscle tissue, shown in Figure 11.15B, is not striated. For this reason, it lacks A bands, I bands, and sarcomeres. Smooth muscle cells tend to be long, thin, and spindle-shaped with a single, centrally located nucleus. All smooth muscle cells are involuntary, and most require extrinsic innervation to contract (some populations do have pacemaker cells and so are autorhythmic). Smooth muscle is found in many places in the body: the iris and ciliary muscle of the eye; the arrector pili muscles in the dermis; and lining the walls of all hollow organs.

11

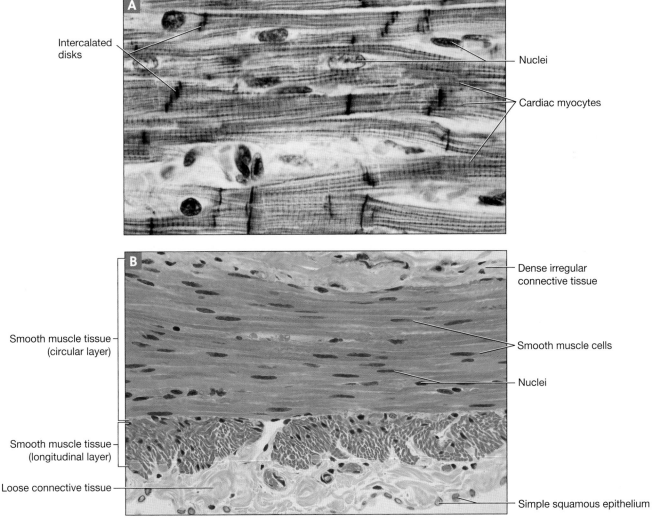

FIGURE **11.15** Other types of muscle tissue: (**A**) cardiac muscle tissue; (**B**) smooth muscle tissue.

How to Distinguish Between Types of Muscle Tissue

With a bit of practice, distinguishing between the three types of muscle tissue on microscope slides becomes fairly easy. Following are some hints to help you differentiate these three tissues:

Striations If striations are present, the muscle is either skeletal or cardiac. If there are no striations, it is smooth muscle.

Shape of the cells Skeletal muscle fibers are long and thin, whereas cardiac myocytes are short, wide, and branching. Smooth muscle cells are thin and flat. My past students have remarked that smooth muscle cells somewhat resemble stratified squamous epithelium or dense regular collagenous connective tissue (see pp. 120 and 127).

Location of the nucleus Each skeletal muscle fiber has multiple nuclei located next to the sarcolemma. Cardiac myocytes usually have a single, large nucleus located among the myofibrils. The single, flattened nucleus of a smooth muscle cell is usually in the middle of the cell.

Other features

ⓘ The intercalated discs of cardiac muscle tissue appear as black lines oriented parallel to the striations. No other tissue type has a similar feature, so intercalated discs are an immediate giveaway that you are looking at cardiac muscle tissue.

ⓘ Smooth muscle tissue is typically found on a slide with other types of tissue because it lines hollow organs. Scroll through the slide to see if you can find any additional tissue types, such as epithelial and/or connective tissue. If these other tissue types are on top of or below the muscle cells, there is a good chance you are examining smooth muscle tissue.

---

1 PROCEDURE

Examining Cardiac and Smooth Muscle Tissue with Microscopy

Obtain prepared slides of cardiac and smooth muscle tissue. Use your colored pencils to draw what you see, and label your drawing with the following terms. After you have completed the activity, answer Check Your Understanding Question 6 (p. 322).

1 Cardiac Muscle

- Striations
  - A band
  - I band
- Sarcolemma
- Nucleus
- Intercalated discs
- Cardiac myocytes

2 Smooth Muscle

- Nucleus
- Smooth muscle cells
- Connective tissue

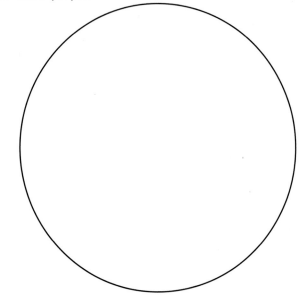

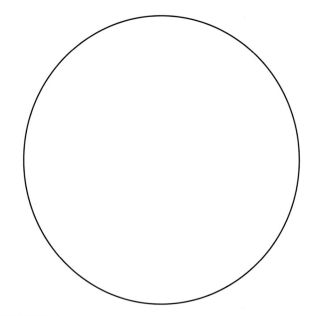

Check Your Recall

1 Label the following terms on Figure 11.16.

- ❏ A band
- ❏ Elastic filament
- ❏ Endomysium
- ❏ Epimysium
- ❏ Fascicle
- ❏ H zone
- ❏ I band
- ❏ Myofibril
- ❏ Perimysium
- ❏ Sarcomere
- ❏ Sarcoplasmic reticulum
- ❏ T-tubules
- ❏ Thick filament
- ❏ Thin filament
- ❏ Z disc

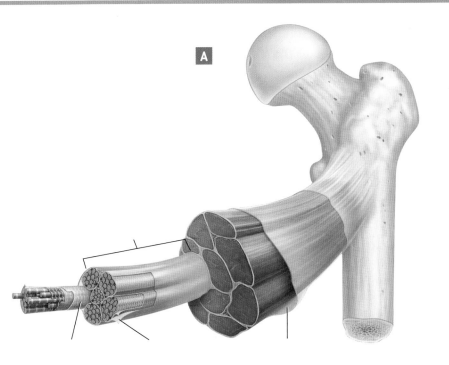

A

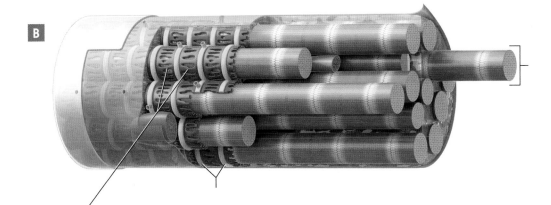

B

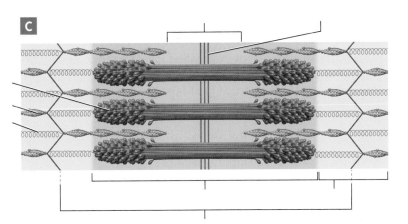

C

FIGURE **11.16**
Skeletal muscle structure and microanatomy:
(**A**) muscle structural levels of organization;
(**B**) myofibrils and organelles;
(**C**) myofilaments.

2 *Circle all that apply.* Which of the following proteins make(s) up an elastic filament?

a. Tropomyosin.
b. Actin.
c. Titin.
d. Myosin.
e. Troponin.

3 A triad

a. consists of a T-tubule and two terminal cisternae.
b. is made of contractile proteins.
c. consists of a muscle fiber, the sarcolemma, and the endomysium.
d. is made of myofilaments.

4 Regarding striations:

a What creates the striations in a skeletal muscle fiber? _____

_____

b What are the dark regions of the striations, and what are the light regions? _____

_____

c What makes them dark and light, respectively? _____

5 *Fill in the blanks:* A sarcomere is the _____ of contraction, and is defined as the

space from one _____ to the next _____ .

6 At the neuromuscular junction,

a. an action potential in a motor neuron triggers the release of neurotransmitters from synaptic vesicles into the synaptic cleft.
b. a muscle fiber stimulates a neuronal action potential.
c. tension is generated.
d. the energy from ATP hydrolysis "cocks" the myosin head.

7 Each of the following statements is false. Correct each to make it a true statement.

a. The resting membrane potential in a skeletal muscle fiber is about +90 mV.
b. During the depolarization phase of an action potential, potassium ions diffuse into the sarcoplasm.
c. Acetylcholinesterase degrades ACh, which initiates a skeletal muscle contraction.
d. Calcium ions bind to tropomyosin, which causes it to shift position and pull troponin away from the actin active site.

8 What are the roles of ATP in the sliding-filament mechanism of contraction?

_____

_____

9 Why does a muscle fiber generate maximum tension when at 100–120% of its resting length?

a. The shortened sarcomeres have a large zone of overlap.
b. More ATP is released when the muscle fiber is at this length.
c. More calcium ions are released when the muscle fiber is at this length.
d. The sarcomeres at this length have a zone of overlap that is ideal for tension generation.

10 *True/False:* Mark the following statements as true (T) or false (F). If the statement is false, correct it to make it a true statement.

_____ a. The primary function of all types of muscle tissue is to generate tension.

_____ b. Cardiac muscle tissue lines hollow organs.

_____ c. The cells of skeletal muscle tissue are multinucleate.

_____ d. The cells of smooth and cardiac muscle tissue contract voluntarily.

Name _____

Section _____ Date _____

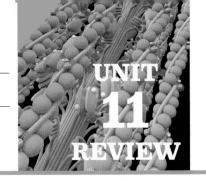

Check Your Understanding

Critical Thinking and Application Questions

1 Muscle diseases may be caused by mutations in the gene coding for the protein *titin*. Given the functions of titin, predict the effects of such diseases.

2 The drug *neostigmine* binds to acetylcholinesterase and blocks its actions. How would this affect the duration of a skeletal muscle contraction?

3 Serial killer Genene Jones was a nurse convicted of murdering her patients. One of the murder weapons she used was *succinylcholine*, a drug that binds to acetylcholine receptors. The drug causes depolarization of the muscle fibers, but is not broken down by acetylcholinesterase, preventing the muscle fiber from repolarizing. Why was succinylcholine an effective murder weapon?

4 You added ATP to your skeletal muscle fibers in Procedure 1 of Exercise 11-2.

    a Why was ATP needed in the experiment? _____

    b What are the roles of ATP in living muscle tissue? _____

c After death, skeletal muscles enter a state of sustained contraction called *rigor mortis*, which is caused by a depletion of ATP. Why would a lack of ATP cause a sustained skeletal muscle contraction?

5 A hypothetical genetic mutation causes the sarcoplasmic reticulum to be underdeveloped in skeletal muscle fibers. Predict how this would affect the ability of the cells to contract.

6 You are examining cells from an unknown tissue in a petri dish. Upon closer inspection, you notice that the cells are contracting in unison, on their own, with no outside stimulation. When you look at the cells under a microscope, you notice they are connected by wavy lines.

a What type of tissue is this?

b What are the wavy lines?

c Why are the cells contracting spontaneously? How are they able to contract in unison?

Introduction to the Nervous System

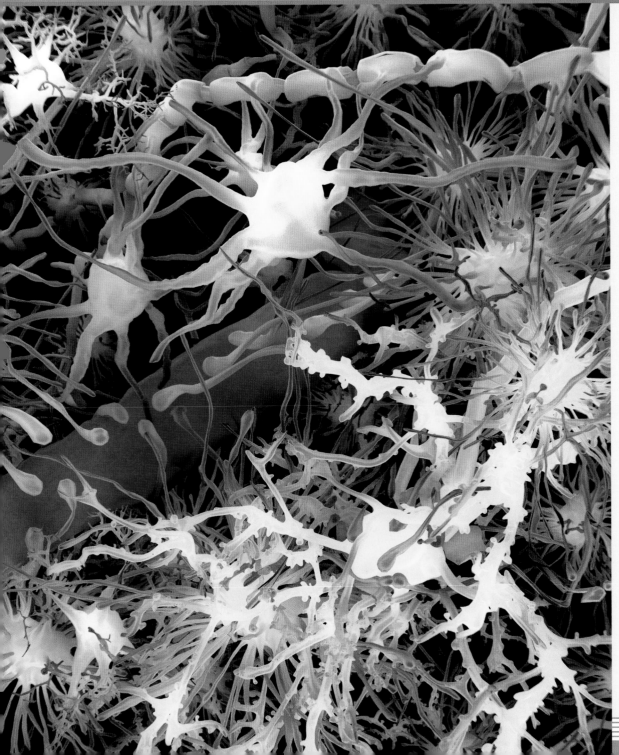

When you have completed this unit, you should be able to:

1 Describe the microanatomy of nervous tissue and the parts of a synapse.

2 Identify structures of the neuron and neuroglial cell on anatomical models and microscope slides.

3 Describe and diagram the sequence of events of a neuronal action potential and chemical synaptic transmission.

PRE-LAB EXERCISES

Complete the following exercises prior to coming to lab, using your lab manual and textbook for reference.

PRE-LAB

12-1 Key Terms

You should be familiar with the following terms before coming to lab.

Term	Definition

Components of Nervous Tissue

Neuron

Neuroglial cell

Parts of the Neuron

Cell body

Axon

Dendrite

Telodendria

Myelin sheath

Myelin sheath gap

Neurophysiology Terms

Synapse

Neurotransmitters

Resting membrane potential

Action potential

Axon terminal

Synaptic vesicle

Synaptic cleft

Presynaptic neuron

Postsynaptic neuron

Color the microscopic anatomy of nervous tissue in Figure 12.1, and label it with the terms from Exercise 12-1 (p. 327). Use your text and Exercise 12-1 in this unit for reference.

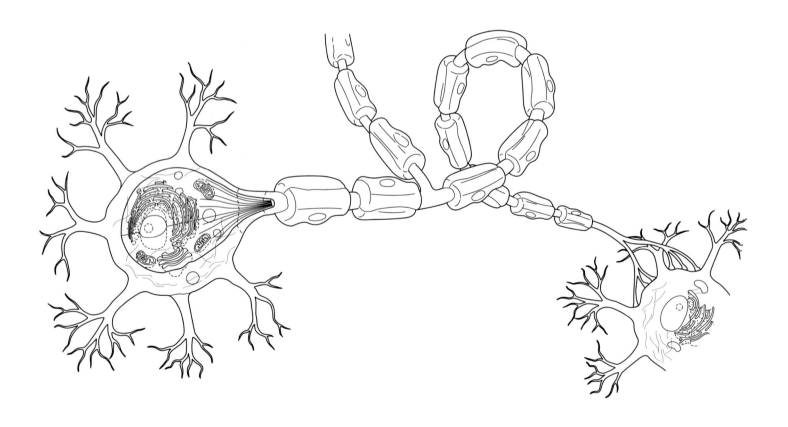

FIGURE **12.1** Multipolar neuron.

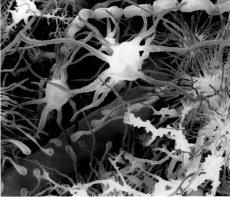

We begin our study of the **nervous system** in this unit, and we explore it further over the next three units. The nervous system consists of the *brain, spinal cord,* and *peripheral nerves.* Within these organs, we find cells called *neurons* that maintain homeostasis in the body by regulating the activity of other cells. They accomplish this by sending nerve impulses, also known as **action potentials,** to their target cells. Neurons are supported by a variety of smaller cells collectively called *neuroglial cells.* These two cell types, along with a specialized extracellular matrix, make up **nervous tissue.**

In the following exercises, we examine the cells and structure of nervous tissue. Then we find out how the structure of neurons relates to their function as we explore nervous system physiology.

Neurons and other nervous system structures.

EXERCISE
12-1

MATERIALS

- ☐ Anatomical models and diagrams:
  - neuron
  - synapse
- ☐ Slides:
  - nervous tissue
  - myelin sheath
- ☐ Light microscope
- ☐ Colored pencils

Neurons and Neuroglia

There are two types of cells within nervous tissue: neurons and neuroglial cells. **Neurons** (NOOR-ahnz; *neuro-* = "nerve") are large cells that transmit and generate messages in the form of nerve impulses, or *neuronal action potentials.* Although they vary widely in size and structure, most have the following three components: the cell body, one axon, and one or more dendrites (Fig. 12.2).

1. **Cell body.** The **cell body** is the biosynthetic center of the neuron, containing the nucleus and many of the organelles. Its cytoskeleton consists of densely packed intermediate filaments known as **neurofilaments** that compartmentalize the rough endoplasmic reticulum into dark-staining structures called **Nissl bodies.** Near the axon and dendrites, neurofilaments form larger **neurofibrils,** which extend out into these processes. Cell bodies are often found in clusters.

2. **Axon.** A single **axon** exits the cell body at the **axon hillock.** Just distal to the axon hillock is a region called the **initial segment,** also known as the *trigger zone,* which generates signals in

12

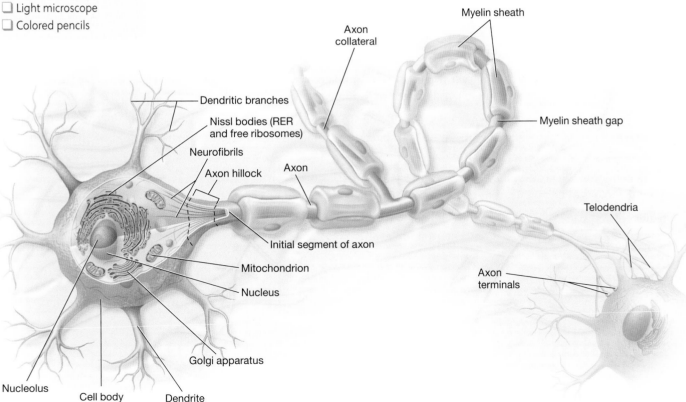

FIGURE **12.2** A multipolar neuron, illustration.

the form of action potentials that are transmitted to other neurons, muscle cells, and glands. Action potentials are generated across an axon's plasma membrane, known as the **axolemma** (ax-oh-LEM-uh; -*lemma* = "husk"). The action potential spreads, or *propagates*, down the entire length of the axon. Some axons have branches known as **axon collaterals** that stem off of the main axon at right angles. Both the main axon and the axon collaterals end in multiple terminal branches called **telodendria** (tee-loh-DEN-dree-uh; *telo-* = "end;" *dendr-* = "tree"). At the end of each telodendrion is an **axon terminal**, which is sometimes called a synaptic bulb. Recall from Unit 11 that the axon terminal contains synaptic vesicles with neurotransmitters that communicate with the axon's target cell.

3. **Dendrites.** Most neurons have one or more branching processes called **dendrites** (DEN-dryt′z) that receive signals from other neurons. They can transmit these signals to the neuron's cell body, but they are not capable of generating action potentials.

Neurons are classified structurally based on the number of processes extending from the cell body (Fig. 12.3). The most common type of neuron is the large **multipolar neuron,** which has three or more processes—specifically, one axon and two or more dendrites. Most multipolar neurons resemble highly branched trees and have hundreds to thousands of dendrites.

Both bipolar neurons and pseudounipolar neurons are rarer than multipolar neurons and are associated with the senses. **Bipolar neurons** (*bi-* = "two") have two processes: one axon and one dendrite. They are found in special sense organs such as the olfactory epithelium and the retina of the eye. **Pseudounipolar neurons** (soo-doh-yoo-nih-POHL-uhr; *pseudo-* = "false;" *uni-* = "one") are found in the skin and have only one process. A short distance from the cell body, the process branches like a "T" into a **peripheral process,** which brings a stimulus from a sensory receptor to the cell body, and into a **central process,** which transmits a signal from the cell body to the spinal cord. Both the central process and the peripheral process can generate action potentials, which makes them axons. Pseudounipolar neurons are sensory neurons that detect stimuli such as fine touch, pressure, and pain.

Neuroglial cells (noor-oh-GLEE-uhl; *glia* = "glue") are much smaller than neurons, and they outnumber neurons about 50 to 1—no small feat considering that the nervous system contains about a trillion neurons. Following are the neuroglial cells of the central nervous system (CNS; brain and spinal cord) and the peripheral nervous system (PNS; cranial and spinal nerves). The neuroglia are shown in Figure 12.4, but note that this figure shows only neuroglial cells of the CNS.

1. **Astrocytes. Astrocytes** are the most numerous neuroglial cell type in the CNS. These star-shaped cells have many functions, including anchoring neurons and blood vessels in place with processes called **perivascular feet,** and regulating the extracellular environment of the brain. In addition, they facilitate the formation of the **blood-brain barrier,** created by tight junctions in the brain capillaries. The blood-brain barrier prevents many substances in the blood from entering the brain tissue.

2. **Oligodendrocytes. Oligodendrocytes** (oh-lig-oh-DEN-droh-syt′z; *oligo-* = "a few") have long extensions that wrap around the axons of certain neurons in the CNS to form a structure called the *myelin sheath*. Note that one oligodendrocyte can myelinate segments of several axons.

3. **Microglial cells.** The small **microglial cells** (my-kroh-GLEE-uhl) are very active phagocytes that clean up debris surrounding neurons. Microglia also degrade and ingest damaged or dead neurons.

4. **Ependymal cells.** The ciliated **ependymal cells** (eh-PEN-dih-muhl) line the hollow spaces of the brain and spinal cord. They assist in forming the fluid that bathes the brain and spinal cord, which is called **cerebrospinal fluid,** and circulate it with their cilia.

5. **Neurolemmocytes. Neurolemmocytes** (noor-oh-LEM-oh-syt′z), also known as **Schwann cells,** form the myelin sheath around the axons of certain neurons in the PNS. A neurolemmocyte can myelinate a segment of only one axon.

6. **Satellite cells. Satellite cells** surround the cell bodies of neurons in the PNS. These cells enclose and support the cell bodies, and regulate the extracellular environment around them.

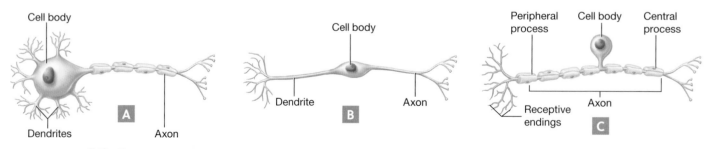

FIGURE **12.3** Types of neurons: (**A**) multipolar neuron; (**B**) bipolar neuron; (**C**) pseudounipolar neuron.

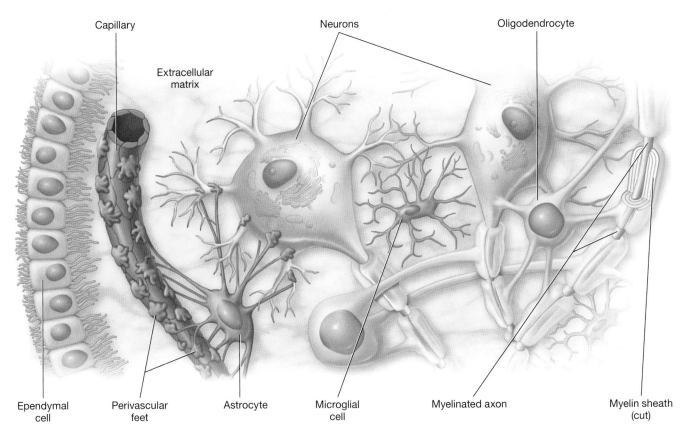

FIGURE **12.4** Neuroglial cells of the CNS.

The **myelin sheath** (MY-lin) is composed of many layers of the plasma membrane of the oligodendrocyte or neurolemmocyte wrapped around an axon. It performs critical functions within the nervous system, including protecting and insulating the axons and speeding up conduction of action potentials. As you can see in Figure 12.5, neurolemmocytes and oligodendrocytes myelinate axons differently. Neurolemmocytes, which myelinate a segment of only a single axon, wrap clockwise around the axon (Fig. 12.5A). The outer edge of the neurolemmocyte, called the **neurilemma** (noor-ih-LEM-uh), contains most of its cytoplasm and the nucleus. Oligodendrocytes, on the other hand, wrap segments of multiple axons in a counterclockwise direction (Fig. 12.5B).

Notice that there are small gaps in the myelin sheath in between each oligodendrocyte arm or neurolemmocyte where the plasma membrane of the axon is exposed (Figs. 12.6 and 12.7). Accordingly, these gaps are called **myelin sheath gaps** (also known as *neurofibril nodes* or *nodes of Ranvier* [rahn-vee-ay]). The myelin-covered segments between the nodes are **internodes**. When action potentials are generated in a myelinated axon, the current is conducted through the internode, and the action potential is regenerated at each myelin sheath gap. This type of conduction is known as **saltatory conduction** (sahl-tuh-TOHR-ee; *saltare* = "leap") because the action potential "leaps" from gap to gap. The "leaping" nature of saltatory conduction makes it significantly

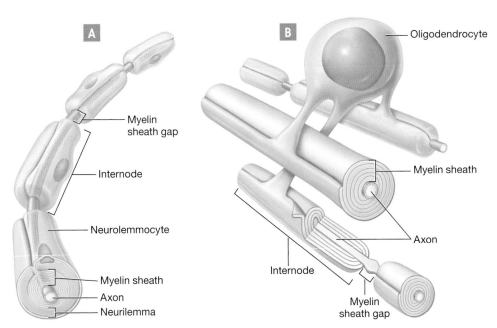

FIGURE **12.5** Myelin sheath: (**A**) neurolemmocytes around a PNS axon; (**B**) an oligodendrocyte around multiple CNS axons.

faster than **continuous conduction**, which occurs in unmyelinated axons. In continuous conduction, the action potential must continuously regenerate along the axon's entire length.

1 PROCEDURE
Model Inventory for Nervous Tissue

Identify the following structures of nervous tissue on models and diagrams using your textbook and this unit for reference. As you examine the anatomical models and diagrams, record the name of the model and the structures you were able to identify on the model inventory in Table 12.1. When you have completed the activity, answer Check Your Understanding Questions 1 through 3 (p. 339).

1. Neuron
   a. Cell body
      (1) Nissl bodies
      (2) Neurofibrils
   b. Axon
      (1) Axon hillock
      (2) Initial segment (trigger zone)
      (3) Axolemma
      (4) Telodendria
   c. Dendrite(s)

2. Multipolar neuron
3. Bipolar neuron
4. Pseudounipolar neuron
5. Neuroglial cells
   a. Astrocytes
   b. Oligodendrocytes
   c. Microglial cells
   d. Ependymal cells
   e. Neurolemmocytes
   f. Satellite cells

6. Other structures
   a. Myelin sheath
   b. Neurilemma
   c. Myelin sheath gap
   d. Internode

12

TABLE **12.1** Model Inventory for Nervous Tissue

Model/Diagram	Structures Identified

Let's now identify some of the structures from the previous procedures on microscope slides. You will examine the following tissue sections:

- **Motor neuron smear.** On this slide, you should see many multipolar neurons surrounded by many, much smaller, neuroglial cells (they may look like purple dots; Fig. 12.6). As you scan the slide with the low-power objective, find a well-stained neuron, and move the objective lens to high power. Look for Nissl bodies, and try to identify the single axon and the axon hillock. (This may be difficult, so don't get discouraged if all processes look similar.)

- **Myelin sheath.** A longitudinal section of axons treated with a stain specific for the components of myelin (often osmium) is useful for seeing the sheath itself and also the myelin sheath gaps (Fig. 12.7). You will likely need to use the high-power objective to see the myelin sheath gaps.

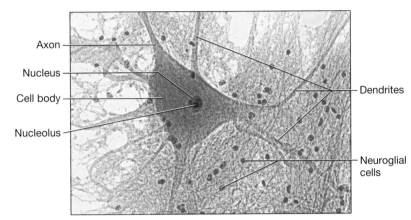

FIGURE **12.6** Nervous tissue, photomicrograph (motor neuron smear).

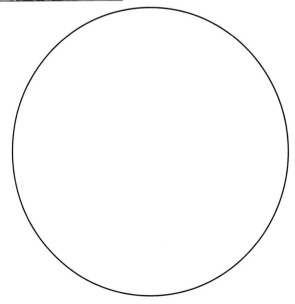

FIGURE **12.7** Myelin sheath, photomicrograph.

Obtain prepared slides of a motor neuron smear and the myelin sheath. Use your colored pencils to draw what you see, and label your drawing with the following terms.

1 Nervous Tissue
- Cell body
- Axon
- Dendrites
- Neuroglial cells

2 Myelin Sheath

- Axon with myelin sheath
- Myelin sheath gap
- Internode

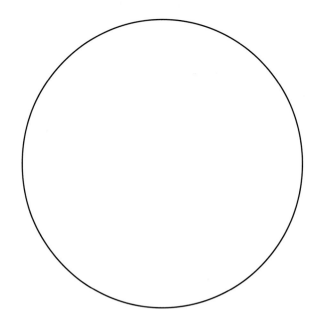

3 **PROCEDURE**

12

Time to Draw

In the space provided, draw, color, and label one of the neuron models that you examined. In addition, write the function of each structure that you label.

Nervous Tissue Physiology

A neuron communicates with its target cell by using chemicals called **neurotransmitters**. Neurotransmitters cause an effect in the target neuron by altering its *membrane potential*. You have seen an example of this before in the skeletal muscle fiber. As with muscle fibers, neurons have a separation of charges across their membranes, with a thin layer of positive charges on the outer membrane and a thin layer of negative charges on the inner membrane (Fig. 12.8). This creates an electrical gradient, which is known as the **membrane potential**—the potential when a neuron is not being stimulated is the **resting membrane potential**. In Figure 12.8, you'll notice that the resting membrane potential in neurons is about –70 mV.

When neurotransmitters bind to receptors on the target neuron, they open different ion channels. This causes ions to cross the membrane, which alters the resting membrane potential. This produces one of two effects known as **local potentials**, which are shown in Figure 12. 9:

- **Excitatory postsynaptic potential.** The neurotransmitter may open cation channels that allow positive charges—such as sodium ions—to enter the cytosol (Fig. 12.9A). The entry of positive charges makes the membrane potential less negative, a change known as **depolarization**. This small, local depolarization is called an **excitatory postsynaptic potential** or **EPSP**.

- **Inhibitory postsynaptic potential.** The neurotransmitter may open cation channels that allow positive ions—such as potassium ions—to leave the cytosol. It may also open anion channels that allow negative ions—such as chloride ions—to enter the cytosol (Fig. 12.9B). The exit of positive charges or entry of negative charges makes the membrane potential more negative, a change known as **hyperpolarization**. This small, local hyperpolarization is called an **inhibitory postsynaptic potential** or **IPSP**.

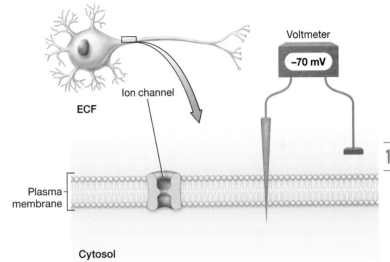

FIGURE **12.8** The resting membrane potential in a neuron.

If a target neuron is stimulated to have enough EPSPs, these small depolarizations will **summate**, or add together. As they summate, they **propagate**, or spread, through the neuron's plasma membrane and may reach a region of the axon known as the *trigger zone*. If they reach the trigger zone and the depolarization attains a value called **threshold**, an *action potential* is generated across the axolemma.

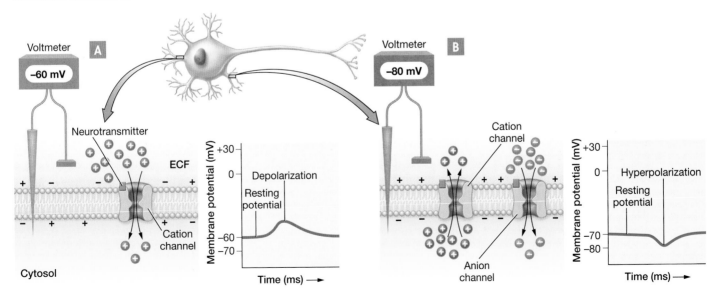

FIGURE **12.9** Local potentials: (**A**) excitatory postsynaptic potential; (**B**) inhibitory postsynaptic potential.

Recall from Unit 11 (p. 299) that an **action potential** is a quick, temporary reversal in the resting membrane potential from negative to positive and back to negative (Fig. 12.10). Let's walk through a quick review, starting with the depolarization stage of the action potential:

Is the resting membrane potential negative or positive? _____

Where do we have more sodium ions—inside the cell or outside? _____

So, when sodium ion channels in the plasma membrane open, will sodium ions diffuse into the cytosol or out of it?

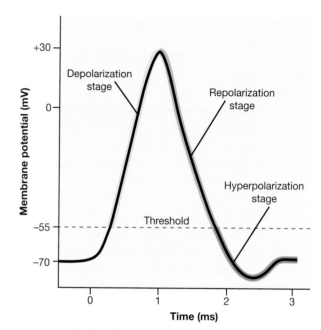

As the cytosol gains positive charges, what happens to the membrane potential? _____

Now, let's walk through the repolarization stage:

After sodium ion channels close, which channels open?

_____

Where do we have more potassium ions—inside the cell or outside? _____

So, when potassium ion channels in the plasma membrane open, will potassium ions diffuse into the cytosol or out of it?

_____

As the cytosol loses positive charges, what will happen to the membrane potential? _____

FIGURE **12.10** A neuronal action potential.

In the muscle fiber, these are the only two parts of the action potential. However, a neuron has a third part—the hyperpolarization stage. During hyperpolarization, potassium ion channels remain open, even after the membrane returns to the resting membrane potential.

In which direction will potassium ions diffuse, into the cytosol or out? _____

What will this do to the neurons' membrane potential? _____

Neurons communicate with one another and with their target cells at a junction called a **synapse** (SIN-apz). In Unit 11, you learned about a type of synapse called the *neuromuscular junction* (NMJ). The synapse between two neurons is similar to the NMJ and consists of three parts:

- **Presynaptic neuron.** The neuron that sends the signal is the **presynaptic neuron.** The axon terminals of the presynaptic neuron contain **synaptic vesicles** with neurotransmitters.
- **Synaptic cleft.** As we saw with the NMJ, the two neurons in a neuronal synapse are also separated by a narrow space. This space, called the **synaptic cleft,** is filled with extracellular fluid, enzymes, and other proteins.
- **Postsynaptic neuron.** The neuron that receives the message is the **postsynaptic neuron.** Its plasma membrane contains **receptors** for neurotransmitters.

As you can see in Figure 12.11, after the action potential is generated at the trigger zone of the presynaptic neuron, (1) it is propagated down the length of the axon to its axon terminals in much the same way current is conducted along a wire. As the action potential reaches the axon terminal, (2) voltage-gated calcium ion channels in the membrane open. The influx of calcium ions into the axon terminal triggers a process that releases neurotransmitters into the synaptic cleft by exocytosis. (3) The neurotransmitters diffuse across the synaptic cleft and bind to receptors on the membrane of the postsynaptic neuron. (4) The effects of these neurotransmitters depend upon the type of neurotransmitter released and the type of receptor to which it binds, but it will usually be an EPSP or an IPSP.

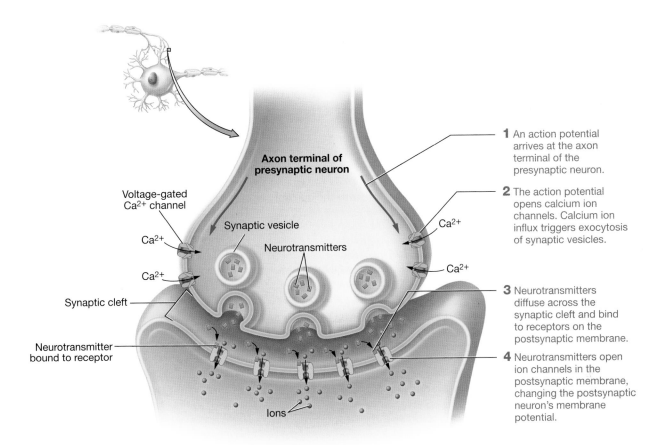

Axon terminal of presynaptic neuron

Voltage-gated Ca²⁺ channel

Ca²⁺

Synaptic vesicle

Ca²⁺

Neurotransmitters

Synaptic cleft

Neurotransmitter bound to receptor

Ca²⁺

Ca²⁺

Ions

1 An action potential arrives at the axon terminal of the presynaptic neuron.

2 The action potential opens calcium ion channels. Calcium ion influx triggers exocytosis of synaptic vesicles.

3 Neurotransmitters diffuse across the synaptic cleft and bind to receptors on the postsynaptic membrane.

4 Neurotransmitters open ion channels in the postsynaptic membrane, changing the postsynaptic neuron's membrane potential.

Postsynaptic neuron

FIGURE **12.11** Structure of a neuronal synapse.

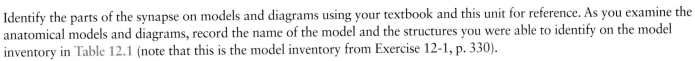

1 PROCEDURE

Model Inventory for Parts of the Synapse

Identify the parts of the synapse on models and diagrams using your textbook and this unit for reference. As you examine the anatomical models and diagrams, record the name of the model and the structures you were able to identify on the model inventory in Table 12.1 (note that this is the model inventory from Exercise 12-1, p. 330).

1. Presynaptic neuron
2. Axon terminal
3. Synaptic vesicle
4. Synaptic cleft
5. Postsynaptic neuron
6. Neurotransmitter receptors

PROCEDURE

Time to Trace!

Let's now trace the entire series of events through a three-neuron loop, including the steps of synaptic transmission between Neurons 1 and 2, the propagation of the action potential down the axon of Neuron 2, and the steps of synaptic transmission that occur between Neurons 2 and 3. Hints are included to ensure that you stay on the right track as you trace. You may wish to consult your textbook for more details on this process. When you have completed the activity, answer Check Your Understanding Questions 4 and 5 (pp. 339–340).

Start: neuronal action potential reaches the axon terminal of Neuron 1 → _____ channels in the axon terminal open and _____ diffuse into the cytosol → the process of _____ is triggered → _____ are released from synaptic vesicles and diffuse across the _____ , binding to _____ on the postsynaptic membrane of Neuron 2 → positive ions enter the cytosol of Neuron 2, generating an _____ potential → if the neuron is stimulated enough times, these potentials _____ and spread through the neuron's plasma membrane toward the axon → when the trigger zone is depolarized to _____ , an _____ potential is generated → _____ channels open and _____ diffuse into the cytosol during the _____ phase → _____ channels open and _____ diffuse out the cytosol during the _____ phase → the _____ potential _____ down the axon until it reaches the axon terminals → _____ channels in the axon terminal open and _____ diffuse into the cytosol → the process of _____ is triggered → _____ are released from synaptic vesicles and diffuse across the _____ , binding to _____ on the postsynaptic membrane of Neuron 3, generating an excitatory or inhibitory local potential. **End**

3

PROCEDURE

Diagramming Your Tracing

Take the pathway that you just traced, and turn it into a diagram that contains the three neurons. Your diagram does not have to be a work of art—only a simple schematic representation of each neuron and each process is necessary. You may use the figures in this unit and your text for reference, but it is best to compose and organize your diagram in a way that makes sense to you so you may return to it for study purposes.

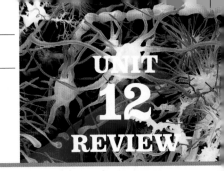

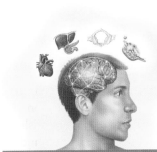

Name _____

Section _____ Date _____

Check Your Recall

UNIT
12
REVIEW

1 **Label the following structures on Figure 12.12.**

- ❏ Axon collateral
- ❏ Axon hillock
- ❏ Axon terminals
- ❏ Cell body
- ❏ Dendrite
- ❏ Initial segment
- ❏ Myelin sheath
- ❏ Myelin sheath gap
- ❏ Telodendria

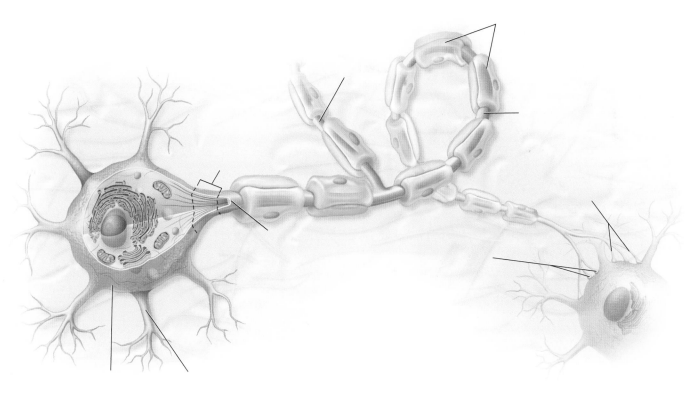

FIGURE **12.12** Neuron.

2 **The neuron pictured in Figure 12.13 is a**

a. pseudounipolar neuron.

b. bipolar neuron.

c. multipolar neuron.

d. unipolar neuron.

3 **The main function of the cell body is to**

a. regulate the external environment around the neuron.

b. generate and transmit signals in the form of action potentials.

c. function as the biosynthetic center of the neuron.

d. form the myelin sheath.

FIGURE **12.13** Neuron.

4 **Action potentials are generated across the plasma membrane of**

a. cell bodies.

b. dendrites.

c. an axon.

d. the myelin sheath.

e. More than one of the above can generate action potentials.

5 *Fill in the blanks.* _____ are neuroglial cells that form the myelin sheath in the peripheral nervous system. _____ are neuroglial cells that form the myelin sheath in the central nervous system.

6 Which of the following cell types circulates cerebrospinal fluid with cilia?
  a. Microglial cells.
  b. Astrocytes.
  c. Neurolemmocytes.
  d. Ependymal cells.

7 Label the following structures on Figure 12.14. Then, fill in the four boxes with the steps of synaptic transmission.
  ❏ Neurotransmitter receptor
  ❏ Postsynaptic neuron
  ❏ Presynaptic neuron
  ❏ Synaptic cleft
  ❏ Synaptic vesicle
  ❏ Voltage-gated Ca²⁺ channel

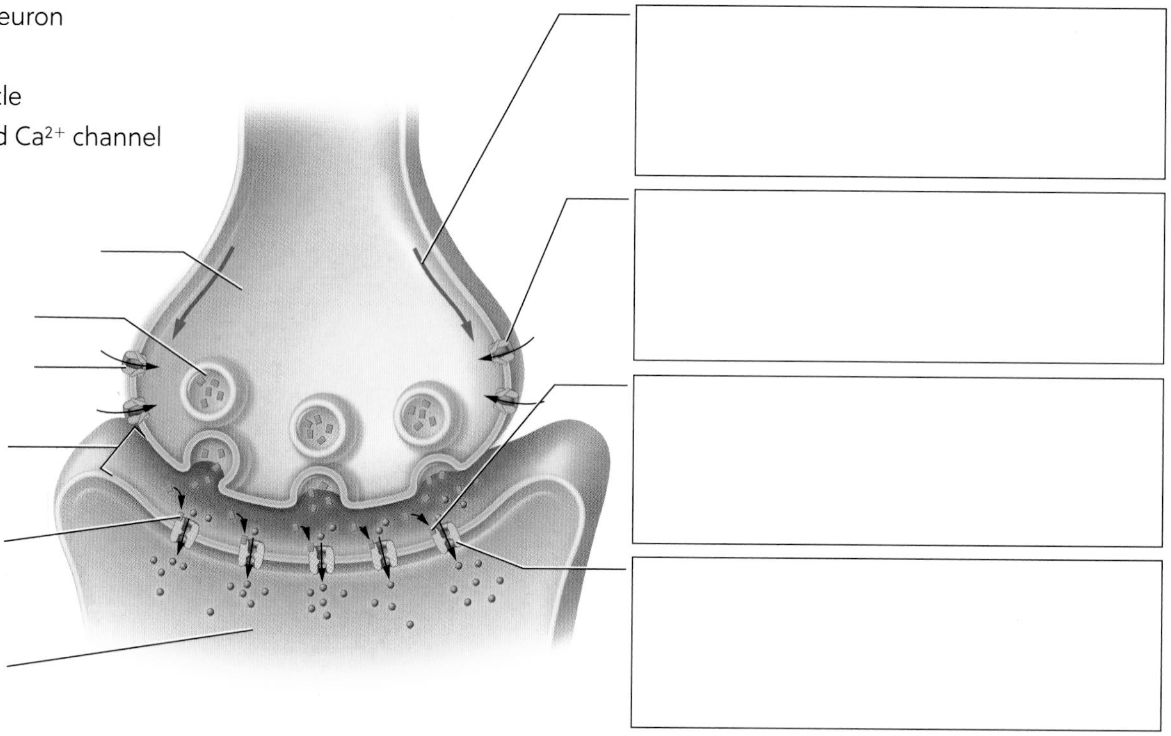

FIGURE **12.14** Structure of a neuronal synapse.

8 What happens during the hyperpolarization stage of a neuronal action potential?
  a. Sodium ions diffuse into the cell, making the membrane potential more positive than resting.
  b. Sodium ions diffuse out of the cell, making the membrane potential more negative than resting.
  c. Potassium ions diffuse into the cell, making the membrane potential more positive than resting.
  d. Potassium ions diffuse out of the cell, making the membrane potential more negative than resting.
  e. Potassium ions diffuse out of the cell, returning the membrane to the resting value.

9 An excitatory postsynaptic potential
  a. brings the cell closer to threshold and more likely to have an action potential.
  b. brings the cell closer to threshold and less likely to have an action potential.
  c. brings the cell farther away from threshold and more likely to have an action potential.
  d. brings the cell farther away from threshold and less likely to have an action potential.

10 The influx of calcium ions into the axon terminal of the presynaptic neuron triggers
  a. the opening of ion channels in the membrane of the postsynaptic neuron.
  b. the release of neurotransmitters from synaptic vesicles by exocytosis.
  c. hyperpolarization of the postsynaptic membrane.
  d. an inhibitory postsynaptic potential in the postsynaptic neuron.

Name _____

Section _____ Date_____

Check Your Understanding

Critical Thinking and Application Questions

1 You are examining a neuron under the microscope and notice it is damaged—missing its entire axon. What processes will this neuron be unable to perform? Why?

2 You are examining another neuron, and find that it has two processes, only one of which generates action potentials. What is the structural class of this neuron? How did you come to this conclusion?

3 The disease *metachromatic leukodystrophy* is characterized by the buildup of a certain type of lipid, which is toxic to oligodendrocytes. Predict the effects of this disease. Would it affect the central or peripheral nervous system? Why?

4 A hypothetical poison blocks potassium ion channels in the neuron. What phase(s) of the action potential would this block? How would it affect the ability of the neuron to function? Explain.

5 One of the ways a presynaptic neuron controls the release of neurotransmitters is by altering the calcium ion channels in the axon terminal.

    a What would happen to synaptic transmission if more calcium ion channels opened, and for a longer period? Explain.

    b What would happen to synaptic transmission if fewer calcium ion channels opened, and for a shorter period? Explain.

12

Central Nervous System

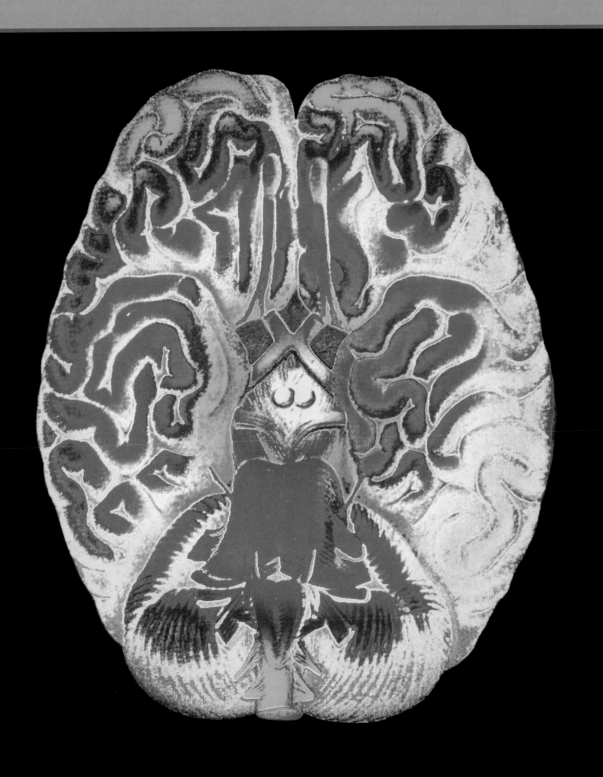

When you have completed this unit, you should be able to:

1 Identify structures of the brain, and describe its gross anatomy.

2 Identify structures of the spinal cord, and describe its anatomical organization.

PRE-LAB EXERCISES

Complete the following exercises prior to coming to lab, using your lab manual and textbook for reference.

PRE-LAB

13-1

Key Terms

You should be familiar with the following terms before coming to lab.

Term	Definition

Structures of the Brain

Cerebral hemispheres _____

Gray matter _____

Cerebral cortex _____

Basal nuclei _____

White matter _____

Diencephalon _____

Thalamus _____

Hypothalamus _____

Midbrain _____

Pons _____

Medulla oblongata _____

Cerebellum _____

Dura mater _____

Arachnoid mater _____

_____

Pia mater _____

_____

Ventricles _____

_____

Structures of the Spinal Cord

Anterior horn of the spinal cord _____

_____

Posterior horn of the spinal cord _____

_____

Lateral horn of the spinal cord _____

_____

Conus medullaris _____

_____

Filum terminale _____

_____

Cauda equina _____

_____

Epidural space _____

_____

Color the diagrams of the brain in Figures 13.1, 13.2, and 13.3, and label them with the terms from Exercise 13-1 (p. 347). Use your text and Exercise 13-1 in this unit for reference.

13

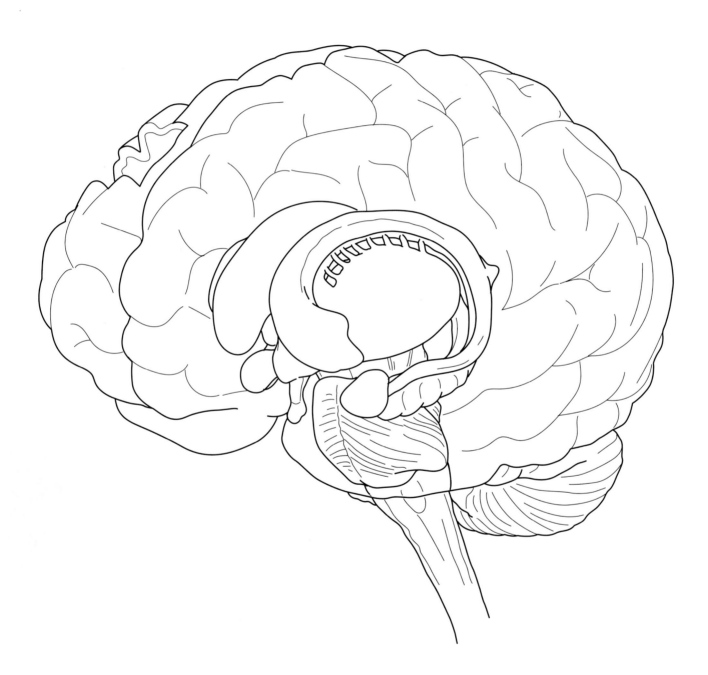

FIGURE **13.1** The main structures of the brain.

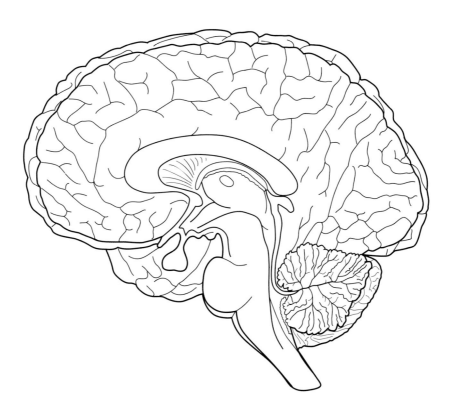

FIGURE **13.2** Midsagittal section of the brain.

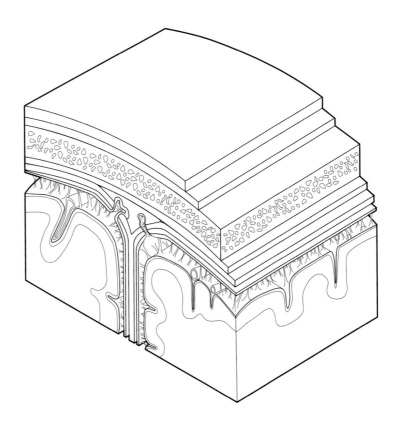

FIGURE **13.3** Brain and meninges, frontal and parasagittal section.

Color the diagrams of the spinal cord in Figure 13.4, and label them with the terms from Exercise 13-2 (p. 357). Use your text and Exercise 13-2 in this unit for reference.

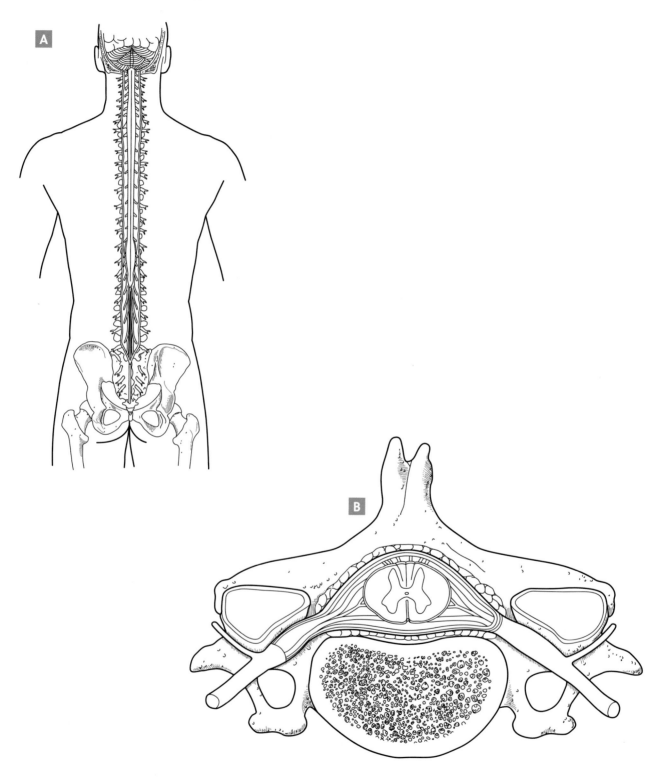

FIGURE **13.4** Spinal cord: (**A**) posterior view of the brain and spinal cord; (**B**) transverse section of the spinal cord in the vertebral column (showing the spinal meninges and associated spaces).

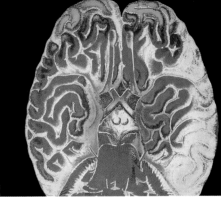

Computer-enhanced Mascagni artwork of the brain.

EXERCISES

R ecall from our study of nervous tissue that we divide the nervous system into two structural divisions: the **central nervous system** (**CNS**), which consists of the *brain* and *spinal cord*, and the **peripheral nervous system** (**PNS**), which consists of the *cranial* and *spinal nerves*. We address the structure and function of the CNS in this unit.

The anatomy of the brain and the spinal cord may seem complex, but really it simply consists of a hollow, folded tube with an enlarged end (the brain). Together these two organs monitor and maintain many homeostatic variables, interpret sensation, plan and execute movement, and control our higher brain functions. The anatomy of both organs will be explored in the two exercises in this unit.

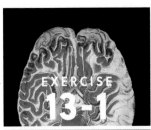

EXERCISE
13-1

MATERIALS

❏ Anatomical models and diagrams:
  ▪ brains, whole and sectioned
  ▪ brain ventricles
  ▪ brainstems
  ▪ dural sinuses
❏ Sheep brains
❏ Dissection equipment and trays
❏ Colored pencils

Anatomy of the Brain

The **brain** is the most complex organ of the nervous system, consisting of a folded, hollow, whitish-gray mass of nervous tissue, connective tissue, and modified epithelium. It is divided into four regions: the *cerebral hemispheres* (collectively called the *cerebrum*), the *diencephalon*, the *cerebellum*, and the *brainstem*. The brain contains hollow spaces called **ventricles** that are filled with a fluid similar to plasma called **cerebrospinal fluid** (seh-ree-broh-SPY-nuhl; **CSF**; *cerebr-* = "brain"). As you can see in Figure 13.5, the largest of the ventricles, called the **lateral ventricles**, are located in the right and left cerebral hemispheres. Note in Figure 13.5A that the lateral ventricles resemble rams' horns when viewed from the anterior side. Indeed, the different regions of each lateral ventricle are named *horns*: the *anterior, posterior,* and *inferior horns*.

The anterior horns of the two lateral ventricles are connected by a small opening called the *interventricular foramen* (remember from the bone units that "foramen" means "hole"). This foramen leads to the smaller **third ventricle**, which is housed within the diencephalon. The third ventricle is continuous with the **fourth ventricle**, found in the brainstem, via a small canal called the **cerebral aqueduct.** The fourth ventricle is continuous with the **central canal,** a hollow passageway that runs down the central spinal cord.

Within each of the four ventricles, we find collections of blood vessels known as **choroid plexuses** (KOHR-oyd; see Fig. 13.8). As blood flows through the choroid plexuses, fluid filters out into the ventricles, and, at that point, is called CSF. The largest choroid plexuses are within the lateral ventricles. Recall from Unit 12 that the ventricles are lined by neuroglial cells called ependymal cells, whose cilia beat to circulate CSF. One of the main functions of CSF is to reduce brain weight, as the brain is buoyant in the CSF. Without CSF, your brain literally would crush itself under its own weight.

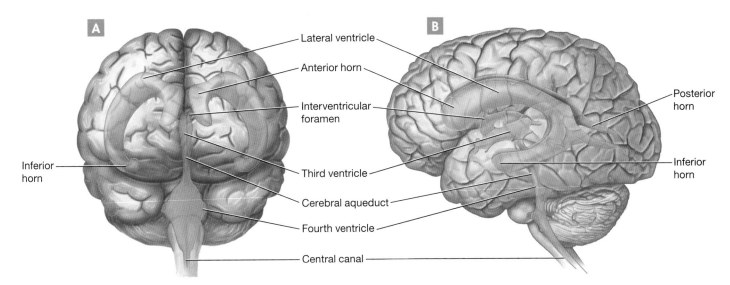

FIGURE **13.5** Ventricles: (**A**) anterior view; (**B**) left lateral view.

The **cerebrum** (seh-REE-brum) is the most superior portion of the brain and is responsible for the brain's cognitive functions, including learning and language, conscious interpretation of sensory information, conscious planning of movement, and personality (Fig. 13.6). The two cerebral hemispheres are separated from one another by a deep groove called the **longitudinal fissure**, and they are separated from the cerebellum by the **transverse fissure**.

The cerebral surface consists of elevated ridges called **gyri** (JY-ree) and shallow grooves called **sulci** (SUL-kee; "wrinkle"), an adaptation that increases the brain's surface area and makes it a more compact structure. The brain folding into gyri and sulci also seems to increase the speed at which cerebral neurons communicate.

The cerebrum consists of five lobes: the **frontal, parietal, temporal, occipital,** and deep **insula** lobes (remember this last one by the mnemonic "the *insula* is *insula*ted"; note the insula is not visible in the figure). Notice that the **lateral sulcus** separates the frontal and temporal lobes and the **central sulcus** separates the frontal and parietal lobes. On either side of the central sulcus are two prominent gyri: the anterior **precentral gyrus**, which houses the primary motor cortex, and the posterior **postcentral gyrus**, which houses the primary somatosensory cortex. A less prominent sulcus, the *parieto-occipital sulcus*, separates the parietal and occipital lobes.

The outer 2 mm of the cerebrum is a region known as the **cerebral cortex** (Fig. 13.7). Here we find unmyelinated parts of the cerebral neurons, including cell bodies, dendrites, and unmyelinated axons. As you can see in the figure, the lack of myelin

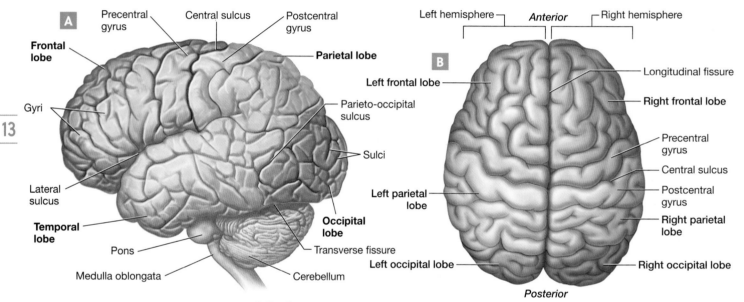

FIGURE **13.6** Brain: (**A**) lateral view; (**B**) superior view.

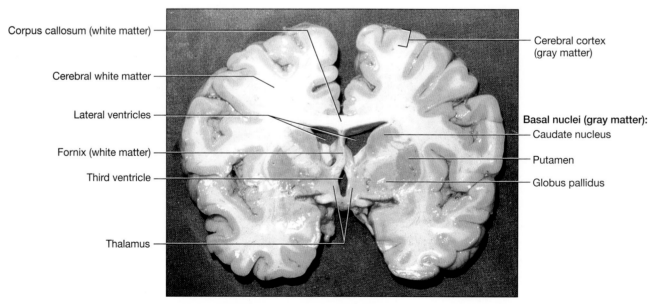

FIGURE **13.7** Frontal section through the brain.

gives the cerebral cortex a gray-brown color, and for this reason it is called **gray matter**. The cell bodies and processes of the cerebral cortex communicate with other parts of the nervous system by bundles of myelinated axons called **white matter**. The largest tract of cerebral white matter is called the **corpus callosum** (KOHR-puhs kal-OH-sum; "large body"), which connects the right and left cerebral hemispheres. Another prominent tract of white matter visible inferior to the corpus callosum is the **fornix**.

Gray matter isn't confined to the cerebral cortex. Clusters of cell bodies called **nuclei** are found throughout the white matter of the cerebrum. Some nuclei are grouped together into functional systems. One such system is the **basal nuclei**: the *caudate nucleus*, *putamen*, and *globus pallidus* (see Fig. 13.10). These three nuclei are responsible for the smooth onset of voluntary motion and inhibiting unwanted movement. The neurons of these nuclei are connected to other parts of the nervous system by various tracts of cerebral white matter.

Another functional system is the **limbic system,** which contains some of the most evolutionarily ancient parts of the mammalian brain (see Fig. 13.10). A key component of the limbic system is the "limbic lobe" of the cerebrum—a ring of gray matter on the medial side of the cerebral hemisphere. Lateral to the limbic lobe, embedded in the temporal lobe, is a seahorse-shaped nucleus called the **hippocampus** (hip-poh-CAM-pus; "seahorse"), which has a critical role in learning and memory. Note the hippocampus is connected to the fornix, through which its output is delivered to other parts of the brain. Anterior to the hippocampus is an almond-shaped nucleus called the **amygdala** (uh-MIG-duh-luh; "almond"), which plays a role in emotional expression, particularly fear.

Deep to the cerebral hemispheres in the central core of the brain, we find the **diencephalon** (dy-en-SEF-ah-lahn; *di-* = "across;" *encephala-* = "brain"), which is composed of three main parts (Fig. 13.8):

1. **Thalamus.** The **thalamus** (THAL-uh-muhs), which makes up 80% of the diencephalon, is the large, central, egg-shaped mass of gray and white matter. There

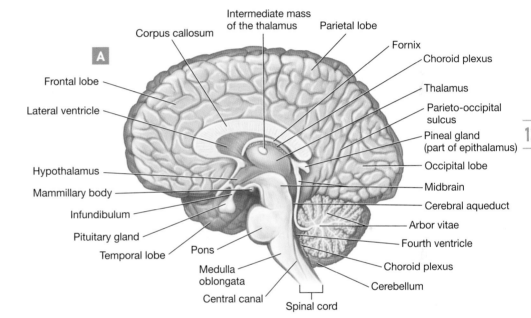

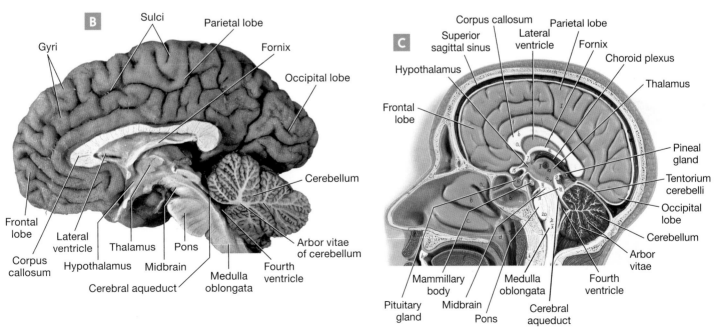

FIGURE **13.8** Midsagittal section of the brain: (**A**) illustration; (**B**) photograph; (**C**) anatomical model.

13

are two thalamic lobes that are connected by a small band of white matter called the *intermediate mass of the thalamus*. Functionally, the thalamus is a major integration center and a major relay center that edit and sort information going into the cerebrum. It essentially functions as the "gateway" into the cerebrum.

2. **Hypothalamus.** The **hypothalamus** (hy-poh-THAL-uh-muhs; *hypo-* = "below") is the anterior and inferior component of the diencephalon. It is a deceptively small structure that contains the nuclei whose neurons help to regulate the endocrine system; monitor the sleep-wake cycle; control thirst, hunger, and body temperature; and monitor the autonomic nervous system (good things do come in small packages, after all). An endocrine organ called the **pituitary gland** (pih-TOO-ih-tehr-ee) is connected to the hypothalamus by a stalk called the **infundibulum** (in-fun-DIB-yoo-lum; "funnel"). On the posteroinferior surface of the hypothalamus is a pair of gray matter clusters called **mammillary bodies**, which play a role in learning and memory.

3. **Epithalamus.** The **epithalamus** (ep-ih-THAL-uh-muss) is the posterior and superior part of the diencephalon. It contains an endocrine organ called the **pineal gland** (pin-EE-uhl; *pinea-* = "pine cone") that secretes the hormone **melatonin** (mel-uh-TOH-nin), which helps to regulate the sleep-wake cycle.

The third major component of the brain is the large, posterior **cerebellum** (sehr-eh-BELL-um). It consists of two highly convoluted lobes connected by a piece called the **vermis** (VER-miss; "worm"). Like the cerebral hemispheres, the outer portion of the cerebellum, known as the **cerebellar cortex**, is gray matter, while the inner region is white matter. The cerebellar white matter is called the **arbor vitae** (AHR-bohr VEE-tay; "tree of life") because of its resemblance to the branches of a tree. The cerebellum coordinates and plans ongoing motor activities and is critical in reducing and preventing motor error with movement.

The final division of the brain, the **brainstem**, influences the automatic functions of the body (Fig. 13.9). The most superior portion of the brainstem is the **midbrain**, which has roles in movement, sensation, and certain reflexes. Posterior to the midbrain are two projections called the **superior** and **inferior colliculi** (koll-IK-yoo-lye; *collicul-* = "hill"), which relay visual and auditory stimuli to the thalamus, respectively. Inferior to the midbrain, we find the rounded **pons** (PAHNZ; "bridge"), which bulges anteriorly. Nuclei of the pons are involved in controlling the rhythm for breathing and the sleep cycle. The last segment of the brainstem, the **medulla oblongata** (meh-DOOL-uh ahb-lahn-GAH-tuh), or simply *medulla*, is continuous inferiorly with the spinal cord. The nuclei in the medulla work with those of the pons to control ventilation and are also involved in regulating heart rate, blood pressure, and certain reflexes such as vomiting. The brainstem and the other main structures of the brain are illustrated in Figure 13.10.

A set of three membranes, collectively called the **meninges** (meh-NIN-jeez; singular: *meninx*; "membrane"), surrounds the brain (Fig. 13.11). The meninges include the following:

1. **Dura mater.** The outermost meninx is the thick, leathery, double-layered **dura mater** (DOO-rah MAH-tur; "tough mother"). The superficial *periosteal layer* is fused to the skull, and the deeper *meningeal layer* is continuous with the dura mater of

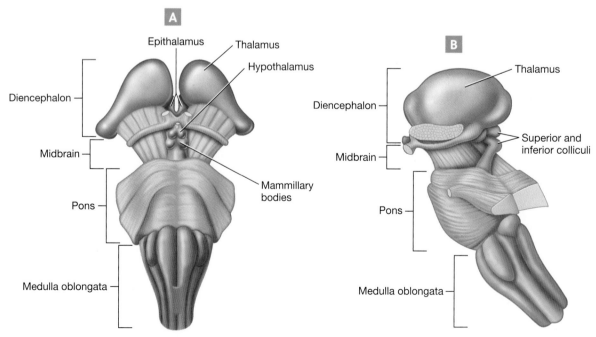

FIGURE **13.9** Diencephalon and brainstem: (**A**) anterior view; (**B**) lateral view.

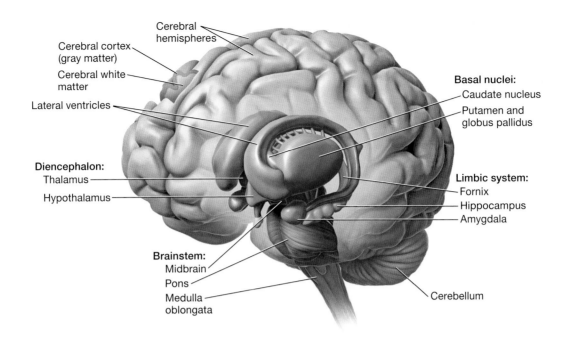

Cerebral hemispheres

Cerebral cortex (gray matter)

Cerebral white matter

Lateral ventricles

Basal nuclei:
Caudate nucleus
Putamen and globus pallidus

Diencephalon:
Thalamus
Hypothalamus

Limbic system:
Fornix
Hippocampus
Amygdala

Brainstem:
Midbrain
Pons
Medulla oblongata

Cerebellum

FIGURE **13.10** The main structures of the brain.

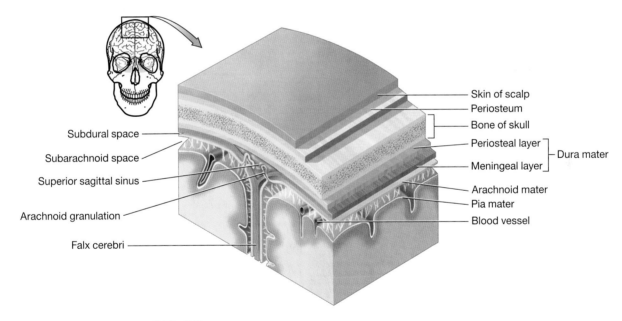

Subdural space

Subarachnoid space

Superior sagittal sinus

Arachnoid granulation

Falx cerebri

Skin of scalp
Periosteum
Bone of skull

Periosteal layer ⎤
⎬ Dura mater
Meningeal layer ⎦

Arachnoid mater
Pia mater

Blood vessel

FIGURE **13.11** Brain and meninges, frontal and parasagittal section.

the spinal cord. The two layers of the dura are fused, but in three regions the meningeal layer separates from the periosteal layer and dives into the brain to form three structures:

a. The **falx cerebri** (FALS seh-REE-bree) resides in the longitudinal fissure and forms a partition between the right and left cerebral hemispheres. Its attachment to the crista galli of the ethmoid bone anchors it in place.

b. The **falx cerebelli** (FALS sehr-eh-BELL-ee) separates the two cerebellar hemispheres.

c. The **tentorium cerebelli** resides in the transverse fissure and separates the cerebrum from the cerebellum (see Fig. 13.8C).

At these locations, the two layers of the dura separate, forming spaces collectively called the **dural sinuses** (see Fig. 18.12, p. 492). All deoxygenated blood from the brain drains into the dural sinuses, which in turn drain into veins exiting the head and neck. You can see the large **superior sagittal sinus**, which runs along the longitudinal fissure, in Figures 13.11 and 13.12.

2. **Arachnoid mater.** The middle meninx, the **arachnoid mater** (ah-RAK-noyd MAH-tur), is separated from the dura by a potential space called the **subdural space**. Small bundles of the arachnoid mater called the **arachnoid granulations** (or **arachnoid villi**) project into the dural sinuses and allow CSF to reenter the blood. You can see the pattern of CSF circulation from its formation by the choroid plexuses to its return to the blood in Figure 13.12.

3. **Pia mater.** The thinnest, innermost meninx is the **pia mater** (PEE-ah MAH-tur; "tender mother"). The pia mater clings to the surface of the cerebral hemispheres and follows the contours of the sulci and gyri. It is richly supplied with blood vessels. There is a space between the pia mater and the arachnoid mater, called the **subarachnoid space**, which is filled with CSF.

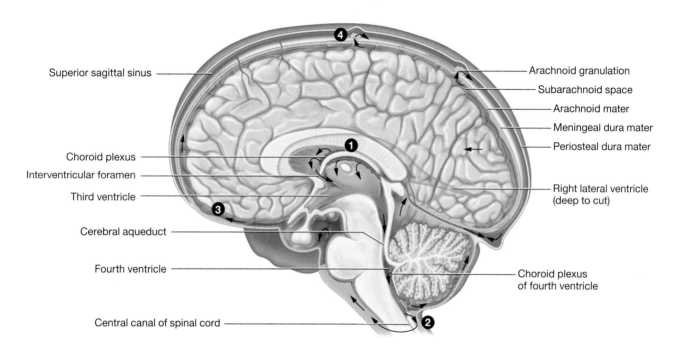

1 CSF is produced by the choroid plexuses of each ventricle.

2 CSF flows through the ventricles and into the subarachnoid space. Some CSF flows through the central canal of the spinal cord.

3 CSF flows through the subarachnoid space.

4 CSF is absorbed into the dural venous sinuses via the arachnoid granulations.

FIGURE **13.12** Circulation of CSF through the brain and spinal cord.

PROCEDURE

Model Inventory for the Brain

Identify the following structures of the brain on models and diagrams, using your textbook and this unit for reference. As you examine the anatomical models and diagrams, record the name of the model and the structures you were able to identify on the model inventory in Table 13.1. The brain's structure is complex, and it's best to examine models in as many different planes of section as possible. When you have completed the activity, answer Check Your Understanding Questions 1 through 3 (p. 365).

1. Ventricles
   a. Lateral ventricles
   b. Third ventricle
   c. Fourth ventricle
   d. Cerebral aqueduct
   e. Choroid plexuses
2. Cerebrum
   a. Cerebral hemispheres
   b. Fissures
      (1) Longitudinal fissure
      (2) Transverse fissure
   c. Lobes of the cerebrum
      (1) Frontal lobe
      (2) Parietal lobe
      (3) Temporal lobe
      (4) Occipital lobe
      (5) Insula lobe
   d. Sulci
      (1) Lateral sulcus

   (2) Central sulcus
      (a) Precentral gyrus
      (b) Postcentral gyrus
   (3) Parieto-occipital sulcus
   e. Cerebral cortex
   f. Corpus callosum
   g. Fornix
   h. Basal nuclei (these will only be visible on certain sections of the brain)
3. Diencephalon
   a. Thalamus
   b. Hypothalamus
      (1) Pituitary gland
      (2) Infundibulum
      (3) Mammillary bodies
   c. Epithalamus
      (1) Pineal gland
4. Cerebellum

   a. Vermis
   b. Cerebellar cortex
   c. Arbor vitae
5. Brainstem
   a. Midbrain
   b. Pons
   c. Medulla oblongata
6. Brain coverings
   a. Dura mater
      (1) Falx cerebri
      (2) Falx cerebelli
      (3) Tentorium cerebelli
      (4) Dural sinuses
      (5) Superior sagittal sinus
   b. Arachnoid mater
      (1) Subdural space
      (2) Arachnoid granulations
   c. Pia mater
      (1) Subarachnoid space

13

TABLE **13.1** Model Inventory for the Brain

Model/Diagram	Structures Identified

2 PROCEDURE
Dissecting the Brain

Often, structures of the brain and spinal cord are difficult to see on anatomical models. By dissecting a preserved sheep brain in this procedure, you will be able to examine these structures more closely. You will note that certain structures, such as the frontal lobes of the cerebral hemispheres, are proportionally smaller in the sheep than in the human brain. Note that the process of preservation makes many structures of the brain much tougher than they would be in a fresh specimen.

⚠ **SAFETY NOTE**
Goggles and gloves are required!

1 Examine the external surface of the brain. Note the thick part of the dura covering the longitudinal fissure. If you cut through this with scissors, you will enter the superior sagittal sinus.

2 Next, remove the dura to reveal the thin membrane on top of the brain. This is the arachnoid mater.

3 Remove an area of the arachnoid mater to see the shiny inner membrane—the pia mater—directly touching the surface of the brain. Note how the pia mater follows the convolutions of the gyri and sulci.

4 Examine the surface anatomy of both the superior and the inferior surfaces of the sheep brain (Figs. 13.13 and 13.14).

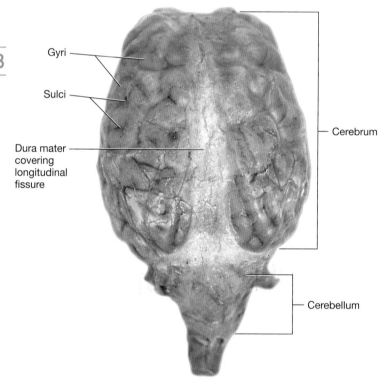

FIGURE **13.13** Superior view of the sheep brain.

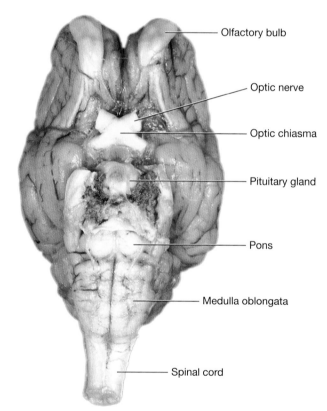

FIGURE **13.14** Inferior view of the sheep brain.

In the space provided, draw what you see on both surfaces, and label your drawing with the following structures:

❏ Arachnoid mater   ❏ Dura mater   ❏ Medulla oblongata   ❏ Sulci
❏ Cerebellum   ❏ Gyri   ❏ Pituitary gland
❏ Cerebrum   ❏ Longitudinal fissure   ❏ Pons

5 Spread the two cerebral hemispheres, and identify the corpus callosum.

6 Make a cut down the brain's midsagittal plane to separate the two cerebral hemispheres.

7 Examine the brain's internal anatomy (Fig. 13.15), and stick your finger in the lateral ventricle. You will see (or feel) that it is much larger than it appears.

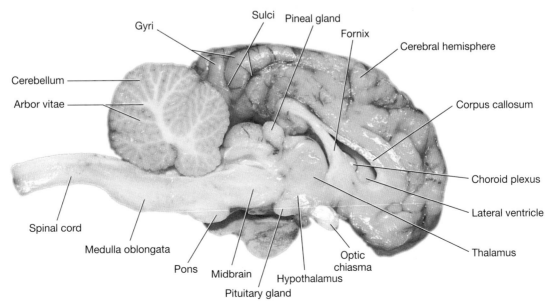

FIGURE **13.15** Lateral view of the sheep brain, midsagittal section.

In the space provided, draw what you see, and label your drawing with the following structures:

- ❏ Arbor vitae
- ❏ Choroid plexus
- ❏ Corpus callosum
- ❏ Fornix
- ❏ Hypothalamus
- ❏ Lateral ventricle
- ❏ Medulla oblongata
- ❏ Midbrain
- ❏ Pineal gland
- ❏ Pons
- ❏ Thalamus

8 Section one of the halves of the brain in the frontal plane, approximately along the central sulcus. Note the outer cerebral cortex (the gray matter) and the inner white matter. From this view, you also can see the lateral and third ventricles. Again, draw what you see in the space provided and label your drawing with the following structures (see Fig. 13.7 for reference):

- ❏ Cerebral cortex
- ❏ Cerebral white matter
- ❏ Falx cerebri
- ❏ Lateral ventricle
- ❏ Thalamus
- ❏ Third ventricle

MATERIALS

☐ Anatomical models and diagrams: spinal cord, whole and sectioned
☐ Colored pencils

Anatomy of the Spinal Cord

The medulla oblongata passes through the foramen magnum of the occipital bone and becomes the **spinal cord** (Fig. 13.16). Along its length are two notable bulges: the **cervical** and **lumbar enlargements**. The spinal cord is wider in these areas due to the high number of nerve roots that attach at these locations going to and coming from the upper and lower limbs. Notice in Figure 13.16 that the spinal cord does not extend the entire length of the vertebral column; rather, it ends between the first and second lumbar vertebrae. At this point, it tapers to form the end of the spinal cord, called the **conus medullaris** (KOHN-uhs med-yoo-LEHR-uhs). Extending from the conus medullaris is a tuft of nerve roots called the **cauda equina** (KOW-dah eh-KWY-nah; "horse's tail").

The cauda equina fills the remainder of the vertebral column to the sacrum and the nerve roots exit out of the appropriate foramina to become spinal nerves. These nerve roots give off spinal nerves that supply the lower limbs and the pelvis; they are also involved in voluntary control of urination and defecation.

Like the brain, the spinal cord is protected by a set of meninges (called **spinal meninges**), which are continuous with the cranial meninges (Figs. 13.17 and 13.18). The cranial and spinal meninges are similar in name and structure: the dura mater is the outer meninx; the arachnoid mater is the middle meninx, which is separated from the dura by a thin potential space called the subdural space; and the pia mater is the inner meninx, which is separated from the arachnoid mater by the CSF-filled subarachnoid space.

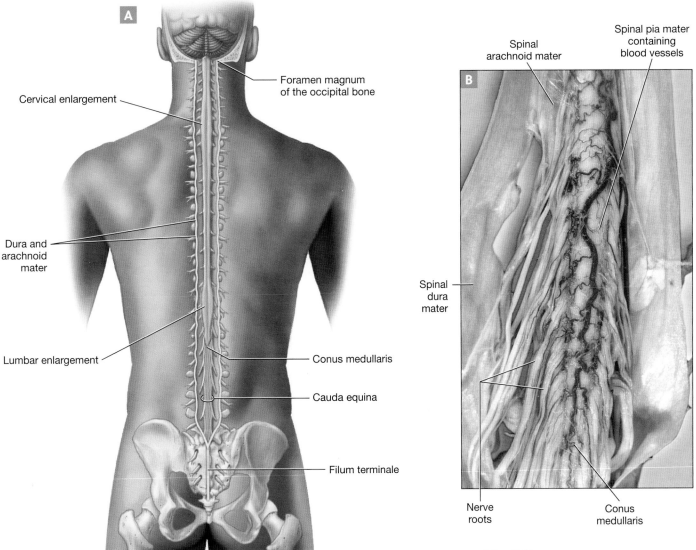

FIGURE **13.16** Spinal cord, posterior view: (**A**) illustration; (**B**) photograph.

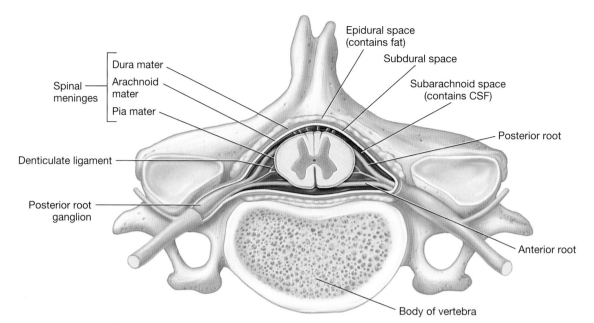

FIGURE **13.17** Transverse section of the spinal cord in the vertebral column (showing spinal meninges and associated spaces).

There are a few notable differences between the cranial and spinal meninges. For one, the spinal dura mater consists of only *one* layer rather than two like the cranial dura does. This single dural layer does not attach to the vertebral column, creating a fat-filled **epidural space** (ep-ih-DOO-ruhl) between the spinal dura and the interior vertebral foramen. There is no epidural space around the brain because the periosteal layer of the cranial dura is fused to the skull.

Notice in **Figure 13.17** another key difference between the cranial and spinal meninges: In the spinal cord are small extensions of pia mater called **denticulate ligaments** (den-TIK-yoo-lit). These tiny ligaments secure the spinal cord to the vertebral column. In addition, the pia mater continues long after the spinal cord ends, forming a long, fibrous extension called the **filum terminale** (FY-lum ter-mee-NAL-ay) that eventually attaches to the coccyx (see **Fig. 13.16**).

The external surface of the spinal cord features two indentations. Anteriorly, we find the relatively wide **anterior median fissure**, and posteriorly is the much narrower **posterior median sulcus** (**Fig. 13.18**). Internally, the spinal cord consists of a butterfly-shaped core of gray matter that surrounds the CSF-filled **central canal**. Notice that this arrangement is different from what we

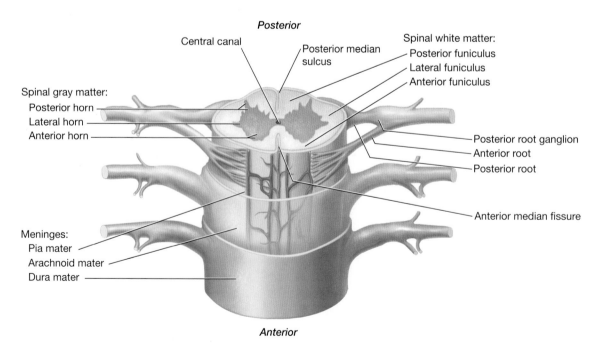

FIGURE **13.18** Transverse section showing the internal anatomy of the spinal cord.

saw in the brain, where the gray matter was on the outside and the white matter on the inside. The gray matter is divided into regions, or **horns:**

- The **anterior horns** contain the cell bodies of motor neurons. The axons of the neurons of the anterior horn exit the spinal cord, forming the **anterior root**, which eventually becomes part of a spinal nerve.

- The **posterior horns** contain the cell bodies of sensory neurons. These cell bodies receive input from the axons of pseudounipolar neurons in the PNS that enter the spinal cord via the **posterior root**. The cell bodies of these pseudo-unipolar neurons are located just lateral to the spinal cord in a swollen knob called the **posterior root ganglion**.

- The **lateral horns** are found in the thoracic and lumbar regions of the spinal cord. They contain the cell bodies of auto-nomic neurons from the sympathetic nervous system. This division of the autonomic nervous system maintains the homeostasis of variables such as heart rate and blood pressure during periods of exercise, excitement, and emergency.

As you can see in Figure 13.18, it is possible to tell the anterior and posterior spinal cord apart by looking at the shapes of the anterior and posterior horns. The anterior horns are broad and flat on the ends, whereas the posterior horns are more tapered, and they extend farther out toward the edge.

Surrounding the spinal gray matter is the spinal white matter, which can be divided into three *columns* or **funiculi** (fun-IK-yoo-lye; "rope"): the **anterior, posterior,** and **lateral funiculi**. Each funiculus contains myelinated axons grouped into bundles called **tracts**. Tracts contain axons that have the same beginning and end points and the same general function. *Ascending tracts* carry sensory information from sensory neurons to the brain, and *descending tracts* carry motor information from the brain to motor neurons.

1 PROCEDURE
Model Inventory for the Spinal Cord

13

Identify the following structures of the spinal cord on models and diagrams, using your textbook and this unit for reference. As you examine the anatomical models and diagrams, record the name of the model and the structures you were able to identify on the model inventory in Table 13.2. When you have completed the activity, answer Check Your Understanding Questions 4 through 6 (p. 366).

1. Cervical enlargement
2. Lumbar enlargement
3. Conus medullaris
4. Cauda equina
5. Meninges
   a. Dura mater
      (1) Epidural space
   b. Arachnoid mater
      (1) Subdural space
   c. Pia mater
      (1) Subarachnoid space
      (2) Denticulate ligaments
      (3) Filum terminale
6. Anterior median fissure

7. Posterior median sulcus
8. Central canal
9. Spinal gray matter
   a. Anterior horn
   b. Posterior horn
   c. Lateral horn
10. Spinal nerve roots
    a. Anterior root
    b. Posterior root
       (1) Posterior root ganglion
11. Spinal white matter
    a. Anterior funiculus
    b. Lateral funiculus
    c. Posterior funiculus

TABLE **13.2** Model Inventory for the Spinal Cord

Model/Diagram	Structures Identified

13

2 **PROCEDURE**

Time to Draw

In the space provided, draw, color, and label one of the transverse sections of the spinal cord models that you examined. In addition, write the function of each structure that you label.

Name _____

Section _____ Date _____

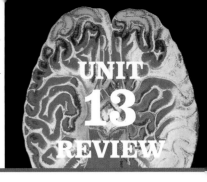

Check Your Recall

1 Label the following parts of the brain in Figures 13.19 and 13.20.

❑ Central sulcus
❑ Cerebral aqueduct
❑ Corpus callosum
❑ Fourth ventricle
❑ Frontal lobe
❑ Lateral sulcus
❑ Parietal lobe
❑ Pineal gland
❑ Postcentral gyrus
❑ Precentral gyrus
❑ Temporal lobe
❑ Thalamus

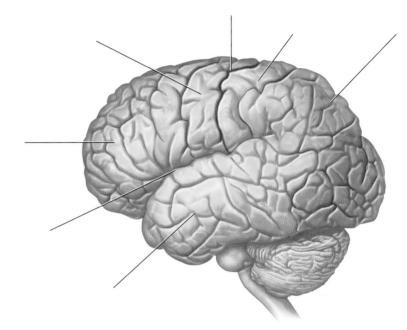

FIGURE **13.19** Lateral view of the brain.

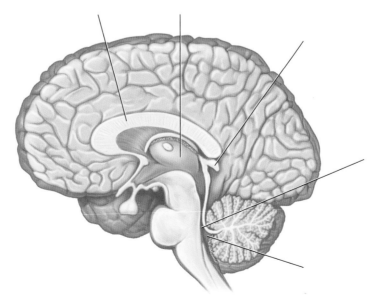

FIGURE **13.20** Midsagittal section of the brain.

2 Label the following structures in Figure 13.21.

❑ Amygdala
❑ Caudate nucleus
❑ Cerebellum
❑ Cerebral cortex
❑ Fornix
❑ Hippocampus
❑ Hypothalamus
❑ Lateral ventricle
❑ Medulla oblongata
❑ Pons

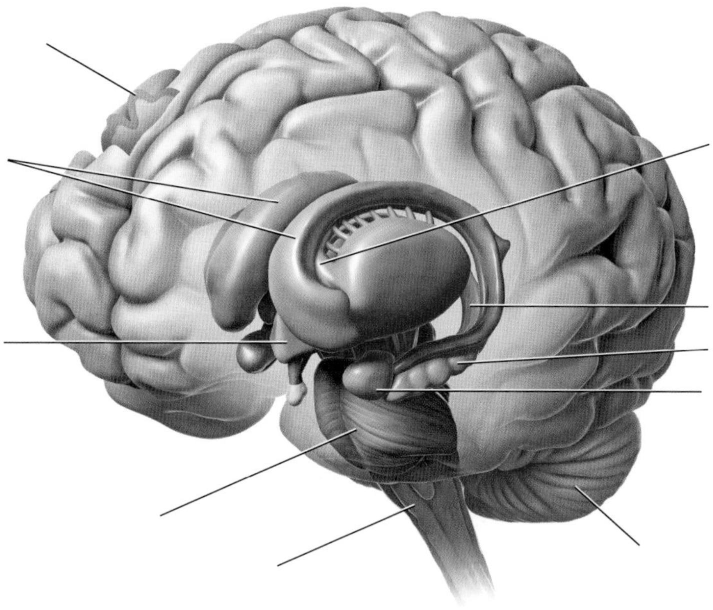

FIGURE **13.21** The main structures of the brain.

3 The longitudinal fissure separates the
a. cerebrum from the cerebellum.
b. two cerebral hemispheres.
c. cerebral cortex from cerebral white matter.
d. temporal lobe from the frontal and parietal lobes.

4 The deep lobe of the cerebrum is the
a. temporal lobe.
b. occipital lobe.
c. parietal lobe.
d. insula lobe.

5 *True/False:* Mark the following statements as true (T) or false (F). If the statement is false, correct it to make it a true statement.

_____ The diencephalon consists of the thalamus, epithalamus, and hypothalamus.

_____ The thin, inner membrane around the brain is the arachnoid mater.

_____ The cerebellum is responsible for the smooth onset of voluntary motion.

_____ Gray matter consists of myelinated axons.

_____ The hippocampus has a critical role in learning and memory.

6 The part of the brain that acts as the "gateway" to the cerebrum is the
a. thalamus.
b. epithalamus.
c. medulla oblongata.
d. midbrain.

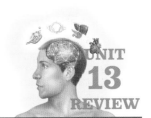
7 Cerebrospinal fluid is produced by the

   a. dural sinuses.

   b. choroid plexuses.

   c. ventricles.

   d. meninges.

8 Label the following parts of the spinal cord in Figure 13.22.

   ❏ Anterior funiculus

   ❏ Anterior root

   ❏ Arachnoid mater

   ❏ Cauda equina

   ❏ Central canal

   ❏ Dura mater

   ❏ Epidural space

   ❏ Lumbar enlargement

   ❏ Pia mater

   ❏ Posterior horn

   ❏ Posterior root ganglion

   ❏ Subarachnoid space

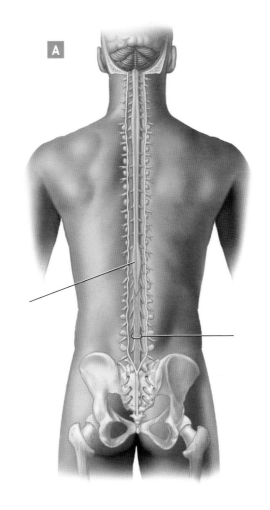

FIGURE **13.22** Spinal cord: (**A**) transverse section in the vertebral column; (**B**) internal anatomy.

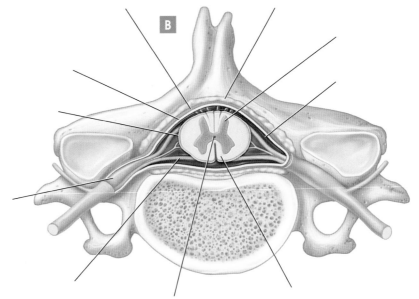

13

9 The end of the spinal cord is known as the

    a. filum terminale.

    b. lumbar enlargement.

    c. cauda equina.

    d. conus medullaris.

10 Which of the following spaces around the spinal cord is filled with adipose tissue?

    a. Epidural space.

    b. Subdural space.

    c. Subarachnoid space.

    d. All of the above.

13

Name _____

Section _____ Date _____

Check Your Understanding

Critical Thinking and Application Questions

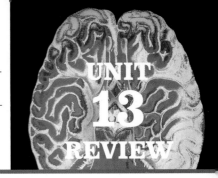

1 *Cauda equina syndrome* is caused by compression or impingement of the cauda equina. What symptoms might someone experience with this syndrome? Explain.

_____

_____

_____

_____

_____

2 Predict the effects of injuries to the following structures:

a Basal nuclei

_____

_____

b Medulla oblongata

_____

_____

c Hippocampus

_____

_____

3 Bettina fell down the stairs and hit her head. She now has a "blinding" headache, clear fluid leaking out of her nose, and she is dizzy. An x-ray reveals a fracture of the ethmoid bone. What has likely happened? What is the fluid leaking out of her nose, and how does it explain her symptoms?

_____

_____

_____

_____

4 A common way to deliver anesthesia for surgery and childbirth is to inject the anesthetic agent into the epidural space around the lower lumbar portion of the spinal column (*epidural anesthesia*). Why isn't it possible to deliver epidural anesthesia around the brain?

5 You are a medical resident and are administering an epidural anesthetic. You pull back the plunger and the syringe fills with cerebrospinal fluid. What has happened? How can you fix this mistake?

6 Omar was in an automobile accident, and sustained an injury to the right side of his lower thoracic spinal cord. Since his injury, Omar has suffered from unstable blood pressure and heart rate and has been unable to move any muscles of his right lower limb. Which gray matter horn(s) was/were affected by his injury? Explain.

13

Peripheral and Autonomic Nervous System

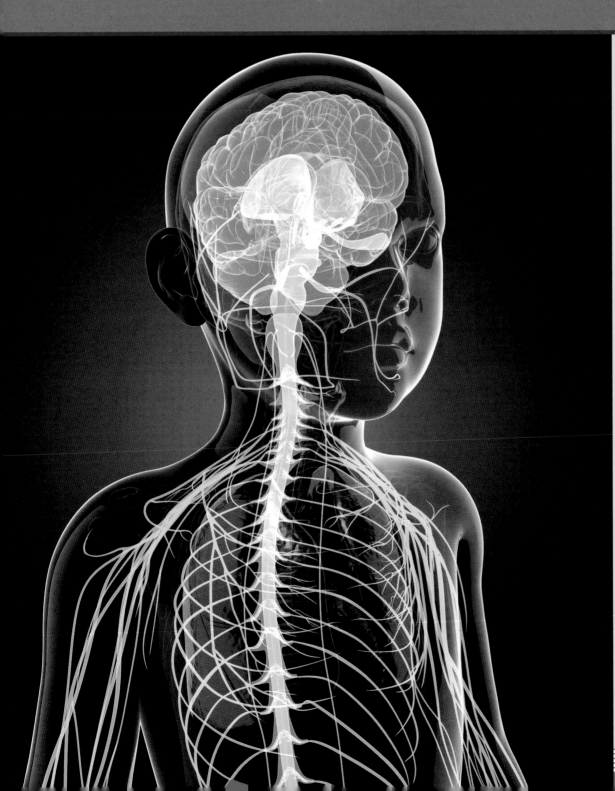

When you have completed this unit, you should be able to:

1 Identify structures of a peripheral nerve on anatomical models or microscope slides.

2 Identify, describe, and demonstrate functions of cranial nerves.

3 Identify spinal nerves and plexuses on anatomical models.

4 Describe a simple spinal reflex arc and explain how mental concentration affects the patellar tendon (knee-jerk) reflex.

5 Describe the effects of the two branches of the autonomic nervous system on the body systems.

PRE-LAB EXERCISES

Complete the following exercises prior to coming to lab, using your lab manual and textbook for reference.

PRE-LAB

14-1 Key Terms

You should be familiar with the following terms before coming to lab. Please note that the individual cranial and spinal nerves are covered in Pre-Lab Exercises 14-2 (p. 370) and 14-3 (p. 371), respectively.

Term	Definition

General Terms

Peripheral nerve _____

_____

Cranial nerve _____

_____

Spinal nerve _____

_____

Sympathetic nervous system _____

_____

Parasympathetic nervous system _____

_____

Parts of a Peripheral Nerve

Fascicle _____

_____

Epineurium _____

_____

Perineurium _____

_____

Endoneurium _____

_____

Spinal Nerve Plexuses

Cervical plexus _____

_____

Brachial plexus _____

_____

Lumbar plexus _____

_____

Sacral plexus _____

_____

Complete Table 14.1 by listing the functions of each pair of cranial nerves, and indicating whether the nerve is primarily motor, sensory, or mixed. Use Exercise 14-2 (p. 375) in this unit for reference.

TABLE **14.1** Cranial Nerve Functions

Cranial Nerve	Functions	Motor, Sensory, or Mixed
CN I: Olfactory nerve		
CN II: Optic nerve		
CN III: Oculomotor nerve		
CN IV: Trochlear nerve		
CN V: Trigeminal nerve		
CN VI: Abducens nerve		
CN VII: Facial nerve		
CN VIII: Vestibulocochlear nerve		
CN IX: Glossopharyngeal nerve		
CN X: Vagus nerve		
CN XI: Accessory nerve		
CN XII: Hypoglossal nerve		

PRE-LAB

14-3

Spinal Nerve Plexuses and the Anterior Rami of the Spinal Nerves

Label **Figure 14.1**, which shows the spinal nerve plexuses and the anterior rami of the spinal nerves, with the terms from Exercise 14-3 (p. 380). Use your text and Exercise 14-3 in this unit for reference. Note that this diagram is presented in color to make identification of the nerves easier.

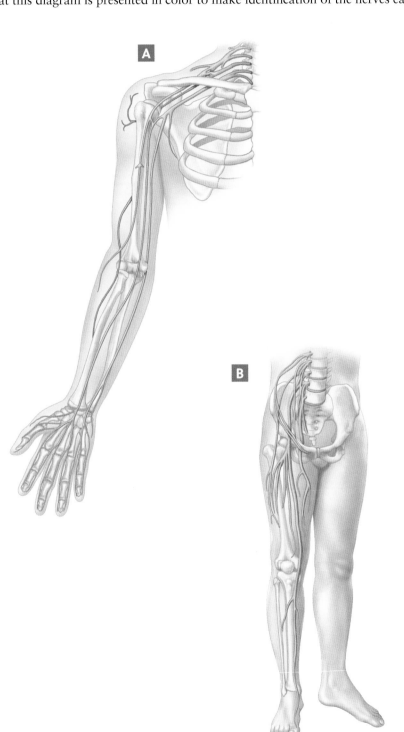

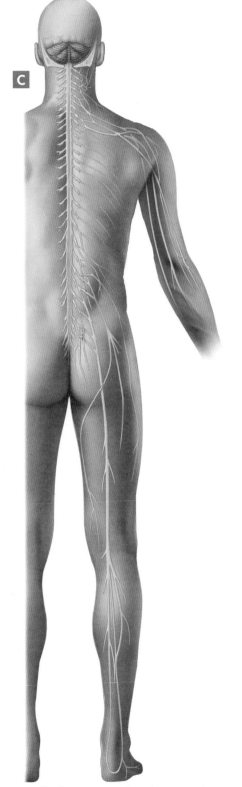

FIGURE **14.1** Nerve plexuses and the anterior rami of the spinal nerves:
(**A**) brachial plexus; (**B**) lumbar plexus; (**C**) posterior view of the full body showing all plexuses and major anterior rami.

14-4

Branches of the Autonomic Nervous System

The autonomic nervous system (ANS) has two subdivisions: (a) the sympathetic nervous system (SNS), and (b) the parasympathetic nervous system (PSNS). Fill in Table 14.2 with the general characteristics of each branch of the ANS and the effects of each system on its target organs, using your text and Exercise 14-4 (p. 387) in this unit for reference.

TABLE **14.2** Characteristics of the Sympathetic and Parasympathetic Nervous Systems

Characteristic	SNS	PSNS
Main function		
Location of nerve roots		
Neurotransmitter(s)		
Effects on Target Organs and Physiological Processes		
Heart		
Bronchioles (airway passages of the lungs)		
Blood vessels to abdominal organs and skin		
Blood vessels to skeletal muscle		
Secretion from digestive glands		
Urine formation/ micturition (urination)		
Pupils of the eye		

14

EXERCISES

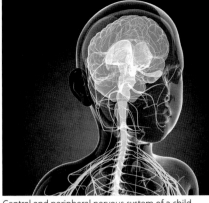

Central and peripheral nervous system of a child.

In Unit 13, we discussed the central nervous system (CNS), and now we turn to the other division of the nervous system—the **peripheral nervous system (PNS)**. The organs of the PNS are called **peripheral nerves**, or simply *nerves*. There are two types of nerves classified by location: (1) nerves that bring information to and from the brain and the brainstem, called **cranial nerves**, and (2) nerves that bring information to and from the spinal cord, called **spinal nerves**.

The PNS may be divided broadly into two divisions based upon function: the **motor** or **efferent division** (EF-uhr-int; "carry out"), which innervates muscle cells and glands, and the **sensory** or **afferent division** (AF-uhr-int; "bring to"), which innervates the skin, joints, special sensory organs, and other sensory receptors. The motor and sensory divisions may be further subdivided based upon the structures that are served: (a) the **somatic sensory** and **somatic motor divisions**, which serve skin and skeletal muscles, respectively, and (b) the **visceral sensory** and **visceral motor divisions**, which serve smooth muscle, cardiac muscle, and glands. The visceral motor division controls most of our automatic functions such as heart rate, blood pressure, digestion, and urine production, and is also known as the **autonomic nervous system (ANS)**.

In the following exercises, we examine the structure and functions of the organs and divisions of the PNS. As you study the PNS, bear in mind that its functions are closely interwoven with the CNS, and the branches of the nervous system cannot function independently of one another.

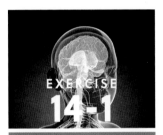

EXERCISE 14-1

MATERIALS

- ☐ Anatomical models or charts: peripheral nerves
- ☐ Slide: peripheral nerve
- ☐ Light microscope with three objectives
- ☐ Colored pencils

Peripheral Nerve Anatomy

The organs of the peripheral nervous system are known as **peripheral nerves**, or simply **nerves**. Each nerve consists of myelinated and unmyelinated axons (also known as *nerve fibers*), blood vessels, lymphatic vessels, and connective tissue sheaths (Figs. 14.2A and B). Each individual axon is covered by its axolemma (plasma membrane), superficial to which we find a connective tissue sheath called the **endoneurium** (in-doh-NOOR-ee-um). Axons are grouped into bundles called **fascicles** (FASS-ih-kullz), which are in turn covered with another connective tissue sheath called the **perineurium** (pehr-ih-NOOR-ee-um). Groups of fascicles, blood vessels, and lymphatic vessels are surrounded by the most superficial connective tissue sheath: the **epineurium** (ep-ih-NOOR-ee-um).

14

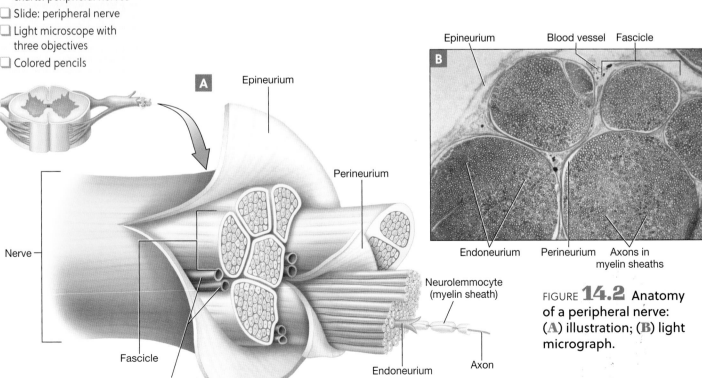

FIGURE **14.2** Anatomy of a peripheral nerve: (**A**) illustration; (**B**) light micrograph.

Examining a Peripheral Nerve with Microscopy

Examine a prepared slide of a sectioned peripheral nerve. Start on low power, and then advance to higher powers to see more details. Draw what you see, and label your drawing with the following terms, using Figure 14.2B for reference. When you have finished the procedure, answer Check Your Understanding Question 1 (p. 391).

- Fascicle
- Axon
- Blood vessels
- Nerve sheaths
- Epineurium
- Perineurium
- Endoneurium
- Myelin sheath

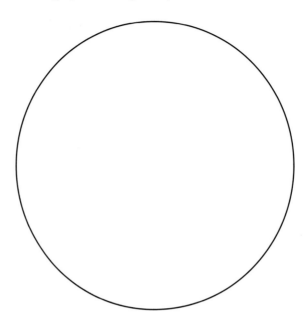

MATERIALS

- Anatomical models and diagrams: brain
- Preserved brain specimens
- Penlight
- Snellen vision chart
- Tuning fork
- Unknown samples (for smelling)
- PTC, thiourea, and sodium benzoate tasting papers

Cranial Nerve Structure and Function

The 12 pairs of **cranial nerves** originate from or bring information to the brain (Fig. 14.3). Each nerve is given two names: (1) a sequential Roman numeral in order of its attachment to the brain, and (2) a name that describes the nerve's location or function. For example, cranial nerve III is the third cranial nerve that attaches to the brain. It is also called the oculomotor nerve because one of its functions is to provide motor axons to some of the muscles that move the eyeball.

Most cranial nerves innervate structures of the head and neck. Three cranial nerves are **sensory nerves** whose axons have purely sensory functions, four are **mixed nerves** that contain both sensory and motor axons, and five are **motor nerves** that primarily contain motor axons. Following is an overview of the main functions of each cranial nerve (note that CN = "cranial nerve"):

1. **CN I: Olfactory Nerve.** The **olfactory nerve** (ohl-FAK-toh-ree; *olfact-* = "smell") is a purely sensory nerve that consists of the axons of olfactory neurons in the olfactory epithelium in the superior nasal cavity. It provides for the sense of smell.

2. **CN II: Optic Nerve.** The **optic nerve** (AHP-tik; *opt-* = "vision") is also a purely sensory nerve that provides for the sense of vision. Its axons emerge from the retina of the eye and meet at the **optic chiasma** (ky-AZ-mah; *chiasm-* = "X-shaped"). Here, the nerves partially exchange axons before diverging to form the **optic tracts.** Due to this axon exchange, visual input from each eye is carried to both lobes of the brain.

3. **CN III: Oculomotor Nerve.** The **oculomotor nerve** (ahk-yoo-loh-MOH-tohr; *ocul-* = "eye") is a motor cranial nerve. It innervates four of the six extrinsic eye muscles that move the eyeball; the muscle that opens the eyelid; the muscle that constricts the pupil; and the muscle that changes the shape of the lens for near vision, an adjustment called **accommodation.**

4. **CN IV: Trochlear Nerve.** The **trochlear nerve** (TROH-klee-ur) is a small motor nerve that innervates one of the six extrinsic eye muscles that moves the eyeball (the *superior oblique muscle*).

5. **CN V: Trigeminal Nerve.** The **trigeminal nerve** (try-JEM-in-uhl; "threefold") is a large mixed nerve named for its three branches. It provides sensory innervation from the face and motor innervation to the muscles of mastication (chewing).

6. **CN VI: Abducens Nerve.** The **abducens nerve** (ab-DOO-senz; *abduc-* = "pulling to the side") is a small motor nerve that innervates the final extrinsic eye muscle (the *lateral rectus muscle*).

14

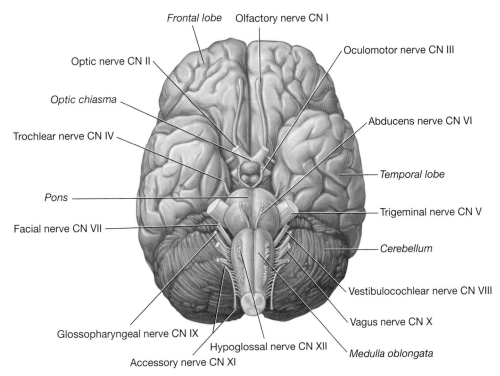

FIGURE **14.3** Inferior view of the brain with the cranial nerves.

7. **CN VII: Facial Nerve.** The mixed fibers of the **facial nerve** innervate many structures and provide for the following: motor to the muscles of facial expression; taste from the anterior two-thirds of the tongue; motor to the glands that produce tears (the lacrimal glands), mucus, and saliva; and sensory from part of the face and mouth.

8. **CN VIII: Vestibulocochlear Nerve.** The final sensory nerve, the **vestibulocochlear nerve** (ves-tib-yoo-loh-KOHK-lee-ur), innervates the structures of the inner ear. It provides for the senses of hearing and equilibrium (balance).

9. **CN IX: Glossopharyngeal Nerve.** The small, mixed **glossopharyngeal nerve** (glah-soh-fehr-IN-jee-uhl; *gloss-* = "tongue;" *pharyng-* = "throat") provides motor axons to the muscles of the pharynx (throat) involved in swallowing. It also contains sensory fibers from the posterior one-third of the tongue for taste sensation.

10. **CN X: Vagus Nerve.** The mixed **vagus nerve** (VAY-guhs) is the only cranial nerve that "wanders" outside of the head and neck ("vagus" means "wanderer"). In the head and the neck, it provides some sensory innervation from the skin of the head and the pharynx, motor axons to muscles involved in speech and swallowing, and motor axons to certain salivary glands. Outside the head and the neck, it innervates most of the thoracic and abdominal viscera as the main nerve of the parasympathetic nervous system.

Remembering the Order of the Cranial Nerves

Many cranial nerve mnemonics have been created over the years to help students remember their correct order. Following is one of my favorite mnemonics, but if this one doesn't stick for you, try making up your own or doing an Internet search for "cranial nerve mnemonics":

Oh (Olfactory)
Once (Optic)
One (Oculomotor)
Takes (Trochlear)
The (Trigeminal)
Anatomy (Abducens)
Final (Facial)
Very (Vestibulocochlear)
Good (Glossopharyngeal)
Vacations (Vagus)
Are (Accessory)
Happening (Hypoglossal)

You also can help yourself remember the olfactory and optic nerves by reminding yourself that you have one nose (CN I, the *olfactory* nerve) and two eyes (CN II, the *optic* nerve).

11. **CN XI: Accessory Nerve.** The **accessory nerve,** a motor nerve, is the only cranial nerve that has both a cranial component originating from the brainstem and a spinal component originating from the spinal cord. Its motor axons innervate the muscles that move the head and the neck, such as the trapezius and sternocleidomastoid muscles.

12. **CN XII: Hypoglossal Nerve.** The **hypoglossal nerve** (hy-poh-GLAHS-uhl; *hypo-* = "below") is a small motor nerve that innervates the muscles that move the tongue. Note that the hypoglossal nerve *moves* the tongue but does not carry any taste sensation from the tongue.

1 PROCEDURE
Model Inventory for the Cranial Nerves

Identify cranial nerves I through XII and associated structures on anatomical models and/or preserved specimens of the brain. List the structures you are able to identify in the model inventory in Table 14.3.

1. Olfactory nerves
   a. Olfactory bulbs
2. Optic nerves
   a. Optic chiasma
   b. Optic tract
3. Oculomotor nerves
4. Trochlear nerves
5. Trigeminal nerves
6. Abducens nerves
7. Facial nerves
8. Vestibulocochlear nerves
9. Glossopharyngeal nerves
10. Vagus nerves
11. Accessory nerves
12. Hypoglossal nerves

TABLE **14.3** Model Inventory for the Cranial Nerves

Model/Diagram	Structures Identified

---

2 PROCEDURE
Testing the Cranial Nerves

A component of every complete physical examination performed by healthcare professionals is the cranial nerve exam. In this procedure, you will put on your "doctor hat" and perform the same tests of the cranial nerves done during a physical examination. Pair up with one or more classmates, and take turns performing the following tests. For each test, first document your observations (in many cases, this will be "able to perform" or "unable to perform"). Then, state which cranial nerve(s) you have checked with each test. Keep in mind that some tests check more than one cranial nerve, some cranial nerves are tested more than once, and each nerve is tested in this procedure at least once. When you have completed the activity, answer Check Your Understanding Questions 2 through 4 (p. 391).

1 Have your partners perform the following actions one at a time (not all at once—they may have difficulty smiling and frowning at the same time): smile, frown, raise their eyebrows, and puff their cheeks.

Observations: _____

CN(s) tested: _____

2 Have your partners open and close their jaws and clench their teeth.

Observations: _____

CN(s) tested: _____

3 Have your partners elevate and depress their shoulders and turn their heads to the right and the left.

Observations: _____

CN(s) tested: _____

4 Draw large, imaginary letter "Zs" in the air with your fingers. Have your partners follow your fingers with their eyes without moving their heads. Repeat the procedure, this time drawing "Hs" in the air with your fingers.

Observations: _____

CN(s) tested: _____

5 Test pupillary response:

 a Dim the lights in the room about halfway.

 b Place your hand vertically against the bridge of your partner's nose as illustrated in Figure 14.4. This forms a light shield to separate the right and left visual fields.

 c Shine the penlight indirectly into the left eye from an angle as illustrated in Figure 14.4. Watch what happens to the pupil in the left eye.

 d Move the penlight away, and watch what happens to the left pupil.

 e Shine the light into the left eye again, and watch what happens to the pupil in the right eye. Move the penlight away, and watch what happens to the right pupil.

 f Repeat this process with the right eye.

 g Record your results in Table 14.4.

CN(s) tested: _____

_____

FIGURE **14.4** Method for testing the pupillary response.

6 Have your partners focus on an object on the far side of the room (e.g., the chalkboard or a chart) for 1 minute. Then have them switch their focus to an object in your hands (e.g., a pencil). Watch your partners' pupils carefully as the point of focus is changed from far to near.

Observations: _____

_____

_____

CN(s) tested: _____

_____

TABLE **14.4** Pupillary Response Results

Action	Response of Left Pupil	Response of Right Pupil
Light shined into left eye		
Light removed from left eye		
Light shined into right eye		
Light removed from right eye		

7 Place your hands lightly on their throats, and have them swallow and speak. Feel for symmetrical movement of the larynx (throat) in your partners.

Observations: _____

CN(s) tested: _____

8 Have your partners protrude their tongues. Check for any abnormal deviations or movements (e.g., do the tongues move straight forward or do they move to one side?).

Observations: _____

CN(s) tested: _____

9 To test vision, have your partners stand 20 ft. from a Snellen chart and cover their right eyes. They should read the chart with their left eyes only, starting with the largest line and stopping with the smallest line they can read clearly. Identify the ratios (e.g., 20/30) printed next to the final lines they can read and record them in your observations. Now, have your partners cover their left eyes and repeat the process, reading the chart with their right eyes only.

Observations: _____

CN(s) tested: _____

14

10 Hold a tuning fork by its handle and tap the tines lightly on the lab tables to start it ringing. Touch the stem to the top of each of your partners' heads along the midsagittal lines in the manner shown in Figure 14.5. This is called the Weber test. Ask your partners whether they hear the vibrations better in one ear, or whether they hear the sounds equally well in both ears.

Observations: _____

_____

CN(s) tested: _____

_____

11 Have your partners stand with their eyes closed and their arms at their sides for several seconds. Evaluate their abilities to remain balanced.

Observations: _____

_____

CN(s) tested: _____

_____

FIGURE **14.5** Weber test for hearing.

12 Test your partners' sense of smell by holding unknown samples near their noses and fanning the odors toward them. Have them identify the substances by their scents.

Observations: _____

CN(s) tested: _____

13 Evaluate your partners' ability to taste by having them place PTC paper on their tongues (the ability to taste PTC is genetically determined; about half of the population can taste it). For anyone who cannot taste the PTC, try the thiourea paper instead (a word of warning—thiourea tastes bad). Some people cannot taste either of these papers; in these cases, try the sodium benzoate paper.

Observations: _____

CN(s) tested: _____

14-3

MATERIALS

☐ Anatomical models and diagrams: spinal nerves

☐ Reflex hammer

Spinal Nerves and Reflexes

Each of the 31 pairs of **spinal nerves** forms from the fusion of the anterior and posterior roots of the spinal cord. Recall that the anterior roots carry motor axons emerging from the spinal cord, and the posterior roots carry sensory axons to the spinal cord. Each spinal nerve carries both motor and sensory axons, so all spinal nerves are mixed nerves.

Shortly after the anterior and posterior roots fuse to form the spinal nerve, it splits into three branches: a posterior ramus, an anterior ramus, and a small meningeal branch. The posterior rami serve the skin, joints, and musculature of the posterior trunk. The meningeal branches reenter the vertebral canal to innervate spinal structures. The larger **anterior rami** (RAY-mee; *ramus*, singular; "branch") travel anteriorly to supply the muscles of the upper and lower limbs, the anterior thorax and abdomen, and part of the back. The general distribution of the anterior rami is illustrated in Figures 14.6 and 14.7.

The anterior rami of the thoracic spinal nerves travel between the ribs as 11 separate pairs of **intercostal nerves** that innervate the intercostal muscles, the abdominal muscles, and the skin of the chest and abdomen. The anterior rami of the cervical, lumbar, and sacral nerves combine to form four large **plexuses**, or networks, of nerves: the *cervical*, *brachial*, *lumbar*, and *sacral plexuses*. The major nerves of these plexuses are as follows:

1. **Cervical plexuses.** The **cervical plexuses** consist of the anterior rami of C1–C4 with small contributions from C5. The branches of each cervical plexus serve the skin of the head and the neck and certain neck muscles. The major branch is the **phrenic nerve** (FREN-ik; *phren-* = "diaphragm;" C3–C5), which serves the diaphragm muscle, and triggers the process of inspiration during breathing.

2. **Brachial plexuses.** The complicated-looking **brachial plexuses** consist of the anterior rami of C5–T1 (Fig. 14.8). The first structures formed in each brachial plexus are its large **trunks**. Typically, C5 and C6 unite to form the *superior trunk*, C7 forms the *middle trunk*, and C8 and T1 unite to form the *inferior trunk*. Each trunk splits into an anterior division and a posterior division that become the **cords** of the plexus. The anterior division of the inferior trunk forms the *medial cord*, which descends in the medial arm. The anterior divisions of the superior and middle trunks unite to form the *lateral cord*, which descends

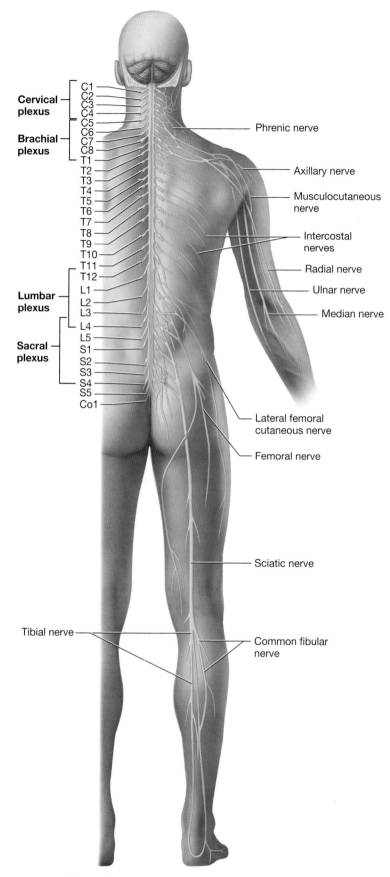

FIGURE **14.6** Nerve plexuses and the anterior rami of the spinal nerves.

in the lateral arm. The posterior divisions of each trunk unite to form the *posterior cord*, which is located in the posterior arm. Several nerves originate from the brachial plexuses' cords and trunks, including the following:

a. **Axillary nerve.** The **axillary nerve** is a branch of the posterior cord and serves structures near the axilla, including the deltoid muscle, which abducts the arm; teres minor muscle, which stabilizes the scapula; and the skin around this region.

b. **Musculocutaneous nerve.** The **musculocutaneous nerve** (musk-yoo-loh-kyoo-TAY-nee-uhs) is the distal continuation of the lateral cord, and as a result it is located in the lateral arm. It provides motor innervation to the muscles that flex the forearm (such as the biceps brachii muscle) and sensory innervation from the skin of the lateral forearm.

c. **Radial nerve.** The **radial nerve** is the distal continuation of the posterior cord and is located in the posterior upper limb. It serves the muscles that extend the forearm and hand. In addition, it provides sensory innervation from the skin in the lateral hand.

d. **Ulnar nerve.** The **ulnar nerve**, which you likely know as the "funny bone nerve," is the distal

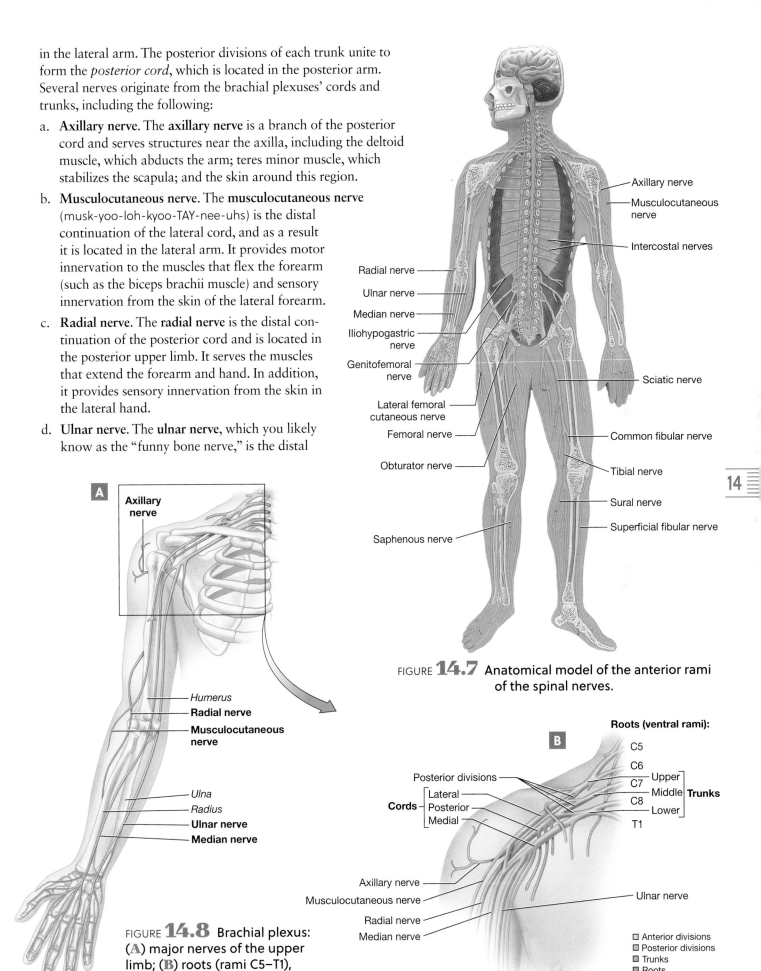

Axillary nerve
Musculocutaneous nerve
Intercostal nerves
Radial nerve
Ulnar nerve
Median nerve
Iliohypogastric nerve
Genitofemoral nerve
Sciatic nerve
Lateral femoral cutaneous nerve
Femoral nerve
Common fibular nerve
Obturator nerve
Tibial nerve
Sural nerve
Superficial fibular nerve
Saphenous nerve

14

FIGURE **14.7** Anatomical model of the anterior rami of the spinal nerves.

A
Axillary nerve

Humerus
Radial nerve
Musculocutaneous nerve

Ulna
Radius
Ulnar nerve
Median nerve

FIGURE **14.8** Brachial plexus: (**A**) major nerves of the upper limb; (**B**) roots (rami C5–T1), trunks, divisions, and cords.

B

Roots (ventral rami):
C5
C6
C7
C8
T1

Posterior divisions
Upper
Middle **Trunks**
Lower

Cords — Lateral
Posterior
Medial

Axillary nerve
Musculocutaneous nerve
Radial nerve
Median nerve

Ulnar nerve

☐ Anterior divisions
☐ Posterior divisions
☐ Trunks
☐ Roots

continuation of the medial cord. It begins posteriorly but then curves around the medial epicondyle of the humerus, crossing over to the anterior side of the forearm. At this location, the nerve is superficial and is easily injured when you whack your elbow. The ulnar nerve provides motor innervation to certain muscles in the forearm that flex the hand and most of the intrinsic muscles of the hand. It also provides sensory innervation from the skin over the medial hand.

e. **Median nerve.** The **median nerve** results from the fusion of portions of the medial and lateral cords. It is named as such because it travels approximately down the middle of the arm and forearm. The median nerve supplies motor innervation to most of the muscles of the forearm that flex the hand and certain intrinsic hand muscles. It supplies sensory innervation from the skin over the anterior and lateral hand. As the median nerve enters the wrist, it travels under a band of connective tissue called the *flexor retinaculum*. Occasionally the median nerve becomes trapped and inflamed under the flexor retinaculum, which results in *carpal tunnel syndrome*.

3. **Lumbar plexuses.** Each **lumbar plexus** consists of the anterior rami of L1–L4 with a small contribution from T12 (Fig. 14.9). The branches of the lumbar plexus include the following:

a. **Iliohypogastric and ilioinguinal nerves.** The small **iliohypogastric** (ill-ee-oh-hy-poh-GAS-trik) and **ilioinguinal nerves** (ill-ee-oh-IN-gwin-uhl) both provide motor innervation to the transversus abdominis muscle, which compresses abdominal contents, and the internal oblique muscle, which laterally flexes and rotates the vertebral column. Its sensory branches supply the skin of the pelvic area.

b. **Genitofemoral nerve.** The **genitofemoral nerve** curves around medially to provide motor innervation to the cremaster muscle in males. It also provides sensory innervation from the skin around the anteromedial thigh and genitals in both sexes.

c. **Femoral nerve.** The largest nerve of this plexus is the **femoral nerve,** which provides motor innervation to most of the anterior thigh muscles that extend the knee and sensory innervation from the skin of the anterior and medial thigh. It gives off a large sensory branch called the **saphenous nerve** (SAF-en-uhs), which supplies the knee joint, medial leg, and foot.

d. **Lateral femoral cutaneous nerve.** As implied by its name, the **lateral femoral cutaneous nerve** provides mainly sensory innervation from the skin of the anterolateral thigh.

e. **Obturator nerve.** The **obturator nerve** (AHB-too-ray-tur) is located in the medial thigh. Here it supplies motor innervation to the medial thigh muscles (which adduct the thigh) and sensory innervation from the skin of the proximal, medial thigh.

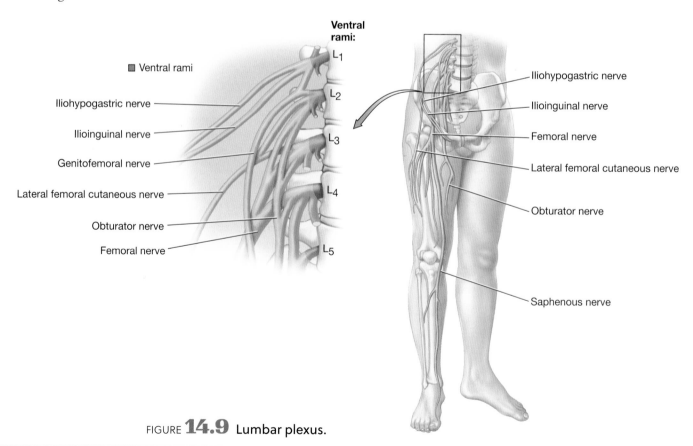

FIGURE **14.9** Lumbar plexus.

4. **Sacral plexuses.** Each **sacral plexus** forms from anterior rami of L4–S4 (Fig. 14.10). It forms the following nerves:

   a. **Superior gluteal nerve.** The first branch of the sacral plexus is the **superior gluteal nerve**, which supplies motor innervation to the muscles that abduct the thigh, including the gluteus medius, gluteus minimus, and tensor fascia lata muscles.

   b. **Inferior gluteal nerve.** The next branch, the **inferior gluteal nerve**, provides motor innervation to the gluteus maximus muscle, which extends the thigh.

   c. **Pudendal nerve.** A smaller branch of the sacral plexus is the **pudendal nerve** (poo-DEN-duhl). It provides motor innervation to the muscles of the pelvic floor and anogenital sphincters. The pudendal nerve also provides sensory innervation from the genitalia.

   d. **Posterior femoral cutaneous nerve.** The function and location of the **posterior femoral cutaneous nerve** is evident from its name—it is located in the posterior thigh where it provides sensory innervation from the skin.

   e. **Sciatic nerve.** The largest nerve of the sacral plexus—and indeed the largest nerve in the body—is the **sciatic nerve** (sy-Ă-tik; *sciat-* = "hip joint"). The sciatic nerve travels in the posterior thigh, where it splits into two branches: the tibial nerve and the common fibular nerve. The **tibial nerve** provides motor innervation to muscles that flex the leg (posterior thigh muscles), plantarflex the foot (posterior leg muscles), and flex the toes (intrinsic foot muscles). It gives off a small superficial sensory branch, the **sural nerve**, which supplies the skin of the posterior leg and foot. The **common fibular nerve** divides into superficial and deep branches. The superficial branch provides motor innervation to the lateral leg. The deep branch supplies motor innervation to the anterior muscles of the leg that dorsiflex the foot and the intrinsic muscles of the foot. The common fibular nerve also contributes a branch to the sural nerve.

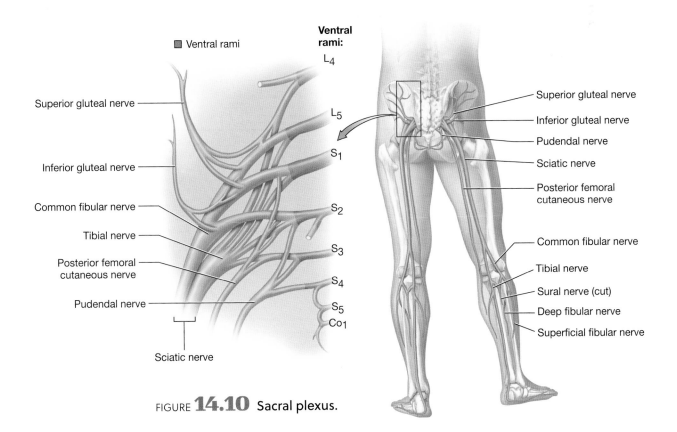

FIGURE **14.10** Sacral plexus.

Model Inventory for Nerves and Nerve Plexuses

Identify the following nerves and nerve plexuses on models and diagrams, using your textbook and this unit for reference. As you examine the anatomical models and diagrams, record the name of the model and the structures you were able to identify on the model inventory in Table 14.5. When you have completed the activity, answer Check Your Understanding Questions 5 and 6 (pp. 391–392).

1. Intercostal nerves
2. Cervical plexus
   a. Phrenic nerve
3. Brachial plexus
   a. Axillary nerve
   b. Musculocutaneous nerve
   c. Radial nerve
   d. Ulnar nerve
   e. Median nerve
4. Lumbar plexus
   a. Iliohypogastric nerve
   b. Ilioinguinal nerve
   c. Genitofemoral nerve
   d. Femoral nerve
      (1) Saphenous nerve
   e. Lateral femoral cutaneous nerve
   f. Obturator nerve
5. Sacral plexus
   a. Superior gluteal nerve
   b. Inferior gluteal nerve
   c. Pudendal nerve
   d. Posterior femoral cutaneous nerve
   e. Sciatic nerve
      (1) Tibial nerve
         (a) Sural nerve
      (2) Common fibular nerve

TABLE **14.5** Model Inventory for the Anterior Rami of the Spinal Nerves

Model/Diagram	Structures Identified

14

A **reflex** is an involuntary, predictable motor response to a stimulus. The pathway through which information travels, shown here and in Figure 14.11, is called a **reflex arc:**

sensory receptor detects the stimulus ➔

sensory afferent neurons bring the stimulus to the CNS ➔ the CNS processes and integrates the information ➔ the CNS sends its output via motor efferent neurons to an effector ➔

the effector performs the triggered action

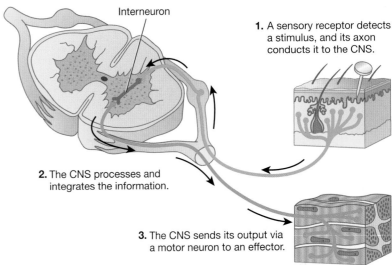

1. A sensory receptor detects a stimulus, and its axon conducts it to the CNS.

Interneuron

2. The CNS processes and integrates the information.

3. The CNS sends its output via a motor neuron to an effector.

FIGURE **14.11** Reflex arc.

The human body has many different reflex arcs, one of the simplest of which is the **stretch reflex**. Stretch reflexes—initiated when a muscle is stretched—are important in maintaining posture and balance. The stretch is detected by **muscle spindles,** which are specialized stretch receptors in the muscles; these stimuli are sent via sensory afferent neurons to the CNS. The CNS then sends impulses down the motor efferent neurons to the muscle, triggering a muscle contraction to counter the stretch.

You can demonstrate the stretch reflex easily: Sit down with your knees bent and relaxed, and palpate (feel) the musculature of your posterior thigh. How do the muscles feel (taut or soft)? Now, stand up, and bend over to touch your toes. Palpate the muscles of your posterior thigh again. How do they feel? The reason they feel different in this position is that you stretched the hamstring muscles when you bent over to touch your toes. This triggered a stretch reflex that resulted in shortening (or tightening) of those muscles.

Technically, this reflex can be carried out without the help of the cerebral cortex and can be mediated solely by the spinal cord. But does this mean that the cortex plays no role in these reflexes at all? Let's find out, using the simplest example of a stretch reflex— the patellar tendon (knee-jerk) reflex, shown in Figure 14.12.

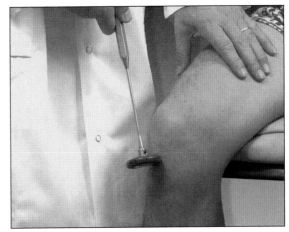

FIGURE **14.12** Patellar tendon reflex.

> **Hypothesis:** How do you think mental concentration will affect the patellar tendon reflex?

1 Have your lab partner sit in a chair with legs dangling freely.

2 Palpate your partner's patellar tendon between the tibial tuberosity and the patella.

3 Tap this area with the flat end of a reflex hammer (sometimes a few taps are necessary to hit the right spot). What is the result?

4 Now, give your partner a difficult math problem to work (long division with decimals usually does the trick). As your partner works the problem, tap the tendon again. Is this response different from the original response? If yes, how, and why?

_____

_____

_____

5 Compare your results to your hypothesis.

_____

_____

_____

14

EXERCISE 14-4

MATERIALS

- ☐ Automated or manual sphygmomanometer
- ☐ Stethoscope

The Autonomic Nervous System

The **autonomic nervous system** (ANS) is the largely involuntary branch of the peripheral nervous system charged with maintaining homeostasis of several different physiological variables in the face of changing conditions. The ANS has two branches: the **sympathetic nervous system** (SNS) and the **parasympathetic nervous system** (PSNS).

The cell bodies of the neurons of the SNS are located in the thoracic and lumbar regions of the spinal cord. Functionally, the SNS is often described in terms of the "fight-or-flight" response, in which the body prepares to respond to an emergency situation (e.g., running from an angry alligator). This gives rise to a useful mnemonic: Your body is *sympathetic* to your emergency situation, so your *sympathetic* nervous system comes to the rescue. Although reaction to an emergency is a primary function of the SNS, it isn't the whole story. The SNS is activated by *any* excitement, emotion, or exercise, even something as simple as standing up. The axons of the SNS release the neurotransmitters **epinephrine, norepinephrine,** and **acetylcholine.** These neurotransmitters trigger the following effects in their target tissues:

- Increased rate and force of heart contraction, which increases the blood pressure;
- Constriction of the blood vessels serving the abdominal viscera and the skin, which also increases the blood pressure;
- Dilation of the blood vessels serving the skeletal muscles;
- Dilation of the bronchioles (airway passages in the lungs);
- Decreased secretion from digestive glands;
- Decreased production of urine;
- Increased metabolic rate;
- Increased release of fatty acids and glucose;
- Dilation of the pupils; and
- The release of epinephrine from the adrenal medulla.

The cell bodies of the neurons of the PSNS are located in cranial nerve nuclei and in the sacral portion of the spinal cord. Functionally, the PSNS is discussed in terms of its "rest and recovery" role, in which it promotes functions associated with digestion, defecation, and diuresis (urine production). The axons of the PSNS release the neurotransmitter acetylcholine, which has the following effects on its target tissues:

- Decreased heart rate, which decreases blood pressure;
- Dilation of the blood vessels serving the skin and abdominal viscera, which decreases blood pressure (note that this is *not* a direct effect of the PSNS on the blood vessels, but rather an indirect effect resulting from sympathetic nerves' inhibition);
- Mild constriction of the bronchioles;
- Increased activity of smooth muscle of the digestive tract and increased secretion from digestive glands;
- Increased urine production;
- Storage of fats and glucose;
- Constriction of the pupils; and
- Adjustment of the lens for near vision.

Notice the effects of the SNS and PSNS are exactly opposite. Generally, the PSNS is subordinate to the SNS (digesting that doughnut isn't all that important when you're being chased by an angry alligator); however, neither branch of the ANS is ever completely quiet. The divisions work together constantly to provide the proper balance for any given situation.

---

1 PROCEDURE
Testing Blood Pressure and Heart Rate Response to Exercise

One of the simplest ways to observe the effects of the SNS is with exercise. In this activity, in order to see the SNS in action, you will be measuring the effects of exercise on a partner's heart rate and blood pressure. When you have completed this activity, answer Check Your Understanding Question 7 (p. 392).

1 Have your partner sit quietly for 2 minutes.

2 After 2 minutes, measure resting heart rate by placing two fingers on your partner's radial pulse (on the lateral side of the wrist). Count the number of beats for 1 minute. Record the rate in Table 14.6. Be sure to record the units (beats per minute).

3 Obtain a stethoscope, and listen to your partner's heart. How does the heartbeat sound (quiet, loud, etc.)? _____

4 Measure your partner's resting blood pressure using a sphygmomanometer (blood pressure cuff) and a stethoscope (instructions for taking blood pressures are found in Unit 19; pp. 523–524). You may also use an automated sphygmomanometer if one is available. Record the blood pressure in Table 14.6. Be sure to record the units (mmHg).

5 Have your partner perform vigorous exercise for several minutes (running up and down stairs or doing jumping jacks works well). Note that even minor exercise will produce changes in blood pressure and pulse, but the changes are more apparent after vigorous exercise (especially for those who are novices at taking blood pressure).

6 Immediately after the vigorous exercise, repeat the heart rate and blood pressure measurements, and record these data in Table 14.6. Then, listen to your partner's heart with a stethoscope. How does the heartbeat sound compared with the sounds you heard at rest?

_____

_____

TABLE **14.6** Results of Exercise and ANS Experiment

Situation	Blood Pressure	Heart Rate
Seated (at rest)		
Immediately after exercise		
After resting for 5 minutes		

7 Have your partner rest while seated for 5 minutes. After 5 minutes, repeat the heart rate and blood pressure measurements, record these data in Table 14.6, and again listen to the heartbeat. Does the heart sound different after rest?

_____

_____

8 Interpret your results:

a In which situation(s) did the SNS dominate? How do you know?

_____

_____

_____

_____

b In which situation(s) did the PSNS dominate? How do you know?

_____

_____

_____

_____

9 Compare your results to your hypothesis.

_____

Check Your Recall

1 Axons are grouped into bundles called _____, which are wrapped in a connective tissue sheath called the _____.

a. nerve fibers; epineurium
b. fascicles; epineurium
c. nerve fibers; perineurium
d. fascicles; perineurium

2 The main nerve of the parasympathetic nervous system is the

a. hypoglossal nerve.
b. vagus nerve.
c. trochlear nerve.
d. trigeminal nerve.

3 Which of the following cranial nerves is a mixed motor and sensory nerve?

a. Optic nerve.
b. Glossopharyngeal nerve.
c. Hypoglossal nerve.
d. Abducens nerve.

4 *Matching:* Match the cranial nerve with its main functions.

_____ Facial nerve

_____ Trochlear nerve

_____ Hypoglossal nerve

_____ Oculomotor nerve

_____ Vagus nerve

_____ Olfactory nerve

_____ Abducens nerve

_____ Glossopharyngeal nerve

_____ Vestibulocochlear nerve

_____ Optic nerve

_____ Trigeminal nerve

_____ Accessory nerve

A. Vision
B. Motor to the muscles of swallowing; taste to the posterior one-third of the tongue
C. Motor to the muscles of swallowing and speaking; motor to the thoracic and abdominal viscera
D. Motor to four of six extrinsic eye muscles; dilates the pupil, opens the eye, and changes the shape of the lens
E. Motor to the trapezius and sternocleidomastoid muscles
F. Motor to one of six extrinsic eye muscles (superior oblique muscle)
G. Motor to the muscles of facial expression; taste to the anterior two-thirds of the tongue
H. Motor to one of six extrinsic eye muscles (lateral rectus muscle)
I. Motor to the tongue
J. Olfaction (smell)
K. Hearing and equilibrium
L. Sensory to the face; motor to the muscles of mastication

5 The portion of a spinal nerve that serves the upper limbs, lower limbs, and much of the trunk is the

a. anterior ramus.
b. meningeal branch.
c. posterior root ganglion.
d. posterior ramus.

6 Stretch is detected by

a. motor efferent neurons.
b. Golgi tendon organs.
c. muscle spindles.
d. motor afferent neurons.

7 *Matching:* Match each spinal nerve with the main structure(s) it supplies.

_____ Axillary nerve

_____ Intercostal nerves

_____ Iliohypogastric nerve

_____ Phrenic nerve

_____ Tibial nerve

_____ Superior gluteal nerve

_____ Lateral femoral cutaneous nerve

_____ Musculocutaneous nerve

A. Gluteus medius, gluteus minimus, and tensor fascia lata muscles

B. Muscles that flex the leg and plantarflex the foot; skin of posterior leg and foot

C. Anterior arm muscles that flex the forearm; skin of the lateral forearm

D. Deltoid and teres minor muscles; skin around the area

E. Transversus abdominis and internal oblique muscles; skin around the pelvis

F. Skin of the anterolateral thigh

G. Intercostal and abdominal muscles; skin of the chest and abdomen

H. Diaphragm muscle

8 Label the following nerves and plexuses on Figure 14.13.

❏ Axillary nerve
❏ Brachial plexus
❏ Common fibular nerve
❏ Femoral nerve
❏ Intercostal nerves
❏ Lumbar plexus
❏ Median nerve
❏ Sacral plexus
❏ Sciatic nerve
❏ Tibial nerve
❏ Ulnar nerve

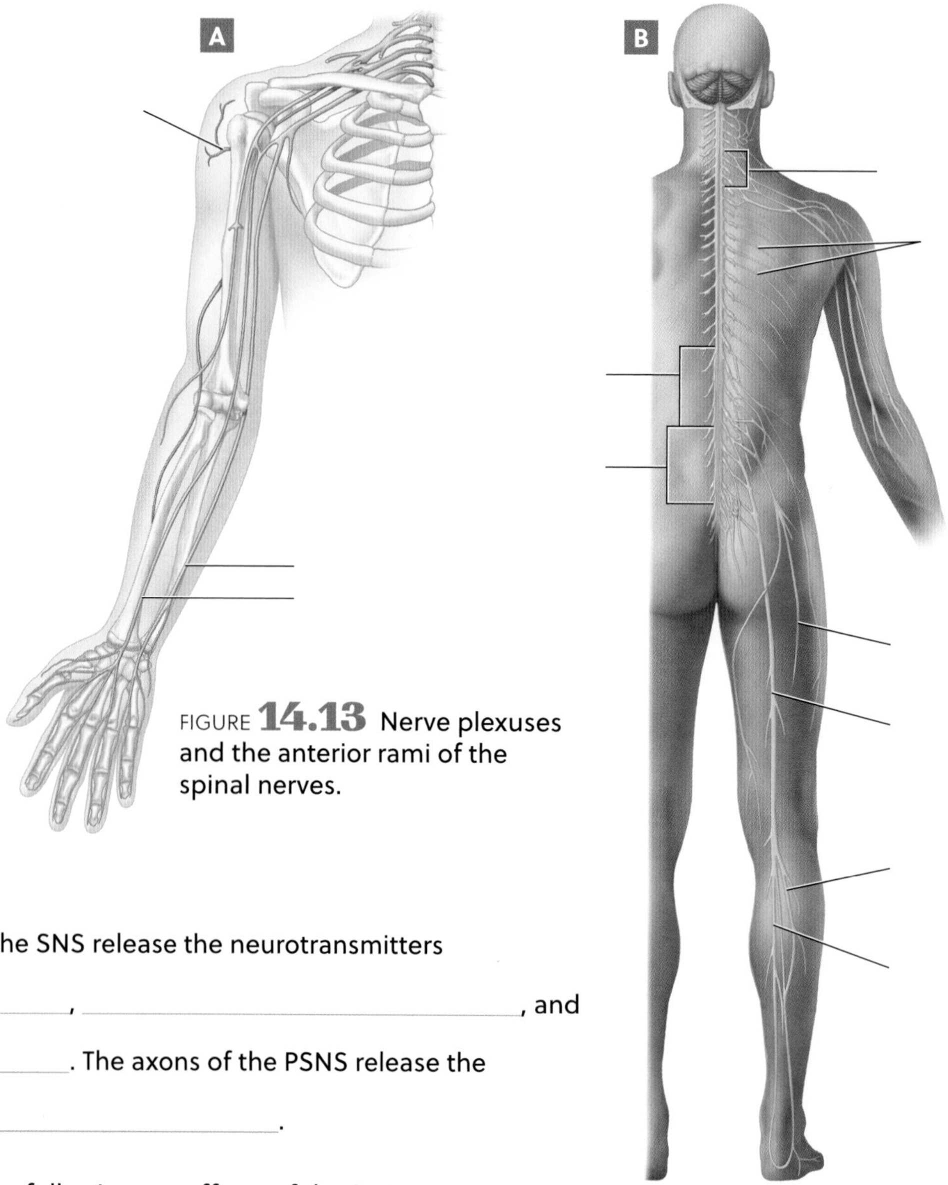

FIGURE **14.13** Nerve plexuses and the anterior rami of the spinal nerves.

9 *Fill in the blanks:* The axons of the SNS release the neurotransmitters

_____ , _____ , and

_____ . The axons of the PSNS release the

neurotransmitter _____ .

10 *Circle all that apply.* Which of the following are effects of the SNS?

a. Increase in heart rate and force of contraction.

b. Increase in metabolic rate.

c. Increased digestive functions.

d. Dilation of the pupils.

e. Increased urine production.

f. Adjustment of the lens for near vision.

g. Dilation of the bronchioles.

h. Increased release of fatty acids and glucose.

Name _____

Section _____ Date_____

Check Your Understanding

Critical Thinking and Application Questions

1 Explain why a peripheral nerve is considered an organ. (***Hint***: Consider the definition of an organ.)

_____

_____

_____

2 The condition *Bell's palsy* results from the dysfunction of one of the facial nerves (meaning it affects only one side of the face). Predict the symptoms of this condition. Which tests that you performed in Exercise 14-2, Procedure 2, would show abnormal results?

_____

_____

_____

_____

3 Injury to which cranial bone could result in a loss of smell? Why?

_____

_____

_____

4 Your patient, Mr. Pratchett, suffered a head injury in an automobile accident. You test his pupillary response and find that one pupil responds normally to light, whereas the other has no response at all—the pupil is fixed and dilated. Which cranial nerve or nerves may be responsible for his abnormal pupillary response? Explain your reasoning.

_____

_____

_____

_____

5 Damage to which spinal nerve(s) might produce the following physical findings?

   a Inability to abduct the arm _____

   b Inability to flex the hand or feel skin over the anterior and lateral hand _____

   c Inability to feel the skin over the posterior thigh _____

   d Inability to plantarflex the foot or flex the toes_____

6 Trina is an avid jogger. One day, during her morning jog, she accidentally steps in a hole, causing pain in her lower back. The next morning, she wakes up with pain shooting down her posterior thigh and leg. Which nerve did she likely "tweak" during her jog? Why is she having pain in the lower limb? Could she develop muscle weakness, too? If so, in which muscle groups?

7 The active ingredients in the herbal supplement *ephedra* mimic the effects of the SNS on body systems. Consequently, this drug has been banned in several countries. Predict the effects of this drug and why dangerous side effects are more likely for certain people.

14

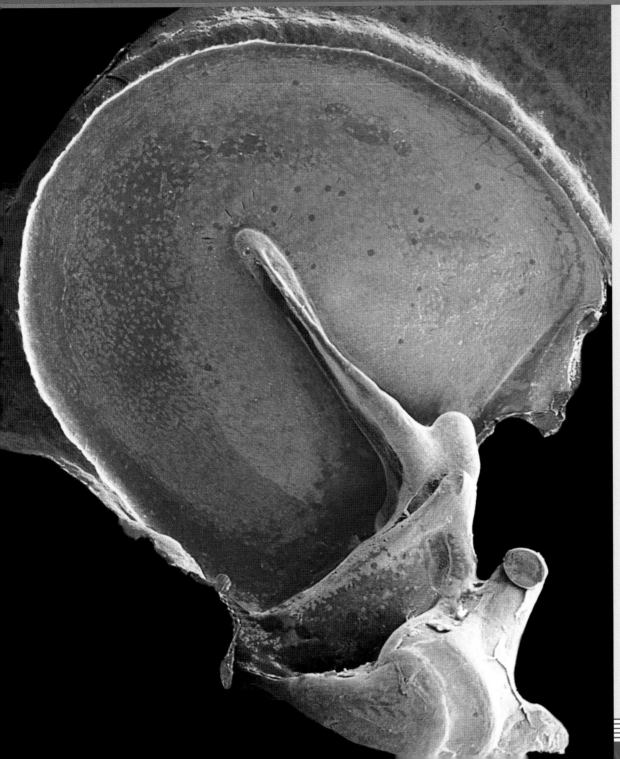

General and Special Senses

When you have completed this unit, you should be able to:

1 Describe and identify structures of the eye.

2 Compare and contrast the functions of the rods and cones.

3 Describe and identify structures of the ear.

4 Perform tests of hearing and equilibrium.

5 Identify structures of the olfactory and taste senses.

6 Determine the relative concentration of cutaneous sensory receptors in different regions of the body.

PRE-LAB EXERCISES

Complete the following exercises prior to coming to lab, using your lab manual and textbook for reference.

PRE-LAB

15-1 Key Terms

You should be familiar with the following terms before coming to lab.

Term	Definition

Structures of the Eye

Conjunctiva _____

Lacrimal gland _____

Sclera _____

Cornea _____

Iris _____

Pupil _____

Lens _____

Ciliary body _____

Choroid _____

Retina _____

Rods _____

Cones _____

15

Structures of the Ear

Auricle
_____
_____

External auditory canal
_____
_____

Tympanic membrane
_____
_____

Auditory ossicles
_____
_____

Pharyngotympanic tube
_____
_____

Vestibule
_____
_____

Semicircular canals
_____
_____

Cochlea
_____
_____

Structures of Taste and Smell

Chemosenses
_____
_____

Olfactory epithelium
_____
_____

Tongue papillae
_____
_____

PRE-LAB

15-2 **Anatomy of the Eye**

Color the structures of the eye in Figures 15.1 and 15.2, and label them with the terms from Exercise 15-1 (p. 399). Use your text and Exercise 15-1 in this unit for reference.

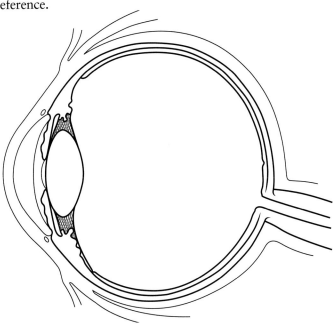

FIGURE **15.1** Sagittal section of the eyeball.

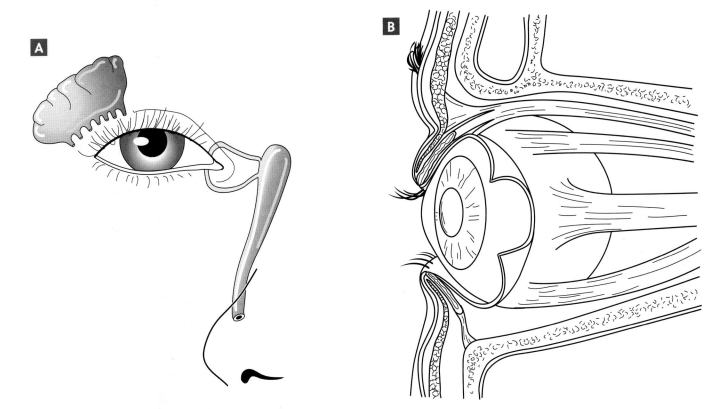

FIGURE **15.2** External structures of the eye: (**A**) anterior view; (**B**) lateral view.

Anatomy of the Ear

Color the structures of the ear in Figure 15.3, and label them with the terms from Exercise 15-2 (p. 408).

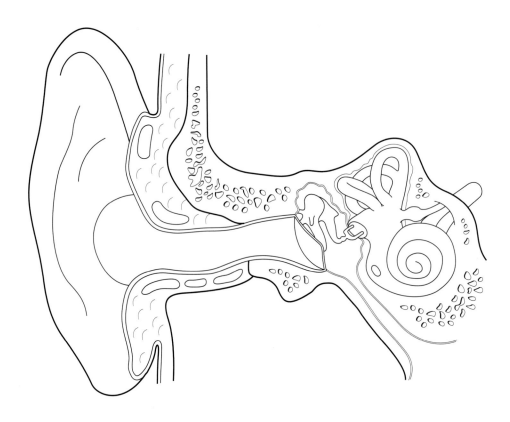

FIGURE **15.3** Anatomy of the ear.

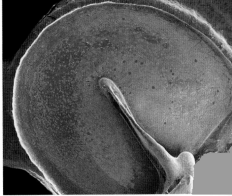

EXERCISES

Sensation is broadly defined as the detection of changes in the internal and external environments. Sensation may be conscious or subconscious, depending on the destination of the sensory information. For example, certain blood vessels have receptors that detect blood pressure. These stimuli are transmitted to the brainstem, which makes changes as necessary to ensure that blood pressure adjusts to meet the body's needs. This information never makes it to the cerebral cortex, so you are not consciously aware of it. However, information eventually taken to the cerebral cortex for integration and inter-pretation (e.g., the taste of your food or the level of light in a room) is something of which you are consciously aware. This is called **perception**, and it is the focus of this unit. Each sense relies on the process of *sensory transduction*—the conversion of a stimulus into an electrical signal—and each has specialized structures to perform this process.

Scanning electron micrograph of an eardrum

The following exercises ask you to examine the anatomy and physiology of the **special senses**: vision, hearing and equilibrium, taste, and smell. You also will examine the **general senses** in this unit, which include the senses of touch, pain, and temperature.

EXERCISE

15-1

MATERIALS

- ❑ Anatomical models and diagrams: eye
- ❑ Preserved eyeballs
- ❑ Dissection equipment
- ❑ Dissection trays
- ❑ Snellen eye chart
- ❑ Paper: white and dark green or blue
- ❑ Ruler
- ❑ Lenses:
  - ▪ convex
  - ▪ concave
- ❑ Flashlight

Anatomy of the Eye and Vision

The eye is a complex organ consisting of two main components: external structures (such as the eyelids) and the eyeball itself. Many of the external structures of the eye protect the delicate eyeball, and others move the eyeball.

One of the most prominent external structures of the eye is the **lacrimal apparatus** (LAK-ruh-muhl; *lacr-* = "tear"), which produces and drains tears. The lacrimal apparatus includes the **lacrimal gland**—located in the superolateral orbit—which produces the aqueous component of tears called *lacrimal fluid*. Lacrimal fluid protects the eyeball. Its water and solutes keep the eyeball moist, lubricate it, and wash away debris. In addition, immune proteins in lacrimal fluid protect the eyeball from bacteria and other pathogens.

As you can see in Figure 15.4A, tears drain into small **lacrimal canals** near the medial canthus, and then drain into the **lacrimal sac**, which is found in a depression in the lacrimal bone. From here, tears travel through the **nasolacrimal duct**, and finally empty into the nasal cavity just inferior to the inferior nasal concha (which is why your nose runs when you cry).

Anteriorly, the eye is covered by the eyelids, or **palpebrae** (pal-PEE-bree). The palpebrae meet medially and laterally at the **medial** and **lateral canthi** (or *commissures*), respectively. At the medial canthus is the **lacrimal caruncle** (kar-UN-kuhl), which contains sebaceous and sweat glands that lubricate the palpebrae. There are several structures in and around the palpebrae. For example, two muscles that open and close the eye insert into and around the palpebrae: the *levator palpebrae superioris muscle* and the *orbicularis oculi muscle*.

Other accessory structures associated with the palpebrae are shown in Figure 15.4B. As you can see, each palpebra has a stiff **tarsal plate** composed of dense connective tissue, which is associated with a sebaceous gland known as a **tarsal gland**. The tarsal glands produce the lipid component of tears, which coats the aqueous portion and facilitates tear drainage into the lacrimal canals.

The internal surfaces of the palpebrae are lined with a thin mucous membrane called the **palpebral conjunctiva** (kahn-junk-TY-vah). Where this mucous membrane contacts the eyeball, it curls around and becomes the **bulbar conjunctiva**, which lines much of the eyeball's superficial surface. Goblet cells within the conjunctiva produce mucus, which lubricates the eyeball and helps tears distribute evenly across it.

The other major external structures of the eye are the **extrinsic eye muscles**, which move the eyeball. As you learned in Unit 14, there are six extrinsic eye muscles (Fig. 15.5), including the

1. **lateral rectus muscle**, which moves the eyeball laterally;
2. **medial rectus muscle**, which moves the eyeball medially;
3. **superior rectus muscle**, which moves the eyeball superiorly;
4. **inferior rectus muscle**, which moves the eyeball inferiorly;

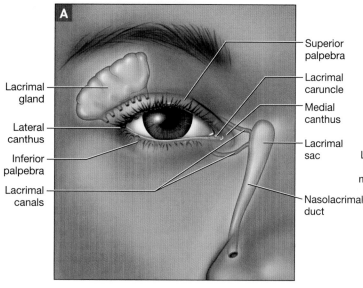

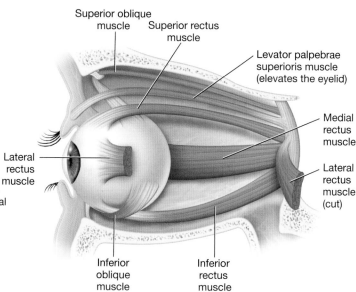

FIGURE **15.5** Extrinsic eye muscles.

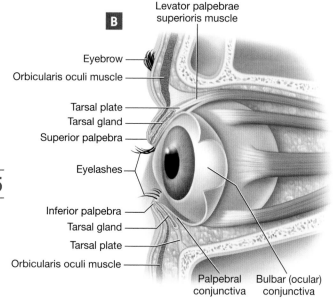

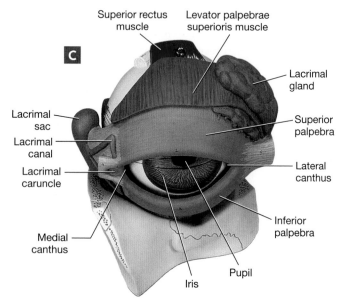

FIGURE **15.4** External structures of the eye:
(**A**) anterior view; (**B**) lateral view; (**C**) anatomical
model photo.

5. **superior oblique muscle,** which moves the eyeball inferiorly and laterally; and

6. **inferior oblique muscle,** which moves the eyeball superiorly and laterally.

The **eyeball** itself is a hollow organ that is divided into two main portions: the anterior cavity and the posterior cavity. The boundary for the cavities is a crystalline structure known as the **lens,** which is one of the structures in the eye that refracts (bends) light coming into the eye to focus it. The **anterior cavity** is anterior to the lens and is filled with a watery fluid called **aqueous humor.** Aqueous humor is produced relatively constantly and drained by a structure called the **scleral venous sinus.** The **posterior cavity** is posterior to the lens and contains a thicker fluid called **vitreous humor** (VIT-ree-uhs; *vitre-* = "glass"). Unlike aqueous humor, vitreous humor is present at birth and remains relatively unchanged throughout life. Both fluids help to refract light coming into the eye.

The eyeball has three distinct tissue layers, or tunics (Fig. 15.6):

1. **Fibrous tunic.** This outermost layer of the eyeball is the **fibrous tunic,** which consists mostly of dense irregular connective tissue. It is avascular (lacks a blood supply) and consists of two parts:

a. **Sclera.** The **sclera** (SKLEHR-ah) is the white part of the eyeball that makes up the posterior five-sixths of the fibrous tunic. It is white because of numerous collagen fibers that contribute to its thickness and toughness (in the same way a joint capsule or a ligament is tough and white).

b. **Cornea.** The clear **cornea** (KOHR-nee-ah) makes up the anterior one-sixth of the fibrous tunic. It is the fourth refractory medium of the eyeball, and accounts for about two-thirds of the eye's refractive power.

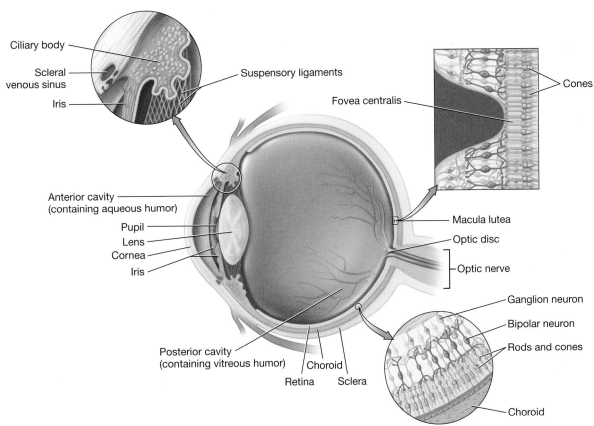

FIGURE **15.6** Sagittal section of the eyeball.

2. **Vascular tunic.** Also called the **uvea** (YOO-vee-uh), the **vascular tunic** carries most of the blood supply to the tissues of the eye. It is composed of three main parts:

   a. **Choroid.** The highly vascular **choroid** (KOHR-oyd; *chorio-* = "membrane") makes up the posterior part of the vascular tunic. The choroid is brown in color to prevent light scattering in the eye.

   b. **Ciliary body.** The **ciliary body** (SILL-ee-ehr-ee) is located on the anterior aspect of the vascular tunic. It is made chiefly of the **ciliary muscle**—smooth muscle fibers that control the shape of the lens. The muscle attaches to the lens via small **suspensory ligaments.** The ciliary body also produces aqueous humor.

   c. **Iris.** The pigmented **iris** (AYE-riss; *iri-* = "rainbow") is the most anterior portion of the vascular tunic. It consists of smooth muscle fibers arranged around an opening called the **pupil.** As the fibers contract, the pupil either constricts or dilates. The iris also divides the anterior cavity into two smaller subdivisions: the *anterior segment*, which is anterior to the iris, and the *posterior segment*, which is posterior to the iris.

3. **Sensory tunic.** The **sensory tunic** consists of the retina and the optic nerve. The **retina** (RET-in-ah) is a thin, delicate structure that contains three layers of neurons: **photoreceptors** (*phot-* = "light") called rods and cones that detect light; **bipolar neurons** that receive input from photoreceptors; and **ganglion cells** (GAYN-glee-ahn) whose axons converge to form the **optic nerve** (AHP-tik; *opt-* = "vision"), or cranial nerve II. Recall from Unit 14 that the optic nerves exit from the posterior orbit, then partially exchange axons at the X-shaped *optic chiasma* before diverging into the two *optic tracts* (see Fig. 14.3, p. 375). The input is eventually delivered to the visual cortex in the occipital lobe of the brain.

   a. **Rods.** The photoreceptors known as **rods** are scattered throughout the retina and are responsible for vision in dim light and for peripheral vision. They can produce vision in black and white only.

   b. **Cones.** The second type of photoreceptors, **cones,** are concentrated at the posterior portion of the retina. They are found in highest numbers in an area called the **macula lutea** (MAK-yoo-lah LOO-tee-ah; "yellow spot"). At the center of the macula lutea is the **fovea centralis** (FOH-vee-uh sin-TRAL-iss; "central pit"), which contains only cones. Cones are responsible for color and high-acuity (sharp) vision in bright light.

   Note that there are no rods or cones at the posteriormost aspect of the eyeball where the optic nerve leaves the eyeball. This location is called the **optic disc.** It is also known as the *blind spot* because its lack of photoreceptors means that this region can produce no images.

Vision is produced when rays of light, also known as **photons** (FOH-tahns), stimulate rods and cones. Rays of light travel nearly parallel to one another. When light passes through a translucent medium, it bends, or **refracts**. The amount of refraction produced depends on the medium's *refractive index*. A medium with a refractive index of 1.0, such as air, does not significantly bend light. Anything with a refractive index greater than 1.0, such as water, can bend light. Refraction is why a spoon placed halfway into a glass of water looks broken—the light rays hitting the part of the spoon sticking out of the water are not bent, but those hitting the spoon in the water are bent.

Notice in Figure 15.6 that light has to pass through four refractive media before it hits the retina: the cornea, the aqueous humor, the lens, and the vitreous humor. Of these four, the cornea and the lens have the greatest refractive power. This is because light refracts more when it strikes an object's surface at an angle. If a surface is curved—more angled at the edges—light is refracted unevenly, being bent more at the edges than in the middle.

Both the cornea and lens have a *convex* shape—the surface bulges outward. As light rays hit the edges of the lens, where it is bent more, they bend inward, or **converge.** When the light rays converge on the retina at a point known as the **focal point,** the light rays are focused. The cornea is convex enough that it accounts for about two-thirds of the eye's refractive power by itself. Indeed, the cornea alone provides most of the necessary refraction when viewing distant objects.

When viewing nearer objects, however, additional "fine-tuning" refraction is needed by the lens. This is accomplished with the help of the ciliary muscle—when its smooth muscle fibers contract, the ciliary body moves closer to the lens and removes tension on the suspensory ligaments. This causes the lens to become rounder, an adjustment called *accommodation.* **Accommodation** allows the lens to become more convex, providing the additional refraction necessary to focus light on the retina. When the eye switches to a distant object again, the ciliary muscle relaxes, which moves the ciliary body farther away from the lens and puts tension on the suspensory ligaments. This flattens the lens, making it less convex, and allows the cornea to again become the primary refractive medium.

1 PROCEDURE
Model Inventory for the Eye

15 Identify the following structures of the eye and the eyeball on models and diagrams using your textbook and this unit for reference. As you examine the anatomical models and diagrams, record the name of the model and the structures you were able to identify on the model inventory in Table 15.1. When you have finished the activity, answer Check Your Understanding Questions 1 and 2 (p. 423).

Accessory Structures

1. Palpebrae
2. Medial and lateral canthi
3. Lacrimal caruncle
4. Lacrimal apparatus
   a. Lacrimal gland
   b. Lacrimal canals
   c. Lacrimal sac
   d. Nasolacrimal duct
5. Tarsal plate
6. Tarsal gland
7. Palpebral conjunctiva
8. Bulbar conjunctiva
9. Extrinsic eye muscles
   a. Lateral rectus m.
   b. Medial rectus m.
   c. Superior rectus m.
   d. Inferior rectus m.
   e. Superior oblique m.
   f. Inferior oblique m.

Eyeball

1. Lens
2. Anterior cavity
   a. Aqueous humor
   b. Scleral venous sinus
3. Posterior cavity
   a. Vitreous humor
4. Fibrous tunic
   a. Sclera
   b. Cornea
5. Vascular tunic (uvea)
   a. Choroid
   b. Ciliary body
      (1) Ciliary muscle
      (2) Suspensory ligaments
   c. Iris
      (1) Pupil
6. Sensory tunic
   a. Retina
   b. Optic nerve (cranial nerve II)
   c. Macula lutea
   d. Fovea centralis
   e. Optic disc

TABLE **15.1** Model Inventory for the Eye

Model/Diagram	Structures Identified

2 **PROCEDURE**

Dissecting the Eyeball

In this procedure, you will examine the structures of the eyeball on a fresh or preserved eyeball. Eyeball dissection isn't as gross as it sounds—I promise!

1 Examine the external anatomy of the eyeball (Fig. 15.7), and record the structures you can identify.

15

> ⚠ **SAFETY NOTE**
>
> Safety glasses and gloves are required!

2 Use scissors to remove the adipose tissue surrounding the eyeball. Identify the optic nerve.

3 Hold the eyeball at its anterior and posterior poles, and use a sharp scalpel or scissors to make an incision in the frontal plane. Watch out, as aqueous humor and vitreous humor are likely to spill everywhere.

4 Complete the incision, and separate the anterior and posterior portions of the eyeball (Fig. 15.8). Take care to preserve the fragile retina—the thin, delicate, yellow-tinted inner layer.

5 List the structures in the anterior half of the eyeball that you can identify (Fig. 15.9):

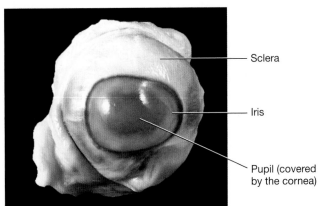

FIGURE **15.7** Anterior view of an eyeball.

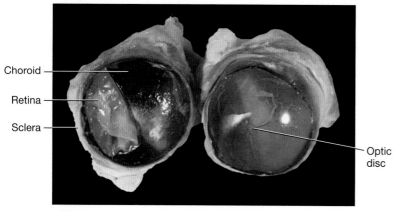

FIGURE **15.8** Frontal section of an eyeball showing the tunics.

Choroid

Retina

Sclera

Optic disc

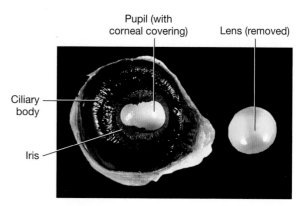

Pupil (with corneal covering)

Lens (removed)

Ciliary body

Iris

FIGURE **15.9** Anterior portion of the eyeball and lens shown from the posterior side.

6 List the structures in the posterior half of the eyeball that you can identify:

_____

_____

_____

_____

---

3 PROCEDURE

Comparing the Distribution of Rods and Cones

We discussed earlier the unequal distribution of the photoreceptors in the retina. In this procedure, you will see (no pun intended) the differences in the rods and the cones. You will compare your ability to see clearly in front of your eyes versus with your peripheral vision, and in bright light versus the dark. After you have completed the activity, answer Check Your Understanding Question 3 (p. 423).

Hypothesis: How will vision differ in front of your eyes versus with your peripheral vision? How will it differ in bright light versus the dark?

_____

1 On a small sheet of paper, write the phrase "Anatomy is fun" in your regular-size print.

2 Hold this piece of paper about 25 cm (10 in.) directly in front of your lab partner's eyes, and have your lab partner read the phrase.

Can your partner read the phrase clearly? _____

Which photoreceptors are producing the image? _____

3 Now, write a second phrase on the paper, and don't tell your partner what the phrase says. Hold the paper about 10 in. from your partner's peripheral vision field. Have the partner continue to stare forward and attempt to read what you have written.

Can your partner read the phrase clearly? _____

Which photoreceptors are producing the image? _____

4 For the next test, dim the lights in the room. Have your partner stand 20 ft. in front of a Snellen eye chart and read down the chart, stopping with the smallest line read accurately. (You should stand next to the chart to verify your partner has read the correct letters.) The numbers next to the line indicate your partner's vision relative to someone with perfect vision (i.e., 20/20), a measurement known as **visual acuity**. For example, a person with 20/40 vision can see at 20 ft. what someone with perfect vision could see at 40 ft. Record your partner's ratio (e.g., 20/40).

Visual acuity: _____

5 With the lights still dimmed and your partner standing in the same place, hold a piece of dark green or dark blue paper over the Snellen chart. Ask your partner to identify the color of the paper you are holding. Record your partner's response.

Paper color: _____

6 Repeat the previous processes with the lights illuminated. Record your partner's visual acuity and paper color responses.

Visual acuity: _____   Paper color: _____

7 In which scenario were visual acuity and color vision better? Explain your findings.

_____

_____

_____

8 Compare your results to your hypothesis.

_____

_____

---

4 **PROCEDURE**

Comparing Convex and Concave Lenses

As you read earlier, light hitting a curved surface is refracted unevenly. We saw the example of the convex lens, which bulges outward, shown in Figure 15.10A. A convex lens causes light rays to converge. In contrast, a *concave lens* has a surface that bends inwardly, or "caves in." Notice in Figure 15.10B how a concave lens bends the light hitting the edges of the lens outward so it scatters, or **diverges**. In this procedure, you'll see how convex and concave lenses affect vision when you look through them. When you have completed the procedure, answer Check Your Understanding Question 4 (p. 423).

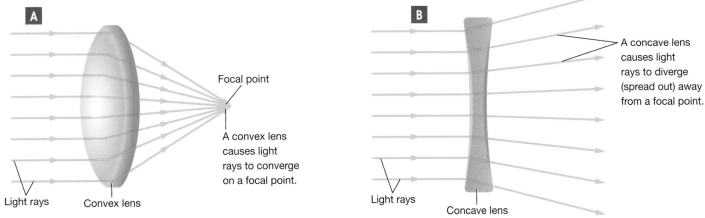

FIGURE **15.10** Types of lenses: (**A**) convex lens; (**B**) concave lens.

Hypothesis: How will an image be affected by viewing it with a concave lens? How will it be affected by viewing it with a convex lens?

_____

_____

1 At your table are two lenses: one that is convex and one that is concave. Closely examine the convex lens. How is it shaped?

_____

2 Look through the convex lens at a page of this book. How does the convex lens affect the image you are seeing?

_____

3 Shine a flashlight through the convex lens onto a piece of white paper.

   a How does the lens bend the light rays from the flashlight?

_____

   b How does this explain your results from Number 2?

_____

_____

4 Now, closely examine the concave lens. How is it shaped?

_____

5 Look through the concave lens at a different page of this book. How does the concave lens affect the image you are seeing?

_____

6 Shine a flashlight through the concave lens onto a piece of white paper.

   a How does the lens bend the light rays from the flashlight?

_____

   b How does this explain your results from Number 2?

_____

_____

7 Compare your results to your hypothesis.

_____

_____

5 PROCEDURE
Finding the Blind Spot

Recall that the location where the optic nerve exits the eyeball lacks photoreceptors and so leaves a "blind spot"—a place that can produce no images. You can find the blind spot with the simple diagram shown in Figure 15.11.

1 Close your left eye, and hold Figure 15.11 about 56 cm (18 in.) in front of your right eye so that the "+" is directly in line with your right eye.

2 Slowly move Figure 15.11 toward your right eye while staring at the "+" until the large dot disappears. When it disappears, it is in your blind spot.

3 Have your lab partner measure the distance from the page to your eye with a ruler.

Distance in cm: _____

4 Repeat the process for your left eye.

Distance in cm: _____

FIGURE **15.11** Blind spot test.

6 PROCEDURE
Testing for Astigmatism

The condition called **astigmatism** (uh-STIG-muh-tiz′m; *a-* = "without;" *stigma* = "point") is characterized by irregularities in the surfaces in the cornea and/or the lens. These irregularities cause the vision to become blurred because these structures are unable to focus light precisely on the retina. You can test for astigmatism by using a chart like the one shown in Figure 15.12.

1 Hold Figure 15.12 a comfortable reading distance from your eyes, about 35 cm (14 in.).

2 Cover one eye, and stare at the center of Figure 15.12. All lines should appear equally distinct and black. If any of the lines appear blurry or gray, astigmatism may be present.

3 Cover the other eye and repeat the process.

4 Was astigmatism present in either eye? Explain. _____

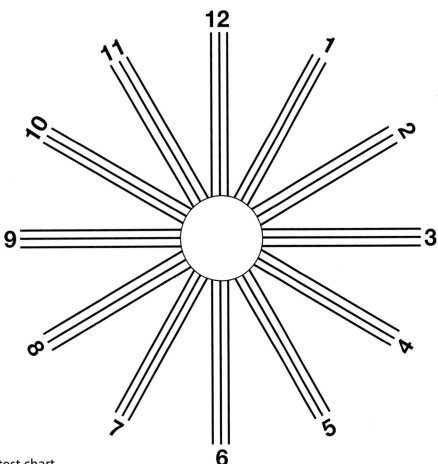

FIGURE **15.12** Astigmatism test chart.

MATERIALS

☐ Anatomical models and diagrams: ear
☐ Tuning fork (500–1,000 Hz)
☐ Whiteboard markers

Anatomy of the Ear, Hearing, and Equilibrium

The ear contains structures both for hearing and equilibrium. It is divided into three regions: the outer, middle, and inner ear (Fig. 15.13).

1. **Outer ear.** The **outer ear** begins with the **auricle** (OHR-ih-kuhl; *auric-* = "ear"), or *pinna*, a shell-shaped structure composed primarily of elastic cartilage that surrounds the opening to the **external auditory canal**. The external auditory canal extends about 2.5 cm into the temporal bone. Here it ends in the **tympanic membrane** (tim-PAN-ik; *tympan-* = "drum"), a thin sheet of epithelium and connective tissue that separates the outer ear from the middle ear.

2. **Middle ear.** The **middle ear** is a small air-filled cavity within the temporal bone that houses tiny bones called the **auditory ossicles** (AH-sih-kullz; "little bones"): the **malleus** (MAL-ee-uhs; hammer), **incus** (ING-kuhs; anvil), and **stapes** (STAY-peez; stirrup). When sound waves hit the tympanic membrane, it vibrates and transmits those vibration to the ossicles. This sets the ossicles vibrating, and they transmit these vibrations to the inner ear through the **oval window**, to which the stapes is attached. An additional structure in the middle ear is the **pharyngotympanic tube** (fah-ring-oh-tim-PAN-ik; *pharyng-* = "throat") or *auditory tube*, which connects the middle ear to the pharynx and equalizes pressure in the middle ear.

3. **Inner ear.** The **inner ear** contains the sense organs for hearing and equilibrium. It consists of cavities, collectively called the **bony labyrinth**, filled with a fluid called **perilymph** (PEHR-ee-limf; *lymph* = "clear water"). Within the perilymph is a series

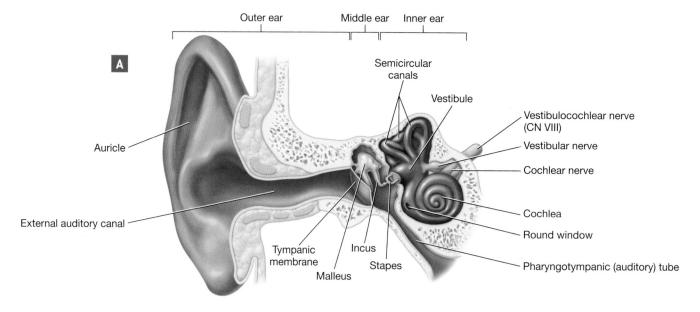

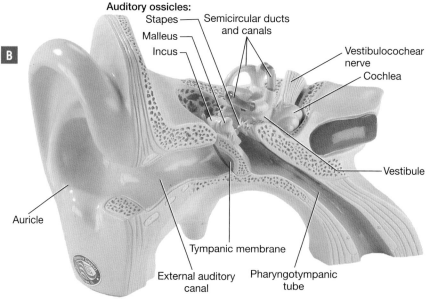

FIGURE **15.13** Anatomy of the ear: (**A**) illustration; (**B**) anatomical model photo.

15

of membranes, called the **membranous labyrinth,** that contain a thicker fluid called **endolymph** (IN-doh-limf; Fig. 15.14). The bony labyrinth has three regions:

a. **Vestibule.** The **vestibule** is an egg-shaped bony cavity that houses two structures responsible for equilibrium: the **saccule** (SAK-yool) and the **utricle** (YOO-trih-kuhl). Both structures transmit impulses down the vestibular portion of the vestibulocochlear nerve. The saccule and the utricle are responsible for a type of equilibrium called *static equilibrium*. This refers to maintaining balance when the body is not moving—hence the word "static"—but the head is tilted.

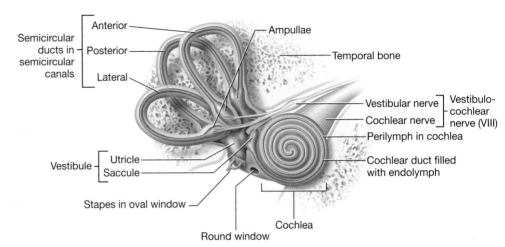

b. **Semicircular canals.** Situated at right angles to one another, the **semicircular canals** house the **semicircular ducts** and the **ampullae,** which work together with the organs of the vestibule to maintain equilibrium.

FIGURE **15.14** Membranous labyrinth of the inner ear.

Their orientation allows them to be responsible for a type of equilibrium called *rotational equilibrium*. This refers to the ability to maintain balance when the body or head is moving. Like the saccule and utricle, the semicircular ducts and the ampulla transmit impulses down the vestibular portion of the vestibulocochlear nerve.

c. **Cochlea.** The **cochlea** (KOHK-lee-ah; *cochlea* = "snail shell") is a spiral bony canal that contains a part of the membranous labyrinth called the **cochlear duct.** Within the cochlear duct is a structure known as the **spiral organ** (or the *organ of Corti*) whose specialized **hair cells** depolarize in response to sound wave vibrations. The depolarized hair cells transmit sound impulses to the cochlear portion of the vestibulocochlear nerve. The cochlea has a hole in its lateral wall called the **round window,** which allows the perilymph in the cochlea to vibrate.

15

1 | PROCEDURE
Model Inventory for the Ear

Identify the following structures of the ear on models and diagrams, using your textbook and this unit for reference. As you examine the anatomical models and diagrams, record the name of the model and the structures you were able to identify on the model inventory in Table 15.2. After you have completed the activity, answer Check Your Understanding Question 5 (p. 423).

1. Outer ear
   a. Auricle (pinna)
   b. External auditory canal
2. Middle ear
   a. Tympanic membrane
   b. Ossicles
      (1) Malleus
      (2) Incus
      (3) Stapes
   c. Oval window
   d. Pharyngotympanic (auditory) tube
3. Inner ear

   a. Vestibule
      (1) Saccule
      (2) Utricle
   b. Semicircular canals
      (1) Semicircular duct
      (2) Ampullae
   c. Cochlea
      (1) Cochlear duct
      (2) Round window
   d. Vestibulocochlear nerve (cranial nerve VIII)
      (1) Vestibular nerve
      (2) Cochlear nerve

TABLE **15.2** Model Inventory for the Ear

Model/Diagram	Structures Identified

Hearing Acuity

There are two possible types of hearing loss:

1. **Conductive hearing loss** results from interference of sound conduction through the outer and/or middle ear.

2. **Sensorineural hearing loss** results from damage to the inner ear or the vestibulocochlear nerve.

Two clinical tests can help a healthcare professional determine whether hearing loss is conductive or sensorineural: the Weber test and the Rinne (rinn-ay) test. Both tests use tuning forks that vibrate at specific frequencies when struck. The tuning forks are placed directly on the bones of the skull to evaluate bone conduction—the ability to hear the vibrations transmitted through the bone. They are also placed in front of the ear to evaluate air conduction—the ability to hear the vibrations transmitted through the air. After you have completed both tests, answer Check Your Understanding Question 6 (p. 424).

2 PROCEDURE

Performing the Weber Test

Hypothesis: Will you detect conduction and/or sensorineural deafness in your partner?

1 Obtain a tuning fork with a frequency of 500 to 1,000 Hz (cycles per second).

2 Hold the tuning fork by the base, and tap it on the edge of the table. The fork should begin ringing softly. If it is ringing too loudly, grasp the tines to stop it from ringing, and try again.

3 Place the base of the vibrating tuning fork on the midline of your partner's head, as shown in Figure 15.15.

4 Ask your partner whether the sound is heard better in one ear or whether the sound is heard equally in both ears. If the sound is heard better in one ear, this is called *lateralization*.

Was the sound lateralized? If yes, to which ear? _____

5 To illustrate what it would sound like if the sound were lateralized, have your partner place a finger in one ear. Repeat the test.

   a In which ear was the sound heard better? _____

   b If a patient has conduction deafness, in which ear do you think the sound will be heard most clearly (the deaf ear or the good ear)?

      _____

      Why? (If you are confused, think about your results when one ear was plugged.)

      _____

      _____

   c If a patient has sensorineural deafness, in which ear do you think the sound will be best heard? Why?

      _____

      _____

6 Compare your results to your hypothesis.

_____

FIGURE **15.15** Weber test.

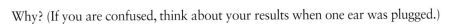

3 PROCEDURE
Performing the Rinne Test

Hypothesis: Will your partner hear bone-conducted sound or air-conducted sound better?

_____

1 Strike the tuning fork lightly to start it ringing.

2 Place the base of the tuning fork on your partner's mastoid process, as shown in Figure 15.16.

3 Time the interval during which your partner can hear the sound. Your partner will have to tell you when he or she can no longer hear the ringing.

Time interval in seconds: _____

4 After your partner can no longer hear the ringing, quickly move the still-vibrating tuning fork 1 to 2 cm lateral to the external auditory canal (the fork should not be touching your partner at this point).

5 Time the interval from the point when you moved the tuning fork in front of the external auditory canal to when your partner can no longer hear the sound.

Time interval in seconds: _____

Which situation tested bone conduction?

_____

Which situation tested air conduction?

_____

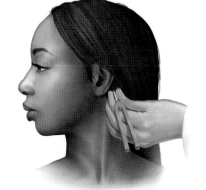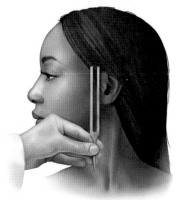

FIGURE **15.16** Rinne test.

6 Typically, the air-conducted sound is heard twice as long as the bone-conducted sound. For example, if the bone-conducted sound was heard for 15 seconds, the air-conducted sound should be heard for 30 seconds.

Were your results normal? _____

What type of deafness is present if the bone-conducted sound is heard longer than the air-conducted sound? Explain.

_____
_____

7 Compare your results to your hypothesis.

_____
_____

Equilibrium

A common and simple test of equilibrium is the **Romberg test,** in which the person is asked to stand still, first with the eyes open and then with the eyes closed. Under normal conditions, the vestibular apparatus should be able to maintain equilibrium in the absence of visual input. If the vestibular apparatus is impaired, however, the brain relies on visual cues to maintain balance.

4 PROCEDURE
Performing the Romberg Test

Hypothesis: How will removing visual cues affect your partner's balance?

_____

1 Have your partner stand erect with the feet together and the arms at the sides in front of a whiteboard.

2 Use a whiteboard marker to draw lines on the board on either side of your partner's torso. These lines are for your reference in the next part.

3 Have your partner stand in front of the whiteboard for 1 minute, staring forward with eyes open. Use the lines on either side of the torso to note how much your partner sways while standing. Record the amount of side-to-side swaying (i.e., minimal or significant):

_____

4 Now, have your partner stand in the same position for 1 minute with eyes closed. Again, note the amount of side-to-side swaying, using the marker lines for reference.

Was the amount of swaying more or less with the eyes closed? _____
Why do you think this is so?

_____
_____

What do you predict would be the result for a person with an impaired vestibular apparatus? Explain.

_____
_____

5 Compare your results to your hypothesis.

EXERCISE
15-3

MATERIALS

☐ Anatomical models and diagrams:
  - head
  - neck
  - tongue

Olfactory and Taste Senses

Olfaction is referred to as a **chemosense**—because it relies on chemoreceptors to relay information about the environment to the brain. The chemoreceptors of the olfactory sense are located in a small patch in the roof of the nasal cavity called the **olfactory epithelium** (Fig. 15.17). The olfactory epithelium contains three types of cells:

- **Olfactory neurons.** The cells that detect odorants are bipolar neurons called **olfactory neurons** (*olfac-* = "smell"). The axons of olfactory neurons are collectively called **cranial nerve I** or the **olfactory nerve.** These axons penetrate the holes in the cribriform plate to synapse on the **olfactory bulb,** which then sends the impulses down the axons of the **olfactory tract** to the olfactory cortex.

- **Basal cells.** Olfactory neurons have a lifespan of only 30–60 days. For this reason, they are replaced by stem cells known as **basal cells,** which surround olfactory neurons in the olfactory epithelium. Basal cells have a relatively rapid rate of cell division to continually replace dying olfactory neurons.

- **Sustentacular cells.** *Sustentacular cells,* also known as *supporting cells,* surround olfactory neurons, where they provide structural and metabolic support.

The other chemosense is taste, also known as **gustation** (guh-STAY-shun; *gustare* = "to taste"). The chemoreceptors that detect taste are located on **taste buds,** which are housed on projections from the tongue called **papillae** (Fig. 15.18). Of the four types of papillae—filiform, fungiform, foliate, and circumvallate—all but filiform papillae house taste buds. **Fungiform papillae** are scattered over the surface of the tongue, whereas the large **vallate papillae** are located at the posterior aspect of the tongue, arranged in a "V" shape. **Foliate papillae** contain taste buds primarily during childhood; they are located on the lateral aspects of the tongue.

We generally find taste buds on the lateral surfaces of the papillae. Taste buds feature three types of cells:

- **Gustatory (taste) cells.** Chemoreceptors are located on specialized epithelial cells called **gustatory cells** (GUHS-tuh-tohr-ee). The apical surface of the cells features microvilli that project into a **taste pore,** which is an indentation on the surface of the papilla.

- **Basal cells.** Gustatory cells have a short lifespan of only 10–14 days. For this reason, there is a population of stem cells called **basal cells** that differentiate into new gustatory cells.

- **Supporting cells.** Surrounding gustatory cells are **supporting cells** that provide structural and metabolic support.

Taste sensation tends to decline as people age because the number of basal cells decreases, and so the gustatory cells are not replaced when they degenerate. We are typically born with approximately 10,000 taste buds but lose half of them by adulthood—the rate of decline is greatest after age 50.

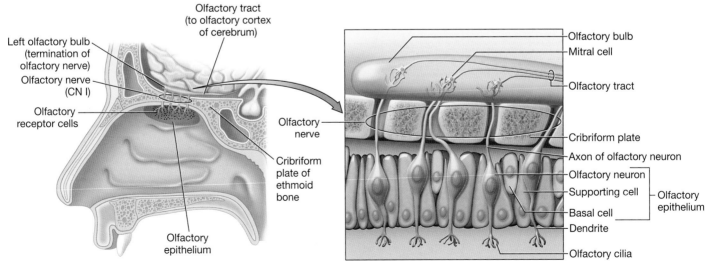

FIGURE **15.17** Nasal cavity and olfactory epithelium.

15

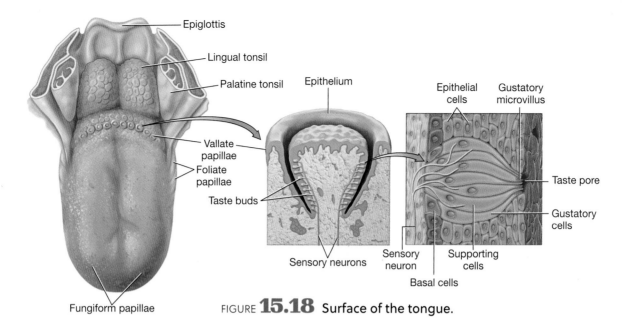

FIGURE **15.18** Surface of the tongue.

1 **PROCEDURE**

Model Inventory for Olfaction and Taste

Identify the following structures of the olfactory and taste senses on anatomical models and charts. As you examine the anatomical models and diagrams, record the name of the model and the structures you were able to identify on the model inventory in Table 15.3. After you have completed the activity, answer Check Your Understanding Question 7 (p. 424).

Olfaction

1. Nasal cavity
   a. Cribriform plate
2. Olfactory epithelium
   a. Olfactory receptor cells
3. Olfactory nerve (cranial nerve I)
4. Olfactory bulbs
5. Olfactory tract

Taste

1. Taste buds
2. Papillae
   a. Fungiform papillae
   b. Circumvallate papillae
   c. Foliate papillae

TABLE **15.3** Model Inventory for Olfaction and Taste

Model/Diagram	Structures Identified

MATERIALS

- ☐ Water-soluble marking pens (2 colors)
- ☐ Ruler
- ☐ Wooden applicator sticks or toothpicks (2)
- ☐ Alcohol swabs

Physiology of the General Senses: Cutaneous Sensation

We have been examining the special senses; let's now turn to the *general somatic senses*—those relating to touch, stretch, joint position, temperature, and pain. There are two types of touch stimuli:

- **Discriminative touch**, also known as the *tactile senses*, pertains to fine touch that allows you to discriminate among different shapes and textures. Discriminative touch allows you to discern the feel of an orange versus an apple with your eyes closed.

- **Nondiscriminative touch** pertains to crude sensations such as deep pressure. Discriminative touch allows you to feel the weight of an orange in your hand, but not feel the texture of its peel.

Discriminative and nondiscriminative touch are detected and transmitted by *somatic sensory neurons*—pseudounipolar neurons whose cell bodies are located in posterior root ganglia. Recall that a pseudounipolar neuron has two processes (both of which are axons): a peripheral process that transmits the stimulus to the cell body, and a central process that transmits it to the central nervous system. The distal end of a peripheral process is split into multiple small *nerve endings* where sensory transduction takes place.

Nerve endings contain **sensory receptors** that detect the initial stimulus. We classify sensory receptors by the type of stimulus they detect—those that detect touch are cutaneous **mechanoreceptors** (mek-uh-noh-reh-SEP-terz), which respond to stimuli that *mechanically* deform the skin. There are five types of cutaneous mechanoreceptors (Fig. 15.19):

- **Tactile cells.** In Unit 6, you learned about **tactile cells** (or *Merkel cells*), receptors located in the deepest layer of the epidermis. Each tactile cell is associated with a **tactile nerve ending**. These receptors have the finest spatial resolution of any mechanoreceptor and detect discriminative touch stimuli.

- **Tactile corpuscles.** You also learned about **tactile corpuscles** in Unit 6 (also known as *Meissner corpuscles*), which are located in the superficial part of the dermis. Tactile corpuscles also detect and transmit discriminative touch stimuli, although they do not have the fine spatial resolution of tactile cells.

- **Lamellated corpuscles.** The third example of a mechanoreceptor you learned about in Unit 6 is the **lamellated corpuscle**—nondiscriminative touch receptors located in the deep dermis. The word root for "lamellated" means "layer," and these receptors are indeed layered like an onion. The layers act like filters, permitting only high-frequency vibrations and deep pressure stimuli to activate the receptor.

- **Bulbous corpuscles.** In the dermis and hypodermis, we find **bulbous corpuscles**, also called *Ruffini endings*. These receptors respond to the nondiscriminative stimulus of stretch, such as that created by the rapid indentation of the skin.

- **Hair follicle receptors.** The final cutaneous mechanoreceptors are the **hair follicle receptors**—nondiscriminative touch receptors that wrap around the base of a hair follicle. These receptors detect stimuli that bend a hair, such as a breeze. (Note these receptors are not visible in Fig. 15.19).

Mechanoreceptor distribution in the skin is one factor that determines how sensitive a body part is to touch stimuli. In the following experiments, you will examine the relative distribution of tactile corpuscles and tactile cells in the skin. You will also examine other factors that affect sensitivity by performing two tests: the error of localization and two-point discrimination. After you complete the activities, answer Check Your Understanding Question 8 (p. 424).

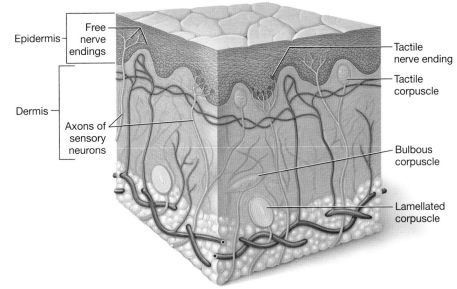

FIGURE **15.19** Cutaneous mechanoreceptors.

Error of Localization

Mechanoreceptor density is an important factor that determines a body region's sensitivity. However, it's not the only factor. Every region of the skin corresponds to an area of the primary somatosensory cortex of the cerebrum. Some regions are better represented than others and so are capable of localizing stimuli with greater precision than are less well-represented areas. The **error of localization** (also called *tactile localization*) tests the ability to determine the location of the skin touched and demonstrates how well-represented each region of the skin is in the cerebral cortex. Here, you will compare the error of localization in different locations, including the shoulder, anterior tibia, palm of the hand, and fingertip.

1 PROCEDURE
Testing Error of Localization

> **Hypothesis:** Where will error of localization be greatest? Where will it be smallest?
>
> _____

1 Have your partner sit with eyes closed.

2 Use a water-soluble marking pen to place a mark on your partner's anterior forearm.

3 Using a different color of marker, have your partner, still with eyes closed, place a mark as close as possible to where they believe the original spot is located.

4 Use a ruler to measure the distance between the two points in millimeters. This is your error of localization.

5 Repeat this procedure for each of the following locations:

   a shoulder

   b anterior tibia

   c palm of hand

   d fingertip

6 Record your data in Table 15.4.

7 Compare your results to your hypothesis.

_____

_____

_____

_____

_____

TABLE **15.4** Error of Localization

Location	Error of Localization (mm)
Anterior forearm	
Shoulder	
Anterior tibia	
Palm of hand	
Fingertip	

Two-Point Discrimination

Another factor that determines a region's sensitivity to tactile stimuli is the size of the area innervated by the somatic sensory neuron. Such neurons branch extensively in the skin—the more branches, the larger the **receptive field**, or the region of the skin served by a single neuron. Areas of the body that are innervated by more neurons with smaller receptive fields tend to have the greatest sensitivity, particularly to discriminative touch.

One test that examines the size of receptive fields and the density of mechanoreceptors is the **two-point discrimination test**. In this test, you assess the ability to detect the number of stimuli ("points") placed on the skin. Areas that have a higher density of touch receptors with smaller receptive fields are better able to distinguish between multiple stimuli than those with fewer touch receptors and larger receptive fields. In the following procedure, you will compare two-point discrimination in locations such as the shoulder, anterior tibia, palm of the hand, and fingertip.

2 PROCEDURE

Testing Two-Point Discrimination

Hypothesis: Where will two-point discrimination be greatest? Where will it be smallest?

1 Have your partner sit with eyes closed.

2 Place the ends of two wooden applicator sticks close together (they should be nearly touching) on your partner's skin on the anterior forearm. Ask how many points your partner can discriminate—one or two?

3 If your partner can sense only one point, move the sticks farther apart. Repeat this procedure until your partner can distinguish two separate points touching the skin.

4 Use a ruler to measure the distance between the two sticks in millimeters. This is your two-point discrimination.

5 Repeat this procedure for each of the following locations:
  a shoulder
  b anterior tibia
  c palm of the hand
  d fingertip

6 Record your data in Table 15.5.

7 Compare your results to your hypothesis.

TABLE **15.5** Two-Point Discrimination

Location	Two-Point Discrimination (mm)
Anterior forearm	
Shoulder	
Anterior tibia	
Palm of hand	
Fingertip	

1 Label the following external structures of the eye on Figure 15.20.

❏ Bulbar conjunctiva   ❏ Lacrimal sac   ❏ Nasolacrimal duct   ❏ Tarsal gland

❏ Lacrimal caruncle   ❏ Lateral canthus   ❏ Superior palpebra

❏ Lacrimal gland   ❏ Medial canthus   ❏ Tarsal plate

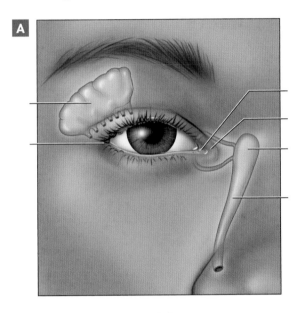
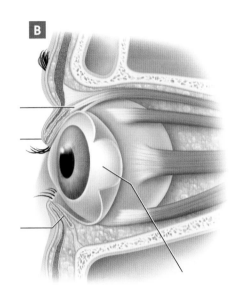

FIGURE **15.20** External structures of the eye: (**A**) anterior view; (**B**) lateral view.

2 Matching: Match the following terms with the correct description.

_____ Aqueous humor

_____ Rods

_____ Lacrimal gland

_____ Iris

_____ Optic disc

_____ Tarsal gland

_____ Vitreous humor

_____ Cornea

_____ Pupil

_____ Cones

A. Opening surrounded by the iris through which light enters the eye

B. Structure that secretes the aqueous component of tears

C. The anterior 1/6 of the fibrous tunic; the most powerful refractive medium of the eyeball

D. Watery fluid located in the anterior cavity of the eyeball

E. Thick fluid located in the posterior cavity of the eyeball

F. Sebaceous gland that secretes the lipid component of tears

G. Photoreceptors that detect peripheral and dim light vision

H. Pigmented portion of the vascular tunic that consists of smooth muscle fibers

I. Photoreceptors that detect color and high-acuity vision

J. Location with no photoreceptors at the posterior eyeball where the optic nerve exits the eyeball

3 Label the following parts of the eyeball on Figure 15.21.

❏ Choroid ❏ Fovea centralis ❏ Optic nerve ❏ Sclera
❏ Ciliary body ❏ Lens ❏ Posterior cavity ❏ Suspensory ligaments
❏ Cornea ❏ Macula lutea ❏ Retina

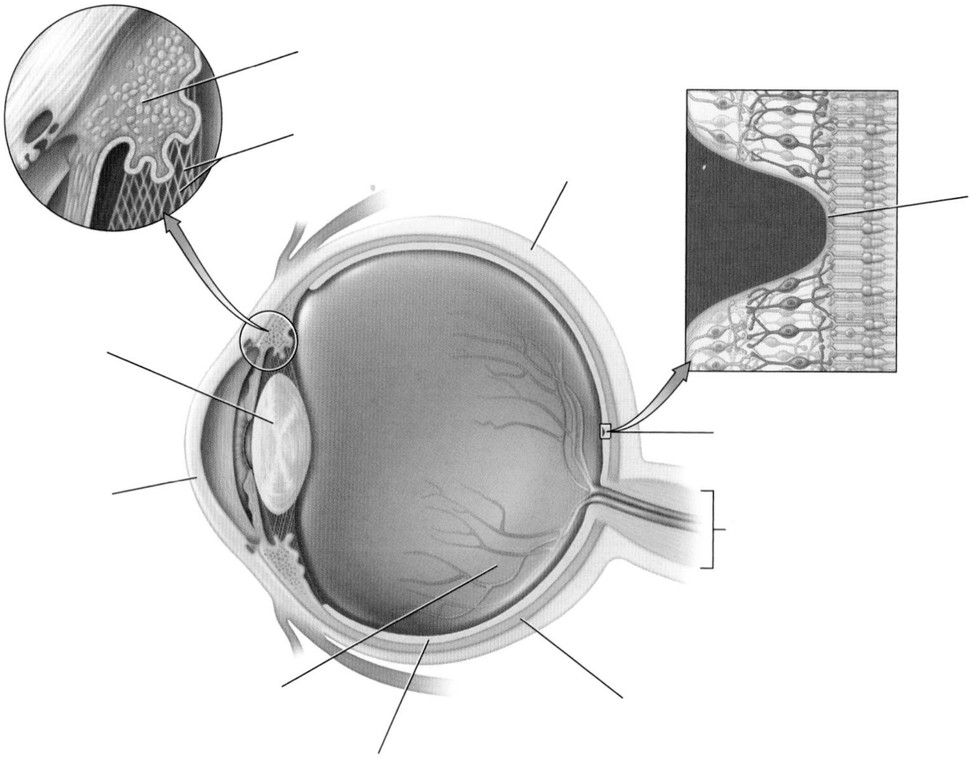

FIGURE **15.21** Sagittal section of the eyeball.

4 *Fill in the blanks:* A concave lens causes light to _____, whereas a convex lens causes light to _____ onto a _____ _____ .

5 The auditory ossicles transmit vibrations to the inner ear through the
a. pharyngotympanic tube.
b. oval window.
c. external auditory canal.
d. round window.

6 *True/False:* Mark the following statements as true (T) or false (F). If the statement is false, correct it so it is a true statement.

_____ a. Hair cells in the semicircular canals depolarize in response to sound wave vibrations.

_____ b. The saccule and utricle in the vestibule are responsible for static equilibrium.

_____ c. The membranous labyrinth is filled with endolymph.

_____ d. The tympanic membrane separates the middle ear and the inner ear.

_____ e. Smell and taste are chemosenses.

_____ f. Accommodation is the adjustment of the cornea necessary for near vision.

7 The axons of olfactory neurons are collectively known as the
   a. olfactory bulb.
   b. olfactory epithelium.
   c. olfactory nerve.
   d. olfactory tract.

8 Label the following parts of the ear on Figure 15.22.

❏ Ampullae   ❏ Incus   ❏ Semicircular ducts
❏ Cochlear duct   ❏ Pharyngotympanic tube ❏ Stapes
❏ Cochlear nerve   ❏ Round window   ❏ Tympanic membrane
❏ External auditory canal ❏ Saccule   ❏ Vestibular nerve

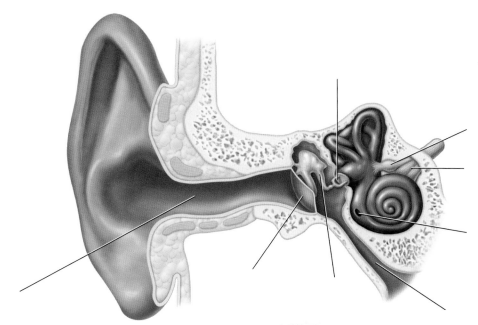

FIGURE **15.22** Anatomy of the ear.

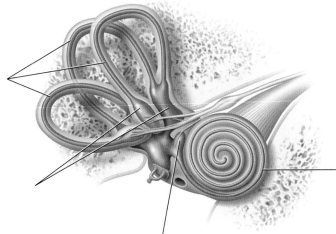

9 Chemoreceptors that detect taste are located on cells called

    a. gustatory cells.

    b. basal cells.

    c. olfactory receptor cells.

    d. sustentacular cells.

10 The mechanoreceptors with the finest spatial resolution for discriminative touch are the

    a. lamellated corpuscles.

    b. hair follicle receptors.

    c. bulbous corpuscles.

    d. tactile cells.

15

Name _____

Section _____ Date _____

Check Your Understanding

Critical Thinking and Application Questions

1 Inflammation or dysfunction of the lacrimal gland may result in insufficient production of lacrimal fluid. Why does this put a person at increased risk for eye infections?

_____

_____

_____

2 *Corneal dystrophy* is a condition that causes the cornea to swell. How would this affect vision, and why?

_____

_____

_____

_____

3 *Cone-rod dystrophy* is a group of disorders that cause the progressive degeneration of the rods and cones. What kind of vision will be affected in cone-rod dystrophy, and why? Be specific.

_____

_____

_____

_____

_____

4 Side mirrors on vehicles are made of concave glass. How does this explain why these mirrors usually feature the phrase, "objects in mirror are closer than they appear"?

_____

_____

_____

5 *Middle ear infections* commonly result in fluid buildup in the middle ear, which puts pressure on the tympanic membrane. Explain why this may diminish hearing in the affected ear.

_____

_____

_____

6 Two types of implanted devices can restore hearing in individuals with hearing impairment.

  a A *cochlear implant* is a device that directly stimulates the cochlear nerve. Would this device be indicated for conductive or sensorineural hearing loss? Explain.

  b A *bone-anchored hearing system* is a device implanted in bone that transmits vibrations directly to the inner ear. Would this device be indicated for conductive or sensorineural hearing loss? Explain.

7 One of the most notable symptoms of COVID-19, the disease caused by the virus SARS-CoV2, is *anosmia*, or the loss of smell. Researchers have determined that the receptor to which SARS-CoV2 binds in order to infect cells is located on basal cells in the olfactory epithelium.

  a How does this explain the anosmia reported with COVID-19?

  b How does this explain why people generally recover their sense of smell after COVID-19 resolves?

8 Braille is a system of raised dots on a page that visually impaired individuals can use to read. What touch receptors allow us to read braille? Given the results of your experiments in Exercise 15-4, explain why we can read braille with our fingertips, but not with our shoulder.

15

Lab Practical Practice Quiz 2

1 The tissue in Figure Q.2.1 is
   a. smooth muscle.
   b. skeletal muscle.
   c. dense irregular connective tissue.
   d. dense regular collagenous connective tissue.

2 The structure marked number 2 in Figure Q.2.1 is
   a. a nucleus.
   b. the endomysium.
   c. an A band.
   d. an I band.

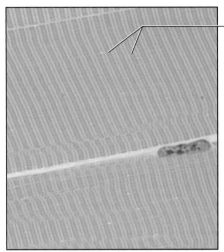

FIGURE **Q.2.1** Unknown tissue for Questions 1–2.

3 The structure marked number 3 in Figure Q.2.2 is the
   a. anterior cruciate ligament.
   b. posterior cruciate ligament.
   c. joint capsule.
   d. bursa.

4 The joint in Figure Q.2.2 is a
   a. fibrous joint.
   b. syndesmosis.
   c. cartilaginous joint.
   d. synovial joint.

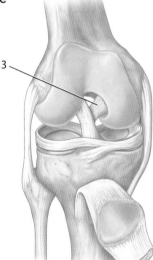

FIGURE **Q.2.2** Unknown joint for Questions 3–4.

5 The structure marked number 5 in Figure Q.2.3 is the
   a. myelin sheath.
   b. myelin sheath gap.
   c. dendrite.
   d. cell body.

6 The structure marked number 6 in Figure Q.2.3 is the
   a. axon.
   b. dendrite.
   c. axon terminal.
   d. axon collateral.

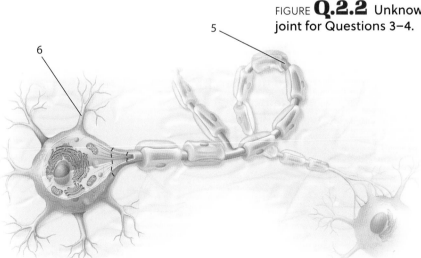

FIGURE **Q.2.3** Neuronal structures for Questions 5–6.

7 The muscle marked number 7 in Figure Q.2.4 is the
   a. masseter muscle.
   b. zygomaticus minor muscle.
   c. orbicularis oris muscle.
   d. orbicularis oculi muscle.

8 The muscle marked number 8 in Figure Q.2.4 is the
   a. sternocleidomastoid muscle.
   b. trapezius muscle.
   c. deltoid muscle.
   d. latissimus dorsi muscle.

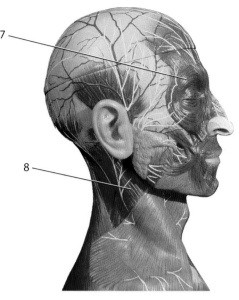

FIGURE **Q.2.4** Lateral view of the musculature of the head and neck for Questions 7–8.

9 The muscle marked number 9 in Figure Q.2.5 is the
   a. pectoralis major muscle.
   b. pectoralis minor muscle.
   c. rectus abdominis muscle.
   d. risorious muscle.

10 The muscle marked number 10 in Figure Q.2.5 is the
   a. biceps brachii muscle.
   b. triceps brachii muscle.
   c. brachioradialis muscle.
   d. deltoid muscle.

11 The muscle marked number 11 in Figure Q.2.5 is the
   a. rectus abdominis muscle.
   b. latissimus dorsi muscle.
   c. external oblique muscle.
   d. transversus abdominis muscle.

12 The muscle marked number 12 in Figure Q.2.5 is the
   a. tibialis anterior muscle.
   b. vastus lateralis muscle.
   c. sartorius muscle.
   d. rectus femoris muscle.

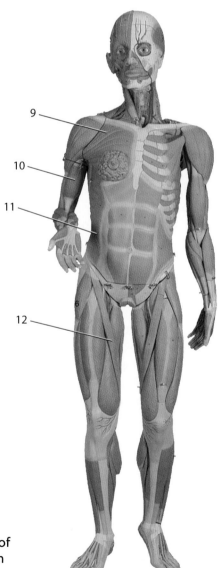

FIGURE **Q.2.5** Anterior view of the musculature of the human body for Questions 9–12.

13 The muscle marked number 13 in Figure Q.2.6 is the
 a. biceps femoris muscle.
 b. semitendinosus muscle.
 c. semimembranosus muscle.
 d. gracilis muscle.

14 The muscle marked number 14 in Figure Q.2.6 is the
 a. gastrocnemius muscle.
 b. gracilis muscle.
 c. tibialis anterior muscle.
 d. soleus muscle.

15 The muscle marked number 15 in Figure Q.2.6 is the
 a. soleus muscle.
 b. gluteus maximus muscle.
 c. gluteus medius muscle.
 d. gastrocnemius muscle.

16 The muscle marked number 16 in Figure Q.2.6 is the
 a. erector spinae muscle.
 b. latissimus dorsi muscle.
 c. rhomboid major muscle.
 d. trapezius muscle.

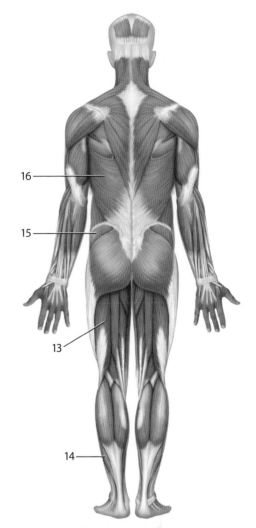

FIGURE **Q.2.6** Posterior view of the musculature of the human body for Questions 13–16.

17 The structure marked number 17 in Figure Q.2.7 is the
 a. frontal lobe.
 b. parietal lobe.
 c. occipital lobe.
 d. temporal lobe.

18 The structure marked number 18 in Figure Q.2.7 is the
 a. thalamus.
 b. hypothalamus.
 c. pineal gland.
 d. optic nerve.

19 The structure marked number 19 in Figure Q.2.7 is the
 a. pons.
 b. midbrain.
 c. medulla oblongata.
 d. cerebellum.

20 The structure marked number 20 in Figure Q.2.7 is the
 a. lateral ventricle.
 b. cerebral aqueduct.
 c. third ventricle.
 d. fourth ventricle.

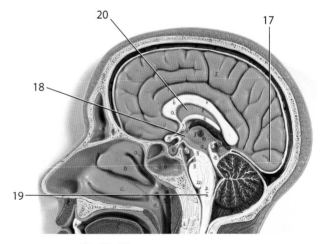

FIGURE **Q.2.7** Midsagittal section through the head and neck for Questions 17–20.

21 The structure marked number 21 in Figure Q.2.8 is the
   a. anterior root.
   b. dura mater.
   c. posterior root ganglion.
   d. posterior horn.

22 The structure marked number 22 in Figure Q.2.8 is the
   a. anterior horn.
   b. epidural space.
   c. lateral horn.
   d. central canal.

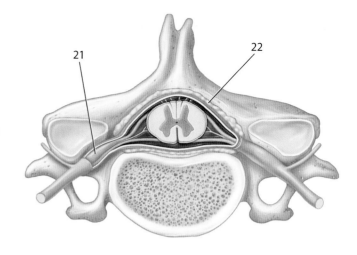

FIGURE **Q.2.8** Transverse section through the spinal cord for Questions 21–22.

23 The structure marked number 23 in Figure Q.2.9 is the
   a. phrenic nerve.
   b. femoral nerve.
   c. musculocutaneous nerve.
   d. intercostal nerve.

24 The structure marked number 24 in Figure Q.2.9 is the
   a. sciatic nerve.
   b. ulnar nerve.
   c. axillary nerve.
   d. radial nerve.

25 The structure marked number 25 in Figure Q.2.9 is the
   a. common fibular nerve.
   b. sural nerve.
   c. femoral nerve.
   d. musculocutaneous nerve.

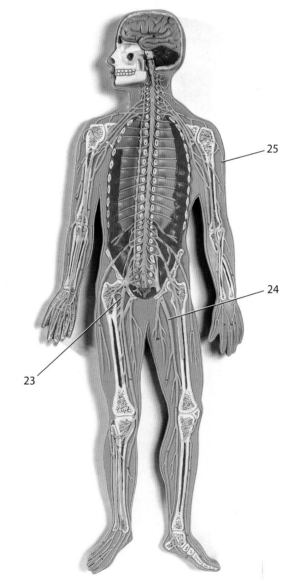

FIGURE **Q.2.9** The nerve plexuses and the anterior rami of major spinal nerves for Questions 23–25.

26 The structure marked number 26 in Figure Q.2.10 is the

    a. cornea.

    b. lens.

    c. sclera.

    d. suspensory ligaments.

27 The structure marked number 27 in Figure Q.2.10 is the

    a. iris.

    b. pupil.

    c. sclera.

    d. choroid.

28 The structure marked number 28 in Figure Q.2.10 is the

    a. fovea centralis.

    b. pupil.

    c. optic disc.

    d. choroid.

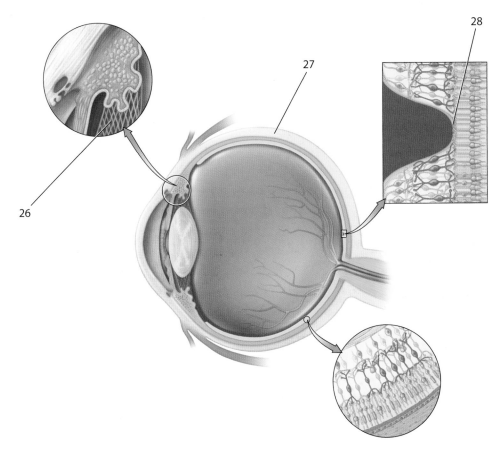

FIGURE **Q.2.10** Structures of the eye for Questions 26–28.

29 The structure marked number 29 in Figure Q.2.11 is the
   a. tympanic membrane.
   b. pharyngotympanic (auditory or Eustachian) tube.
   c. auricle.
   d. external auditory canal.

30 The structure(s) marked number 30 in Figure Q.2.11 is/are the
   a. semicircular canals.
   b. malleus.
   c. cochlea.
   d. vestibule.

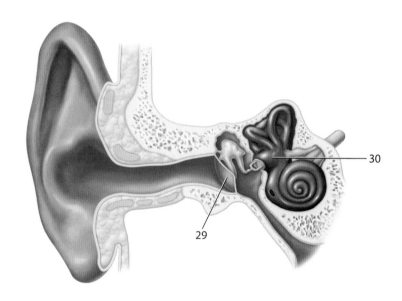

FIGURE **Q.2.11** Structures of the ear for Questions 29–30.

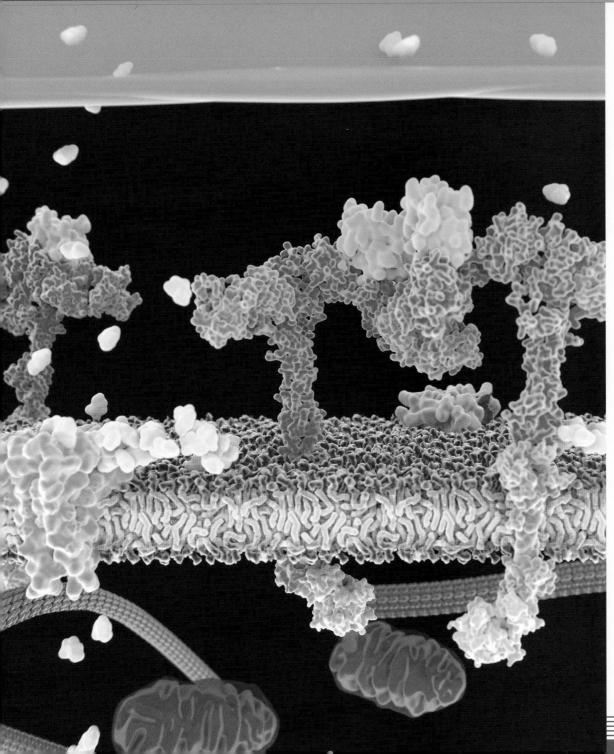

Endocrine System

When you have completed this unit, you should be able to:

1 Describe and identify endocrine organs and structures.

2 Identify microscopic structures of endocrine organs.

3 Trace the functions, stimulus for secretion, and target tissues of various hormones.

4 Describe the negative feedback mechanisms that control hormone secretion.

5 Apply principles of the endocrine system to clinical cases.

PRE-LAB EXERCISES

Complete the following exercises prior to coming to lab, using your lab manual and textbook for reference.

16-1 Key Terms

You should be familiar with the following terms before coming to lab. Please note that key hormones are covered in Pre-Lab Exercise 16-3 (p. 435).

Term	Definition

General Terms

Primary endocrine organ (gland)

Hormone

Target tissue

Negative feedback

Endocrine Organs

16

Hypothalamus

Anterior pituitary

Posterior pituitary

Thyroid gland

Thyroid follicle

Parathyroid glands

Pineal gland

Thymus

Pancreas _____

Pancreatic islet _____

Adrenal cortex _____

Adrenal medulla _____

Ovaries _____

Testes _____

16

16-2 Endocrine System Anatomy

Color the structures of the endocrine system in Figure 16.1, and label them with the terms from Exercise 16-1 (p. 439). Use your text and Exercise 16-1 in this unit for reference.

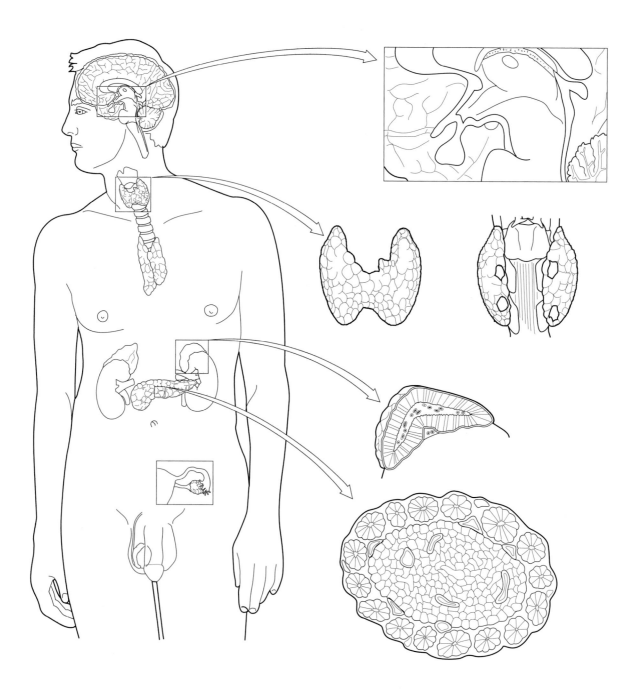

FIGURE **16.1** Organs and tissues of the endocrine system.

16-3 Hormones: Target Tissues and Effects

Fill in Table 16.1 with the following information for each hormone: the organ that secretes the hormone, the hormone's target tissue(s), and its main effects.

TABLE **16.1** Properties of Hormones

Hormone	Organ that Secretes the Hormone	Target Tissue(s)	Main Effects
Antidiuretic hormone			
Oxytocin			
Thyroid-stimulating hormone			
Adrenocorticotropic hormone			
Growth hormone			
Prolactin			
Melatonin			
Thyroxine and triiodothyronine (T4 and T3)			

(continues)

TABLE **16.1** Properties of Hormones *(cont.)*

Hormone	Organ that Secretes the Hormone	Target Tissue(s)	Main Effects
Calcitonin			
Thymosin and thymopoietin			
Parathyroid hormone			
Cortisol			
Aldosterone			
Epinephrine and norepinephrine			
Insulin			
Glucagon			

16

EXERCISES

Insulin binding to an insulin receptor, illustration

The **endocrine system** is a diverse group of ductless glands. The system works closely with the nervous system—and together they maintain the homeostasis of multiple physiological variables. Although these two systems both work toward the same goal, the methods by which they do so differ. The nervous system functions via action potentials (nerve impulses) and releases *neurotransmitters* that directly affect target cells. The effects are nearly immediate, but they are short in duration. In contrast, the endocrine system brings about its effects via the secretion of **hormones**—chemicals released into the bloodstream that typically act on distant targets. Hormones' effects are not immediate, but they are longer-lasting than those of the nervous system.

How the endocrine system works is illustrated in Figure 16.2. There are four general steps:

1. **A deviation in a regulated physiological variable away from the normal range triggers an endocrine organ to release a hormone.** In the figure, we are using the example of the *anterior pituitary gland* and its hormone *adrenocorticotropic hormone*, or *ACTH*.

2. **The secreted hormone diffuses into the blood, which transports it to the hormone's target tissue.** The cells in a hormone's **target tissue** have receptors that bind to the hormone.

3. **Hormone molecules diffuse out of the blood and bind to receptors on or inside target cells.** The receptors in our figure for ACTH are within the plasma membrane of cells in the *adrenal cortex*. Some hormone receptors, however, are located in the target cell's cytosol.

4. **The hormone triggers an effect in its target cell, such as causing the cell to secrete another hormone.** In our example, the binding of ACTH to adrenal cortex cells triggers them to release another hormone, *cortisol*. In general, hormones regulate the processes of other cells. They may turn on or off genes, which could induce synthesis of enzymes or other hormones. They may also change a cell's metabolic rate or alter the permeability of its plasma membrane. You might think of hormones as the "middle managers" of the body, because they communicate the messages from their "bosses" (the endocrine glands) and tell the "workers" (other cells) what to do.

Some endocrine glands, such as the anterior pituitary and thyroid glands, are **primary endocrine organs** that secrete hormones as their primary function. Others, however, are *secondary endocrine glands* that secrete hormones as a secondary function. Examples include the heart (atrial natriuretic peptide), adipose tissue (leptin), the kidneys (erythropoietin), and the stomach (gastrin).

This unit introduces you to the anatomy, histology, and physiology of the endocrine organs and hormones. To close out this unit, you will play "endocrine detective" and solve three "endocrine mysteries."

16

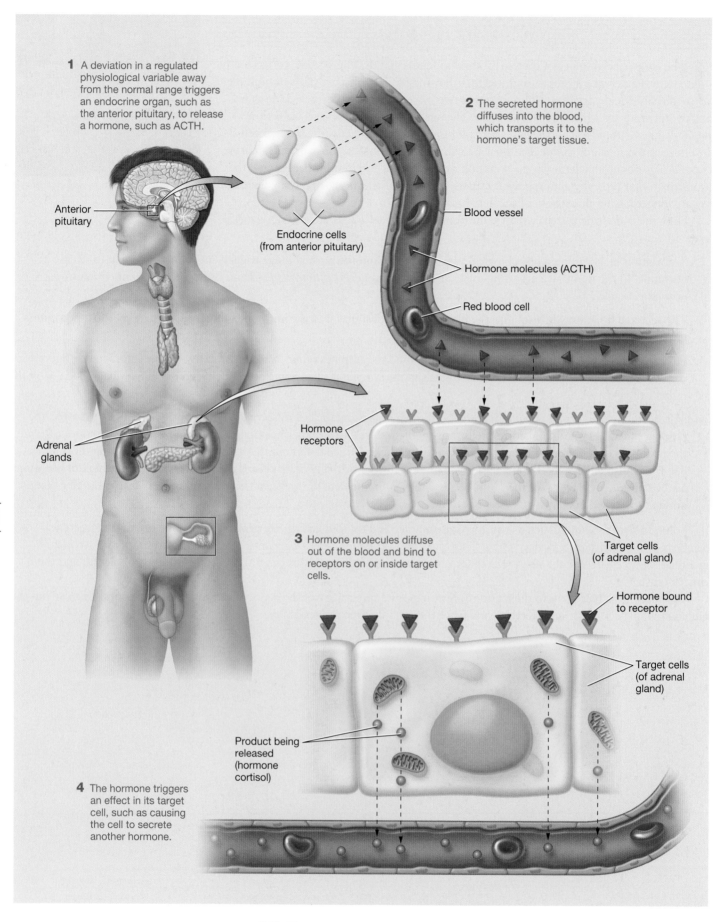

1 A deviation in a regulated physiological variable away from the normal range triggers an endocrine organ, such as the anterior pituitary, to release a hormone, such as ACTH.

Anterior pituitary

Endocrine cells (from anterior pituitary)

2 The secreted hormone diffuses into the blood, which transports it to the hormone's target tissue.

Blood vessel

Hormone molecules (ACTH)

Red blood cell

Adrenal glands

Hormone receptors

Target cells (of adrenal gland)

3 Hormone molecules diffuse out of the blood and bind to receptors on or inside target cells.

Hormone bound to receptor

Target cells (of adrenal gland)

Product being released (hormone cortisol)

4 The hormone triggers an effect in its target cell, such as causing the cell to secrete another hormone.

FIGURE **16.2** How the endocrine system works.

16

Endocrine System Anatomy

The 10 primary endocrine organs are the hypothalamus, the pituitary gland, the pineal gland, the thyroid gland, the parathyroid glands, the thymus, the adrenal gland, the pancreas, and the ovaries or testes (Fig. 16.3). Let's take a closer look at each of these organs (note that we discuss the ovaries and testes only briefly here; they are discussed fully in Unit 27).

1. **Hypothalamus and pituitary gland.** The **hypothalamus,** the inferior part of the diencephalon, is known as a **neuroendocrine organ.** It can be likened to the endocrine system's chief executive officer (CEO). It has a close working relationship with the **pituitary gland** (pih-TOO-ih-tehr-ee), to which it is attached by a stalk called the **infundibulum** (in-fun-DIB-yoo-lum; "funnel"). Notice in **Figure 16.4** that the pituitary gland is actually two separate structures: The **anterior pituitary gland,** or **adenohypophysis** (ăd-in-oh-hy-PAHF-ih-sis; "glandular undergrowth"), is composed of glandular epithelium and secretes a variety of hormones that affect other tissues in the body. The **posterior pituitary,** or **neurohypophysis** (noor-oh-hy-PAHF-ih-sis; "neural undergrowth"), is composed of nervous tissue rather than glandular tissue.

The hypothalamus produces two types of hormones. The first, called **inhibiting** and **releasing hormones** respectively, are those that inhibit and stimulate secretion from the anterior pituitary gland, respectively. In response to hypothalamic-releasing hormones, the anterior pituitary gland secretes hormones that stimulate other endocrine and exocrine glands in the body. In **Figure 16.4A,** you can see how the hypothalamus communicates with the anterior pituitary gland via a specialized

MATERIALS
❏ Anatomical models and diagrams:
- endocrine system
- human torso
- head and neck
- fetus

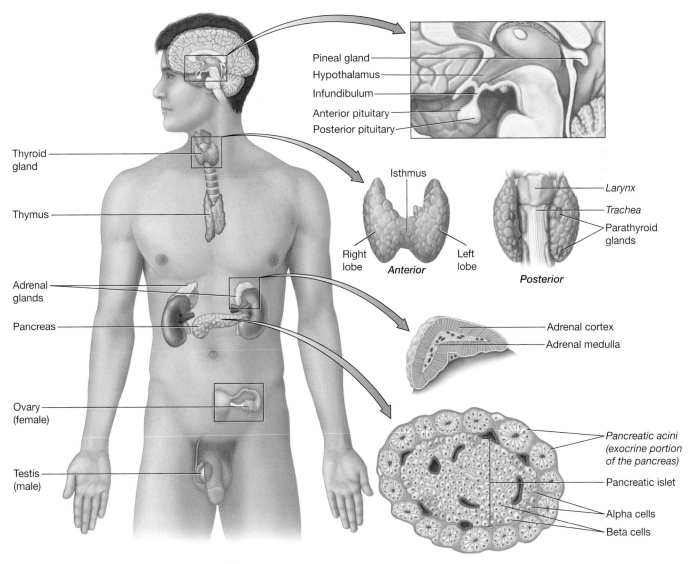

FIGURE **16.3** Organs and tissues of the endocrine system.

set of blood vessels collectively called the **hypothalamic-hypophyseal portal system** (hy-PAH-fih-see-uhl). The releasing and inhibiting hormones are synthesized by hypothalamic neurons and enter capillaries in the hypothalamus, after which they travel through small *portal veins* in the infundibulum. They then enter a second capillary bed in the anterior pituitary, where they exit the blood and interact with anterior pituitary cells to influence their functions.

In addition to inhibiting and releasing hormones, the hypothalamus makes the hormone **oxytocin** (ahks-ee-TOH-sin; "sudden childbirth"), which triggers uterine contraction and milk ejection from the mammary glands. It also produces **antidiuretic hormone** or **ADH** (an-tee-dy-yoo-RET-ik; *di-* = "through;" *uret-* = "urine"), which causes water retention from the kidneys when the solute concentration of the blood increases. These hormones are produced by hypothalamic neurons that extend the length of the infundibulum down into the posterior pituitary, where they are stored (Fig. 16.4B).

a. The **anterior pituitary gland** mostly produces hormones known as *tropic hormones*, or those that influence the functions of other glands. Examples include **thyroid-stimulating hormone (TSH)**, which stimulates growth of and secretion from the thyroid; **prolactin** (*lact-* = "milk"), which stimulates milk production from mammary glands; **adrenocorticotropic hormone** (uh-dree-noh-kohr-tih-koh-TROH-pik; **ACTH**), which stimulates secretion from the adrenal cortex; and two reproductive hormones, **luteinizing hormone** (LOO-tee-in-aye-zing) and **follicle-stimulating hormone**, which affect primarily the testes and ovaries. An exception is **growth hormone (GH)**, which increases the rate of cell division and protein synthesis in all tissues and has both tropic and nontropic effects. As implied by its name, GH promotes longitudinal bone growth and muscle development. In the short-term, GH increases blood glucose concentration, but in the long-term, GH lowers it by indirectly promoting its uptake into cells.

b. The posterior pituitary doesn't produce any hormones at all and functions merely as a place to store the oxytocin and ADH produced by the hypothalamus.

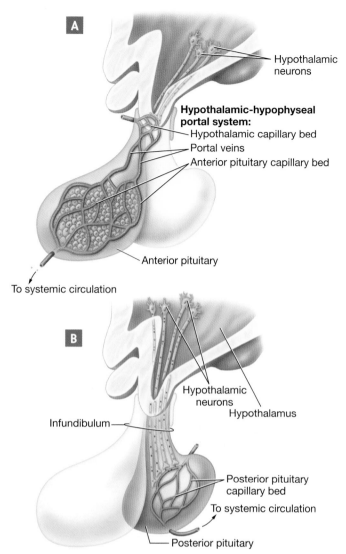

FIGURE **16.4** Hypothalamus and pituitary gland: **(A)** hypothalamus and anterior pituitary; **(B)** hypothalamus and posterior pituitary.

2. **Pineal gland.** Recall from Unit 13 (p. 341) that the tiny **pineal gland** (pin-EE-uhl; *pineal* = "pinecone") is located in the posterior and superior diencephalon. This neuroendocrine organ secretes the hormone **melatonin** (mel-uh-TOH-nin) in response to decreased light levels. It acts on the reticular formation of the brainstem to trigger sleep.

3. **Thyroid gland.** The **thyroid gland** (THY-royd; "shield-shaped") is located in the anterior and inferior neck superficial to the larynx. It consists of right and left lobes connected by a thin band of tissue called the **isthmus**. Microscopically, it is composed of hollow spheres called **thyroid follicles** (Fig. 16.5). The cells that line the thyroid follicles are simple cuboidal cells called **follicle cells**, and they surround a gelatinous, iodine-rich substance called **colloid** (KAHL-oyd; *coll-* = "glue").

The follicle cells are part of a multi-tiered feedback loop system known as the hypothalamic-pituitary-thyroid axis. The hypothalamus releases *thyrotropin-releasing hormone* (TRH) in response to a variety of hormonal, metabolic, and environmental stimuli (such as cold temperatures). TRH, in turn, stimulates the release of TSH from the anterior pituitary. TSH then triggers follicle cells to secrete a chemical into the colloid that reacts with iodine. The result is two different hormones: **thyroxine** or **T4**, which has four iodine atoms, and **triiodothyronine** (try-aye-oh-doh-THY-roh-neen) or **T3**, which has three iodine atoms. T3 is the most active of the two hormones and acts on essentially all cells in the body to

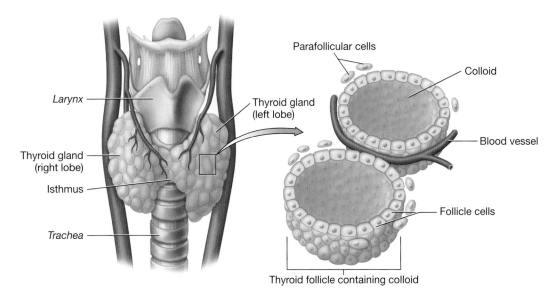

FIGURE **16.5** Thyroid gland and thyroid follicles.

increase the metabolic rate, increase protein synthesis, and regulate the heart rate and blood pressure, among other things. By increasing the metabolic rate, T3 increases heat production, which gives it an important role in thermoregulation—the maintenance of body temperature homeostasis. About 10 times as much T4 is produced as T3, and the body converts T4 to T3 when the T3 level in the blood drops.

    Between the follicles we find another cell type called the **parafollicular cells** (*para-* = "around"). These cells produce the hormone **calcitonin** (kal-sih-TOH-nin), which is a hormone that plays a role in calcium ion homeostasis. Calcitonin is secreted when calcium ion levels in the blood rise, triggering osteoblast activity and bone deposition.

4. **Parathyroid glands.** Refer back to Figure 16.3, where you can see the small **parathyroid glands** on the posterior thyroid gland. They secrete the hormone **parathyroid hormone (PTH)**, which is the main hormone in the body that maintains calcium ion homeostasis. PTH is secreted in response to a decreased level of calcium ions in the blood. It triggers osteoclast activity and the breakdown of bone tissue, increased calcium ion absorption from the intestines, and increased calcium ion reabsorption from the kidneys. Hormones with opposite actions, such as PTH and calcitonin, are called **antagonists**.

5. **Thymus.** The **thymus** sits in the superior mediastinum. It is large and active in infancy and early childhood, during which time it secretes the hormones **thymosin** and **thymopoietin** (thy-moh-POY-eh-tin; *poiet-* = "to make"). Both hormones stimulate the development of T lymphocytes within the thymus. In adults most of the thymic tissue is gradually replaced by fat and other connective tissue.

6. **Adrenal gland.** As the name implies, the **adrenal glands** (uh-DREE-nuhl; *ad-* = "next to;" *ren-* = "kidney") sit atop the superior pole of each kidney. Like the pituitary gland, the adrenal gland is actually composed of two separate structures, the adrenal cortex and the adrenal medulla, which are surrounded by a connective tissue capsule (Fig. 16.6).

   a. **Adrenal cortex.** The superficial region of the adrenal gland consists of glandular tissue called the **adrenal cortex**, which secretes **steroid hormones** in response to stimulation by ACTH and other factors. The outermost zone of the adrenal cortex, the **zona glomerulosa** (gloh-mehr-yoo-LOH-sah), secretes **mineralocorticoids** (min-er-al-oh-KORT-ih-koydz) such as **aldosterone** (al-DAHS-tur-ohn). As implied by their name, these hormones maintain the homeostasis of various *minerals* in the body. Aldosterone acts on the kidneys to trigger the retention of sodium and chloride ions. In addition, it triggers the loss of potassium and hydrogen ions to the urine. Together, these effects help maintain fluid, electrolyte, acid-base, and blood pressure homeostasis.

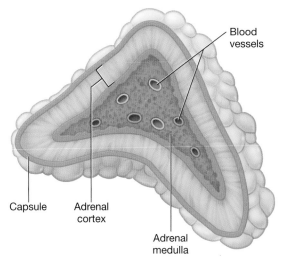

FIGURE **16.6** Adrenal gland.

The middle zone of the adrenal cortex, the **zona fasciculata** (fah-SIK-yoo-lah-tah), secretes **glucocorticoids** (gloo-koh-KORT-ih-koydz), such as **cortisol** (KOHR-tih-sahl). Glucocorticoids affect a variety of tissues as an important part of the stress response. They also help maintain blood glucose homeostasis by triggering the release of glucose from glycogen and the formation of new glucose by gluconeogenesis. In addition, glucocorticoids cause fluid retention and suppress the inflammatory response.

The innermost zone, the **zona reticularis**, secretes glucocorticoids and **gonadocorticoids** (goh-nad-oh-KORT-ih-koydz) such as *testosterone*, *estrogens*, and *progesterone*. These hormones affect the gonads and other tissues; we'll discuss their functions shortly.

b. **Adrenal medulla.** The deep region of the adrenal gland, called the **adrenal medulla** (meh-DOOL-uh), consists of modified postsynaptic sympathetic neurons that secrete *catecholamines*—**epinephrine** and **norepinephrine**—into the blood in response to stimulation from the sympathetic nervous system. The adrenal catecholamines have the same effects on target cells as the norepinephrine and epinephrine released by sympathetic neurons: dilation of bronchioles; increase in the rate and force of contraction of the heart; constriction of blood vessels serving the skin and abdominal viscera; dilation of the pupil; and more (see Unit 14). Secretion of adrenal catecholamines prolongs the sympathetic response, as the effects of neuronal catecholamines are terminated after only a few seconds. In addition, these hormones are able to act on target cells that are not innervated by sympathetic neurons.

7. **Pancreas.** The **pancreas** (PAYN-kree-uhs) has both endocrine and exocrine functions. Its exocrine functions are carried out by groups of cells called *pancreatic acini*, which release their products into ducts. Embedded within the pancreatic acini are small, round "islands" called **pancreatic islets** (Fig. 16.7) that carry out the pancreas' endocrine functions. The cells within the pancreatic islets secrete the hormones *insulin* and *glucagon* (GLOO-kah-gahn), which play a major role in regulating blood glucose levels. **Insulin**, which is produced by cells called **beta (β) cells**, triggers the uptake of glucose by cells, which decreases the concentration of glucose in the blood. The hormone **glucagon**, which is produced by **alpha (α) cells**, is insulin's antagonist. Glucagon triggers glycogenolysis and gluconeogenesis in the liver. Both actions increase the concentration of glucose in the blood.

8. **Testes.** The **testes** are the male reproductive organs that produce sperm cells, which are the male gametes. Cells within the testes called **interstitial cells** produce a steroid hormone called **testosterone**. This hormone promotes the production of sperm cells and the development of male secondary sex characteristics such as a deeper voice, greater bone and muscle mass, and facial hair.

9. **Ovaries.** The **ovaries** are the female reproductive organs that produce oocytes, which are the female gametes. The ovaries produce steroid hormones called **estrogens** and **progesterone**. Estrogens play a role in the development of oocytes, female secondary sex characteristics such as breasts and subcutaneous fat stores, and a variety of other processes. Progesterone has a number of effects that prepare the body for pregnancy.

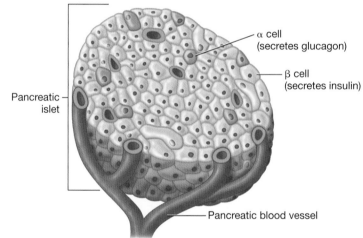

FIGURE **16.7** Pancreatic islet.

Let's now examine these structures on models and charts. Note that human torso models are typically a good place to start when studying the endocrine system, because most of the organs are easy to find. The one exception is the thymus; many torsos and models choose not to show this structure because it is fairly inactive in adults. Fetal models, however, typically show well-developed thymus glands.

Model Inventory of the Endocrine System

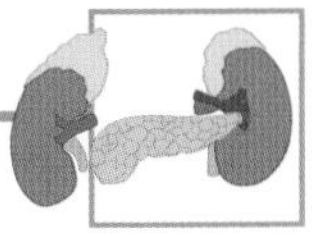

Identify the following structures of the endocrine system on models and diagrams, using your textbook and this unit for reference. As you examine the anatomical models and diagrams, record the name of the model and the structures you were able to identify on the model inventory in Table 16.2. After you have completed this activity, answer Check Your Understanding Questions 1 through 4 (p. 457).

Endocrine Glands

1. Hypothalamus
   a. Infundibulum
2. Pituitary gland
   a. Anterior pituitary
   b. Posterior pituitary
3. Pineal gland
4. Thyroid gland
   a. Right and left lobes
   b. Isthmus

5. Parathyroid glands
6. Thymus gland
7. Adrenal glands
   a. Adrenal cortex
   b. Adrenal medulla
8. Pancreas
   a. Pancreatic islets
9. Testes
10. Ovaries

TABLE **16.2** Model Inventory for the Endocrine System

Model/Diagram	Structures Identified

MATERIALS

- ❏ Slides:
  - ▪ thyroid gland
  - ▪ adrenal gland
  - ▪ pancreas
- ❏ Light microscope
- ❏ Colored pencils

Endocrine Organ Histology

In this exercise, we examine the histology of three endocrine organs: the thyroid gland, the adrenal gland, and the pancreas. (We examine the ovary and testis in the reproductive system unit.) Following are keys to identification of each tissue:

1. **Thyroid gland.** Thyroid follicles are perhaps one of the easiest structures to identify (Fig. 16.8). Look for a ring of simple cuboidal epithelium surrounding the reddish-brown, acellular colloid. In between the follicles, note that you can see large, clear parafollicular cells.

2. **Adrenal gland.** The zones of the adrenal cortex each appear differently and so are fairly easy to tell apart on a slide. Notice in Figure 16.9 that the cells in the thin outer zona glomerulosa are arranged in clusters, whereas the cells in the thick middle zona fasciculata are stacked on top of one another and resemble columns. Finally, the cells of the thin inner zona reticularis stain more darkly and are tightly packed. The innermost adrenal medulla is distinguished from the zones of the cortex by its numerous, loosely arranged blood vessels. If you find that you're having a hard time discerning the adrenal medulla from the zona glomerulosa (i.e., you don't know whether you're looking at the top or the bottom of the slide), look for the adrenal gland capsule, which you can see in the figure. It is the most superficial layer of the adrenal gland, and so is the "top" of the slide.

   The regions of the adrenal gland are best viewed on low or medium power. Switch to high power to get more detail of the individual cells.

3. **Pancreas.** As you read earlier, there are two main groups of cells in the pancreas: (1) the pancreatic islets, and (2) the exocrine, enzyme-secreting *acinar cells*. Most of the pancreas is composed of acinar cells; however, note the small "islands" of tissue in Figure 16.10. These islands are the insulin- and glucagon-secreting pancreatic islets. Typically, the islets are lighter in color than the surrounding acinar cells. On high power, the differences between the two tissues are easily seen: The acinar cells are slightly cuboidal and are arranged around a duct, whereas the islet cells have no distinctive arrangement (there also may be larger, stain-free spaces between the islet cells).

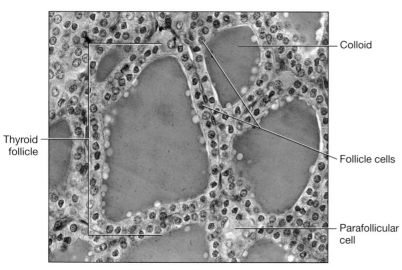

FIGURE **16.8** Thyroid gland, photomicrograph.

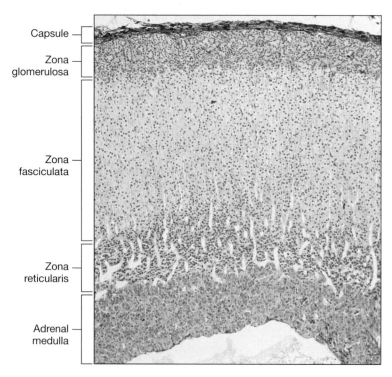

FIGURE **16.9** Zones of the adrenal gland, photomicrograph.

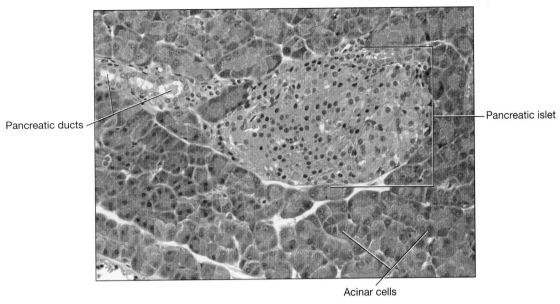

Pancreatic ducts

Pancreatic islet

Acinar cells

FIGURE **16.10** Pancreas, photomicrograph.

PROCEDURE
Examining Endocrine Tissues with Microscopy

Obtain prepared slides of the thyroid gland, the adrenal gland, and the pancreas. Place each slide on the stage of the microscope, and scan it on low power. Advance to higher power to see the cells and associated structures in greater detail. Use your colored pencils to draw what you see in the field of view, and label your drawing with the terms as indicated.

1 Thyroid

- Follicle cells
- Colloid
- Parafollicular cells

16

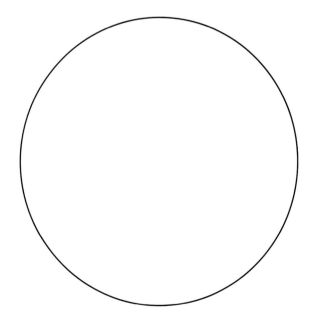

2 Adrenal Gland

- Zones of the adrenal cortex:
  - Zona glomerulosa
  - Zona fasciculata
  - Zona reticularis
  - Adrenal medulla

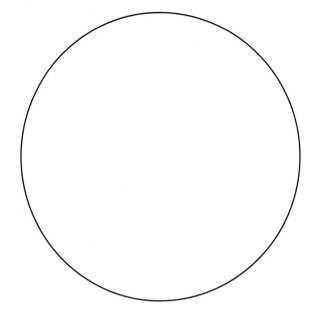

3 Pancreas

- Pancreatic acini (exocrine portion)
- Pancreatic islets (endocrine portion)

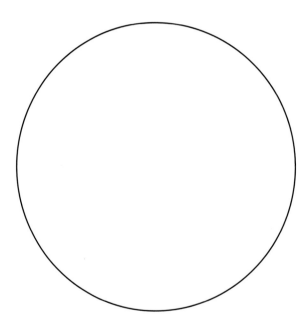

16

Time to Trace! Negative Feedback Loops

Hormone secretion is regulated through control mechanisms called **feedback loops**, in which a change in a regulated variable, such as body temperature, triggers effects that *feed back* and affect that same variable—for example, warming or cooling the body. Feedback loops are composed of events that lead to an effect, or *output*. This output, in turn, influences the loops themselves.

There are two types of feedback loops: negative and positive. Most hormone secretion is regulated by **negative feedback loops**, which generally work by the following process:

1. The loops begin with a disturbance in the homeostasis of a regulated variable such as heart rate or the amount of water in the body.
2. This disturbance in homeostasis triggers an endocrine gland to secrete a hormone to restore the imbalance.
3. The hormone acts on distant target cells to cause changes that restore the variable to its normal range.
4. When homeostasis is restored, the activity of the gland and concentration of the hormone declines.

Occasionally, hormone secretion occurs via a **positive feedback loop**. As opposed to a negative feedback loop, in which the endocrine gland works to counter the initial stimulus, a positive feedback loop reinforces the initial stimulus. This is best illustrated by the release of oxytocin during childbirth. As birth nears, the head of the fetus stretches the mother's cervix, a stimulus that triggers the release of oxytocin. Oxytocin causes the uterus to contract, which further stretches the cervix, which stimulates the release of more oxytocin. More oxytocin leads to stronger contractions, more cervical stretching, and more oxytocin release. In this way, the initial stimulus—cervical stretching—actually leads to more stretching.

In this exercise, we'll focus on negative feedback loops, since they are most common. You will be tracing a hormone's negative feedback loop from the initial homeostatic disturbance. Remember that sometimes a homeostatic imbalance causes an *increase* in hormone secretion, but it may also cause a *decrease* in hormone secretion. Following is an example of an increase:

Start: the concentration of glucose in the blood rises ⟶ the pancreas releases insulin ⟶ the concentration of the hormone in the blood rises ⟶ the hormone causes insulin uptake by cells ⟶ the concentration of glucose in the blood decreases ⟶ the concentration of the hormone in the blood decreases ⟶ **End**

1 PROCEDURE
Tracing Negative Feedback Loops

Now, it's your turn! After you have completed the activity, answer Check Your Understanding Questions 5 and 6 (p. 458).

1 Start: the concentration of glucose in the blood decreases ⟶ the pancreas releases the hormone

⟶ its concentration in the blood _____ ⟶

the hormone causes _____ and _____ ⟶ the concentration

of glucose in the blood _____ ⟶ the concentration of the hormone

in the blood _____ ⟶ **End**

2 Start: neurons of the _____

_____ stimulate the adrenal medulla in response to a stressor such as exercise ⟶ the adrenal

medulla releases the hormones _____ and _____

⟶ the concentration of the hormones in the blood _____ ⟶ the hormone causes

_____ ⟶ homeostasis is restored ⟶ the concentration of the hormones

in the blood _____ ⟶ **End**

16

3 Start: the level of light outside decreases → the pineal gland releases the hormone _____

→ the concentration of the hormone in the blood _____ → the hormone causes

_____ → the concentration of the hormone in the blood _____ →

End

4 Start: the body is exposed to cold temperatures → the hypothalamus releases _____

_____ → this hormone stimulates the release of the

hormone _____

from the anterior pituitary gland → this hormone stimulates the release of the hormones _____ and

_____ from the thyroid gland → the concentration of these hormones in the blood _____

→ the hormones cause _____

→ the body temperature increases → the concentration of the hypothalamic hormone _____

_____ in the

blood _____ → the concentration of the anterior pituitary hormone _____

_____ in the

blood _____ → the concentration of the hormones _____ and

_____ from the thyroid gland in the blood _____ → **End**

5 Start: the concentration of the blood decreases (i.e., there is *too much water* in the blood) → the hypothalamus decreases

the release of the hormone _____ → the amount of the

hormone stored in the posterior pituitary _____ → the concentration of the hormone in the

blood _____ → _____ water is retained from the kidneys →

the concentration of the blood _____ → **End**

Endocrine "Mystery Cases"

In this exercise, you will be playing the role of "endocrine detective" as you solve endocrine disease mysteries. In each case, you will have a victim who has suddenly fallen ill with a mysterious malady. You will be presented a set of "witnesses," each of whom will give you a clue as to the nature of the illness. Other clues will come from samples you send off to the lab for analysis. You will solve the mystery by providing the victim a diagnosis. You may wish to use your textbook for assistance with these cases. When you have completed the cases, answer Check Your Understanding Question 7 (p. 458).

---

1 PROCEDURE

Solving Endocrine Mysteries

Case 1: The Overheated Mr. Olive

You are called upon to visit the ailing Mr. Olive. Before you see him, you speak with three witnesses who were with him when he fell ill.

Witness Statements

- *Ms. Magenta*: "Mr. Olive has been hot-blooded for as long as I've known him. But he's even more hot-blooded than usual. He's always sweating and complaining of being hot."
- *Col. Lemon*: "The old boy eats like a hippopotamus, but he keeps losing weight!"
- *Professor Purple*: "Mr. Olive and I used to go on major expeditions together. Now he's so anxious and hyperactive he can't focus long enough to plan one!"

What are your initial thoughts about the witnesses' statements? Does one hormone come to mind that may be the cause? Explain your reasoning.

16

You see Mr. Olive and collect some blood to send off to the lab. The analysis comes back as follows:

  T3 (triiodothyronine): 0.7 ng/dL (normal: 0.2–0.5 ng/dL)

  T4 (thyroxine): 9.6 μg/dL (normal: 4–7 μg/dL)

  TSH (thyroid-stimulating hormone): 0.02 mU/L (normal: 0.3–4.0 mU/L)

Analyze the Results

Why do you think the T3 and T4 are high and the TSH is low?

Based upon the witness statements and the laboratory analysis, what is your final diagnosis? Given the diagnosis, explain Mr. Olive's symptoms.

Case 2: The Broken Mrs. Blanc

Your next call is to the home of Mrs. Blanc, after she fractured her arm. As before, you have three witnesses to interview.

Witness Statements

- *Ms. Magenta*: "I swear I didn't do it! I was just helping her up! She has been so weak and tired lately."
- *Mr. Olive*: "I don't like to gossip about such things, but this is the fourth time in the past few months she has broken a bone!"
- *Ms. Feather*: "She told me the other day that her bones and joints are always achy. Maybe she needs some of my herbal teas?"

Based upon the witnesses' statements, what are your initial thoughts? Does one hormone come to mind that could produce these effects? Explain your reasoning.

16 You see Ms. Blanc and collect some blood to send off to the lab. The analysis comes back as follows:

Calcium ion concentration: 11.6 mg/dL (normal: 8.6–10.3 mg/dL)

Parathyroid hormone: 120 pg/mL (normal: 10-55 pg/mL)

Analyze the Results

Why do you think the blood calcium ion concentration is high?

Based upon the witness statements and the laboratory analysis, what is your final diagnosis? Given the diagnosis, explain Ms. Blanc's symptoms.

Case 3: The Hypertensive Horatio Lemon

Your last call is to the aid of Col. Horatio Lemon. Three witnesses are present from whom to take statements.

Witness Statements

- *Mr. Olive:* "I think the colonel is letting his health go! His blood pressure has been out of control!"
- *Mrs. Blanc:* "I couldn't help but notice the colonel is rather, well . . . sweaty. He perspires all the time, even when sitting in a cool room!"
- *Ms. Scarlett:* "He said he felt faint the other day. I took his pulse, and his heart was racing out of control. He must have been very happy to see me."

Based upon the witnesses' statements, what are your initial thoughts? Does one type of hormone come to mind that could produce these effects? Explain your reasoning.

You see the colonel, collect some blood to send off to the lab, and order a scan of his abdomen. The analysis comes back as follows:

Epinephrine concentration: 515 pmol/L (normal: 0–140 pmol/L)

Norepinephrine concentration: 1949 pgmol/L (normal: 70-1700 pmol/L)

CT scan of the abdomen: mass found in the left adrenal medulla.

Analyze the Results

How are the elevated levels of epinephrine and norepinephrine related to the tumor in the adrenal medulla?

16

Based upon the witness statements, laboratory analysis, and radiographic findings, what is your final diagnosis? Given the diagnosis, explain Prof. Purple's symptoms.

Check Your Recall

1 Label Figure 16.11 with the following terms.

- ❏ Adrenal cortex
- ❏ Adrenal medulla
- ❏ Anterior pituitary
- ❏ Hypothalamus
- ❏ Ovary
- ❏ Pancreas
- ❏ Pancreatic islet
- ❏ Parathyroid glands
- ❏ Pineal gland
- ❏ Posterior pituitary
- ❏ Testis
- ❏ Thymus

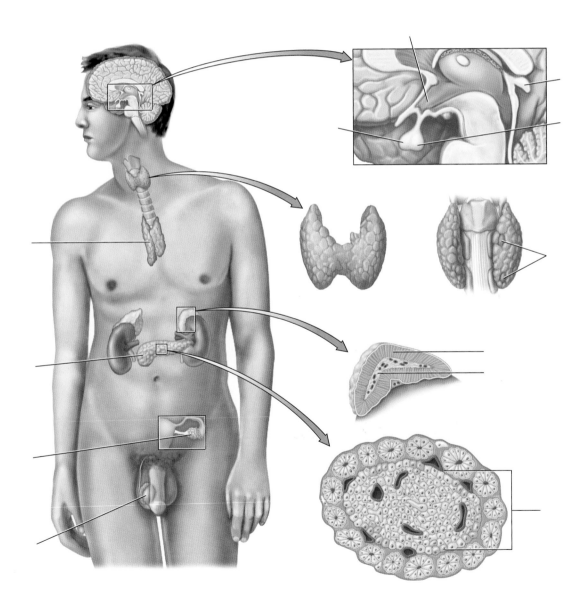

FIGURE **16.11** Organs and tissues of the endocrine system.

2 A hormone exerts its effects by

a. binding to receptors on the plasma membranes of target cells and triggering a change inside the cell.

b. binding to receptors in the cytosol of target cells and triggering a change inside the cell.

c. binding to the glycocalyx and triggering cell-cell adhesion.

d. Both a and b are correct.

e. Both a and c are correct.

3 The hypothalamic-hypophyseal portal system connects the

a. hypothalamus and pineal gland.

b. anterior pituitary gland and posterior pituitary gland.

c. posterior pituitary gland and hypothalamus.

d. anterior pituitary gland and hypothalamus.

4 *True/False:* Mark the following statements as true (T) or false (F). If the statement is false, correct it to make it a true statement.

_____ a. Glucagon triggers actions that raise the concentration of glucose in the blood.

_____ b. The thyroid gland produces thyroxine, triiodothyronine, and parathyroid hormone.

_____ c. The thymus gland produces hormones that regulate the metabolic rate.

_____ d. Aldosterone triggers actions that raise the concentration of calcium ions in the blood.

_____ e. The posterior pituitary produces oxytocin and antidiuretic hormone.

5 Label Figure 16.12 with the following terms.

❏ Colloid

❏ Follicle cells

❏ Isthmus

❏ Left lobe of the thyroid gland

❏ Parafollicular cells

❏ Right lobe of the thyroid gland

❏ Thyroid follicle

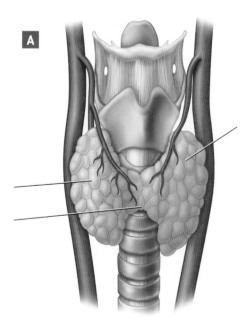
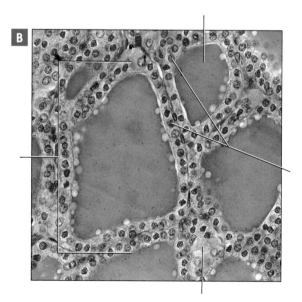

FIGURE **16.12** Thyroid gland: (**A**) illustration; (**B**) photomicrograph.

6 Pairs of hormones with opposite actions are known as

    a. antagonists.

    b. synergists.

    c. co-hormones.

    d. catecholamines.

7 Which of the following organs consists of modified postsynaptic sympathetic neurons?

    a. Anterior pituitary.

    b. Parathyroid glands.

    c. Adrenal cortex.

    d. Adrenal medulla.

8 *Matching:* Match the following hormones with their main action(s).

_____ Cortisol	A. Triggers uterine contraction and milk ejection
_____ Calcitonin	B. Promotes maturation of T lymphocytes
	C. Promotes sleep in response to a low light level
_____ Thymosin	D. Main hormone of the stress response
_____ Growth hormone	E. Promotes sperm cell production, greater bone and muscle mass, and facial hair development
_____ Oxytocin	F. Stimulates muscle development and longitudinal bone growth
_____ Antidiuretic hormone	G. Decreases blood calcium ion concentration
_____ Melatonin	H. Stimulates the retention of water from the kidneys
_____ Testosterone	

16

9 Which of the following is true regarding endocrine organ histology?

    a. The thyroid gland contains calcitonin-secreting follicle cells.

    b. The pancreas has an exocrine portion consisting of pancreatic acinar cells and an endocrine portion consisting of pancreatic islets.

    c. The adrenal medulla has three zones of cells that secrete steroid hormones.

    d. The adrenal cortex is modified nervous tissue of the parasympathetic nervous system.

10 What are the key differences between a negative feedback loop and a positive feedback loop?

Check Your Understanding

Critical Thinking and Application Questions

1 Hormones travel through the blood, allowing them to reach nearly every cell in the body. However, each hormone has effects only on certain cells. Explain.

2 Hitesh learns that his body produces a defective form of ADH that doesn't function properly. What symptoms would you expect Hitesh to be experiencing?

3 Tanisha's parents bring her to the doctor due to concern over her slow growth rate. Tanisha is 8 years old and has always been several inches shorter than her peers. You order bloodwork and discover her growth hormone level is very low.

   a How does this explain her slow growth? Could this be causing other problems, as well?

   b You prescribe synthetic growth hormone for Tanisha. Will this increase her height? Would it still increase her height if she were 28 years old instead of 8? Why or why not?

4 Some blood pressure drugs work by blocking the actions of aldosterone. What sort of negative side effects might result from the use of such drugs?

5 In the condition *hypothyroidism*, patients have a decreased concentration of both T3 and T4 in the blood. Do you think the negative feedback loops would lead to higher TSH secretion or lower TSH secretion? Explain.

6 The secretion of insulin is regulated by a negative feedback loop. Predict the effects on the body if it were instead regulated by a positive feedback loop.

7 In Case 2 of Exercise 16-4 (p. 450), we saw that Ms. Blanc had excess parathyroid hormone (PTH), leading to bone pain and fractures. Interestingly, in the opposite condition—*hypoparathyroidism*—we may also see bone pain and fractures. Considering the function of parathyroid hormone, explain this finding.

The Cardiovascular System, Part I: The Heart

UNIT 17

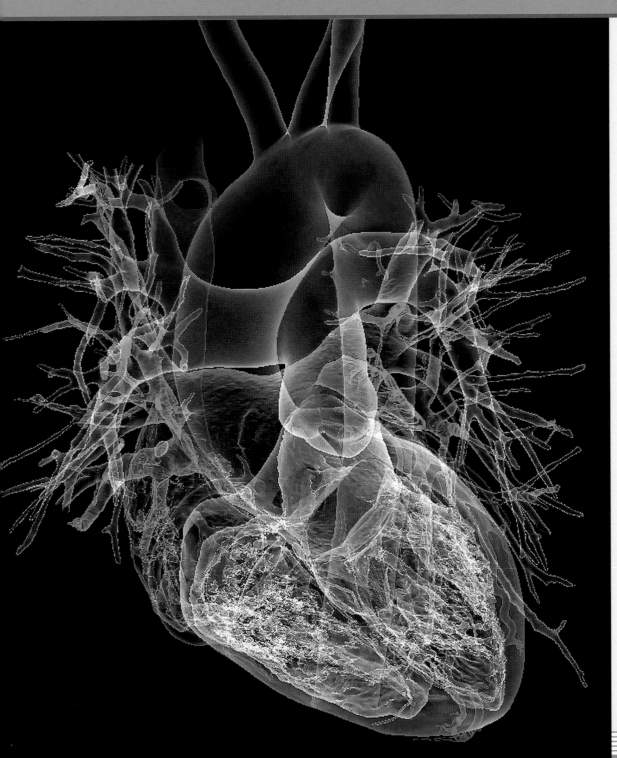

When you have completed this unit, you should be able to:

1 Describe and identify structures of the heart.

2 Trace the pathway of blood flow through the heart and lungs.

3 Describe the histology of cardiac muscle tissue.

PRE-LAB EXERCISES

Complete the following exercises prior to coming to lab, using your lab manual and textbook for reference.

PRE-LAB

17-1 Key Terms

You should be familiar with the following terms before coming to lab.

Term	Definition

Layers of the Heart Wall

Pericardium _____

Pericardial cavity _____

Myocardium _____

Endocardium _____

Structures of the Heart

Atria (right and left) _____

Ventricles (right and left) _____

Tricuspid valve _____

Mitral (bicuspid) valve _____

Pulmonary valve _____

Aortic valve _____

Chordae tendineae _____

Papillary muscles _____

Great Vessels

Superior vena cava _____

_____

Inferior vena cava _____

_____

Pulmonary trunk _____

_____

Pulmonary veins _____

_____

Aorta _____

_____

PRE-LAB

17-2 **Anatomy of the Thoracic Cavity**

Color the structures of the thoracic cavity in Figure 17.1, and label them with the terms from Exercise 17-1 (p. 463). Use your text and Exercise 17-1 in this unit for reference.

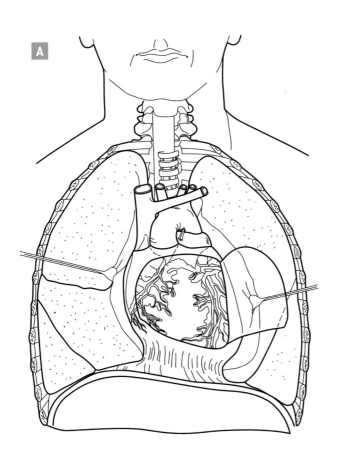

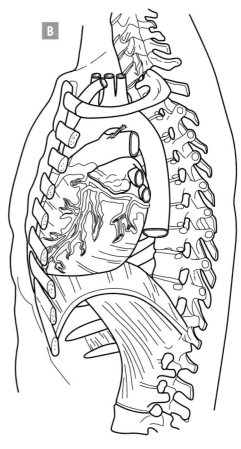

17

FIGURE **17.1** Thoracic cavity: (**A**) anterior view; (**B**) left lateral view.

17-3
Anatomy of the Heart

Color the two views of the heart in Figure 17.2, and label them with the terms from Exercise 17-1 (p. 463). Use your text and Exercise 17-1 in this unit for reference.

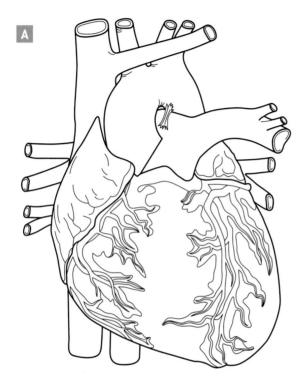

A

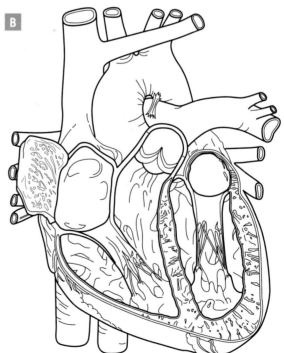

B

FIGURE **17.2** Heart: (**A**) anterior view; (**B**) frontal dissection.

EXERCISES

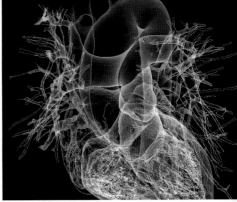

The **cardiovascular system** transports oxygen, nutrients, wastes, other solutes, and cells throughout the body. We now begin our exploration of the cardiovascular system with the pump that drives it—the heart. The heart is a remarkable organ, tirelessly beating more than 100,000 times per day to pump more than 8,000 L of blood around the body. In this unit, we examine the anatomy of this remarkable organ, including the blood flow through the heart and the histology of cardiac muscle.

3D computed tomography scan of a heart.

EXERCISE 17-1

MATERIALS

- ❏ Anatomical models and diagrams:
  - ▪ heart
  - ▪ torso
- ❏ Preserved heart
- ❏ Dissection equipment
- ❏ Dissection tray
- ❏ Blue and red water-soluble marking pens
- ❏ Laminated outline of the heart and lungs
- ❏ Colored pencils

Anatomy of the Heart

The heart is located in the *mediastinum* and is, on average, about the size of a fist (Fig. 17.3A). Its **apex** is its pointy inferior tip, and its **base** is its flattened posterior side (Fig. 17.3B). The heart is composed of four chambers: the small, superior *right* and *left atria*, and the larger, inferior *right* and *left ventricles*. The chambers are separated visually by grooves on the heart's surface: The **atrioventricular sulcus** (ay-tree-oh-ven-TRIK-yoo-lur) is between the atria and ventricles, and the **interventricular sulcus** is between the two ventricles.

As you can see in Figure 17.4, the heart is surrounded by a double-layered membrane called the **pericardium** (pehr-ee-KAR-dee-um; *peri-* = "around;" *card-* = "heart"). The outermost layer of the pericardium, called the **fibrous pericardium**, anchors the heart to surrounding structures. It is made of dense irregular connective tissue that is not very distensible, which helps to prevent the heart from overfilling. The inner layer, called the **serous pericardium**, is itself composed of two layers. The outer portion, called the **parietal pericardium**, is functionally fused to the fibrous pericardium. Notice that, at the edges of the heart, the parietal pericardium folds over on itself to attach to the heart muscle. Here it forms the inner layer of the serous membrane called the **visceral pericardium**, which is also known as the *epicardium*. Between the parietal and visceral layers, we find a thin layer of serous fluid that occupies a narrow potential space called the **pericardial cavity**. The fluid within the pericardial cavity helps the heart to beat with minimal friction.

The heart itself is an organ that consists of three tissue layers:

1. **Epicardium.** The **epicardium** (ep-ih-KAR-dee-um; *epi-* = "on top"), or visceral pericardium, is the outermost layer of the heart wall. It consists of a layer of simple squamous epithelial tissue and loose connective tissue.

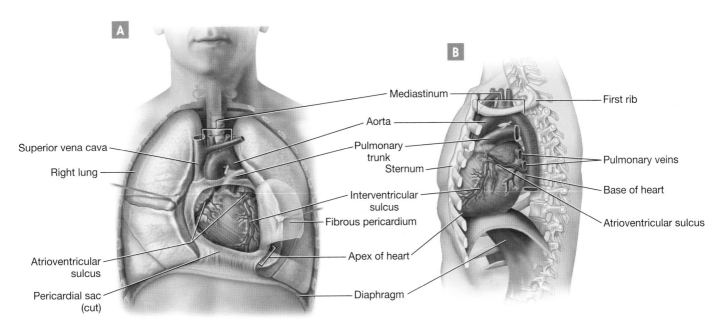

FIGURE **17.3** Thoracic cavity: (**A**) anterior view; (**B**) left lateral view.

Labels, A (anterior view): Superior vena cava · Right lung · Atrioventricular sulcus · Pericardial sac (cut) · Mediastinum · Aorta · Pulmonary trunk · Interventricular sulcus · Fibrous pericardium · Apex of heart · Diaphragm

Labels, B (left lateral view): First rib · Pulmonary veins · Base of heart · Atrioventricular sulcus · Mediastinum · Sternum · Diaphragm

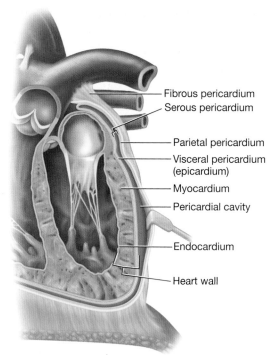

FIGURE **17.4** Layers of the heart wall.

2. **Myocardium.** The middle **myocardium** (my-oh-KAR-dee-um; *my-* = "muscle") is the actual muscle of the heart. It consists of cardiac muscle tissue and its fibrous skeleton.

3. **Endocardium.** The innermost **endocardium** (in-doh-KAR-dee-um; *endo-* = "within") is a type of simple squamous epithelium called *endothelium*. It is continuous with the endothelium lining all blood vessels in the body.

Let's now look at the external anatomy of the heart, which is shown in Figure 17.5. As you can see in the figure, the atria receive blood from *veins*, which are vessels bringing blood to the heart. The ventricles eject blood into *arteries*, which carry blood away from the heart. The vessels entering and exiting the heart are the largest in the body, and so are called **great vessels.** There are four kinds of great vessels:

1. **Superior and inferior venae cavae.** The **superior vena cava** (VEE-nah KAY-vah; "hollow vein") is a large vein that drains deoxygenated blood from structures located, in general, above the diaphragm muscle. In contrast, the **inferior vena cava** drains structures located, in general, below the diaphragm muscle. Both empty into the right atrium. These veins drain a group of blood vessels collectively called the **systemic circuit.** In these vessels, oxygen and nutrients are delivered to cells by *systemic arteries* and deoxygenated blood is returned to the heart by *systemic veins*.

2. **Pulmonary trunk.** The **pulmonary trunk** (PUL-muh-nehr-ee; *pulmon-* = "lung") is a large artery that exits from the right ventricle. Shortly after it forms, it splits into **right** and **left pulmonary arteries,** which deliver deoxygenated blood to the lungs through a series of vessels collectively called the **pulmonary circuit.** Within the pulmonary circuit, gases are exchanged, and the blood becomes oxygenated.

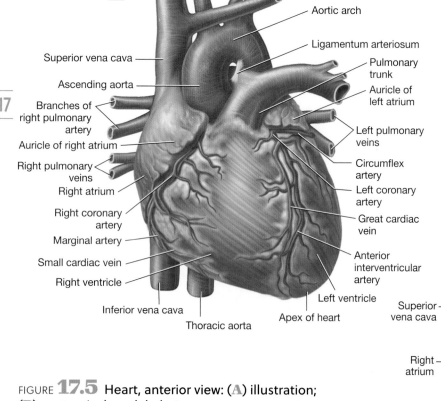

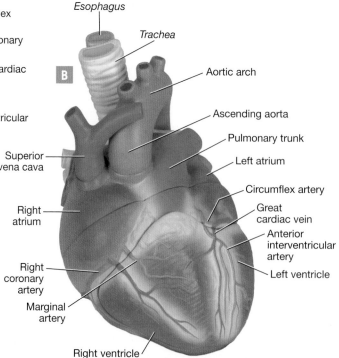

FIGURE **17.5** Heart, anterior view: (**A**) illustration; (**B**) anatomical model photo.

3. **Pulmonary veins.** The **pulmonary veins** are the portion of the pulmonary circuit that brings oxygenated blood back to the heart. There are generally four pulmonary veins, and they empty into the left atrium.

4. **Aorta.** The large **aorta** (ay-OHR-tah) is the first and largest artery of the systemic circuit. It stems from the left ventricle, after which it branches repeatedly to deliver oxygenated blood to the body's cells. Notice in Figure 17.5A there is a fibrous band called the **ligamentum arteriosum** (lig-uh-MEN-tum ahr-teer-ee-OH-sum) that connects the pulmonary trunk and the aorta. This is a remnant of a structure present in the fetal heart—the *ductus arteriosus*. The ductus arteriosus is a "bridge" between the pulmonary trunk and the aorta that diverts blood from the lungs and shunts it to the systemic circulation instead. This prevents blood pressure from becoming too high in the immature fetal lungs.

The other set of blood vessels visible on the external surface of the heart are the vessels collectively called the **coronary circulation** (KOHR-oh-nehr-ee). The **coronary arteries** branch off the base of the aorta and bring oxygenated blood to the cells of the myocardium. The myocardium is drained by a set of **cardiac veins**. The first coronary artery, the **right coronary artery**, travels along the right side of the atrioventricular sulcus. It branches into the **right marginal artery**, which serves the lateral part of the right atrium and right ventricle, and the **posterior interventricular artery**, which serves the posterior heart (see Fig. 17.6).

The other coronary artery is the **left coronary artery**, which splits into two branches shortly after it forms. Its first branch is the **anterior interventricular artery** (also known as the *left anterior descending artery*), which travels along the interventricular sulcus to supply the anterior heart. Its second branch is the **circumflex artery** (SIR-kum-flex), which travels in the left side of the atrioventricular sulcus to supply the left atrium and posterior left ventricle. When a coronary artery is blocked, the reduced blood flow to the myocardium causes a situation known as *myocardial ischemia*. Severe blockage may result in hypoxic injury and death to the tissue, a condition termed **myocardial infarction** (commonly called a heart attack).

The anatomy of the cardiac veins often varies from person to person, but the following three main veins generally are present: (1) the **small cardiac vein**, which drains the right inferolateral heart; (2) the **middle cardiac vein**, which drains the posterior heart; and (3) the **great cardiac vein**, which drains most of the left side of the heart. All three veins drain into the large **coronary sinus** located on the posterior right atrium, as seen in Figure 17.6. The coronary sinus drains into the right atrium.

On a dissection of the heart, as shown in Figure 17.7, we can see that the atria and ventricles are divided by muscular walls called *septa*. Between the two ventricles is the thick **interventricular septum**; the **interatrial septum** (in-ter-AY-tree-uhl) is the thin wall between the two atria. Notice the interatrial septum has a small dent in it called the **fossa ovalis** (FAHS-uh oh-VAL-is), which is another remnant of a fetal heart structure—a hole called the *foramen ovale*. The foramen ovale is a shunt that sends some blood entering the right atrium directly into left atrium, bypassing the immature fetal lungs.

Let's now look more closely at the heart's four chambers.

1. **Right atrium.** The **right atrium** (AY-tree-um) is the superior right chamber. It receives deoxygenated blood from the body's main veins—the superior vena

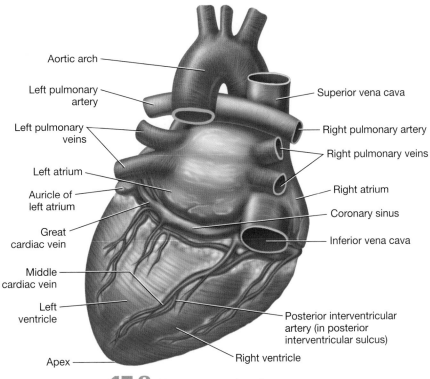

FIGURE **17.6** Heart, posterior view.

Aortic arch
Left pulmonary artery
Left pulmonary veins
Left atrium
Auricle of left atrium
Great cardiac vein
Middle cardiac vein
Left ventricle
Apex

Superior vena cava
Right pulmonary artery
Right pulmonary veins
Right atrium
Coronary sinus
Inferior vena cava
Posterior interventricular artery (in posterior interventricular sulcus)
Right ventricle

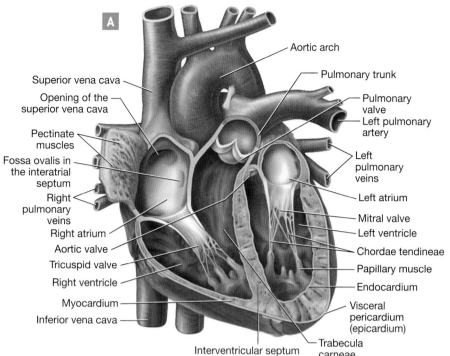

A

Aortic arch

Superior vena cava

Opening of the superior vena cava

Pectinate muscles

Fossa ovalis in the interatrial septum

Right pulmonary veins

Right atrium

Aortic valve

Tricuspid valve

Right ventricle

Myocardium

Inferior vena cava

Interventricular septum

Pulmonary trunk

Pulmonary valve

Left pulmonary artery

Left pulmonary veins

Left atrium

Mitral valve

Left ventricle

Chordae tendineae

Papillary muscle

Endocardium

Visceral pericardium (epicardium)

Trabecula carneae

FIGURE **17.7** Frontal dissection of the heart: (**A**) illustration; (**B**) anatomical model photo.

B

Ascending aorta

Superior vena cava

Opening of the superior vena cava

Right atrium

Pulmonary valve

Right coronary artery

Tricuspid valve

Chordae tendineae

Papillary muscle

Right ventricle

Apex of heart

Aortic arch

Pulmonary trunk

Left pulmonary artery

Pulmonary veins

Left atrium

Anterior interventricular artery

Mitral valve

Left ventricle

Interventricular septum

cava, the inferior vena cava, and the coronary sinus—the openings of which we find on the right atrium's posterior side. Externally, it has a large pouch called the **right auricle** (OHR-ih-kuhl) that allows the right atrium to expand and fill with more blood. Internally, the anterior surface of the right atrium is rough due to muscular ridges called **pectinate muscles** (PEK-tin-et; *pectin-* = "comb").

2. **Right ventricle.** The **right ventricle** is a wide, crescent-shaped, thin-walled chamber inferior to the right atrium, from which it receives deoxygenated blood. It ejects blood into a vessel called the **pulmonary trunk.** Internally, its surface contains ridge-like protrusions of cardiac muscle called **trabeculae carneae** (trah-BEK-yoo-lee kar-NEE-ee; "fleshy beams"). One prominent trabecula is the **moderator band** (or **septomarginal trabecula**), which stretches from the interventricular septum to the base of the anterior papillary muscle (visible in Fig. 17.11). It carries part of the cardiac conduction system (see Exercise 19-5, p. 528) from the septum to the papillary muscle, which helps to coordinate right ventricular contraction.

3. **Left atrium.** The superior left chamber is the **left atrium.** It receives oxygenated blood returning from the pulmonary circuit via four **pulmonary veins.** Externally, it has a **left auricle**, although it is much smaller than the right auricle. Internally, its surface is mostly smooth and it lacks pectinate muscles.

4. **Left ventricle.** The **left ventricle** is a thick, long, circular chamber that receives oxygenated blood from the left atrium and pumps it into the aorta. Notice in the figure that the left ventricle is considerably thicker than the right ventricle. This reflects the fact that the pressure is much higher in the systemic circuit than it is in the pulmonary circuit. The higher pressure requires the left ventricle to pump harder, and so it has greater muscle mass and is thicker. Like the right ventricle, trabeculae carneae line the left ventricle's internal surface.

To ensure that blood in the heart flows only in a single direction, we have structures called **valves** (Figs. 17.7 and 17.8). There are two types of valves in the heart. First are the valves between the atria and ventricles, which are called **atrioventricular valves.** The three-cusped **tricuspid valve** is between the right atrium and right ventricle, and the two-cusped **mitral** (MY-truhl) or **bicuspid valve** is between the left atrium and left ventricle. Each cusp of the atrioventricular valves is attached to collagenous "strings" called **chordae tendineae** (KOHR-dee tin-din-EE-ee; "tendinous cords"), which are themselves attached to muscles within the ventricular wall called **papillary muscles**. When the ventricles contract, the papillary muscles pull the chordae tendineae taut, which puts tension on the cusps and prevents them from everting into the atria, a condition called *prolapse*.

Second are the valves between the ventricles and their arteries, which are called **semilunar valves** (sem-ee-LOON-uhr; "half-moon"). The **pulmonary valve** sits between the right ventricle and the pulmonary trunk, and the **aortic valve** sits between the left ventricle and the aorta. Note that there are no chordae tendineae or papillary muscles attached to the semilunar valves.

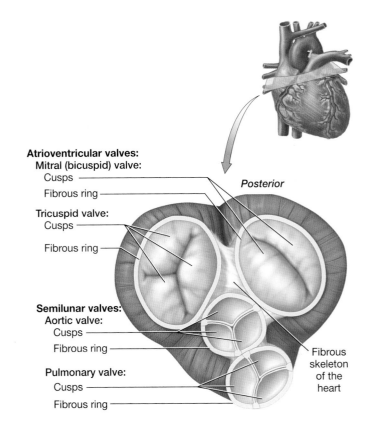

FIGURE **17.8** Transverse section of the heart showing all four valves.

	PROCEDURE
1	Model Inventory for the Heart

Identify the following structures of the heart on models and diagrams, using your textbook and this unit for reference. As you examine the anatomical models and diagrams, record the name of the model and the structures you were able to identify on the model inventory in Table 17.1. When you have completed the activity, answer Check Your Understanding Questions 1 through 3 (pp. 479–480).

1. General structures
   a. Mediastinum
   b. Apex of the heart
   c. Base of the heart
   d. Atrioventricular sulcus
   e. Interventricular sulcus
   f. Pericardium
      (1) Fibrous pericardium
      (2) Serous pericardium
         (a) Parietal pericardium
         (b) Visceral pericardium (epicardium)
         (c) Pericardial cavity
   g. Myocardium
   h. Endocardium
2. Great vessels
   a. Superior vena cava
   b. Inferior vena cava
   c. Pulmonary trunk
   d. Right and left pulmonary arteries

   e. Pulmonary veins
   f. Aorta
3. Coronary arteries
   a. Right coronary artery
   b. Right marginal artery
   c. Posterior interventricular artery
   d. Left coronary artery
   e. Anterior interventricular artery
   f. Circumflex artery
4. Cardiac veins
   a. Small cardiac vein
   b. Middle cardiac vein
   c. Great cardiac vein
   d. Coronary sinus
5. Interatrial septum
   a. Fossa ovalis
6. Interventricular septum
7. Right atrium
   a. Opening of the superior vena cava

   b. Opening of the inferior vena cava
   c. Opening of the coronary sinus
   d. Right auricle
   e. Pectinate muscles
8. Right ventricle
   a. Trabeculae carneae
9. Left atrium
   a. Left auricle
   b. Openings of the pulmonary veins
10. Left ventricle
    a. Trabeculae carneae
11. Atrioventricular valves
    a. Tricuspid valve
    b. Mitral valve
    c. Chordae tendineae
    d. Papillary muscles
12. Semilunar valves
    a. Pulmonary valve
    b. Aortic valve

TABLE **17.1** Model Inventory for the Heart

Model/Diagram	Structures Identified

2 **PROCEDURE**
Time to Draw

17 In the space provided here and on the next page, draw, color, and label one of the heart models that you examined. Draw both the anterior view and the frontal dissection. In addition, write the function of each structure that you label.

3 **PROCEDURE**

Dissecting the Heart

Now, you'll examine a preserved heart or a fresh heart. Follow the procedure as provided to find the structures you just studied on models. When you have completed the dissection, answer Check Your Understanding Question 4 (p. 480).

⚠ **SAFETY NOTE**

Safety glasses and gloves are required!

1   Orient yourself by first determining the superior aspect and the inferior aspect of the heart. The superior aspect of the heart is the broad end, and the inferior aspect (apex) is the pointy tip. Now, orient yourself to the anterior and posterior sides. The easiest way to do this is to locate the pulmonary trunk—the vessel directly in the middle of the anterior side. Find the side from which the pulmonary trunk originates, and you will be on the anterior side, which you can see in Figure 17.9. Locate the following structures:

- a. parietal pericardium (may not be attached)
- b. visceral pericardium (shiny layer over the surface of the heart)
- c. aorta
- d. pulmonary trunk
- e. superior vena cava
- f. inferior vena cava
- g. pulmonary veins
- h. ventricles
- i. atria

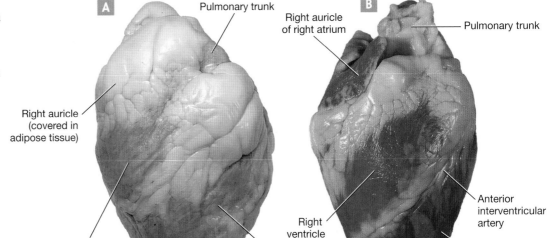

FIGURE **17.9** Anterior view of a sheep heart: (**A**) preserved heart; (**B**) fresh heart.

2 Locate the superior vena cava. Insert scissors or a scalpel into the superior vena cava and cut down into the right atrium. Before moving on to Step 3, note the structure of the tricuspid valve, and draw it in the space provided. How many flaps do you see? What is the function of this valve?

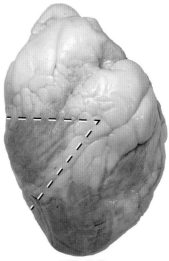

FIGURE **17.10** Cutting a "flap" in the right ventricle of a preserved heart.

3 Now, you will cut a flap into the right ventricle, as pictured in Figure 17.10. When your cut is complete, open the flap you've created to see inside the right ventricle, which is shown in Figure 17.11. Structures to locate include the following:

a. tricuspid valve
b. chordae tendineae
c. papillary muscles
d. myocardium
e. endocardium (shiny layer on the inside of the heart)
f. moderator band

4 Next, insert the scissors into the pulmonary trunk. Note the structure of the pulmonary valve, and draw it in the space provided to the right. How does it differ structurally from the tricuspid valve? What is the function of this valve?

17

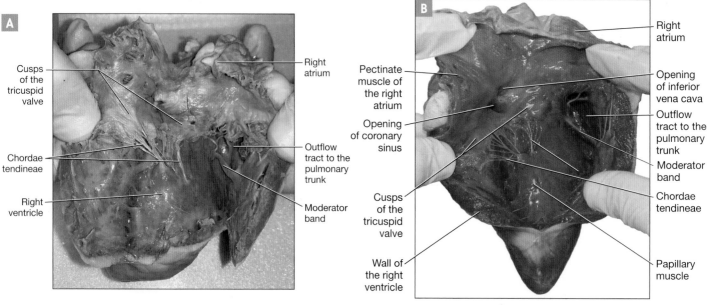

FIGURE **17.11** Right ventricle of a sheep heart: (**A**) preserved heart; (**B**) fresh heart.

5 Insert the scissors into a pulmonary vein. Cut down into the left atrium. Note the structure of the mitral valve, and draw it in the space provided. What is the function of this valve? How does its structure differ from that of the pulmonary and tricuspid valves?

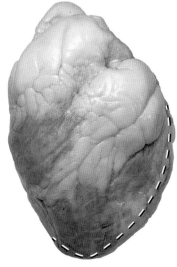

6 Now you'll cut a flap into the left ventricle, as shown in Figure 17.12. When your cut is complete, open the flap you've created to see inside the left ventricle, which is shown in Figure 17.13. Note the thickness of the left ventricle. How does it compare with the thickness of the right ventricle? Why is there a difference?

FIGURE **17.12** Cutting a "flap" in the left ventricle of a preserved heart.

7 Insert the scissors into the aorta. Extend the cut until you can see the aortic valve. Draw the aortic valve in the space provided. Is it structurally more similar to the pulmonary valve or the mitral valve? What is the function of this valve?

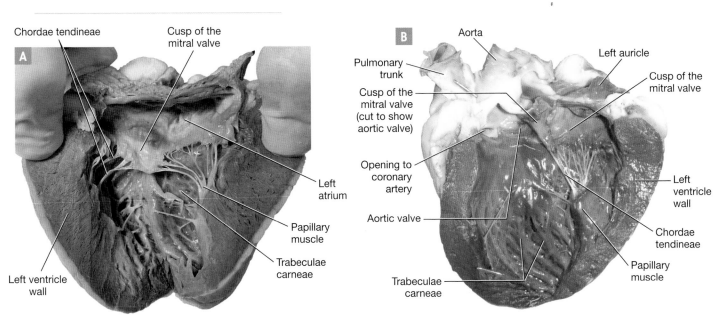

FIGURE **17.13** Left ventricle of a sheep heart: (**A**) preserved heart; (**B**) fresh heart.

Now that you've learned the parts of the heart, put the pieces together and trace the pattern of blood as it flows through the heart and lungs. First, write out the entire pathway, beginning with the main systemic veins that drain into the heart and ending with the main systemic artery into which the heart pumps. Don't forget to include the valves in your tracing. Then, use water-soluble markers and a laminated outline of the heart to draw the pathway of blood as it flows through the heart and pulmonary circulation. Use a blue marker to indicate areas that contain deoxygenated blood and a red marker to indicate areas that contain oxygenated blood. If no laminated outline is available, use colored pencils and Figure 17.14. When you have completed the activity, answer Check Your Understanding Question 5 (p. 480).

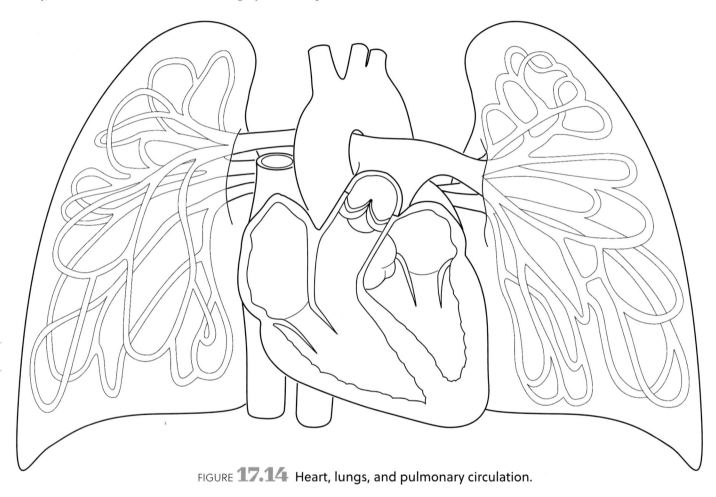

17

FIGURE **17.14** Heart, lungs, and pulmonary circulation.

Start: Inferior/Superior Venae Cavae → _____ atrium → _____ valve →

_____ → _____ valve →

_____ → _____ artery →

_____ capillaries → the blood exchanges the gas _____ for the gas

_____ → _____ veins → _____ atrium

→ _____ valve → _____ →

_____ valve → **End: Aorta**

MATERIALS

❑ Slide: cardiac muscle
tissue

❑ Light microscope

❑ Colored pencils

Cardiac Muscle Histology

Recall from Unit 5 (p. 109) that cardiac muscle tissue is striated like skeletal muscle tissue but otherwise is quite different (Fig. 17.15). Following are some important structural differences:

- Cells of cardiac muscle, known as **cardiac myocytes**, are shorter, wider, and branched, whereas skeletal muscle fibers are long, thin, and unbranched.

- Cardiac muscle cells typically are uninucleate, although some have multiple nuclei. The nucleus is generally located near the center of the cell.

- These cells contain specialized adaptations called **intercalated discs** (in-TER-kuh-lay-t'd) that appear as dark lines parallel to the striations. These discs contain desmosomes and gap junctions that hold adjacent cardiac cells tightly together to allow the cells to communicate chemically and electrically. This adaptation is important to the heart's function: For a heart contraction to occur, all cells of the atria must contract simultaneously as a unit, and then all cells of the ventricles must contract simultaneously as a unit. Contrast this with skeletal muscles, in which the number of muscle fibers that contract is proportional to the strength of the contraction.

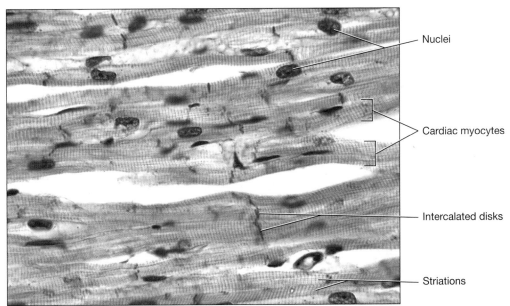

FIGURE **17.15** Cardiac muscle tissue, photomicrograph.

Functionally, skeletal and cardiac muscle tissues have differences, as well. Recall that skeletal muscle cells must be stimulated by a neuron to contract. Cardiac myocytes, however, are *autorhythmic*, meaning they require no external stimulation. Instead, a population of cells within the heart known as *pacemaker cells* depolarizes automatically, setting the rate and rhythm for the heartbeat.

PROCEDURE
Examining Cardiac Muscle Tissue with Microscopy

Examine a prepared slide of cardiac muscle tissue on high power. Use colored pencils to draw what you see, and label the listed structures. When you have completed the activity, answer Check Your Understanding Question 6 (p. 480).

- Cardiac myocyte
- Intercalated discs
- Striations
- Nucleus

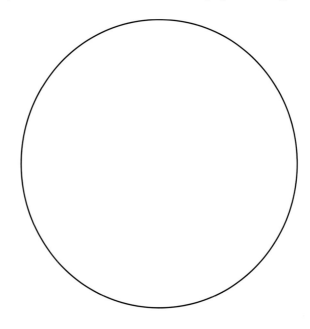

Check Your Recall

1 Label the following parts of the heart on Figure 17.16.

- ❏ Aorta
- ❏ Auricle of right atrium
- ❏ Circumflex artery
- ❏ Coronary sinus
- ❏ Inferior vena cava
- ❏ Left atrium
- ❏ Ligamentum arteriosum
- ❏ Posterior interventricular artery
- ❏ Pulmonary trunk
- ❏ Pulmonary veins
- ❏ Right coronary artery
- ❏ Superior vena cava

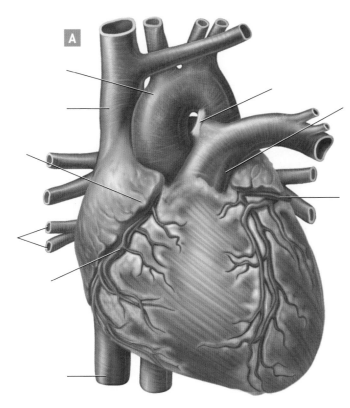

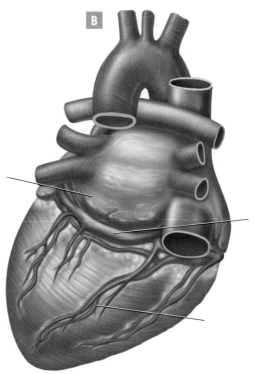

FIGURE **17.16** Heart: (**A**) anterior view;
(**B**) posterior view.

2 Label the following parts of
   the heart on Figure 17.17.
   ❏ Aortic valve
   ❏ Chordae tendineae
   ❏ Fossa ovalis
   ❏ Interventricular septum
   ❏ Mitral valve
   ❏ Papillary muscle
   ❏ Pectinate muscles
   ❏ Pulmonary valve
   ❏ Tricuspid valve

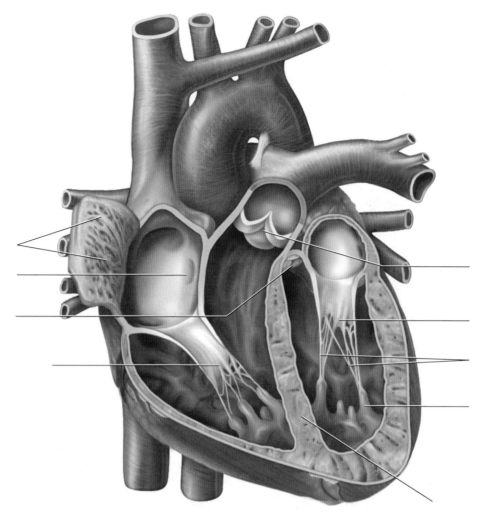

FIGURE **17.17** Frontal dissection of the heart.

3 Label the following parts of the heart on Figure 17.18.
   ❏ Endocardium
   ❏ Fibrous pericardium
   ❏ Myocardium
   ❏ Parietal pericardium
   ❏ Pericardial cavity
   ❏ Visceral pericardium

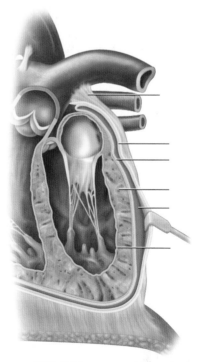

FIGURE **17.18** Layers of the heart wall.

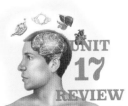

4 *Matching:* Match the following terms with the correct definition.

_____ Endocardium

_____ Parietal pericardium

_____ Tricuspid valve

_____ Aortic valve

_____ Trabeculae carneae

_____ Pulmonary veins

_____ Mitral valve

_____ Visceral pericardium

_____ Pulmonary arteries

_____ Pulmonary valve

A. Structure located between the right atrium and the right ventricle
B. Bring(s) oxygenated blood to the left atrium from the lungs
C. Inner layer of the serous pericardium
D. Structure located between the left atrium and left ventricle
E. Structure located between the right ventricle and the pulmonary trunk
F. Outer layer of the serous pericardium
G. Inner layer of the heart composed of endothelium
H. Muscular ridges in the wall of the right ventricle
I. Bring(s) deoxygenated blood to the lungs
J. Structure located between the left ventricle and the aorta

5 How do the arteries of the systemic circuit and pulmonary circuit differ functionally?

_____

_____

17

6 The pulmonary trunk
a. receives blood from the left ventricle and delivers it to the body.
b. receives blood from the lungs and delivers it to the left atrium.
c. receives blood from the left ventricle and delivers it to the lungs.
d. receives blood from the right ventricle and delivers it to the lungs.

7 The _____ _____ is a remnant of a hole in the interatrial septum of the fetal heart.
a. ductus arteriosus
b. foramen ovale
c. fossa ovalis
d. ligamentum arteriosum

8 Which of the following branches of the left coronary artery supplies the left atrium and posterior left ventricle?
a. Circumflex artery.
b. Anterior interventricular artery.
c. Marginal artery.
d. Posterior interventricular artery.

9 Which of the following vessels transports oxygenated blood?

   a. Superior vena cava.

   b. Pulmonary vein.

   c. Pulmonary artery.

   d. Coronary sinus.

10 What are the functions of intercalated discs?

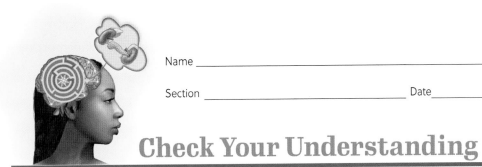

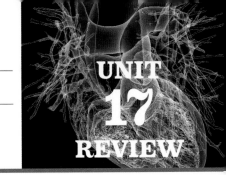

Check Your Understanding

Critical Thinking and Application Questions

1 The condition *mitral valve stenosis* is characterized by narrowing and hardening of the mitral valve, which decreases the amount of blood pumped through it.

  a Predict systemic consequences of mitral valve stenosis. Explain your reasoning. _____

  _____

  _____

  _____

  b How could mitral valve stenosis affect the blood pressure in the pulmonary circuit? Explain. _____

  _____

  _____

  _____

2 Jaina was born with a condition called *dextro-transposition of the great arteries*, in which her aorta arises from her right ventricle and her pulmonary trunk arises from her left ventricle.

  a What is the normal arrangement of great arteries? _____

  _____

  b Why might the arrangement of vessels in Jaina's case cause problems? _____

  _____

  _____

  c Predict the symptoms Jaina will experience if the vessel transposition is not corrected. _____

  _____

  _____

3 Ms. F. visited her physician for a routine physical. During the exam, she explained that over the last two weeks, she had been feeling much more tired than normal and occasionally felt short of breath. Knowing that women usually present with atypical symptoms of a heart attack, her physician ran some diagnostic tests and found that Ms. F. was indeed having a heart attack.

  a Imaging studies showed that Ms. F. had blockages in both her posterior interventricular artery and her circumflex artery. What parts of the heart would be affected by these blockages?

  _____

b Ms. F.'s heart attack damaged one of her papillary muscles. What is the normal function of a papillary muscle? Will a malfunctioning papillary muscle affect the semilunar or atrioventricular valves? Explain.

4 In the heart dissection you performed, you noted that the left ventricle is thicker than the right ventricle. Why is the left ventricle thicker? What might it mean if the right ventricle were thicker than the left?

5 In the condition *patent ductus arteriosus*, the ductus arteriosus fails to close after birth and the "bridge" between the pulmonary trunk and the aorta remains open. How would this condition affect the normal pattern of blood flow? What effect would this have on the oxygenation of the blood?

6 One of the deadliest heart conditions is a disturbance in heart rhythm known as *ventricular fibrillation*, in which the myocytes of the ventricles depolarize and contract individually. How are the cells of the heart supposed to contract? (**Hint:** Think about the functions of the intercalated discs.) Why would it be deadly to have cardiac myocytes of the ventricles contracting individually?

17

The Cardiovascular System, Part II: Blood Vessel Anatomy

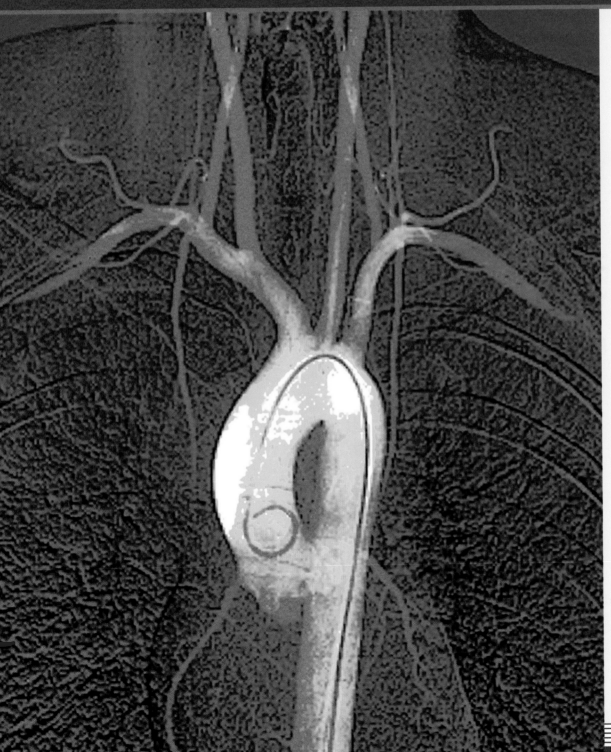

When you have completed this unit, you should be able to:

1. Describe and identify selected arteries and veins.

2. Describe the organs and regions supplied and drained by each artery and vein.

3. Describe the unique blood flow patterns through the brain and the hepatic portal system.

4. Trace the pathway of blood flow through various arterial and venous circuits.

5. Describe the histological differences between arteries and veins.

6. Palpate common pulse points and identify common locations for blood draws.

PRE-LAB EXERCISES

Complete the following exercises prior to coming to lab, using your lab manual and textbook for reference.

PRE-LAB

18-1

Arterial Anatomy

Label the arterial diagrams in Figure 18.1 with the terms from Exercise 18-1 (p. 485). Use your text and Exercise 18-1 in this unit for reference. Note that these diagrams are presented in color to facilitate identification of the vessels.

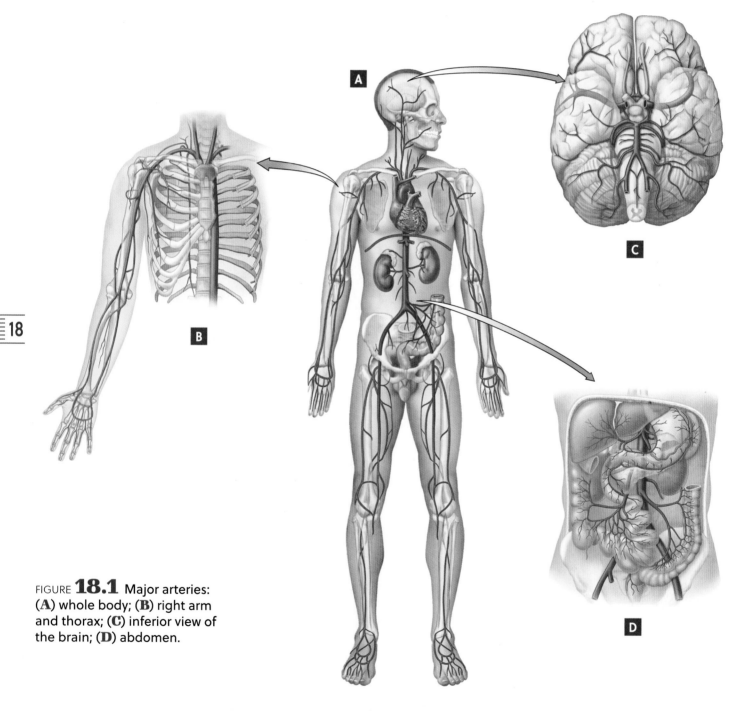

FIGURE **18.1** Major arteries:
(**A**) whole body; (**B**) right arm
and thorax; (**C**) inferior view of
the brain; (**D**) abdomen.

18

PRE-LAB

18-2 Venous Anatomy

Label the venous diagrams in Figure 18.2 with the terms from Exercise 18-2 (p. 491). Use your text and Exercise 18-2 in this unit for reference. Note that these diagrams are presented in color to facilitate identification of the vessels.

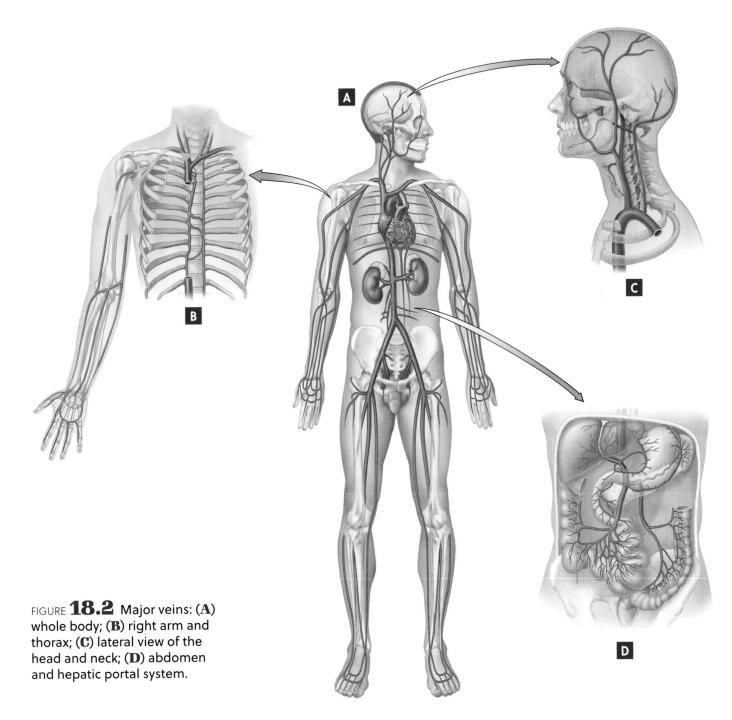

FIGURE **18.2** Major veins: (**A**) whole body; (**B**) right arm and thorax; (**C**) lateral view of the head and neck; (**D**) abdomen and hepatic portal system.

18

Arterial and Venous Anatomy

Label the model diagram in Figure 18.3 with the terms from Exercises 18-1 and 18-2 (pp. 485 and 491). Use your text and Exercises 18-1 and 18-2 in this unit for reference. Note that these diagrams are presented in color to facilitate identification of the vessels.

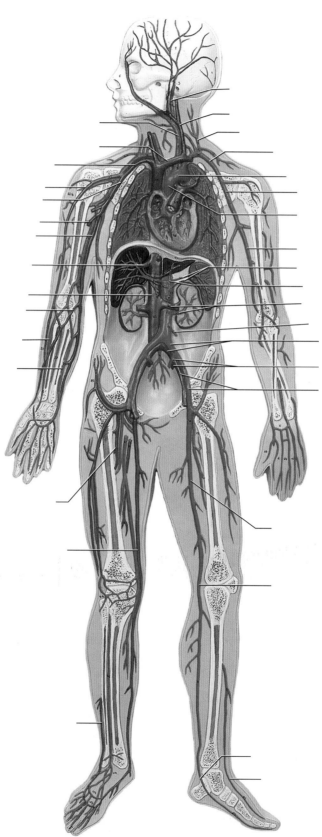

FIGURE **18.3** Arteries and veins of the body, anatomical model photo.

EXERCISES

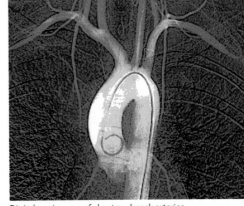

Blood vessels are a closed system of passages that transport blood around the body. The heart pumps blood away from the heart through a series of **arteries**. Arteries branch as they pass through organs and tissues to form progressively smaller vessels until they branch into tiny **capillary beds**, where gas, nutrient, and waste exchange take place. The blood is drained from the capillaries via a series of **veins** that return the blood to the heart.

Digital angiogram of chest and neck arteries.

The three major circuits of blood flow in the body are the following:

1. **Systemic.** The **systemic circuit** consists of a series of arteries that deliver oxygenated blood to capillary beds within the body's tissues, and a set of veins that return deoxygenated blood back to the heart.

2. **Coronary.** The **coronary circuit** is similar to the systemic circuit except its arteries, capillary beds, and veins supply and drain only the heart.

3. **Pulmonary.** The **pulmonary circuit** features a set of arteries that deliver deoxygenated blood to the capillary beds of the lungs, and a set of veins that return oxygenated blood to the heart.

In this unit, we will address primarily the systemic circuit, as the coronary and pulmonary circuits were discussed in Unit 17. In the upcoming exercises, you will identify the systemic circuit's major blood vessels, trace various pathways of blood flow through the body, and examine the histology of the blood vessel wall. In the final exercise, you will perform some clinical examinations of blood vessels.

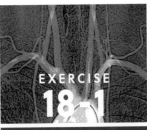

EXERCISE 18-1

MATERIALS

☐ Blood vessel anatomical models and diagrams:
  - human torsos
  - brain
  - head and neck
  - abdomen
  - upper limb
  - lower limb

Major Arteries of the Body

The systemic arterial circuit begins with the largest artery in the body, the **aorta**. An overview of the systemic arterial circuit is shown in Figure 18.4. The aorta originates from the left ventricle as the **ascending aorta,** which ascends until it curves around to form the **aortic arch**. There are three major branches off the aortic arch: the *brachiocephalic trunk*, the *left common carotid artery*, and the *left subclavian artery*. Recall that the heart is positioned in the left side of the thoracic cavity. For this reason, the first branch off the aorta, the **brachiocephalic trunk** (bray-kee-oh-seh-FAL-ik; *brach-* = "arm;" *cephal-* = "head"), veers to the right. Shortly after passing deep to the clavicle, it splits into the right common carotid and right subclavian arteries.

The arterial supply of the head and neck comes primarily from the **right** and **left common carotid arteries** (kuh-RAHT-id; Fig. 18.5). Notice that the right and left common carotid arteries have different origins—the right side branches from the brachiocephalic trunk, and the left side from the aortic arch. In the neck, these arteries branch into the internal and external carotid arteries. The **external carotid artery** gives off many branches that supply the structures of the head, neck, and face. One of its terminal branches is the large **superficial temporal artery**, which crosses the temporal bone to supply the scalp.

The **internal carotid arteries** pass through the carotid canals to enter the cranial cavity, where they give off the **ophthalmic arteries** (ahf-THAL-mik; *ophthal-* = "eye"), which supply the eyeball and structures around the orbit, and the **anterior** and **middle cerebral arteries**, which supply the brain. Notice in Figure 18.6 that the two anterior cerebral arteries are connected by a small **anterior communicating artery**. Also supplying the brain are the **vertebral arteries**, which branch from the subclavian arteries. The vertebral arteries then pass through the vertebral foramina of the cervical vertebrae and enter the cranial cavity through the foramen magnum. At the brainstem on the base of the brain, the two vertebral arteries fuse to become the single **basilar artery** (BAY-zih-lur; *bas-* = "base"), splitting again near the pituitary gland into the **posterior cerebral arteries**. These vessels give off small **posterior communicating arteries**, connecting the circulation of the basilar artery with that of the internal carotid arteries. As you can see in Figure 18.6, these vessels form a continuous structure known as the **cerebral arterial circle**. This vascular "roundabout" provides alternate routes of circulation to the brain if one of the arteries supplying the brain becomes blocked.

The arterial supply to the upper limb, shown in Figure 18.7, begins with the right and left **subclavian arteries** (sub-KLAY-vee-in; *sub-* = "beneath;" *clav-* = "clavicle"). The subclavian artery becomes the **axillary artery** near the axilla. In the arm, the

18

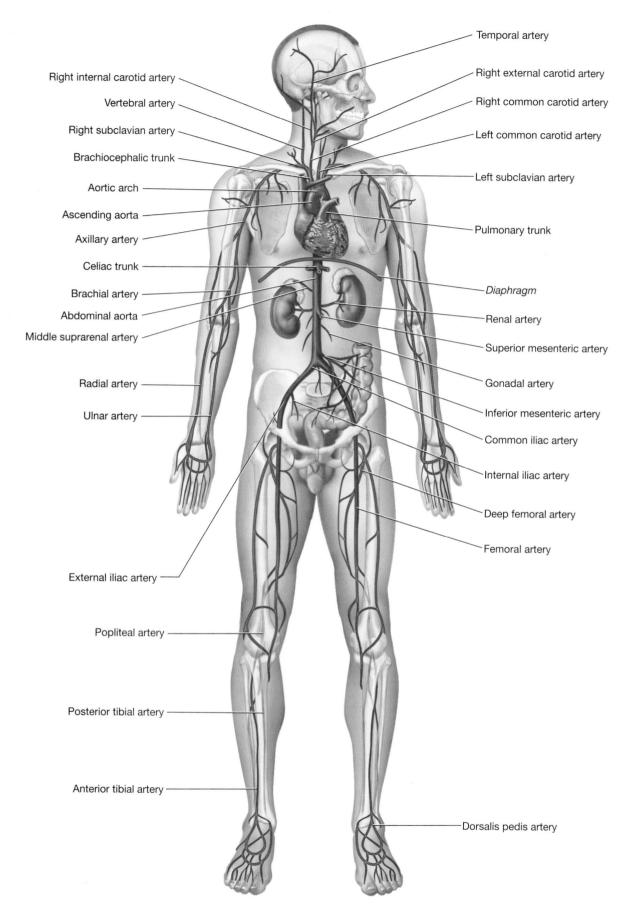

Right internal carotid artery

Vertebral artery

Right subclavian artery

Brachiocephalic trunk

Aortic arch

Ascending aorta

Axillary artery

Celiac trunk

Brachial artery

Abdominal aorta

Middle suprarenal artery

Radial artery

Ulnar artery

External iliac artery

Popliteal artery

Posterior tibial artery

Anterior tibial artery

Temporal artery

Right external carotid artery

Right common carotid artery

Left common carotid artery

Left subclavian artery

Pulmonary trunk

Diaphragm

Renal artery

Superior mesenteric artery

Gonadal artery

Inferior mesenteric artery

Common iliac artery

Internal iliac artery

Deep femoral artery

Femoral artery

Dorsalis pedis artery

FIGURE **18.4** Major arteries of the body.

18

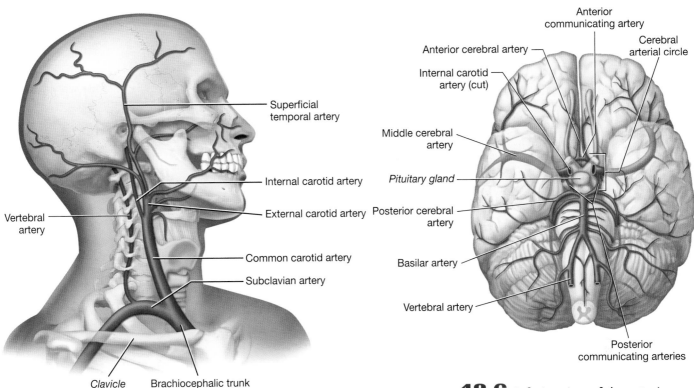

FIGURE **18.5** Arteries of the head and neck.

Labels (Figure 18.5): Superficial temporal artery; Internal carotid artery; External carotid artery; Common carotid artery; Subclavian artery; Vertebral artery; Clavicle; Brachiocephalic trunk

FIGURE **18.6** Inferior view of the arteries of the brain.

Labels (Figure 18.6): Anterior communicating artery; Anterior cerebral artery; Cerebral arterial circle; Internal carotid artery (cut); Middle cerebral artery; Pituitary gland; Posterior cerebral artery; Basilar artery; Vertebral artery; Posterior communicating arteries

axillary artery becomes the **brachial artery** (BRAY-kee-uhl), which splits into the **radial artery** and the **ulnar artery** just distal to the antecubital fossa. As you would expect, these arteries travel alongside the bones for which they are named—the radial artery is lateral and the ulnar artery is medial.

Let's now turn to the thorax and abdomen. Near the left superior sternal border, the aortic arch curves inferiorly to become the **thoracic aorta**. The thoracic aorta descends through the thoracic cavity posterior to the heart, giving off *posterior intercostal arteries*, after which it passes through the diaphragm to become the **abdominal aorta**. The six major branches of the abdominal aorta, shown in Figure 18.8, include the following:

1. **Celiac trunk**. The short, stubby **celiac trunk** (SEE-lee-ak; *celiac* = "belly") is the first branch off the abdominal aorta. It splits almost immediately into the **common hepatic artery** (*hepat-* = liver), which supplies the liver, stomach, pancreas, and duodenum (part of the small intestine); the **splenic artery** (SPLEN-ik), which supplies

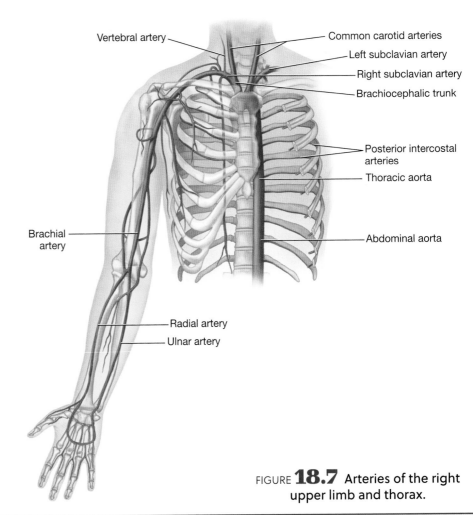

Labels (Figure 18.7): Vertebral artery; Common carotid arteries; Left subclavian artery; Right subclavian artery; Brachiocephalic trunk; Posterior intercostal arteries; Thoracic aorta; Brachial artery; Abdominal aorta; Radial artery; Ulnar artery

FIGURE **18.7** Arteries of the right upper limb and thorax.

the spleen, stomach, and pancreas; and the **left gastric artery** (*gastr-* = "stomach"), which supplies the stomach.

2. **Middle suprarenal arteries.** Just inferior to the celiac trunk are the small **middle suprarenal arteries** (soo-prah-REE-nuhl; *supra-* = "above;" *ren-* = "kidney"), which supply the adrenal glands that are located on top of the kidneys. They are seen more clearly in Figure 18.4.

3. **Renal arteries.** Inferior to the celiac trunk we find the two **renal arteries** (REE-nuhl), which serve the kidneys. Note that the kidneys are posterior to the other abdominal organs in Figure 18.7 and so the renal arteries are slightly obscured by other organs and vessels. They are also seen more clearly in Figure 18.4.

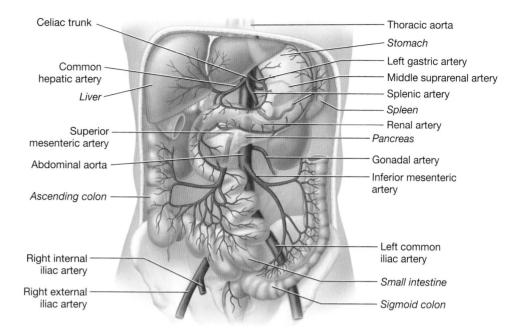

FIGURE **18.8** Arteries of the abdomen.

4. **Superior mesenteric artery.** In the same vicinity of the renal arteries is another branch called the **superior mesenteric artery** (mez-en-TEHR-ik; *mes-* = "middle;" *enter-* = "intestine"). As its name implies, it travels through the membranes of the intestines (called the *mesentery*) and supplies the small and much of the large intestine.

5. **Gonadal arteries.** Inferior to the superior mesenteric arteries we find a small pair of arteries that serve the reproductive organs, or *gonads*, and so are called the **gonadal arteries.**

6. **Inferior mesenteric artery.** The last large branch off the abdominal aorta is the **inferior mesenteric artery**, which supplies the remainder of the large intestine.

The abdominal aorta terminates by bifurcating into two **common iliac arteries** (ILL-ee-ak), which themselves bifurcate into an internal iliac artery and an external iliac artery (Figs. 18.8 and 18.9). The **internal iliac artery** supplies structures of the pelvis, and the **external iliac artery** passes deep to the inguinal ligament to enter the anterior thigh, where it becomes the **femoral artery**. In the proximal thigh, the femoral artery gives off the *deep femoral artery*, which travels posteriorly to supply the hip joint, femur, and other structures in the thigh. The femoral artery remains anterior until about midway down the thigh when it also passes posteriorly to become the **popliteal artery** (pahp-lih-TEE-uhl; named for the popliteal fossa, or the posterior knee). Just distal to the popliteal fossa, the popliteal artery divides into its two main branches: the **anterior tibial artery**, which continues in the anterior foot as the **dorsalis pedis artery** (dohr-SAL-iss PEE-diss; *ped-* = "foot"), and the **posterior tibial artery**, which curls underneath the medial malleolus and continues to the plantar surface of the foot.

Many of the models in your lab likely show both arteries and veins. For this reason, we have included a few photos of anatomical models with arteries and veins to help guide you as you do your model inventories. These photos are in Figures 18.17 through 18.19 on pp. 497–498 (after we discuss veins).

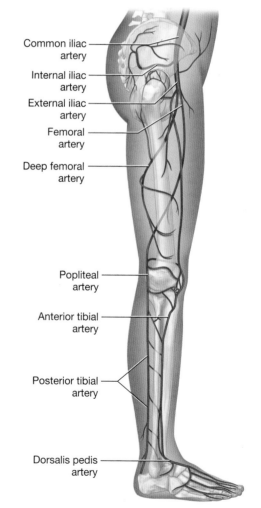

FIGURE **18.9** Lateral view of the arteries of the right lower limb.

Model Inventory for Arteries

Identify the following arteries on models and diagrams, using your textbook and this unit for reference. As you examine the anatomical models and diagrams, record in Table 18.1 the name of the model and the structures you were able to identify on the model inventory. When you have completed the activity, answer Check Your Understanding Questions 1 and 2 (p. 513).

Arteries of the Trunk

1. Aorta
   a. Ascending aorta
   b. Aortic arch
   c. Thoracic aorta
   d. Abdominal aorta
2. Brachiocephalic trunk
3. Subclavian artery
4. Celiac trunk
   a. Common hepatic artery
   b. Splenic artery
   c. Left gastric artery
5. Middle suprarenal arteries
6. Renal arteries
7. Superior mesenteric artery
8. Gonadal arteries
9. Inferior mesenteric artery
10. Common iliac artery
    a. Internal iliac artery
    b. External iliac artery
    c. Posterior tibial artery

Arteries of the Head and Neck

1. Common carotid arteries
   a. Right common carotid artery
   b. Left common carotid artery
2. External carotid artery
   a. Superficial temporal artery
3. Internal carotid artery
   a. Ophthalmic artery
   b. Anterior cerebral artery
   c. Middle cerebral artery
4. Vertebral artery
5. Basilar artery
   a. Posterior cerebral artery
6. Cerebral arterial circle
   a. Anterior communicating artery
   b. Posterior communicating arteries

Arteries of the Upper Limbs

1. Axillary artery
2. Brachial artery
3. Radial artery
4. Ulnar artery

Arteries of the Lower Limbs

1. Femoral artery
2. Popliteal artery
   a. Anterior tibial artery
      (1) Dorsalis pedis artery

TABLE **18.1** Model Inventory for Arteries

Model/Diagram	Structures Identified

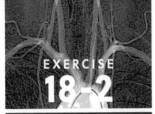

MATERIALS

☐ Blood vessel anatomical models and diagrams:
- human torsos
- brain
- head and neck
- abdomen
- upper limb
- lower limb
- dural sinuses

Major Veins of the Body

Arteries of the systemic circuit deliver oxygenated, nutrient-rich blood to capillary beds. Here, gases, nutrients, and wastes are exchanged. The deoxygenated, carbon dioxide-rich blood is then drained from the capillary beds by a series of veins. The two largest veins in the body are the **superior vena cava**, which drains most structures superior to the diaphragm, and the **inferior vena cava**, which drains most structures inferior to the diaphragm.

The head and the neck are drained primarily by the internal and external jugular veins, with a small contribution from the **vertebral vein** in the posterior neck (Fig. 18.10). The much smaller and more lateral **external jugular vein** (JUG-yoo-lur; *jugul-* = "throat") drains the face and the scalp. The larger **internal jugular vein**, which travels in a sheath with the common carotid artery, drains the brain. Note, however, that venous blood from the brain does not simply drain into one vein and exit the head. Instead, blood from brain capillaries drains into cerebral veins, and then into spaces between the two layers of the dura mater called the **dural sinuses** (Fig. 18.11). As you can see in the figure, two of the sinuses, the **superior** and **inferior sagittal sinuses**, are located within the falx cerebri. Blood from the inferior sagittal sinus drains posteriorly into the **straight sinus**, and then joins with the blood from the superior sagittal sinus by draining into the **transverse sinuses**. From here, blood drains into the **sigmoid sinuses** ("S-shaped"), which also receive blood from the anterior **cavernous sinus**. At this point blood drains into the internal jugular vein.

Blood from the deep structures of the upper limb is drained by the **radial** and **ulnar veins**, both of which parallel the bones for which they are named (Fig. 18.12). These two veins merge in the arm to form the **brachial vein** near the antecubital fossa. The superficial structures of the upper limb are drained by three veins: the lateral **cephalic vein**, the middle **median antebrachial vein**, and the medial **basilic vein** (buh-SIL-ik; *basil-* = "inner"). Notice in the figure that the cephalic vein and the basilic vein are united in the antecubital fossa by the **median cubital vein** (KYOO-bit-uhl). This is a frequent site for drawing blood with a syringe. Around the axilla, the basilic vein joins the brachial vein to form the **axillary vein**. Near the clavicle, the axillary vein becomes the **subclavian vein**, which drains into the **brachiocephalic vein**, and finally into the superior vena cava.

Also shown in Figure 18.12 is the venous drainage system of the posterior thoracic and abdominal walls, which drains into a set of veins called the **azygos system** (ay-ZY-guhs; "unpaired"). This system consists of three unpaired veins: the **azygos vein**, the

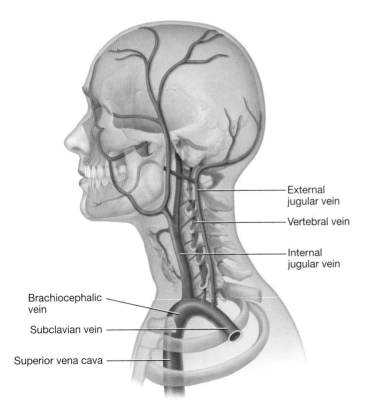

FIGURE **18.10** Superficial veins of the head and neck.

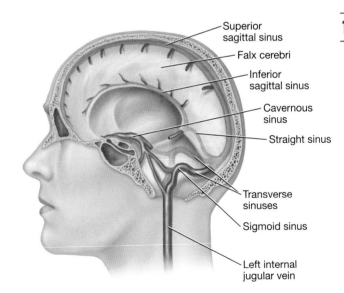

FIGURE **18.11** Dural sinuses draining the brain.

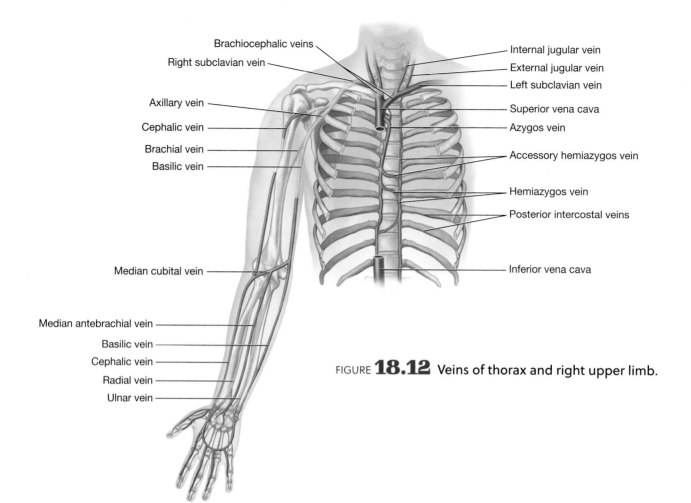

FIGURE **18.12** Veins of thorax and right upper limb.

Labels for Figure 18.12:
- Brachiocephalic veins
- Right subclavian vein
- Axillary vein
- Cephalic vein
- Brachial vein
- Basilic vein
- Median cubital vein
- Median antebrachial vein
- Basilic vein
- Cephalic vein
- Radial vein
- Ulnar vein
- Internal jugular vein
- External jugular vein
- Left subclavian vein
- Superior vena cava
- Azygos vein
- Accessory hemiazygos vein
- Hemiazygos vein
- Posterior intercostal veins
- Inferior vena cava

hemiazygos vein, and the **accessory hemiazygos vein.** The vessels on the left side of the thorax, such as the *posterior intercostal veins*, drain into either the hemiazygos or accessory hemiazygos veins, which then drain into the azygos vein. Vessels on the right side of the thorax drain into the azygos vein. Blood in the azygos vein then drains directly into the superior vena cava.

Veins draining blood from the organs of the abdomen are named largely in parallel with the arteries that serve the organs: The **renal veins** drain the kidneys, the **gonadal veins** drain the gonads, the **suprarenal veins** drain the adrenal glands (Fig. 18.13), the **splenic vein** drains the spleen, the **gastric veins** drain the stomach, the **superior mesenteric vein** drains the small intestine and

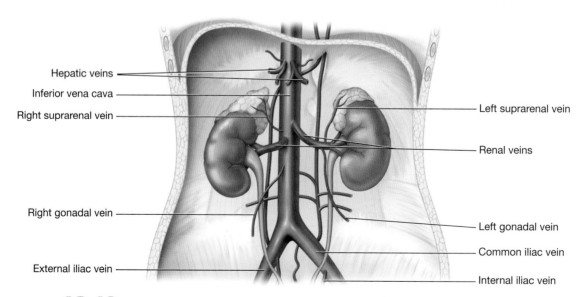

Labels for Figure 18.13:
- Hepatic veins
- Inferior vena cava
- Right suprarenal vein
- Right gonadal vein
- External iliac vein
- Left suprarenal vein
- Renal veins
- Left gonadal vein
- Common iliac vein
- Internal iliac vein

FIGURE **18.13** Veins draining the abdominal area (excluding the hepatic portal system).

much of the large intestine, and the **inferior mesenteric vein** drains the remainder of the large intestine. Although the renal veins and gonadal veins empty into the inferior vena cava, the blood from the latter four veins does not drain into the inferior vena cava directly. Instead, note in Figure 18.14 that each vein drains into a common vein called the **hepatic portal vein**. Here, nutrient-rich blood passes through the **hepatic portal system** in the sinusoids of the liver, where it is processed and detoxified. In this way, everything we ingest (except lipids, which we discuss in Unit 24) must travel through the liver before entering the systemic circulation. After the blood has filtered through the hepatic portal system, it exits via **hepatic veins** and drains into the inferior vena cava.

The deep structures of the leg are drained by the **anterior** and **posterior tibial veins**, which unite in the popliteal fossa to form the **popliteal vein** (Figs. 18.15 and 18.16). A superficial vein called the **small saphenous vein** (SAF-en-uhs) also drains into the popliteal vein. In the distal thigh, the popliteal vein becomes the **femoral vein**. The largest superficial vein of the lower limb is the **great saphenous vein**, which drains the medial leg and thigh and empties into the femoral vein in the proximal thigh.

The femoral vein becomes the **external iliac vein** after it passes deep to the inguinal ligament. In the pelvis, the external iliac vein merges with the **internal iliac vein**, which drains pelvic structures, forming the **common iliac vein**. The two common iliac veins unite to form the inferior vena cava near the superior part of the pelvis.

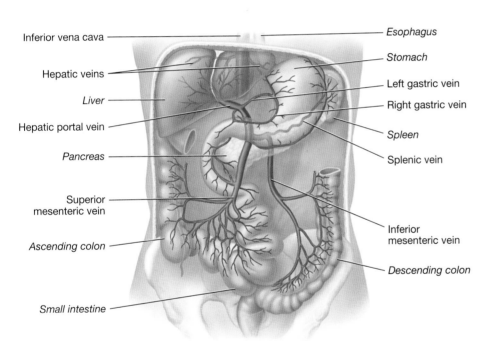

FIGURE **18.14** Veins of the abdomen and the hepatic portal system.

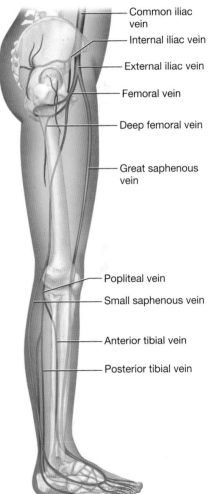

FIGURE **18.15** Lateral view of the veins of the lower limb.

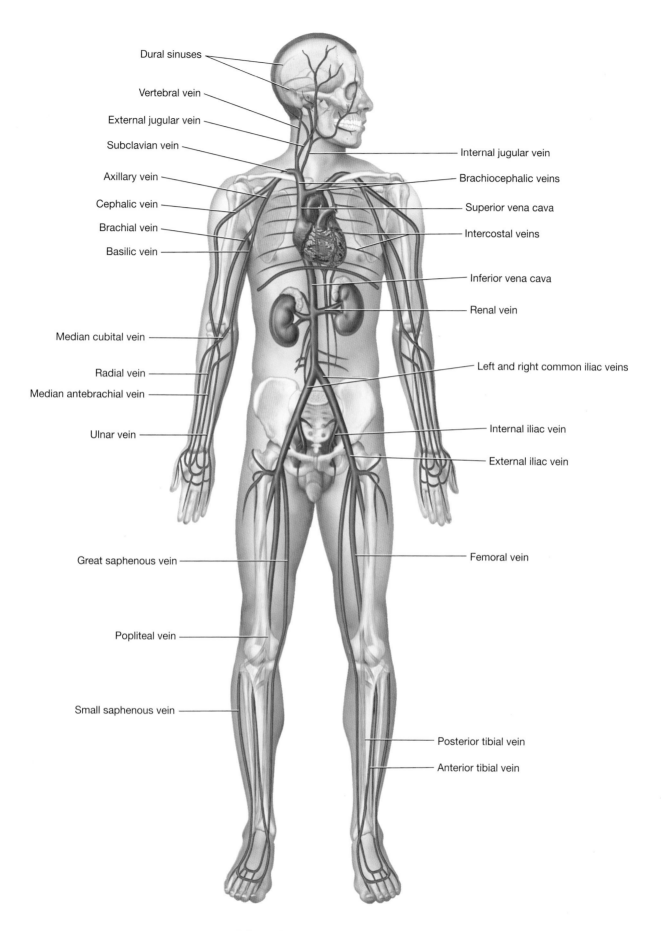

Dural sinuses

Vertebral vein

External jugular vein

Subclavian vein

Axillary vein

Cephalic vein

Brachial vein

Basilic vein

Median cubital vein

Radial vein

Median antebrachial vein

Ulnar vein

Great saphenous vein

Popliteal vein

Small saphenous vein

Internal jugular vein

Brachiocephalic veins

Superior vena cava

Intercostal veins

Inferior vena cava

Renal vein

Left and right common iliac veins

Internal iliac vein

External iliac vein

Femoral vein

Posterior tibial vein

Anterior tibial vein

FIGURE **18.16** Major veins of the body.

Model Inventory for Veins

Identify the following veins on models and diagrams, using your textbook and this unit for reference. As you examine the anatomical models and diagrams, record in Table 18.2 the name of the model and the structures you were able to identify on the model inventory. Figures 18.17 through 18.19 are photos of anatomical models that show both arteries and veins; you may use these to help guide your work as you do your model inventory. When you have completed the activity, answer Check Your Understanding Question 3 (p. 513).

Veins of the Trunk

1. Superior vena cava
2. Inferior vena cava
3. Azygos system
   a. Azygos vein
   b. Hemiazygos vein
   c. Accessory hemiazygos vein
4. Renal vein
5. Gonadal veins
6. Suprarenal vein
7. Splenic vein
8. Gastric veins
9. Superior mesenteric vein
10. Inferior mesenteric vein
11. Hepatic portal vein
12. Hepatic veins

Veins of the Head and Neck

1. Vertebral vein
2. External jugular vein
3. Internal jugular vein
4. Dural sinuses
   a. Superior sagittal sinus
   b. Inferior sagittal sinus
   c. Straight sinus
   d. Transverse sinus
   e. Sigmoid sinus
   f. Cavernous sinus

Veins of the Upper Limbs

1. Radial vein
2. Ulnar vein
3. Brachial vein
4. Cephalic vein
5. Median antebrachial vein
6. Basilic vein
7. Median cubital vein
8. Axillary vein
9. Subclavian vein
10. Brachiocephalic vein

Veins of the Lower Limbs and Pelvis

1. Anterior tibial vein
2. Posterior tibial vein
3. Popliteal vein
4. Small saphenous vein
5. Great saphenous vein
6. Femoral vein
7. External iliac vein
8. Internal iliac vein
9. Common iliac vein

TABLE 18.2 Model Inventory for Veins

Model Inventory	Structures Identified

18

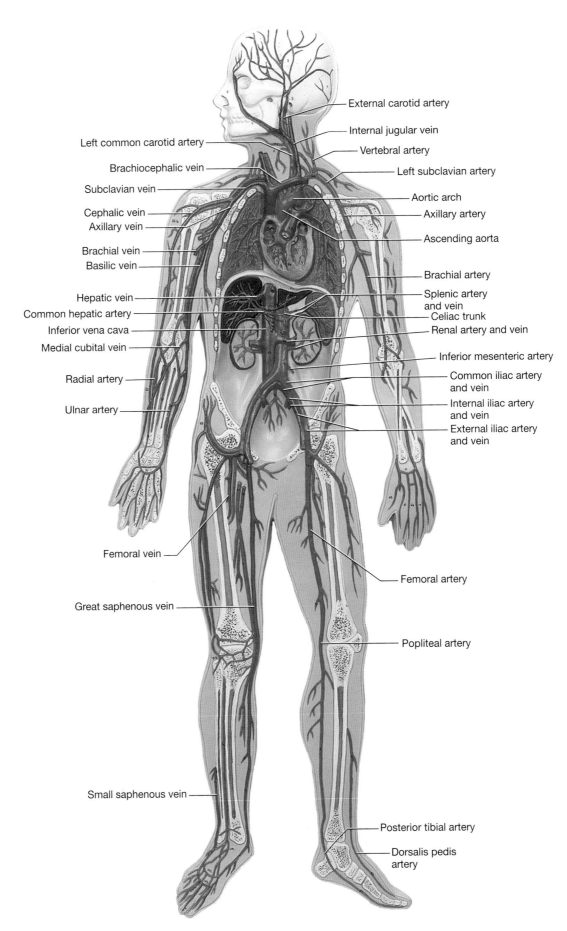

External carotid artery

Internal jugular vein

Vertebral artery

Left common carotid artery

Left subclavian artery

Brachiocephalic vein

Subclavian vein

Aortic arch

Cephalic vein

Axillary artery

Axillary vein

Ascending aorta

Brachial vein

Basilic vein

Brachial artery

Hepatic vein

Splenic artery and vein

Common hepatic artery

Celiac trunk

Inferior vena cava

Renal artery and vein

Medial cubital vein

Inferior mesenteric artery

Radial artery

Common iliac artery and vein

Ulnar artery

Internal iliac artery and vein

External iliac artery and vein

Femoral vein

Femoral artery

Great saphenous vein

Popliteal artery

Small saphenous vein

Posterior tibial artery

Dorsalis pedis artery

FIGURE **18.17** Arteries and veins of the body, anatomical model photo.

18

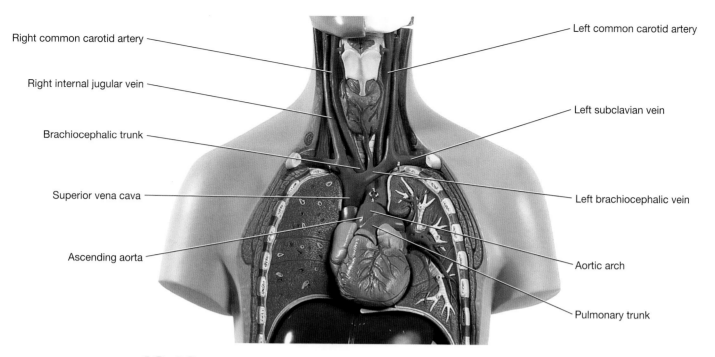

FIGURE **18.18** Arteries and veins of the neck and thorax, anatomical model photo.

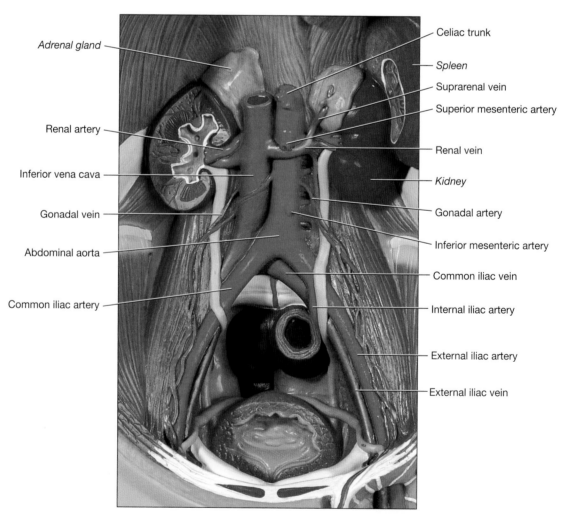

FIGURE **18.19** Arteries and veins of the posterior abdominal wall, anatomical model photo.

EXERCISE

18-3

MATERIALS

- ❑ Laminated outline of the human body
- ❑ Water-soluble marking pen

Time to Trace!

In this exercise, you will trace the blood flow through various circuits in the body. As you trace, keep the following hints in mind:

- Don't forget about the hepatic portal system. Remember that most venous blood coming from the abdominal organs has to go through the hepatic portal vein and the hepatic portal system before it can enter the general circulation.
- Don't forget that the venous blood in the brain drains first into the dural sinuses, and then into the internal jugular vein.

- If you start in a vein, you have to go through the venous system, through the right heart, through the pulmonary circuit, and then through the left heart before you can get back to the arterial system.
- If you start in an artery, you have to go through the arterial system and then through a *capillary bed* before you can get to the venous system. You can't go backward through the arterial system—that's cheating.
- If you start in an artery and end in an artery, you likely will have to go through the arterial circuit, through a capillary bed, through the venous circuit, back to the heart and lungs, and *then* reenter the arterial circuit.

Following is an example in which we have started in the right popliteal vein and ended in the left internal carotid artery:

Start: right popliteal vein → right femoral vein → right external iliac vein → right common iliac vein → inferior vena cava → right atrium → tricuspid valve → right ventricle → pulmonary valve → pulmonary trunk → pulmonary artery → pulmonary capillaries → pulmonary veins → left atrium → mitral valve → left ventricle → aortic valve → ascending aorta → aortic arch → left common carotid artery → left internal carotid artery → **End**

Wasn't that easy?

---

1 **PROCEDURE**

Tracing Blood Flow Patterns

Trace the path of blood flow through the following circuits, using the example above for reference. It is helpful to draw the pathway out on a laminated outline of the human body, and label each vessel as you trace. If a laminated outline is not available, use Figures 18.20 through 18.23 instead. When you have completed your tracings, answer Check Your Understanding Question 4 (p. 514).

18

1 Start: Hepatic Vein →

_____	→
_____	→
_____ valve	→
_____	→
_____ valve	→
_____	→
_____ artery	→
_____ capillaries	→
_____ veins	→
_____	→
_____ valve	→
_____	→
_____ valve	→
ascending _____	→
_____ arch	→
descending _____	→
_____	→
external _____	→
_____	→

End: Left Popliteal Artery

18

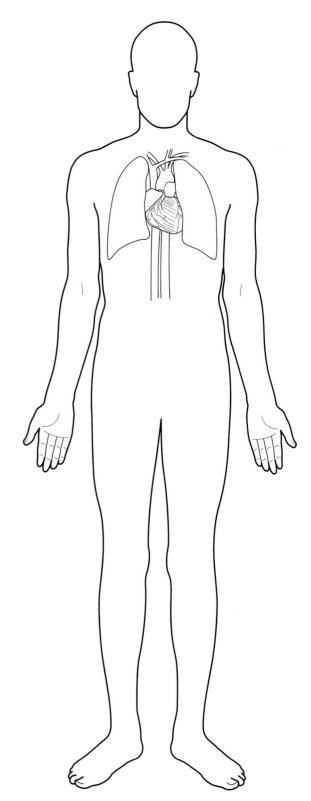

FIGURE **18.20** Outline of the human body.

2 **Start:** Superior Sagittal Sinus →

_____ sinus →
_____ sinus →
_____ vein →
_____ vein →
_____ →
_____ →
_____ valve →
_____ →
_____ valve →
_____ →
_____ artery →
_____ capillaries →
_____ veins →
_____ →
_____ valve →
_____ →
_____ valve →
ascending _____ →
_____ arch →
_____ artery (trunk) →
_____ →
_____ →
_____ →

End: Right Ulnar Artery

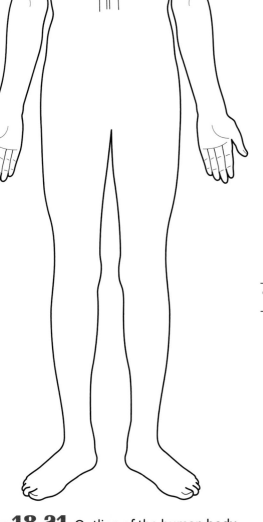

FIGURE **18.21** Outline of the human body.

3 Start: Right Coronary Artery (see Figs. 17.5 and 17.6, pp. 464
and 465) → posterior _____ artery →

_____ capillaries →

middle _____ vein →

_____ sinus →

_____ →

_____ valve →

_____ →

_____ valve →

_____ →

_____ artery →

_____ capillaries →

_____ veins →

_____ →

_____ valve →

_____ →

_____ valve →

ascending _____ →

_____ arch →

descending _____ →

_____ →

End: Inferior Mesenteric Artery

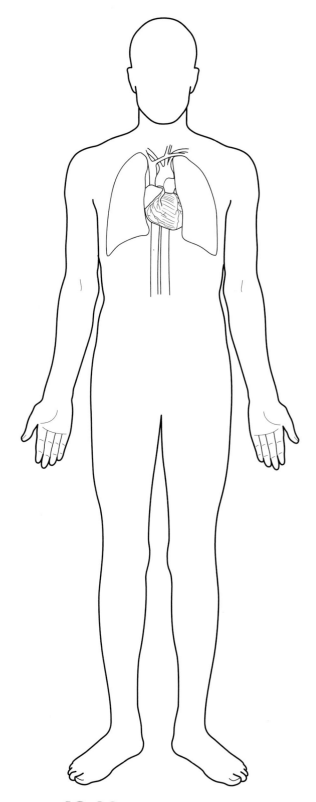

FIGURE **18.22** Outline of the human body.

4 Start: Left Gastric Artery →

_____ capillaries →

_____ vein →

_____ vein →

_____ system →

_____ veins →

_____ →

_____ →

_____ valve →

_____ →

_____ valve →

_____ →

_____ artery →

_____ capillaries →

_____ veins →

_____ →

_____ valve →

_____ →

_____ valve →

ascending _____ →

_____ arch →

_____ artery (trunk) →

_____ →

End: Right Internal Carotid Artery

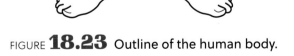

FIGURE **18.23** Outline of the human body.

18

EXERCISE

18-4

MATERIALS

❏ Slides: blood vessel
❏ Light microscope
❏ Colored pencils

Histology of the Blood Vessel Wall

Three distinct tissue layers make up the walls of arteries and veins. The three layers, shown in Figure 18.24, are as follows:

1. **Tunica interna.** The innermost lining of the blood vessel is called the **tunica interna**. It consists of a specialized type of simple squamous epithelium called **endothelium**. It rests on top of a thin layer of extracellular matrix called the *basal lamina*.

2. **Tunica media.** The middle layer of the blood vessel wall is called the **tunica media**, and it consists of smooth muscle tissue and elastic fibers. The smooth muscle, innervated by the sympathetic nervous system, controls the diameter of the vessel and plays an important role in regulating tissue perfusion and blood pressure. The elastic fibers allow the vessel to expand with changing pressure and return to its original diameter.

3. **Tunica externa.** The outermost layer of the blood vessel wall is the **tunica externa** (or **tunica adventitia**), which consists of dense irregular connective tissue with abundant collagen fibers. The collagen fibers reinforce the blood vessel wall and prevent it from rupturing when the pressure in the vessel increases.

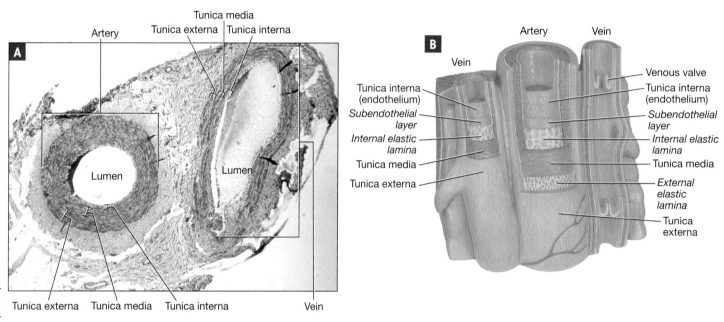

FIGURE **18.24** Artery and vein: (**A**) photomicrograph; (**B**) blood vessel structure, anatomical model photo.

HINTS & TIPS

Like any other organ, the structure of each type of blood vessel follows its function. For this reason, the characteristics of the three layers of the blood vessel wall are considerably different in arteries, veins, and capillaries. They are easy to identify if you bear the following in mind:

ℹ️ Arteries have a much thicker tunica media, with prominent elastic fibers that typically appear as a wavy purple line. They appear circular in cross sections because of their thick walls. Arteries closer to the heart are under high pressure and so have more elastic fibers in the tunica media and more collagen fibers in the tunica externa.

ℹ️ Veins have a thin tunica media with few elastic fibers and little smooth muscle. Because the wall is so much thinner, the lumen is wider, and the vein typically is collapsed on the slide.

ℹ️ Capillaries are extremely thin walled and consist only of a thin tunica interna with a basal lamina. The smallest capillaries are wide enough for only one red blood cell to fit through at a time.

1 PROCEDURE

Examining Blood Vessels with Microscopy

Examine prepared microscope slides of an artery, a capillary, and a vein. The capillary may be on a separate slide. Use colored pencils to draw what you see, and label your diagrams with the terms indicated. When you have completed the activity, answer Check Your Understanding Question 5 (p. 514).

1 Artery
- Tunica interna (endothelium)
- Tunica media
- Smooth muscle
- Elastic fibers
- Tunica externa
- Lumen

2 Capillary
- Tunica interna
- Blood cell(s)

3 Vein
- Tunica interna
- Tunica media
- Tunica externa
- Lumen

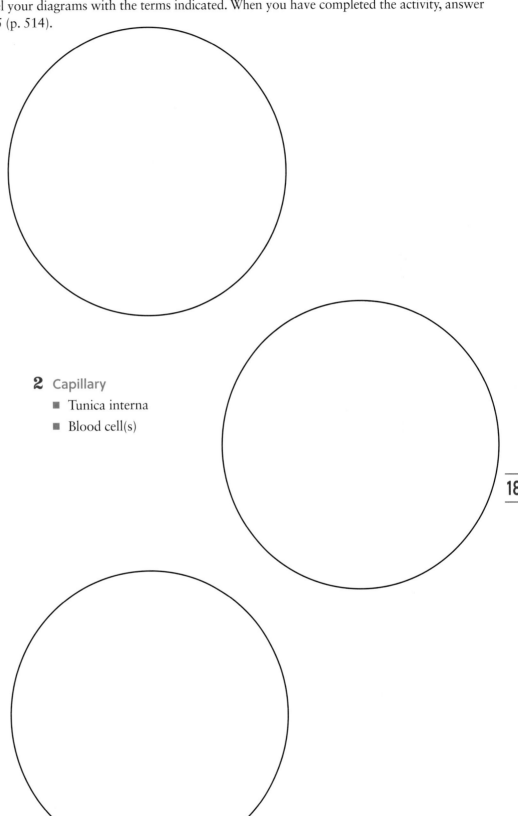

18

EXERCISE

18-5

MATERIALS

❏ Anatomical models or diagrams: blood vessel

❏ Tourniquets

❏ Water-soluble marking pen

❏ Alcohol swabs

Clinical Applications

Knowledge of blood vessel anatomy is important for many different clinical applications. Here we will examine two: (1) pulse palpation, and (2) locating veins for blood draws and intravenous access. Note that you're not actually going to be sticking each other with needles—you're just going to be finding the veins, not putting needles in them.

1 **PROCEDURE**

Palpating the Pulse

Pulse palpation is the process of using the fingertips to feel **pulse points**—locations where the artery is superficial enough that the artery's pulsations with each systole can be felt. It is performed to assess the rate, rhythm, and regularity of the heartbeat, and to assess the arterial circulation to different parts of the body. The pulse points commonly assessed are those found at the radial, ulnar, brachial, carotid, temporal, femoral, popliteal, posterior tibial, and dorsalis pedis arteries, shown in Figure 18.25.

When pulses are palpated, they are **graded** according to a standard scale. This allows healthcare professionals to communicate about a patient unambiguously and to assess the progress or deterioration of a patient's condition. The scale utilizes the following four grades:

- Grade **0/4**: The pulse is absent.
- Grade **1/4**: The pulse is barely or only lightly palpable.
- Grade **2/4**: The pulse is normal.
- Grade **3/4**: The pulse is abnormally strong.
- Grade **4/4**: The pulse is bounding and visible through the skin.

Notice that this scale has no negative numbers or decimal numbers (e.g., you would not use –1/4 or 2.5/4). In a healthy person most pulses are grade 2/4 (read as, "two out of four"), although occasionally a pulse is weak or absent. This is simply normal anatomical variation and does not signify pathology. Students often mistakenly grade any strong pulse as 4/4. If a pulse were truly 4/4, however, this would be a sign of extremely high blood pressure in that artery and would possibly be a medical emergency. Most strong, healthy pulses are graded as 2/4.

Before you begin, please note that you should never palpate both the right and left carotid pulses at the same time. Doing so might initiate the **baroreceptor reflex** (BEHR-oh-reh-sep-ter), in which the parasympathetic nervous system triggers a reflexive and often dramatic drop in blood pressure and heart rate. This could cause your lab partner to momentarily lose consciousness.

When you have completed the procedure, answer Check Your Understanding Question 6 (p. 514).

1 Wash your hands prior to palpating your lab partner's pulses.

2 On a model or diagram, locate the artery you are palpating.

3 Lightly place your index finger and middle finger over the artery. You may increase the pressure slightly, but be careful not to press too hard, because you could cut off blood flow through the artery and also could mistake the pulse in your fingertips for your partner's pulse. If you are unsure whether the pulse is yours or your partner's, feel the lab table. If the lab table "has a pulse," you are feeling the pulse in your own fingertips.

4 Palpate *only* one side (right or left) at a time, especially in the carotid artery.

5 Grade your partner's pulses according to the 0/4 to 4/4 scale, and record the results in Table 18.3.

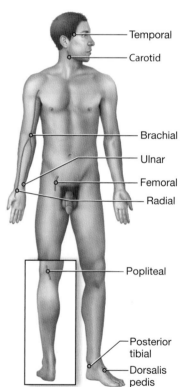

FIGURE **18.25** Common pulse points.

Temporal
Carotid
Brachial
Ulnar
Femoral
Radial
Popliteal
Posterior tibial
Dorsalis pedis

18

TABLE **18.3** Pulse Points Grades

Artery	Right-Side Grade	Left-Side Grade
Carotid		
Temporal		
Brachial		
Radial		
Ulnar		
Dorsalis pedis		
Posterior tibial		

2 PROCEDURE
Locating Common Blood Draw and Intravenous Access Points

The superficial veins of the arm, forearm, and hand provide multiple places that are relatively easy to access when we need to obtain venous blood. When performing a *blood draw*, or the withdrawal of blood for analysis, the most commonly used veins are the median cubital vein, the cephalic vein, or the basilic vein. When placing an *intravenous catheter* into a vein, generally one of the posterior veins of the hand is used.

If you take a look at your arms and hands right now, you'll see that these superficial veins aren't really all that visible. You might see a few small, very superficial veins, but usually none that are large enough in which to place a needle. To get these veins to "pop," medical professionals wrap a tourniquet around the proximal arm, which increases the pressure in the distal veins and decreases venous return. This increases the amount of blood in the veins, and makes them more visible from the surface of the skin (Fig. 18.26). Your goal in this activity is to use a tourniquet to make your lab partner's veins "pop" and for you to identify as many superficial veins as possible.

1 Obtain a tourniquet of the appropriate size and place it around your partner's arm about 7.5–10 cm (3–4 in.) proximal to the antecubital fossa. It should be tight, but avoid pinching your partner's skin or causing too much discomfort.

2 First, look for the veins on the anterior arm. Wait about 15 to 20 seconds for the veins to begin to fill with blood. It may help for your partner to open and close his or her fist once or twice. If you can't see the superficial veins, tapping them lightly may also help make them more visible. Do not leave the tourniquet on your partner's arm for longer than 1 minute.

3 When you can see your partner's veins, trace them lightly with a water-soluble marking pen. Which veins were you able to find and identify?

_____

_____

4 Remove the tourniquet from your partner's arm and repeat the procedure on the opposite arm, this time looking for veins on the posterior hand. Again, do not leave the tourniquet on your partner's arm for longer than 1 minute. Which veins were you able to find and identify?

_____

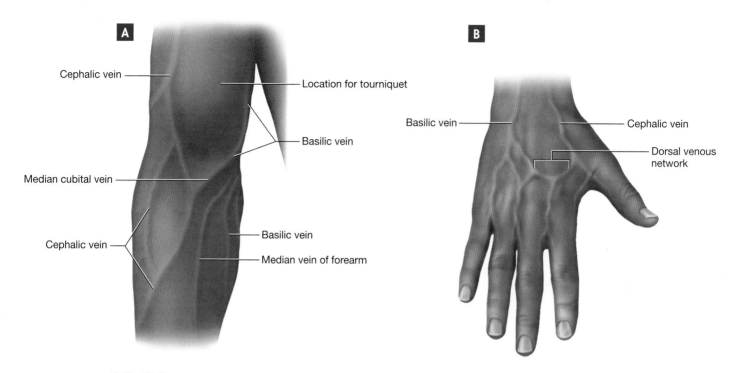

FIGURE **18.26** Surface anatomy of the superficial veins: (**A**) veins of the anterior arm and forearm; (**B**) veins of the posterior hand.

Check Your Recall

1 Label the following arteries in Figure 18.27.

❏ Anterior cerebral artery
❏ Anterior communicating artery
❏ Basilar artery
❏ Cavernous sinus

❏ Cerebral arterial circle
❏ External jugular vein
❏ Inferior sagittal sinus
❏ Internal jugular vein

❏ Superior sagittal sinus
❏ Transverse sinuses
❏ Vertebral artery
❏ Vertebral vein

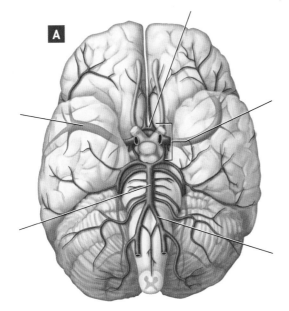

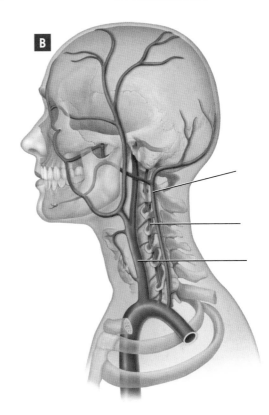

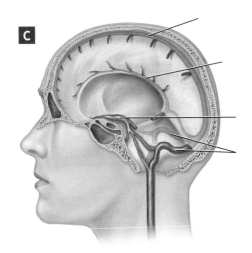

FIGURE **18.27** Blood vessels of the head and neck: (**A**) arteries of the brain; (**B**) superficial veins of the head and neck; (**C**) veins draining the brain.

2 The short artery that branches to serve several abdominal organs is the

a. internal iliac artery.

b. celiac trunk.

c. splenic artery.

d. hepatic portal artery.

3 Label the following veins and arteries on Figure 18.28.

❏ Axillary artery
❏ Basilic vein
❏ Cephalic vein
❏ External iliac vein
❏ Femoral artery
❏ Femoral vein
❏ Great saphenous vein
❏ Hepatic vein
❏ Popliteal artery
❏ Radial artery
❏ Splenic artery
❏ Ulnar artery

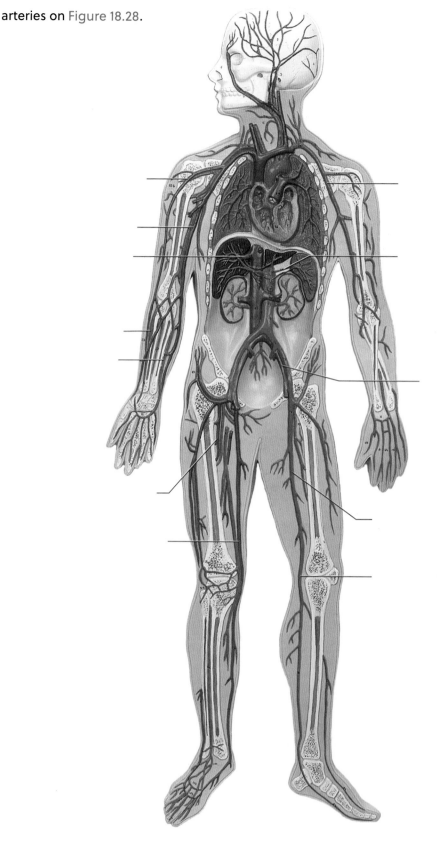

FIGURE **18.28** Arteries and veins of the body, anatomical model photo.

4 The posterior thoracic and abdominal walls are drained by a set of veins called the

a. hepatic portal system.
b. dural sinuses.
c. abdominothoracic system.
d. azygos system.

5 Label the following arteries and veins in Figure 18.29.

- ❏ Brachiocephalic trunk
- ❏ Common iliac artery
- ❏ External iliac artery
- ❏ Gonadal artery

- ❏ Internal iliac artery
- ❏ Left brachiocephalic vein
- ❏ Left common carotid artery
- ❏ Left subclavian vein

- ❏ Renal artery
- ❏ Right common carotid artery
- ❏ Right internal jugular vein
- ❏ Suprarenal vein

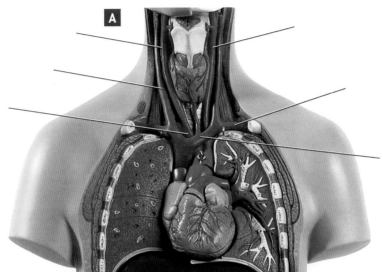

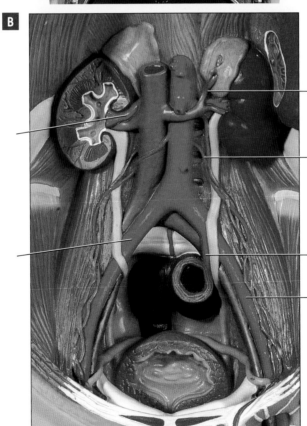

FIGURE **18.29** Major blood vessels: (**A**) neck and thorax, anatomical model photo; (**B**) posterior abdominal wall, anatomical model photo.

6 Which of the following is not a common pulse point?

a. Temporal artery.

b. Common iliac artery.

c. Ulnar artery.

d. Posterior tibial artery.

7 *True/False:* Mark the following statements as true (T) or false (F). If the statement is false, correct it to make it a true statement.

_____ a. The three major circuits of blood flow in the body are the systemic, coronary, and pulmonary circuits.

_____ b. The femoral vein is a superficial leg vein that drains the medial leg and thigh.

_____ c. The external jugular veins drain blood from the brain.

_____ d. Most everything we ingest must pass through the hepatic portal system before entering the systemic circulation.

8 Which of the following veins does not drain into the hepatic portal vein?

a. Renal vein.

b. Splenic vein.

c. Gastric veins.

d. Superior mesenteric vein.

9 The inner layer of the blood vessel wall is the _____ and is composed of _____ .

a. tunica interna; smooth muscle

b. tunica externa; endothelium

c. tunica media; endothelium

d. tunica interna; endothelium

e. tunica media; smooth muscle

10 Blood from the capillaries of the brain drains into the

a. cerebral arterial circle.

b. internal carotid arteries.

c. dural sinuses.

d. vertebral veins.

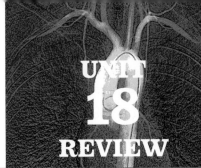
Check Your Understanding

Critical Thinking and Application Questions

1 Nathaniel was injured in a hunting accident during which a bullet severed his left femoral artery. Doctors are now worried he may lose his left leg. Why would an injury to the femoral artery put the whole limb at risk?

2 The condition *giant cell arteritis* is characterized by inflammation of medium-to-large blood vessels, particularly the temporal artery.

   a What symptoms would you expect from inflammation of the temporal artery? Why? _____

   b A potential complication of giant cell arteritis is blockage of the ophthalmic artery. Why is this considered an emergency?

3 Explain why there are right and left brachiocephalic veins, but only one brachiocephalic artery.

4 A blood clot that forms along the wall of a blood vessel is called a *thrombus*. An *embolus* is a piece of a thrombus that breaks off and flows through the blood until it gets stuck in a small blood vessel downstream from the original thrombus.

   a Trace the pathway taken by an embolus that broke off from a thrombus in the subclavian artery (assume it gets stuck in the arterioles of the hand, before it reaches capillary beds):

   _____

   _____

   b Trace the pathway taken by an embolus that broke off from a thrombus in the ulnar vein (assume it gets stuck in arterioles, before it reaches capillary beds):

   _____

   _____

   _____

   _____

5 You are examining unknown vessels under the microscope.

   a Your first vessel has a thick tunica media and a prominent ring of elastic fibers. What type of vessel is it? Explain.

   _____

   _____

   _____

   b Your second vessel has no tunica media and a single red blood cell spans its entire width. What type of vessel is it? Explain.

   _____

   _____

   _____

6 Mr. Goldberg presents to the emergency department complaining of a blinding headache, saying he feels like his head is "pounding." You check his carotid pulses and they are both graded at 4/4. What does this tell you about the possible cause of his headache? Explain.

   _____

   _____

   _____

   _____

   _____

18

The Cardiovascular System, Part III: Cardiovascular Physiology

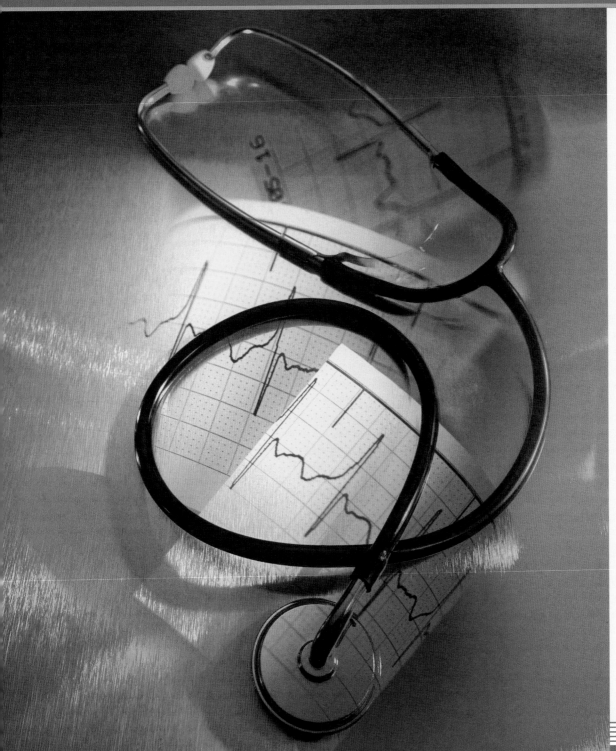

When you have completed this unit, you should be able to:

1 Auscultate the sounds of the heart.

2 Describe and demonstrate common physical examination tests of the blood vessels.

3 Measure blood pressure using a stethoscope and a sphygmomanometer.

4 Describe the effects of the autonomic nervous system on blood pressure and pulse rate.

5 Measure and interpret the ankle–brachial index using a Doppler ultrasound device.

6 Describe the cardiac conduction system, and correlate the electrical activity of the heart with the waves and intervals on an ECG.

PRE-LAB EXERCISES

Complete the following exercises prior to coming to lab, using your lab manual and textbook for reference.

PRE-LAB

19-1 Key Terms

You should be familiar with the following terms before coming to lab.

Term	Definition
Heart Sounds and Pulses	
S1	
S2	
Tachycardia	
Bradycardia	
Pulse point	
Capillary refill time	
Blood Pressure	
Systolic pressure	
Diastolic pressure	
Sounds of Korotkoff	
Electrophysiology	
Sinoatrial node	
Atrioventricular node	

Purkinje fiber system _____

_____

P wave _____

_____

QRS complex _____

_____

T wave _____

_____

R-R interval _____

_____

P-R interval _____

_____

Autonomic Nervous System and the Cardiovascular System

As you learned in Exercise 14-4 (p. 387), the autonomic nervous system (ANS) has profound effects on other body systems and overall homeostasis. The cardiovascular system is no exception, which you will see in this unit's exercises. To refresh your memory, fill in Table 19.1 with the basic effects of the two divisions of the ANS.

TABLE **19.1** Effects of the Divisions of the ANS

Organ or Physiological Variable	Sympathetic Nervous System Effects	Parasympathetic Nervous System Effects
Heart		
Blood vessels serving skin and abdominal viscera		
Net effect on blood pressure		
Lungs (bronchial smooth muscle)		
Metabolic rate		
Urinary functions		
Digestive functions		

19

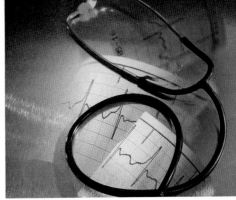

EXERCISES

Every physical examination includes an assessment of the cardiovascular system, in which the heart rate is counted, heart sounds are auscultated, and the blood pressure is measured. In this unit, you will learn how to perform these and other common tests and how they are interpreted. You will also determine the effects of the autonomic nervous system on these measurements and examine the electrocardiogram.

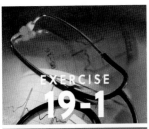

EXERCISE

19-1

MATERIALS

☐ Stethoscope

☐ Cotton swab and alcohol

Heart Auscultation

Heart sounds are produced by the closing of valves at certain points during the cardiac cycle. The first heart sound, called **S1**, is caused by simultaneous closure of the mitral and tricuspid valves when the ventricles begin to contract during *isovolumetric contraction*. The second heart sound, called **S2**, is caused by simultaneous closure of the aortic and pulmonary valves as the ventricles begin to relax during *isovolumetric relaxation*.

The process of listening to heart sounds is known as **auscultation** (ahs-kuhl-TAY-shun; *auscult-* = "listen"). Heart sounds typically are auscultated in four areas, each of which is named for the valve that is best heard at that specific location. The position of each area is described relative to the sternum and the spaces between the ribs, known as *intercostal spaces*. The first intercostal space is located between the first and second rib, which is roughly inferior to the clavicle. From the clavicle you can count down to consecutive spaces to auscultate in the appropriate areas. The four areas, shown in Figure 19.1, are as follows:

1. **Aortic area.** The **aortic area** is the location where the sounds of the aortic valve are best heard. It is located in the second intercostal space (between ribs two and three) at the right sternal border (to the right of the sternum).

2. **Pulmonic area.** The pulmonary valve is best heard over the **pulmonic area**, which is located at the second intercostal space at the left sternal border.

3. **Tricuspid area.** The sounds produced by the tricuspid valve are best heard over the **tricuspid area**, which is found in the fourth intercostal space at the left sternal border.

4. **Mitral area.** The **mitral area** is located in the fifth intercostal space at the left midclavicular line (along an imaginary line you would draw down the middle of the clavicle).

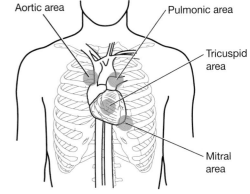

FIGURE **19.1** Areas of auscultation.

The following variables are evaluated during heart auscultation.

■ **Heart rate.** The heart rate refers to the number of heartbeats per minute. If the rate is more than 100, it is termed **tachycardia** (tak-ih-KAR-dee-uh; *tachy-* = "fast"). If the rate is below 60 beats per minute, it is termed **bradycardia** (bray-dih-KAR-dee-uh; *brady-* = "slow").

■ **Heart rhythm.** The heart's **rhythm** refers to the pattern and regularity with which it beats. Some rhythms are *regularly irregular*, in which the rhythm is irregular but still follows a defined pattern. Others are *irregularly irregular*, in which the rhythm follows no set pattern.

■ **Additional heart sounds.** Sometimes sounds in addition to S1 and S2 are heard, which could be a sign of pathology. These sounds are called **S3**, which occurs just after S2, and **S4**, which occurs immediately prior to S1.

■ **Heart murmur.** A heart **murmur** is a clicking or "swooshing" noise heard between the heart sounds. Murmurs are caused by a valve leaking, which is called **regurgitation**, or by a valve that has lost its pliability, which is called **stenosis** (sten-OH-sis; *sten-* = "narrow").

Heart sounds are auscultated with a **stethoscope** (STETH-oh-skohp; *steth-* = "chest")—a tool you will use in this unit. Most stethoscopes contain the following parts (Fig. 19.2):

■ **Earpieces** are gently inserted into the external auditory canal and allow you to auscultate the heart sounds.

- The **diaphragm** is the broad, flat side of the end of the stethoscope. It is used to auscultate higher-pitched sounds and is the side used most often in auscultation of heart sounds.

- The **bell** is the concave, smaller side of the end of the stethoscope. It is used to auscultate lower-pitched sounds.

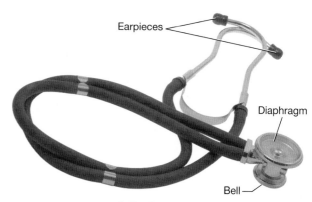

FIGURE **19.2** Stethoscope.

Note that sounds are not audible through both the bell and the diaphragm at the same time. Typically, the end can be flipped from one side to the other by simply turning it clockwise or counterclockwise. Before auscultating with either side, lightly tap the end to ensure that you can hear sound through it. If the sounds are faint or muted, turn the end to the other side and try again. If the end of your stethoscope has only one side (the diaphragm), it works slightly differently. In these stethoscopes, placing light pressure on the end as you are auscultating yields sounds associated with the diaphragm, while placing heavier pressure yields sounds associated with the bell. If you are trying to auscultate with the diaphragm and the sounds are faint, try decreasing the amount of pressure you are placing on the end.

Let's now try auscultating some heart sounds. When you have completed the procedure, answer Check Your Understanding Question 1 (p. 535).

1 PROCEDURE
Auscultating the Heart

1 Obtain a stethoscope and clean the earpieces and diaphragm with cotton swabs and alcohol.

2 Place the earpieces in your ears and gently tap the diaphragm to ensure that it is on the proper side. If it is not, flip it to the other side.

3 Lightly place the diaphragm on your partner's chest in the aortic area. (**Note:** You may wish to have your lab partner place the stethoscope on his or her chest under the shirt, as the sounds are heard best on bare skin.)

4 Auscultate several cardiac cycles and determine which sound is S1 and which sound is S2.

5 Measure the heart rate by counting the number of beats for 15 seconds and multiplying by four. Also, note the rhythm, and whether it is regular, regularly irregular, or irregularly irregular. Finally, note the presence of any extra heart sounds or murmurs.

6 Record your results in Table 19.2.

7 Move on to the next area, and repeat.

TABLE **19.2** Heart Auscultation Results

Area	Rate	Rhythm	Extra Heart Sounds? (Yes/No)	Murmurs Present? (Yes/No)
Aortic area				
Pulmonic area				
Tricuspid area				
Mitral area				

MATERIALS

☐ Stethoscope
☐ Cotton swab and alcohol

Vascular Examination

A vascular examination is the portion of a physical examination that assesses the health of the blood vessels. You performed one common test, pulse palpation, in the blood vessels unit. Two other common tests include auscultating vessels to check for noises called **bruits** (broo-eez) and measuring the time it takes for capillary beds to refill. Each of these procedures is outlined in the sections that follow.

1 PROCEDURE
Auscultating Carotid Bruits

Vascular disease in large vessels may lead to turbulent blood flow through the vessel, producing a bruit. Here we will auscultate for bruits in the carotid arteries.

1 Obtain a stethoscope and switch from the diaphragm to the bell. Clean the earpieces and bell with cotton swabs and alcohol.

2 Place the earpieces in your ears and gently tap the bell to ensure that it is on the proper side. If it's not, flip it to the other side. If your stethoscope has only one side, recall that you will have to use slightly heavier pressure to hear the sounds associated with the bell.

3 Palpate the carotid pulse (remember to palpate only one carotid artery at a time) and place the bell over it. Auscultate for bruits, which sound like a "swooshing" sound with each heartbeat.

4 Repeat the process for the other carotid artery.

5 Were bruits present in either side? _____

Capillary Refill Time

Blood flows through arteries, which branch into successively smaller arteries until they branch into arterioles. Arterioles then feed **capillary beds**, known collectively as the **microcirculation**, where gas, nutrient, and waste exchange takes place (Fig. 19.3). Capillary beds are then drained by venules, which merge to form veins. Capillary beds form interweaving networks, which creates a large surface area for the rapid exchange of substances that occurs across capillary walls.

The amount of blood that flows to a tissue through capillary beds is called **tissue perfusion**. A tissue's perfusion is tightly regulated—if it's too low, the cells will get insufficient oxygen and nutrients and may die, and if it's too high, the high pressure in the capillaries can force excess water out of the blood and into the interstitial fluid.

19

A simple way to assess tissue perfusion in the clinic is by measuring the **capillary refill time,** which is the time it takes for capillary beds to refill after they have been forcibly emptied by pressure. This standard physical examination test is done to evaluate a patient for a variety of vascular diseases, particularly microvascular disease. A normal capillary refill time measures 1–3 seconds; a value greater than 3 seconds may signify some sort of pathology (but be aware that it may also just mean that the patient is cold). Use the following procedure to measure the capillary refill time for each of your lab partner's fingers. When you have completed the activity, answer Check Your Understanding Question 2 (p. 535).

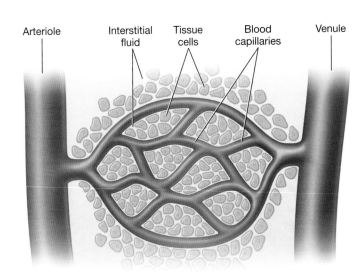

FIGURE **19.3** Structure of a capillary bed.

> **Hypothesis:** Do you think the capillary refill time will be equal on all digits? How fast do you predict the refill time will be?

1 Squeeze the end of the fingertip over the fingernail until the fingernail bed blanches (turns white).

2 Release the fingernail and count the number of seconds it takes for the fingernail bed to return to a pinkish color (note that this may occur immediately, in which case simply record it as 1 second).

3 Repeat for each fingertip of each hand, and record your results in Table 19.3.

TABLE **19.3** Capillary Refill Times

Digits: Right Hand	Refill Time	Digits: Left Hand	Refill Time
1 (thumb)		1 (thumb)	
2		2	
3		3	
4		4	
5		5	

4 Compare your results to your hypothesis.

MATERIALS

❏ Sphygmomanometer
❏ Stethoscope
❏ Cotton swab and alcohol
❏ Bucket of ice water

Blood Pressure

Blood pressure is defined as the pressure exerted by the blood on the walls of the blood vessels. It is determined by the following three factors:

1. **Cardiac output. Cardiac output** is the amount of blood each ventricle pumps in 1 minute. It is a product of heart rate and **stroke volume,** or the amount of blood pumped with each beat.

2. **Peripheral resistance. Resistance** is defined as any impedance to blood flow encountered in the blood vessels. It is determined largely by the degree of vasoconstriction or vasodilation in the systemic circulation. **Vasoconstriction**—narrowing of blood vessels—increases resistance. **Vasodilation**—opening of blood vessels—has the opposite effect. Other factors that influence resistance include obstructions such as atheromatous plaques within the arteries. Resistance is highest away from the heart in the body's periphery, so it is often called **peripheral resistance.**

3. **Blood volume.** The amount of blood found in the blood vessels at any given time is known as the **blood volume.** It is greatly influenced by overall fluid volume and is largely controlled by the kidneys and hormones of the endocrine system.

Note that cardiac output and peripheral resistance are factors that can be altered quickly to change blood pressure. Alterations to blood volume, however, occur relatively slowly and generally require several hours to days to have a noticeable effect.

Arterial blood pressure is measured clinically and experimentally using an instrument called a **sphygmomanometer** (sfig-moh-muh-NAH-muh-tur; *sphygmo-* = "pulse;" *mano-* = "pressure") and a stethoscope. This procedure yields two pressure readings:

1. **Systolic pressure.** The pressure in the arteries during the period of ventricular contraction, called **ventricular systole** (SIS-toh-lee), is known as the **systolic pressure** (sis-TAHL-ik; *syst-* = "contract"). This is the larger of the two readings, averaging between 100 and 120 mmHg.

2. **Diastolic pressure.** The pressure in the arteries during ventricular relaxation, or **ventricular diastole** (dy-Ă-stoh-lee), is the **diastolic pressure** (dy-uh-STAHL-ik; *diastol-* = "expand"). This is the smaller of the two readings, averaging between 60 and 80 mmHg.

Arterial blood pressure is measured by placing the cuff of the sphygmomanometer around the upper arm. When the cuff is inflated, it compresses the brachial artery and cuts off blood flow. When the pressure is released to the level of the systolic arterial pressure, blood flow through the brachial artery resumes but is turbulent. This results in noises known as **Korotkoff sounds** (kuh-RAHT-koff), which may be auscultated with a stethoscope.

---

1 PROCEDURE

Measuring Blood Pressure

19

Practice is necessary to develop the skills to accurately measure arterial blood pressure. Following are the steps that you may use to practice using the sphygmomanometer and stethoscope together, which is shown in Figure 19.4. All readings should be taken with your lab partner seated and relaxed. When you have completed the activity, answer Check Your Understanding Question 3 (p. 535).

1 Obtain a stethoscope and sphygmomanometer of the appropriate size (about 80% of the circumference of the arm).

2 Clean the earpieces and diaphragm as in Exercise 19-1.

3 Wrap the cuff around your partner's arm. It should not be noticeably tight, but it should stay in place when you are not holding it. It should be about 1 1⁄2 in. proximal to the antecubital fossa.

4 Place the stethoscope in your ears and tap the end gently to ensure that it is on the diaphragm side. Palpate for your partner's brachial pulse in the antecubital fossa. When you find it, set the diaphragm of your stethoscope over the pulse. You will *not* hear anything through the stethoscope at this point.

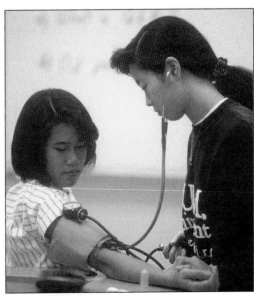

FIGURE **19.4** Measuring blood pressure.

5 Support your partner's arm by cradling it in your arm, or have your partner rest his or her arm on the lab table.

6 Locate the screw of the sphygmomanometer near the bulb, and close it by turning it clockwise. Inflate the cuff by squeezing the bulb several times. Watch the pressure gauge to pay attention to the level of pressure you are applying. Do not inflate it beyond about 30 mmHg above your partner's normal systolic pressure (for most people, this is no higher than 180 mmHg). Your lab partner will likely not be happy with you if you inflate it above about 200 mmHg, as this can be uncomfortable.

7 Slowly open the screw by turning it counterclockwise. Watch the pressure gauge, and listen to the brachial artery with your stethoscope.

8 Eventually, you will see the needle on the pressure gauge begin to bounce; at about the same time, you will begin to hear the pulse in the brachial artery. The pressure you read at that moment should be recorded as the systolic pressure.

9 Continue to listen and watch the gauge. The sound of the pulse will gradually become softer and then finally stop (at this point the needle usually stops bouncing, too). Record as the diastolic pressure the pressure reading from when the sound ends. The numbers should be recorded as a fraction (e.g., 110/70, where 110 is the systolic pressure and 70 is the diastolic pressure).

10 Take your partner's blood pressure twice, and record both readings here:

Blood pressure 1: _____   Blood pressure 2: _____

The Autonomic Nervous System and the Cardiovascular System

The two divisions of the autonomic nervous system (ANS), the sympathetic and parasympathetic nervous systems (SNS and PSNS, respectively), exert a great deal of control over blood pressure through their influence on cardiac output, peripheral resistance, and blood volume.

The SNS is the "fight or flight" branch that helps the body to maintain homeostasis during situations such as exercise, emotion, and emergency. Its neurons release norepinephrine onto cardiac muscle cells and onto the smooth muscle cells lining the walls of blood vessels. We can figure out what the SNS does to blood pressure, and how it does this, by using logic. Look back to Unit 14 (p. 367) to answer the following questions:

What happens to your blood pressure during exercise or emergency? _____

As the SNS is the "fight or flight" branch, what does norepinephrine likely do to heart rate and the force of contraction?

_____

What will this do to cardiac output? _____

What effect does norepinephrine likely have on the blood vessels serving the skin, digestive organs, and urinary organs?

_____

What will this do to peripheral resistance? _____

How will the actions on cardiac output and peripheral resistance affect blood pressure? _____

The PSNS is the "rest and digest" branch of the ANS that helps the body to maintain homeostasis in between those bursts of sympathetic activity. Parasympathetic neurons release acetylcholine onto cardiac muscle cells. Although the vast majority of blood vessels aren't innervated by PSNS neurons, blood vessels do respond to a decrease in sympathetic stimulation. We can similarly figure out what the PSNS does to blood pressure, and how it does this, by using logic.

What happens to your blood pressure during periods of rest? _____

As the PSNS is the "rest and digest" branch, what does acetylcholine likely do to heart rate and the force of contraction?

_____

What will this do to cardiac output? _____

How will a decrease in sympathetic activity affect the blood vessels serving the skin, digestive organs, and urinary organs?

_____

What will this do to peripheral resistance? _____

How will the direct actions on cardiac output and indirect effects on peripheral resistance affect blood pressure?

2 PROCEDURE
Measuring the Effects of the Autonomic Nervous System on the Blood Pressure and Heart Rate

Here, we will witness the effects of the ANS on blood pressure. When you have completed this activity, answer Check Your Understanding Questions 4 and 5 (pp. 535–536).

Hypothesis: What effect will excitement have on heart rate and blood pressure?

1 Have your lab partner remain seated and relaxed for 3 minutes. After 3 minutes, measure your partner's pulse rate by palpating the radial artery and counting the number of beats. Then, take your partner's blood pressure. Record these data in Table 19.4.

2 Have your partner place one hand into a bucket of ice water.

3 Repeat the blood pressure and pulse measurements with your partner's hand still in the ice water. (**Note:** Be kind to your partner and do this quickly!) Record these data in Table 19.4.

4 Have your partner remove the hand from the ice water.

5 Wait 5 minutes, and then repeat the blood pressure and pulse measurements. Record these data in Table 19.4.

> ⚠ **SAFETY NOTE**
>
> Students with health problems or known cardiovascular or vascular disorders should not engage in this activity.

TABLE **19.4** Blood Pressure and Pulse Readings: Ice Water Experiment

Test Situation	Blood Pressure	Pulse Rate
At rest		
While hand immersed in ice water		
5 minutes after removing hand from ice water		

6 Interpret your results:

   a In which situation(s) was the sympathetic nervous system dominant? How can you tell?

   b In which situation(s) was the parasympathetic nervous system dominant? How can you tell?

7 Compare your results to your hypothesis.

MATERIALS

☐ Doppler ultrasound device
☐ Sphygmomanometer
☐ Stethoscope
☐ Cotton swab and alcohol
☐ Ultrasound gel

The Ankle–Brachial Index

Peripheral artery disease (**PAD**), also called *peripheral vascular disease*, is any disease of the arteries outside of the brain and coronary circuit. Although any of these vessels can be affected, it is the arteries of the lower limbs that tend to show the most symptoms of the disease. There are many risk factors for PAD; some of the most common include poorly controlled diabetes mellitus, atherosclerosis, cigarette smoking, and hypertension.

The **ankle–brachial index** (**ABI**) is a test that is used to assess the severity of PAD. The ABI compares the systolic blood pressure in the legs (the "ankle" portion) to the systolic blood pressure in the arms (the "brachial" portion). If an individual has PAD, the ankle pressure is generally much lower than the brachial pressure, which reflects the fact that less blood is flowing to the lower limbs.

The ABI is obtained by dividing the systolic pressure in the ankle by the systolic pressure in the arm. Typically, the ABI is a decimal number because ankle pressure is slightly lower than the brachial pressure. This is because the legs are farther from the heart than the arms, which causes a slight decline in blood pressure. Interpretation of the ABI is as follows:

- 0.9–1.0 = normal
- 0.5–0.9 = peripheral artery disease
- 0.2–0.5 = intermittent claudication (temporary blockages to blood flow)
- <0.2 = severe disease, causing death of tissue

Note that in younger or more athletic persons, the ABI is often greater than 1. This is simply a result of more muscle mass in the lower limb, which is difficult to completely compress with a sphygmomanometer cuff. This falsely elevates the ankle pressure, and so it appears higher than the brachial pressure.

1 PROCEDURE
Measuring the Ankle–Brachial Index

You cannot easily auscultate either of the pedal pulses with a stethoscope, so a Doppler ultrasound device is used to hear the blood flow instead (Fig. 19.5). A Doppler ultrasound device uses sound waves transmitted through a liquid medium (ultrasound gel) to produce audible sounds of the blood flowing through the vessel.

Hypothesis: How will ankle blood pressure compare to the brachial blood pressure?

 19

Following is the procedure for measuring the ankle pressure:

1 Take your partner's brachial pressure in the standard way with a sphygmomanometer and a stethoscope. Record *only* the systolic pressure on the answer blank in Step 7.

2 Wrap the sphygmomanometer cuff around the ankle.

3 Palpate either the dorsalis pedis or the posterior tibial pulses—use whichever is easiest to find and strongest.

4 Place a small amount of ultrasound gel over the pulse. Place the Doppler probe in the gel so it is lightly touching the skin. (*Note:* If you press too hard with the probe, it is possible to cut off blood flow. If you do this, you will hear no sound.)

5 When you can hear sounds of the blood flowing, hold the probe in place as your lab partner inflates the sphygmomanometer cuff. Continue to inflate the cuff until you no longer hear any sound. At this point, the pressure of the cuff has cut off blood flow through the vessel.

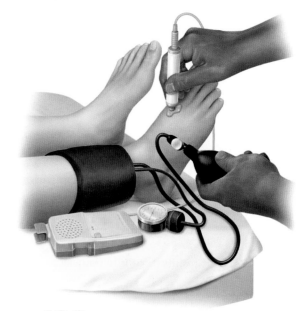

FIGURE **19.5** Performing the ankle–brachial index.

6 Have your lab partner slowly deflate the cuff while you continue to hold the probe in place and watch the pressure gauge. Record the pressure at which you first hear the blood flowing again on the answer blank in Step 7. Note that this is a systolic pressure only; you will not obtain a diastolic pressure for the ankle.

7 Calculate the ABI by dividing the systolic pressure of the ankle by the systolic pressure of the arm. You most likely will get a decimal number, and this is your ABI.

Systolic pressure of the ankle: _____

Systolic pressure of the arm (brachial): _____

Ankle pressure/Brachial pressure: _____

8 Compare your results to your hypothesis.

_____

_____

The Electrocardiogram

Within the heart we find two populations of cardiac muscle cells: *pacemaker cells*, which account for about 1% of the total cells of the heart, and *contractile cells*, which make up the remainder. Pacemaker cells are unique because they rhythmically, spontaneously depolarize and have action potentials. It is their depolarizations that trigger the contractile cells to depolarize and have action potentials. There are three groups of pacemaker cells (Fig. 19.6):

- **Sinoatrial node.** We find the cells of the **sinoatrial node** (sy-noh-AY-tree-uhl), or **SA node**, in the superior portion of the right atrium. The SA node depolarizes about 60 times per minute and is the normal pacemaker of the heart.

- **Atrioventricular node.** The next cluster of pacemaker cells is collectively called the **atrioventricular node**, or **AV node**, which is located posterior and medial to the tricuspid valve. It depolarizes about 40 times per minute and acts as a backup pacemaker should the SA node stop pacing the heart.

- **Purkinje fiber system.** The final series of pacemaker cells is a group that is collectively called the **Purkinje fiber system** (pur-KIN-jee). The system begins with an **atrioventricular bundle** (**AV bundle**) in the inferior interatrial septum and the superior interventricular septum. The AV bundle then splits into the **right** and **left bundle branches**, which run down the right and left sides of the interventricular septum, respectively. Near the apex of the heart, the bundle branches split into the **terminal branches**, which fan out through the ventricles and contact ventricular contractile cells.

Together, these three groups of pacemaker cells make up what is known as the **cardiac conduction system**. This system is named as such because it represents a sort of "hardwiring" of the heart. It allows depolarizations from pacemaker cells to spread extremely rapidly to other pacemaker cells and to contractile cells. You can see in Figure 19.6 how action potentials spread through the heart:

1. The cells of the SA node depolarize; these depolarizations spread through the atria via specialized *atrial conducting fibers*, and the atrial contractile cells depolarize.

2. The impulse reaches the AV node as the atrial cells complete their action potentials and contract. Conduction slows at the AV node, a phenomenon known as the *AV node delay*, which allows the atria to depolarize and contract before the ventricles depolarize and contract.

3. The depolarization next propagates along the Purkinje fiber system, first along the AV bundle.

4. The depolarization spreads down either side of the interventricular septum along the right and left bundle branches.

5. The terminal branches trigger contractile cells of the ventricles to depolarize, have action potentials, and contract.

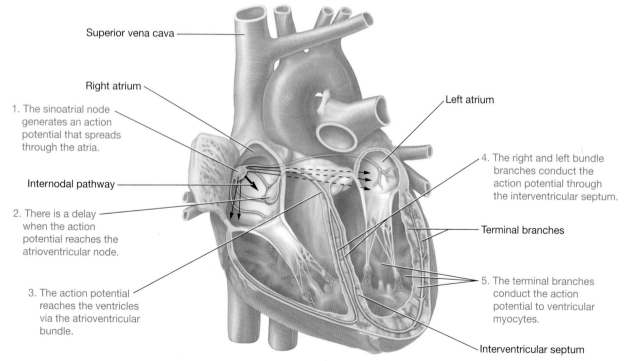

Superior vena cava

Right atrium

Left atrium

1. The sinoatrial node generates an action potential that spreads through the atria.

Internodal pathway

2. There is a delay when the action potential reaches the atrioventricular node.

3. The action potential reaches the ventricles via the atrioventricular bundle.

4. The right and left bundle branches conduct the action potential through the interventricular septum.

Terminal branches

5. The terminal branches conduct the action potential to ventricular myocytes.

Interventricular septum

FIGURE **19.6** Anatomy of the cardiac conduction system.

Note that the AV node electrically connects the atria and ventricles. If the AV node is "blocked," the atria may be paced by the SA node and the ventricles by the AV node or Purkinje fiber system. This leads to different heart rates and rhythms for the atria and ventricles.

The electrical activity of the heart can be examined by taking an **electrocardiogram**, or **ECG**, which is a recording of the changes that occur in the electrical activity of cardiac muscle cells over a period of time. Please note that the ECG illustrates only electrical activity—it does not tell you that the heart is mechanically beating. Although electrical events are generally correlated with the heart's mechanical activity, a heart may have electrical activity without actually contracting.

Electrical activity is recorded by placing electrodes on the surface of the skin that record the changes in electrical activity. The changes in electrical activity are visible on the ECG as **waves**. Note that if there is no *net* change in electrical activity, the line on the ECG is flat. However, even when the ECG is flat between waves, the cells of the heart are in some phase of an action potential. Also note that the ECG appears flat during pacemaker cell action potentials. This is because there are so few pacemaker cells in the heart that their activity isn't detectable with a standard ECG.

A standard ECG recording is shown in Figure 19.7. Notice that it consists of five waves, each of which represents the depolarization or repolarization of different parts of the heart.

- **P wave.** The initial **P wave** shows the depolarization of the cells of the right and left atria. It is fairly small because of the small number of cells in the atria. Note that the flat segment right before the P wave is when the SA node depolarization takes place.

- **QRS complex.** The **QRS complex** is actually a set of three waves that represent the depolarization of the right and left ventricles. The first wave is the **Q wave**, a downward deflection; the next is the **R wave**, a large upward deflection; and the last is the **S wave**, the final downward deflection. The large size of the QRS complex compared with the P wave results from the large number of ventricular cells.

- **T wave.** The small **T wave** is usually the final wave, and it represents the repolarization of the right and left ventricles. Occasionally, after the T wave is a small **U wave**, which is believed to represent repolarization of the terminal branches.

The waves aren't the only important landmarks of the ECG. In addition, we consider the periods between the waves, which show the spread of electrical activity through the heart and phases of the contractile cells' action potentials. We look at two types of periods: *intervals*, which include one or more waves in the measurement, and *segments*, which do not include waves in the measurement.

One important interval is the **P-P interval**, or the period of time between two P waves. A related interval is the **R-R interval**, or the period of time between two R waves. This interval represents the duration of the generation and spread of an action potential through the heart. It can be used to determine the heart rate, which we discuss shortly. Under normal conditions, the P-P interval and R-R intervals should match, as every depolarization from the SA node should lead to depolarization of both the atria and the ventricles.

Another interval we examine is the **P-R interval**, defined as the period from the beginning of the P wave to the beginning of the QRS complex. During the P-R interval, the depolarization from the SA node spreads through the atria to the ventricles via the AV node; this interval includes the AV node delay. A final key interval is the **Q-T interval**, the time from the beginning of the Q wave to the end of the T wave. During the Q-T interval, the ventricular cells are depolarizing and repolarizing.

An important segment that we examine is the **S-T segment**, which is between the end of the S wave and the beginning of the T wave. This segment is recorded during the ventricles' plateau phase. Recall that there is no net change in electrical activity during this phase, and for this reason, the S-T segment is generally flat.

The normal pattern seen on an ECG is known as a **normal sinus rhythm**, which means that the SA node is pacing the heart at a rate between 60 and 100 beats per minute. Any deviation from the normal sinus rhythm is known as a **dysrhythmia** (dis-RITH-mee-uh; *dys-* = "abnormal") or **arrhythmia** (ay-RITH-mee-uh; *a-* = "without").

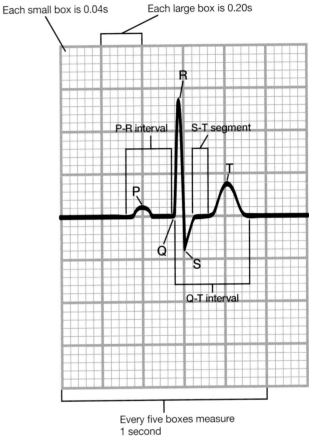

Each small box is 0.04s   Each large box is 0.20s

Every five boxes measure 1 second

FIGURE **19.7** Standard ECG recording.

An electrocardiograph records the tracing at a standard speed of 25 mm/second. This allows us to determine precisely the heart rate and the duration of the intervals we discussed. As you can see in Figure 19.7, each small box on the ECG tracing measures 0.04s, and each large box measures 0.20s. Five large boxes together measure 1 second. Determining the duration of most intervals is simple—just count the small or large boxes, and add the seconds together. Calculating the heart rate is equally simple: count the number of large boxes, and divide 300 by this number. For example, if you count 4.2 boxes, insert 4.2 into the formula as follows: 300/4.2 = 71 beats per minute. The normal values for the periods we discussed are given in Table 19.5.

TABLE **19.5** Normal Values for ECG Periods

Period	Normal Value
Heart rate	60–100 beats per minute
P-P interval	0.60–1.0s
R-R interval	0.60–1.0s
P-R interval	0.12–0.20s
Q-T interval	0.42–0.44s
QRS complex duration	Less than or equal to 0.12s

1 PROCEDURE

Correlating Points on an ECG with Electrical Events of the Heart

Let's start by correlating the following points on the ECG with the electrical activity occurring in the heart. Identify the electrical events taking place in cardiac cells at each of the six points in the ECG in Figure 19.8, and explain the events in the answer lines provided. Do remember though that the ECG shows only *electrical* events, not mechanical events. A heart can have electrical activity but not be beating.

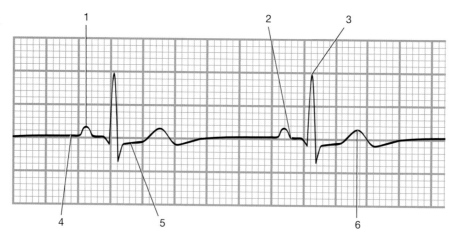

FIGURE **19.8** ECG tracing.

1 _____

2 _____

3 _____

4 _____

5 _____

6 _____

PROCEDURE

Interpreting an ECG

Now that you understand what the wave forms on an ECG mean, you can perform some basic ECG interpretation. Following are two tracings for which you will calculate the heart rate and determine the duration of key intervals of the ECG. When you have completed the activity, answer Check Your Understanding Question 6 (p. 536).

1 Identify and label the P wave, QRS complex, T wave, P-R interval, R-R interval, and Q-T interval on Tracings 1 and 2 in Figure 19.9.

Tracing 1

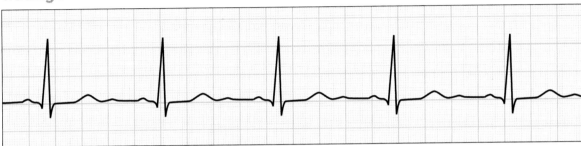

Tracing 2

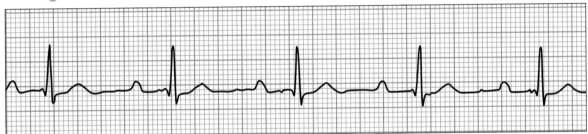

FIGURE **19.9** ECG tracings.

2 Calculate the heart rate for each tracing. Are the values normal or abnormal?

Heart Rate Tracing 1: _____

Heart Rate Tracing 2: _____

19

3 Determine the R-R interval, QRS duration, P-R interval, and Q-T interval for each tracing, and record the values in Table 19.6. Indicate whether the value is normal. If it is abnormal, indicate whether it is higher or lower than normal.

TABLE **19.6** Values for ECG Periods

Value	Tracing 1	Tracing 1 Reading (Normal or Abnormal?)	Tracing 2	Tracing 2 Reading (Normal or Abnormal?)
R-R interval				
P-P interval				
QRS duration				
P-R interval				
Q-T interval				

Check Your Recall

1 The heart sound S2 is caused by
 a. contraction of the ventricles.
 b. closing of the atrioventricular valves.
 c. closing of the semilunar valves.
 d. contraction of the atria.

2 Which of the following terms refers to an abnormally slow heart rate?
 a. Tachycardia.
 b. Murmur.
 c. Dysrhythmia.
 d. Bradycardia.

3 *Fill in the blanks.* Capillary beds are fed by _____ and drained by

_____ .

4 The interweaving networks of capillary beds create a
 a. large surface area for the rapid exchange of substances.
 b. small surface area for the rapid exchange of substances.
 c. large volume of blood to drain into arterioles.
 d. decrease in tissue perfusion.

5 What are the three factors that influence blood pressure, and how does each affect blood pressure?

_____

_____

_____

6 The diastolic pressure is defined as the
 a. pressure in the veins when the ventricles are relaxing.
 b. pressure in the arteries when the atria are relaxing.
 c. pressure in the arteries when the ventricles are relaxing.
 d. pressure in the arteries when the ventricles are contracting.

7 The actions of the sympathetic nervous system trigger a/an _____ in cardiac output and _____ .
 a. increase; vasodilation
 b. increase; vasoconstriction
 c. decrease; vasodilation
 d. decrease; vasoconstriction

8 The QRS complex on an ECG represents

   a. depolarization of the atria.

   b. repolarization of the atria.

   c. depolarization of the ventricles.

   d. repolarization of the ventricles.

9 Draw the parts of the cardiac conduction system on Figure 19.10 and label them with the following terms.

   ❏ Atrioventricular bundle

   ❏ Atrioventricular node

   ❏ Left bundle branch

   ❏ Right bundle branch

   ❏ Sinoatrial node

   ❏ Terminal branches

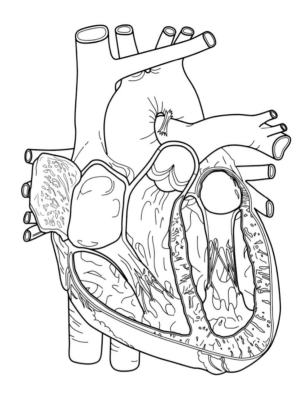

FIGURE **19.10** Frontal dissection of the heart.

10 Label the parts of the electrocardiogram on Figure 19.11.

   ❏ T wave   ❏ P wave   ❏ P-R interval

   ❏ Q-T interval   ❏ QRS complex   ❏ S-T segment

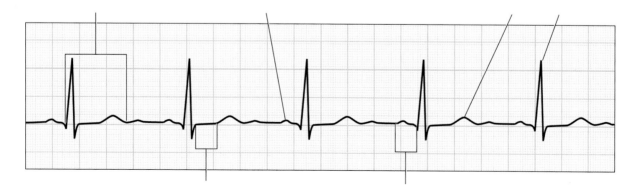

FIGURE **19.11** ECG tracing.

Name _____

Section _____ Date _____

Check Your Understanding

Critical Thinking and Application Questions

1 You are auscultating your patient's chest, and you can hear a noticeable murmur during S1. Is the abnormality in the atrioventricular valves or the semilunar valves? How do you know? Explain.

2 After a motor vehicle accident, Jana presents to the emergency department complaining of severe pain to her right foot and ankle. Upon examination, you notice that her right foot is completely dislocated from her ankle and is cold to the touch. In addition, the capillary refill time is greater than 10 seconds in all five toes of the right foot, whereas it is nearly immediate in the left foot. What has likely happened? Why has it affected capillary refill time? What could happen if the problem isn't corrected immediately?

3 Andrea has been admitted to the emergency room with very low blood pressure. In her medical history, you discover that she takes a diuretic—a drug that increases her urine output. You also note that Andrea has dementia and often can't remember when she last took her medications, causing her to take additional doses sometimes. What has likely caused her low blood pressure?

4 Predict the effects of a drug that increases the output of the sympathetic nervous system on blood pressure and heart rate. How would this drug affect the factors that determine blood pressure?

5 Predict the effects of a drug that increases the output of the parasympathetic nervous system on blood pressure and heart rate. How would this drug affect the factors that determine blood pressure?

6 You are presented with an ECG of a patient with an abnormal heart rhythm. You notice that the PR interval is irregular. In addition, the P-P interval measures 0.80s and the R-R interval measures 1.60s.

a Where is the likely location of the abnormality in the cardiac conduction system that is causing this problem?

b What does the ECG indicate is physically happening in the heart?

Blood

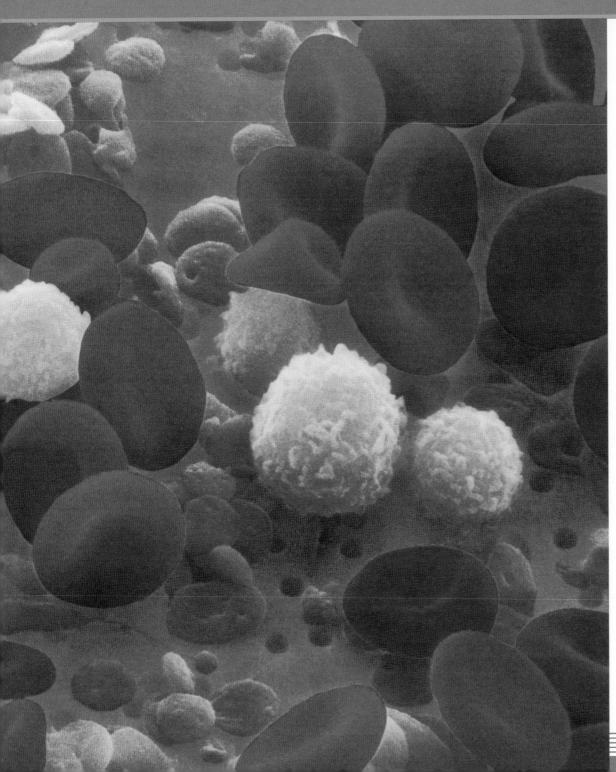

When you have completed this unit, you should be able to:

1 Identify and describe the formed elements of blood.

2 Determine the differential white blood cell count of a blood smear.

3 Perform blood typing of the ABO and Rh blood groups using simulated blood.

4 Explain the basis for blood typing and matching for blood donation.

5 Determine appropriate blood donors for a given recipient.

6 Determine your own blood type and the hemoglobin content of your blood.

PRE-LAB EXERCISES

Complete the following exercises prior to coming to lab, using your lab manual and textbook for reference.

PRE-LAB

20-1 Key Terms

You should be familiar with the following terms before coming to lab.

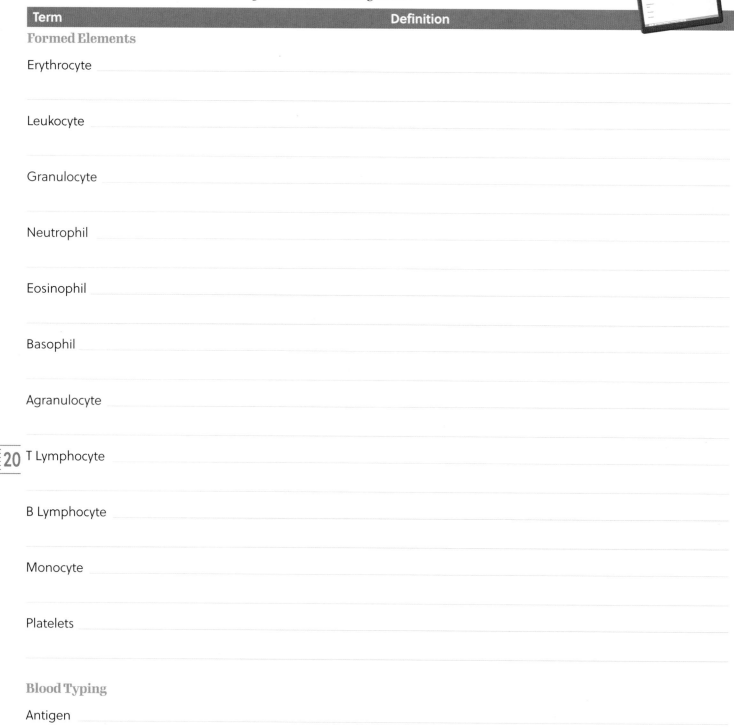

Term	Definition
Formed Elements	
Erythrocyte	
Leukocyte	
Granulocyte	
Neutrophil	
Eosinophil	
Basophil	
Agranulocyte	
T Lymphocyte	
B Lymphocyte	
Monocyte	
Platelets	
Blood Typing	
Antigen	

20

Antiserum

Antibody

Blood Donation

Universal donor

Universal recipient

Formed Elements

In this unit, we will identify the formed elements of blood on a peripheral blood smear. Each formed element has unique morphological characteristics and functions. Use your text and Exercise 20-1 (p. 541) in this unit to fill in Table 20.1 with these functions and characteristics.

TABLE **20.1** Properties of Formed Elements

Formed Element	Nucleus Shape	Cytoplasm and/or Granule Color	Function(s)	Prevalence
Erythrocyte				
Neutrophil				
Eosinophil				
Basophil				
Lymphocyte				
Monocyte				
Platelet				

Scanning electron micrograph of blood cells.

EXERCISES

Blood is a type of connective tissue that is distributed through the body by the cardio-vascular system. It carries out multiple functions, including exchanging gases; distributing solutes; performing functions of the immune system; maintaining acid-base, temperature, and blood pressure homeostasis; and sealing damaged blood vessels with blood clots.

Safety concerns often preclude the use of real blood in the laboratory, but we can still demonstrate important principles of blood by viewing prepared microscope slides of blood cells and by using simulated blood to learn about blood typing. There is no real concern over blood-borne diseases with simulated blood, but do keep in mind that the simulated blood contains chemicals that are hazardous. Therefore, use appropriate safety protocols when handling all materials in this lab.

In this unit, you will identify the formed elements of blood on microscope slides. You will also play a murder mystery game in which you use simulated blood to apply blood-typing techniques, after which you use the same cast of characters to examine blood donation. If your lab has the appropriate protocols for the use of real blood, you will also type your own blood and determine its hemoglobin content.

EXERCISE
20-1

MATERIALS

☐ Slides: blood
☐ Light microscope
☐ Colored pencils

Blood Composition

Whole blood consists of two main components: **plasma,** the fluid portion of blood, and **formed elements,** or the cellular portion of blood. Plasma accounts for about 55% of the volume of whole blood. About 90% of plasma is composed of water. Of the remaining 10%, **plasma proteins** are the most abundant, making up about 9% of the volume of plasma. The remaining 1% of plasma's volume is composed of dissolved solutes such as glucose, amino acids, ions, wastes, and gases.

Most plasma proteins are made by the liver, including **albumin** (al-BYOO-min), a relatively large protein that draws water into the blood via osmosis. Without adequate albumin, water lost to capillary filtration is unable to return to the blood. Other plasma proteins made by the liver include **transport proteins,** which bind and transport lipid-based substances through the water-based environment of the blood, and **clotting proteins,** which are part of the formation of a blood clot via the *clotting cascade*.

Plasma also contains proteins made by cells of the immune system (B lymphocytes) known as *gamma (γ) globulins,* also known as *antibodies.* We discuss antibodies shortly in this unit, and then again in Unit 21 (Lymphatics and Immunity).

Formed elements account for about 45% of the volume of whole blood. There are three classes of formed elements: erythrocytes, platelets, and leukocytes. **Erythrocytes** (eh-RITH-roh-syt′z; *erythr-* = "red"), also known as **red blood cells,** carry oxygen around the body on an iron-containing protein called **hemoglobin** (HEE-moh-glohb-in; *hem-* = "blood"; Fig. 20.1). They are the most numerous blood cells, averaging about 44% of the total blood volume. This value, known as the **hematocrit** (heh-MĂ-toh-krit), is typically higher in males (40 to 50%) than in females (36 to 44%). Erythrocytes are easily distinguished from the other formed elements by their reddish-pink color and the fact that mature erythrocytes lack nuclei and most organelles.

Notice in Figure 20.1 that **platelets** (PLAYT-letz) aren't actually cells at all but are instead just small cellular fragments. As such, they lack nuclei and most organelles and are much smaller than the other formed elements. Platelets are involved in blood clotting and make up less than 1% of the total blood volume.

Leukocytes (LOO-koh-syt′z; *leuk-* = "white"), also known as **white blood cells,** play a role in the immune system and make up less than 1% of the total blood volume. The two subclasses of leukocytes are based upon the presence or absence of visible granules in their cytoplasm.

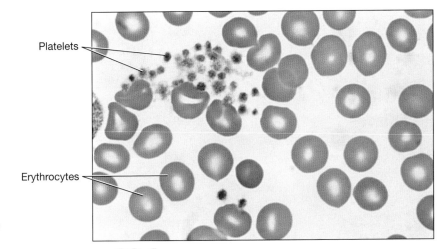

FIGURE **20.1** Erythrocytes and platelets, photomicrograph.

Platelets

Erythrocytes

20

1. **Granulocytes.** As implied by their name, **granulocytes** (GRAN-yoo-loh-syt'z) are cells containing cytoplasmic granules that are visible when stained. The three types of granulocytes stain differently when treated with the dyes hematoxylin and eosin and are named for the type of stain with which they interact.

   a. **Neutrophils** (NOO-troh-filz) do not interact strongly with either type of dye, which causes their granules to stain a light violet-pink color. They are the most numerous type of leukocyte, making up about 60 to 70% of the total leukocytes in the blood. They typically have multilobed nuclei, although their nuclei often vary in appearance, which gives rise to their other name: *polymorphonucleocytes*. One common variation in nucleus shape, shown in Figure 20.2B, is seen in immature neutrophils called *band cells*. As you can see, the nucleus of a band cell has a single lobe that is stretched into a "U" shape (or a single "band"). Neutrophils are attracted to the site of any cellular injury, and are particularly active in ingesting and destroying bacteria.

   b. **Eosinophils** (ee-oh-SIN-oh-filz) interact strongly with the red dye eosin, and so their granules stain bright red. They are far less numerous than neutrophils, accounting for only about 4% of the total leukocytes in the blood. As with neutrophils, their nuclei are segmented into lobes, although eosinophils' nuclei tend to be bilobed. Eosinophils are involved in the allergic response, and respond to infections caused by parasitic worms.

   c. **Basophils** (BAY-zoh-filz) take up the dark purple stain hematoxylin (it is a basic dye, which is why they are named *baso*phils), and so their granules appear dark blue-purple. Like eosinophils, they tend to have bilobed nuclei, but their nuclei are often obscured by their dark granules. They are the least numerous of the leukocytes, making up fewer than 1% of the total leukocyte count, and will likely be the most difficult to find on your slide. Basophils are primarily involved in the allergic response.

2. **Agranulocytes.** The cells known as **agranulocytes** (AY-gran-yoo-loh-syt'z; *a-* = "without") lack specific cytoplasmic granules. The two types of agranulocytes are the following:

   a. **Lymphocytes** (LIMF-oh-syt'z) tend to be smaller than most granulocytes. They have large, spherical nuclei that are surrounded by a rim of light blue-purple cytoplasm. They are the second most numerous type of leukocyte, making up 20 to 25% of the total leukocyte count. There are two populations of lymphocytes. *B lymphocytes* produce *antibodies*, which bind foreign glycoproteins called *antigens*. *T lymphocytes* activate other aspects of the immune response, destroy cancer cells, and destroy cells infected with viruses.

   b. **Monocytes** (MAHN-oh-syt'z) are the largest of the leukocytes. They have U-shaped or horseshoe-shaped nuclei with light blue or light purple cytoplasm. They are the third most numerous type of leukocyte, accounting for 3 to 8% of the total. Monocytes exit the blood to mature into cells called **macrophages** (MAK-roh-feyj-uhz; *macro-* = "large;" *-phage* = "eat"), which are very active phagocytes.

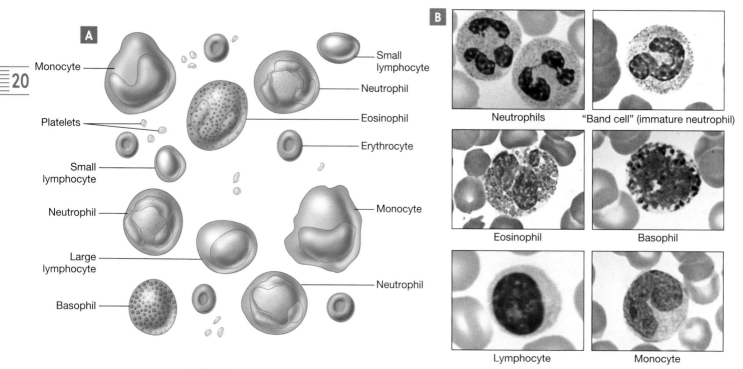

FIGURE **20.2** Formed elements of blood: (**A**) illustration; (**B**) photomicrographs.

1 PROCEDURE
Examining a Peripheral Blood Smear with Microscopy

In this procedure, you will examine a blood slide called a **peripheral blood smear**. Examine the peripheral blood smear on high power, and scroll through to find each of the formed elements. Note that you may have to find a second slide to locate certain cells, because some types are more difficult to find (especially eosinophils and basophils). In the spaces provided, use colored pencils to draw and describe each formed element you locate. When you have finished, answer Check Your Understanding Questions 1 and 2 (p. 559).

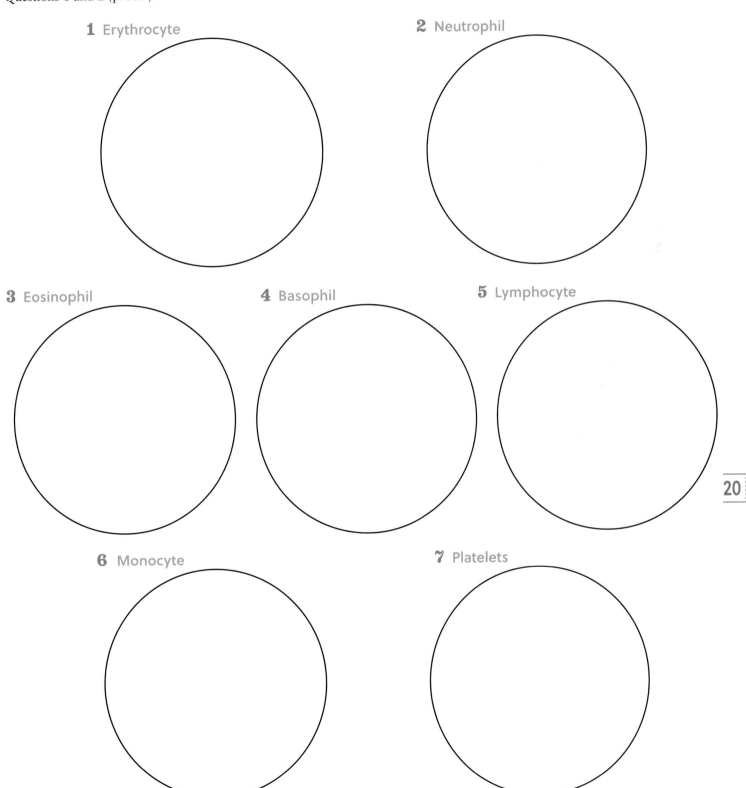

1 Erythrocyte

2 Neutrophil

3 Eosinophil

4 Basophil

5 Lymphocyte

20

6 Monocyte

7 Platelets

Performing a Differential White Blood Cell Count

One of the most common blood analyses performed by a laboratory is a *differential white blood cell count*. In this procedure, the number and types of leukocytes in a blood sample are counted to determine the relative frequency of each type. This can give important information about the cause of a patient's illness, because different conditions will cause an elevation of different types of leukocytes. Differential counts were previously performed manually by a laboratory technician, as you will do here. Now, however, they are generally done by a machine, but the technician will still manually examine the cells if any abnormalities are noted.

1   Obtain a blood smear slide, and scan it on low power to find an area where the cells appear to be evenly distributed.

2   Advance the microscope objective to a power high enough for you to distinguish between the different types of leukocytes. For some microscopes, medium power will suffice, and for others, high power or even oil immersion might be necessary.

3   Scan the slide for leukocytes, and create a running tally of the number of each type in the spaces provided. Do this until you have counted 100 total leukocytes.

Neutrophils   *Eosinophils*   *Basophils*   *Lymphocytes*   *Monocytes*

4   Total the number of each leukocyte you counted, and record these data in Table 20.2. Refer to Table 20.1 in the Pre-Lab Exercises (p. 541) or Exercise 20-1 for the predicted percentage of each type of leukocyte in the blood. How do your totals compare with the predicted percentages?

TABLE **20.2** Differential White Blood Cell Totals

Leukocyte	Number Counted	Percentage (of 100)	Predicted Percentage
Neutrophils			
Eosinophils			
Basophils			
Lymphocytes			
Monocytes			

20

EXERCISE
20-2

MATERIALS

- ❏ Well plates
- ❏ Simulated blood: types A−, B+, AB−, and O+
- ❏ Simulated antisera: anti-A, anti-B, anti-Rh
- ❏ Permanent marker

ABO and Rh Blood Groups

Blood typing is done by checking the blood for the presence or absence of specific glycoproteins called **antigens** (AN-tih-jenz) that are found on the cell surface. Two clinically relevant antigens are the **A antigen** and the **B antigen**. The presence or absence of the A and B antigens determines the blood types known as the **ABO blood group** (Fig. 20.3).

- ■ Type A blood has A antigens on the cell surface.
- ■ Type B blood has B antigens on the cell surface.
- ■ Type AB blood has both A and B antigens on the cell surface.
- ■ Type O blood has neither A nor B antigens on the cell surface.

An additional clinically relevant antigen is the Rh antigen.

- ■ Blood that has the Rh antigen is denoted as Rh positive (e.g., A+).
- ■ Blood that lacks the Rh antigen is denoted as Rh negative (e.g., A−).

The prevalence of different blood types in the United States varies with different ethnic groups. In general, we can say that the most common type is O+, followed by A+, and then B+.

The antigens present on the surface of an erythrocyte can be determined by combining it with a solution called an **antiserum**. An antiserum is a solution that contains proteins, which are produced by B lymphocytes called **antibodies**. Each antibody binds specifically to a unique antigen. When antibodies bind to antigens,

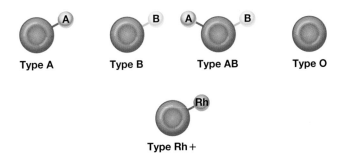

FIGURE 20.3 The basic ABO and Rh blood types.

they cause several effects, including: **agglutination** (uh-gloo-tin-AY-shun), or clumping of the antigen into antigen–antibody complexes, which are easier for phagocytes to ingest; binding and activating phagocytes and immune proteins; neutralizing bacterial toxins, viral proteins, and animal venoms, rendering them inactive; and stimulating inflammation.

Antibodies that bind with antigens on erythrocytes cause the erythrocytes to agglutinate. In this exercise, however, we are using simulated blood, so you won't see agglutination. The antisera used to determine the blood type of a sample are named according to the antigen they bind:

- ■ Anti-A antiserum contains anti-A antibodies that bind to erythrocytes with A antigens.
- ■ Anti-B antiserum contains anti-B antibodies that bind to erythrocytes with B antigens.
- ■ Anti-Rh antiserum contains anti-Rh antibodies that bind to erythrocytes with Rh antigens.

Be careful not to overthink this—if the solution is called anti-A, that just means that it binds to A antigens. Think of it like this: An anti-B solution is *anti* (or against) B antigens, so it binds and "attacks" them. It really is that simple.

20

Antigen–Antibody Reactions

This exercise allows you to examine the antigen–antibody reactions of known blood types. Each table should take one well plate and one set of dropper bottles. The bottles are labeled A−, B+, AB−, and O+ to represent each of those blood types, and anti-A, anti-B, and anti-Rh to represent the different antisera.

When you add a drop of antiserum to your sample, a positive reaction indicates that the antigen is present. So, if you add anti-A and you get a reaction, then you know that the A antigen is present. However, a negative reaction means that the antigen is absent. So, if nothing happens when you add anti-B or anti-Rh to your sample, then neither the B nor the Rh antigens are present.

You can see what a positive reaction looks like in Figure 20.4. Notice that a positive reaction is indicated by the formation of a white, cloudy precipitate. For example, notice in the type A+ sample that the solution is cloudy in the wells to which anti-A and anti-Rh antisera were added, which tells you that A and Rh antigens are present on the cell. Note also that there is no reaction in the well containing anti-B antiserum, which tells you the B antigen is absent. (Note, however, your sample may form either a granular or clumping precipitate, depending on the type of simulated blood used by your lab.).

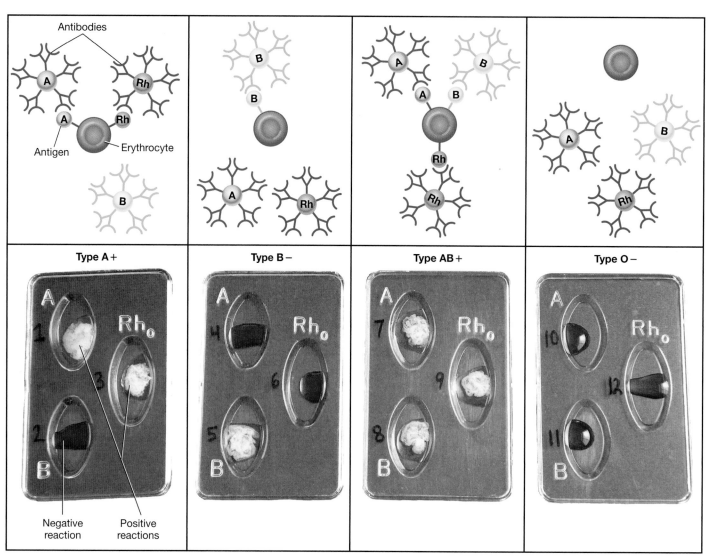

FIGURE **20.4** Reactions of simulated blood with simulated antisera.

20 **1** PROCEDURE

Testing Simulated Blood

Use Figure 20.5 as a guide to placement of samples in the wells. When you have completed the activity, answer Check Your Understanding Question 3 (p. 559).

1 Label wells on the well plate as Wells 1 through 12 with a permanent marker.

2 Drop two drops of type A− blood in Well 1, Well 2, and Well 3.

3 Drop two drops of type B+ blood in Well 4, Well 5, and Well 6.

4 Drop two drops of type AB− blood in Well 7, Well 8, and Well 9.

5 Drop two drops of type O+ blood in Well 10, Well 11, and Well 12.

6 Add two drops of the anti-A antiserum to Wells 1, 4, 7, and 10.

7 Add two drops of the anti-B antiserum to Wells 2, 5, 8, and 11.

8 Add two drops of the anti-Rh antiserum to Wells 3, 6, 9, and 12.

9 Observe the samples for changes in color symbolizing the agglutination or clumping that would normally occur between antisera and specific blood types. Record your results in Table 20.3.

⚠ **SAFETY NOTE**

Safety glasses and gloves are required!

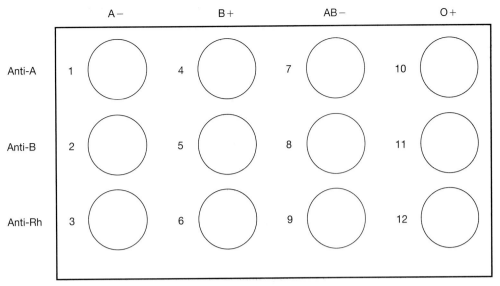

FIGURE **20.5** Well plate diagram.

TABLE **20.3** Blood Typing Results

Blood Type	Reacted with Anti-A? (Yes/No)	Reacted with Anti-B? (Yes/No)	Reacted with Anti-Rh? (Yes/No)	Antigens Present on Cell Surface
A−				
B+				
AB−				
O+				

20

EXERCISE 20-3

MATERIALS

❑ Well plate

❑ Simulated antisera: anti-A, anti-B, and anti-Rh

❑ Murder mystery game

Murder Mystery Game

In this game, you will be applying the blood-typing techniques you learned in Exercise 20-2 (p. 545) to solve a series of murder mysteries. Each of the following cases presents a victim, a murderer, three suspects, three possible murder rooms, and three possible murder weapons. Your job is to play the role of detective and determine the identity of the murderer, which weapon was used, and in which room the crime was committed.

---

1 PROCEDURE

Solving the Murder Mysteries

For each case, a unique set of bottles is marked with a number that corresponds to the specific cases (i.e., the bottles are marked 1 for Case 1, 2 for Case 2, and 3 for Case 3). The murderer, rooms, and murder weapons are different for each case, but the cast of characters remains the same across the cases.

1   To begin the game, assemble into groups of two or three students. Obtain a well plate, and choose one set of samples to test (e.g., the rooms from Case 1, the suspects from Case 2, or the weapons from Case 3).

2   Place two drops of the sample in each of three separate wells. Add two drops of anti-A antiserum to the first well, add two drops of anti-B antiserum to the second well, and add two drops of anti-Rh antiserum to the third well. After you have tested each of the samples, return them to their proper places in the front of the lab.

3   Watch for a reaction with the antisera. Remember that this is simulated blood, just as in Exercise 20-2. A positive reaction is denoted by the formation of a precipitate. Record your results in the spaces provided in your lab manual.

4   To determine the

a   *Murderer:* Match the blood type of one of the **suspects** to that of the murderer.

b   *Weapon and room:* Match the blood type of the **victim** to the blood types found in the rooms and on the weapon.

> **NOTE:** You are <u>not</u> trying to match the blood type of the victim to that of the murderer—that would mean the victim committed suicide!

Case 1: Ms. Magenta

We enter the scene to find the dearly departed Ms. Magenta. Forensic analysis determines that there are two types of blood on the body. One blood type is Ms. Magenta's, and the other blood type is a trace amount left behind from the murderer.

Ms. Magenta's blood type: _____   **Murderer's blood type:** _____

We have three suspects:

1.   *Mrs. Blanc* was being blackmailed by Ms. Magenta and Col. Lemon. They had discovered that Mrs. Blanc had murdered her late husband. Mrs. Blanc knew this would ruin her reputation at the country club.

2.   *Col. Lemon* wanted to keep the blackmail money for himself and wanted Ms. Magenta out of the way.

3.   *Mr. Olive* had been secretly in love with Ms. Magenta for years, and when he told her of his feelings, she rejected him harshly.

Mrs. Blanc's blood type: _____   **Col. Lemon's blood type:** _____

Mr. Olive's blood type: _____

We have three possible murder rooms:

Ballroom blood type: _____   **Library blood type:** _____

Den blood type: _____

We have three possible murder weapons:

Candlestick blood type: _____   **Noose blood type:** _____

Knife blood type: _____

Case 1: Conclusion

Ms. Magenta was killed by _____, in the _____, with the

_____.

Case 2: Col. Lemon

Our next victim is poor Col. Lemon. On his body, we find his blood and, also, trace amounts of the blood of another person, presumably the murderer.

Col. Lemon's blood type: _____   **Murderer's blood type:** _____

We have three potential suspects:

1. *Mrs. Blanc* could easily rid herself of her problem by disposing of the only other person who knows her secret—Col. Lemon.

2. *Professor Purple* believed the colonel had stolen his groundbreaking FrozenForehead™ wrinkle-eraser formula.

3. *Mr. Olive* couldn't stand the colonel because of his close relationship with Ms. Magenta.

Mrs. Blanc's blood type: _____   **Professor Purple's blood type:** _____

Mr. Olive's blood type: _____

We have blood in three different rooms:

Hall blood type: _____   **Kitchen blood type:** _____

Billiards room blood type: _____

Forensics found blood on three different weapons:

Copper pipe blood type: _____   **Hammer blood type:** _____

Revolver blood type: _____

Case 2: Conclusion

Col. Lemon was killed by _____, in the _____, with the _____

_____.

Case 3: Mr. Olive

Our next (and hopefully last) victim is Mr. Olive. Analysis demonstrates two blood types: one belonging to Mr. Olive, and trace amounts of another, belonging to the murderer.

Mr. Olive's blood type: _____   **Murderer's blood type:** _____

We have three potential suspects:

1. *Ms. Feather* simply didn't like Mr. Olive and thought that he had a "bad aura."

2. *Mrs. Blanc* was worried that Mr. Olive knew her secret and wanted him out of the way.

3. *Professor Purple* discovered that Mr. Olive—not Col. Lemon—had actually stolen the FrozenForehead™ formula. Whoops!

Ms. Feather's blood type: _____   **Mrs. Blanc's blood type:** _____

Professor Purple's blood type: _____

Blood was found in three rooms:

Lounge blood type: _____   **Dining room blood type:** _____

Greenhouse blood type: _____

We have three potential murder weapons:

Noose blood type: _____   **Hammer blood type:** _____

Revolver blood type: _____

Case 3: Conclusion

Mr. Olive was killed by _____, in the _____, with the

_____ .

Blood Donation

Blood transfusion, the infusion of a recipient with a donor's blood cells, is a commonly performed medical procedure. Before a recipient is given a blood transfusion, the medical team must first learn the patient's blood type and then find a suitable, or "matching," donor. This is necessary because of the A, B, and Rh antigens on the surface of the donor erythrocytes and the presence of preformed antibodies in the recipient's blood. If a donor's erythrocytes have antigens that the recipient's immune system recognizes as foreign, the recipient's antibodies will agglutinate the foreign erythrocytes. The agglutinated erythrocytes are then destroyed by the immune system, a process known as **hemolysis** (heem-AH-luh-sis; *-lysis* = "split"). This is called a **transfusion reaction,** and it is a medical emergency that can lead to kidney failure and death.

To ensure that a transfusion reaction does not occur, we must make sure the donor blood does not have antigens that the recipient's immune system will recognize as foreign. For the ABO blood group, our immune systems produce antibodies to any antigen *not* present on the surface of our own cells.

■ People with type A blood have A antigens and so produce anti-B antibodies.

■ People with type B blood have B antigens and so produce anti-A antibodies.

■ People with type O blood have neither A nor B antigens and so produce both anti-A and anti-B antibodies.

■ People with type AB blood have both A and B antigens and so produce neither anti-A nor anti-B antibodies.

If you're wondering about the Rh factor, wait just a moment—we're getting there. Let's do an example with the ABO blood group first: Felix has type B blood, which means that he has anti-A antibodies.

What will happen if we give him blood from a donor with:

■ Type A blood? There are A antigens on these donor erythrocytes, and Felix's anti-A antibodies would agglutinate them. ✘

■ Type B blood? Felix's anti-A antibodies would have no effect on the B antigens on these donor erythrocytes, so this blood is safe. ✔

■ Type O blood? There are neither A nor B antigens on these donor erythrocytes, so Felix's anti-A antibodies would have no effect on them, and this blood is safe. ✔

■ Type AB blood? There are both A and B antigens on these donor erythrocytes, and Felix's anti-A antibodies would bind and agglutinate the A antigens. ✘

Now, that's easy, isn't it?

Next, let's address the Rh factor. The blood of an Rh-negative person does *not* contain preformed antibodies to the Rh antigen. However, anti-Rh antibodies are made if an Rh-negative person is exposed to the Rh antigen. In an emergency setting, it is generally not possible to determine whether an Rh-negative person has been exposed to the Rh antigen, so healthcare professionals err on the side of caution and assume that the person has anti-Rh antibodies. For the sake of simplicity, we will assume the same thing in this exercise. So, for our purposes:

■ People with Rh-positive blood *do not* produce anti-Rh antibodies.

■ People with Rh-negative blood *do* produce anti-Rh antibodies.

Let's walk through one more example, taking into account the Rh factor this time: Lourdes has A− blood, which means that she has anti-_____ and anti-_____ antibodies.

What will happen if we give her blood from a donor with:

■ Type A+ blood? There are _____ and _____ antigens on these donor erythrocytes. Lourdes' anti-_____ antibodies would _____ the _____ antigens. ✘ or ✔?

■ Type B− blood? There are _____ antigens on these donor erythrocytes, and Lourdes' anti-_____ antibodies would _____ them. ✘ or ✔?

■ Type O− blood? There are _____ antigens on these donor erythrocytes, so Lourdes' anti-_____ and anti-_____ antibodies would have _____ on them. ✘ or ✔?

■ Type AB+ blood? There are _____, _____, and _____ antigens on these donor erythrocytes, and Lourdes' anti-_____ and anti-_____ antibodies would _____ them. ✘ or ✔?

1

PROCEDURE

Blood Type Matching Practice

Use the information from the preceding section and your text to complete Table 20.4. After you have filled in the table, answer Check Your Understanding Question 4 (p. 559).

TABLE **20.4** Blood Donation

Blood Type	Antigens Present	Antibodies Present	Can Donate Safely to Which Blood Types?	Can Receive Safely from Which Blood Types
A+				
A−				
B+				
B−				
AB+				
AB−				
O+				
O−				

You should notice something from looking at Table 20.4: People with AB+ blood can receive from any donor blood type, and people with O− blood can donate to any recipient blood type. This is because people with AB+ erythrocytes have all three antigens and so their blood contains no ABO or Rh antibodies to bind to donor blood. Conversely, people with type O− erythrocytes have none of the three antigens and so there is nothing for any recipient's antibodies to bind. For these reasons, type AB+ blood is often called the **universal recipient** and type O− blood is often called the **universal donor**.

2

PROCEDURE

Matching Blood Types for Transfusions

Gasp! It turns out that Ms. Magenta, Col. Lemon, and Mr. Olive all survived their injuries! But they have lost blood and need blood transfusions. All the suspects have had a sudden change of heart and have offered to help the three victims by donating blood. When they arrived at the hospital, the blood of all victims and suspects was retested. This was fortunate, as it turned out the results obtained at the crime scenes were inaccurate due to a suspected mole in the police lab. The correct blood types are listed in Table 20.5. Your job is to determine who among the suspects could safely donate blood to whom. After you have finished this activity, answer Check Your Understanding Questions 5 and 6 (p. 560).

TABLE **20.5** Corrected Blood Types of the Suspects and Victims

Suspect/Victim	Blood Type
Ms. Magenta	B+
Ms. Feather	O+
Mrs. Blanc	A−
Prof. Purple	AB−
Col. Lemon	AB+
Mr. Olive	O−

HINTS & TIPS

Remember—when trying to work out who can donate blood to whom, you are concerned with the recipient's antibodies and the donor's antigens. So, first work out which antibodies the recipient has, and then make sure the recipient's antibodies won't bind any antigens on the donor's erythrocytes.

Recipient 1: Ms. Magenta

Ms. Magenta's blood type: _____

Donors:

Ms. Feather's blood type: _____

Mrs. Blanc's blood type: _____

Professor Purple's blood type: _____

Who could safely donate blood to Ms. Magenta? _____

Who could not safely donate blood to Ms. Magenta? _____

Recipient 2: Col. Lemon

Col. Lemon's blood type: _____

Donors:

Ms. Feather's blood type: _____

Mrs. Blanc's blood type: _____

Professor Purple's blood type: _____

Who could safely donate blood to Col. Lemon? _____

Who could not safely donate blood to Col. Lemon? _____

Recipient 3: Mr. Olive

Mr. Olive's blood type: _____

Donors:

Ms. Feather's blood type: _____

Mrs. Blanc's blood type: _____

Professor Purple's blood type: _____

Who could safely donate blood to Mr. Olive? _____

Who could not safely donate blood to Mr. Olive? _____

MATERIALS

- ☐ Lancet
- ☐ Alcohol wipes
- ☐ Simulated antisera: anti-A, anti-B, and anti-Rh
- ☐ Slide: blank
- ☐ Permanent marker
- ☐ Toothpicks
- ☐ Tallquist paper and scale
- ☐ Dissection microscope or magnifying glass

Examination of Your Own Blood Type

If your lab has the appropriate equipment and biohazard disposal means, your instructor may permit you to type and examine your own blood in this optional exercise. Working with blood is actually very safe provided you follow some basic procedures outlined here:

1 Wash your hands with soap and water before starting and after completing the procedures.

2 Prepare your work area by placing a disposable absorbent liner on the lab table.

3 Wear gloves and safety glasses when handling all materials for this lab.

4 Handle only your own lab materials to avoid coming into contact with blood other than your own.

5 Dispose of all lancets and microscope slides in the designated sharps container only.

6 Dispose of all nonsharp materials (disposable pads, gloves, alcohol wipes, and any other materials you have used) in the designated red biohazard bag.

7 When you are finished with the procedures, clean your work area with the disinfectant solution provided by your lab instructor.

In the following procedures, you will determine your blood type and measure the approximate hemoglobin content of your blood. Note that these exercises involve lancing your own finger to stimulate bleeding. If you have any medical conditions that render this activity unsafe, discuss this with your lab instructor.

---

1 PROCEDURE

Determining Your Blood Type

The process of determining the blood type of real blood is similar to the one you performed earlier with simulated blood: You use three blood samples, and apply three different antisera to look for a reaction; in this case, you are looking for agglutination of erythrocytes (Fig. 20.6). The reaction between real blood antigens and antibodies is subtler than in the simulated blood; in particular, the reaction with Rh antigens and the anti-Rh antibodies can be difficult to see. You may wish to examine your samples under a magnifying glass to see the reaction more clearly.

> ⚠ **SAFETY NOTE**
> Safety glasses and gloves are required!

1 Obtain a blank microscope slide, and draw three circles on it with a permanent marker. Label the circles A, B, and Rh.

2 Wash your hands and prepare your work area with a disposable absorbent liner.

3 Place a glove on one hand, and prepare one finger of your ungloved hand by cleaning it with an alcohol wipe.

4 Use a fresh lancet to lance the finger you just cleaned. Dispose of the used lancet in the sharps bin.

5 Squeeze your finger to stimulate bleeding and squeeze a small drop of blood onto each of the three circles on the slide.

6 Place a drop of anti-A antiserum in the circle marked A, anti-B in the circle marked B, and anti-Rh in the circle marked Rh.

7 Use three toothpicks, one for each circle, to gently mix the blood with the antisera. You must use a different toothpick for each circle to avoid cross-contamination. Watch carefully for a reaction, using a dissection

FIGURE **20.6** Erythrocyte agglutination.

microscope or magnifying glass if needed (be sure to hold a magnifying glass in your gloved hand to avoid coming into contact with blood from your classmates).

8 Determine your blood type based upon the reactions with the antisera. Remember, if the blood reacts with an antiserum, that antigen is present. For example, if your blood reacts with anti-B antiserum and anti-Rh antiserum, the B and Rh antigens are present, and the blood type is B+. Record your blood type here: _____

9 Dispose of your microscope slide in the sharps bin when you have completed the blood typing procedure.

2 PROCEDURE
Determining the Hemoglobin Content of Your Blood

As you learned in Exercise 20-1, erythrocytes are filled with the protein hemoglobin, which binds and transports oxygen through the blood. The average amount of hemoglobin in erythrocytes averages about 12–16 g/dL in females and about 14–18 g/dL in males. Medically, this is an important value, because a decreased amount of hemoglobin can indicate conditions such as *iron-deficiency anemia*. In a hospital lab, the amount of hemoglobin in the blood is measured with an instrument known as a *hemoglobinometer*. However, in this lab we will employ an older (and less expensive) method using *Tallquist paper*, which provides an estimate of the blood's hemoglobin content.

1 Squeeze your finger to continue to stimulate bleeding. If you need to lance your finger again, obtain a new lancet, and follow the same steps from the first procedure.

2 Obtain a piece of Tallquist paper. Roll your bleeding finger on the paper.

3 Compare the color the paper turns with the scale on the container while the paper is still slightly wet—do not let the paper dry, or you will need to repeat the procedure.

Estimated hemoglobin value: _____

4 Dispose of any remaining sharps in the sharps container and all other blood-containing materials, including the Tallquist paper, in the red biohazard bag. Clean your work area with the disinfectant provided by your lab instructor.

3 PROCEDURE
Calculating the Average Hemoglobin and Most Common Blood Type for Your Class

After you have completed the first two procedures and cleaned up your work area, you may pool the results for your class to find the most common blood types and the average values for hemoglobin content.

1 Record your blood type on the whiteboard.

2 When everyone in the class has recorded his or her blood type, pool the results, and complete Table 20.6. Calculate the percentage of your class that has each blood type.

3 Your instructor will have two columns for hemoglobin values on the whiteboard, one for female and one for male members of the class. Write your estimated hemoglobin value on the whiteboard under the appropriate column.

4 When all of your classmates have recorded their numbers on the board, calculate the average value for the females and males of your class. Record these data in Table 20.7. How do the values for your class compare with the averages?

TABLE **20.6** Blood Types for Your Class

Blood Type	Number in Class	Percentage of Total
A+		
A−		
B+		
B−		
O+		
O−		
AB+		
AB−		

TABLE **20.7** Average Hemoglobin Values for Your Class

Group	Average Hemoglobin Value (g/dL)
Females	
Males	

Check Your Recall

1 *True/False:* Mark the following statements as true (T) or false (F). If the statement is false, correct it to make it a true statement.

_____ a. The hematocrit is the percent of blood composed of leukocytes.

_____ b. Erythrocytes transport oxygen through the body.

_____ c. Platelets function in blood clotting.

_____ d. Monocytes are the most numerous type of leukocyte.

_____ e. Lymphocytes are primarily involved in the allergic response.

2 Label the formed elements on the peripheral blood smear in Figure 20.7.

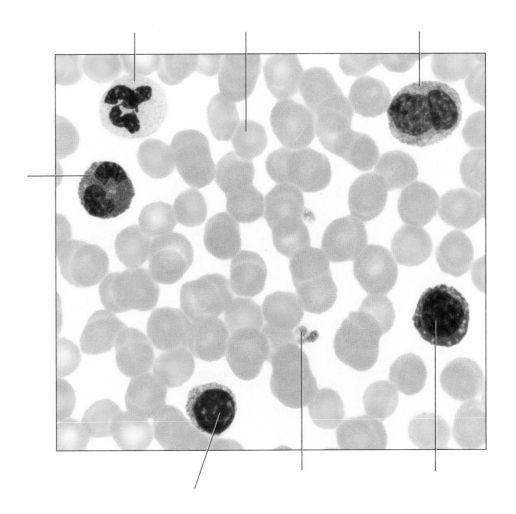

FIGURE **20.7** Peripheral blood smear.

3 Which of the following correctly describes the function of albumin?

a. Transports substances through the blood.

b. Functions in immunity.

c. Is part of the blood clotting cascade.

d. Draws water into blood vessels by osmosis.

4 Blood type O is characterized by having

a. A antigens.

b. B antigens.

c. O antigens.

d. Neither A nor B antigens.

e. Both A and B antigens.

5 Which antigens are present on the surface of erythrocytes of the following blood types?

a AB–

b O+

c O–

d A+

6 Which of the following correctly describes the actions of antibodies on erythrocytes?

a. Antibodies bind to antigens on the erythrocytes and agglutinate them.

b. Antibodies bind to foreign erythrocytes and directly kill them.

c. Antibodies digest dead, damaged, and foreign erythrocytes by phagocytosis.

d. Antibodies trigger the production of B and T lymphocytes.

7 *Circle all that apply.* A person with type A blood has which of the following antibodies?

a. Anti-A antibodies.

b. Anti-B antibodies.

c. Anti-O antibodies.

d. No antibodies.

8 *Circle all that apply.* A person with type O+ blood has which of the following antibodies? (Assume the person has been exposed to Rh antigens.)

a. Anti-A antibodies.

b. Anti-B antibodies.

c. Anti-Rh antibodies.

d. No antibodies.

9 When matching a donor and recipient for a blood transfusion, we are concerned with the

a. donor's antigens and the recipient's antigens.

b. donor's antigens and the recipient's antibodies.

c. donor's antibodies and the recipient's antibodies.

d. donor's antibodies and the recipient's antigens.

10 Why do blood banks ask people with type O– blood to donate, if they are able?

Check Your Understanding

Critical Thinking and Application Questions

1 Your hospital patient has been admitted for a cough, fever, and shortness of breath. Lab analysis of blood work shows an elevated leukocyte count with, specifically, a high lymphocyte count. The nurse practitioner says that, based on this information, the patient likely has a viral infection, although he needs further information to confirm the diagnosis. What led him to conclude that the patient has a viral infection, and why?

2 Most bone marrow transplants require the destruction of the recipient's own bone marrow with radiation and/or drugs. Why does this put patients at an increased risk of infection?

3 Professor Purple develops a poison in his lab that mimics anti-B antibodies. Will this poison be deadly to everyone, or only to certain people? Explain.

4 What effect will Professor Purple's poison have on its victims?

5 List all the blood types from which the following people could receive blood, assuming the recipients have been exposed to Rh antigens:

a Recipient 1: Type A−

b Recipient 2: Type O+

c Recipient 3: Type AB+

d Recipient 4: Type B−

6 List all the blood types to which the following people could donate, assuming the recipients have been exposed to Rh antigens:

a Donor 1: Type O−

b Donor 2: Type B+

c Donor 3: Type A+

d Donor 4: Type AB−

20

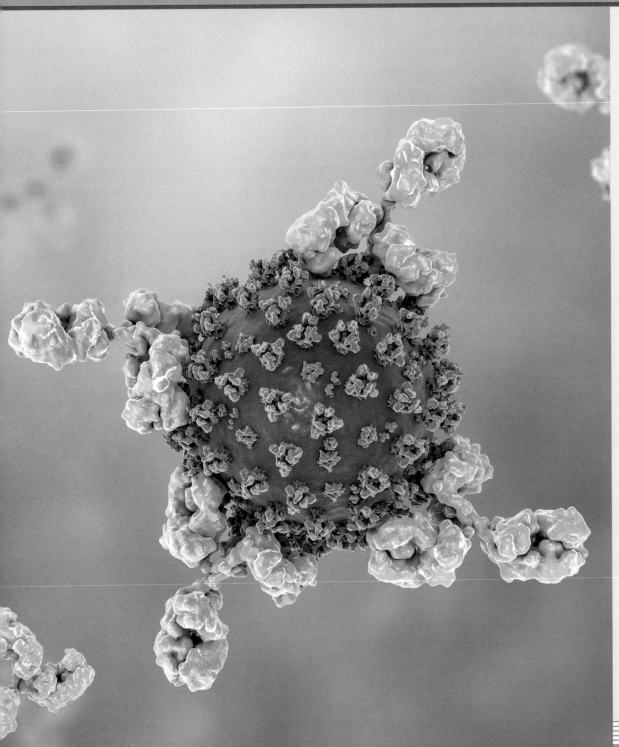

Lymphatics and Immunity

When you have completed this unit, you should be able to:

1. Describe and identify structures of the lymphatic system.

2. Describe the role of the immune system in processing lymph as it is returned to the heart.

3. Trace the pathway of lymph as it is returned to the cardiovascular system.

4. Identify features of lymphatic organs on microscope slides.

5. Describe the three lines of defense of the immune system and trace the immune response to a bacterial and viral infection.

6. Describe the theory behind the ELISA procedure.

PRE-LAB EXERCISES

Complete the following exercises prior to coming to lab, using your lab manual and textbook for reference.

PRE-LAB

21-1 Key Terms

You should be familiar with the following terms before coming to lab.

Term	Definition

Lymphatic Structures

Lymphatic capillary _____

_____

Lymph _____

_____

Lymph-collecting vessel _____

_____

Lymph trunk _____

_____

Thoracic duct _____

_____

Right lymphatic duct _____

_____

Thymus _____

_____

Lymph node _____

_____

Spleen _____

_____

Mucosa-associated lymphatic tissue _____

_____

Tonsil _____

_____

Components of the Immune System

Innate immunity _____

Inflammation _____

_____

Macrophage _____

_____

Adaptive immunity _____

_____

Antigen _____

_____

Humoral (antibody-mediated) immunity _____

_____

Antibody _____

_____

Cell-mediated immunity _____

_____

Helper T lymphocyte _____

_____

Cytotoxic T lymphocyte _____

_____

B lymphocyte _____

_____

21

Color the structures of the lymphatic system in Figure 21.1, and label them with the terms from Exercise 21-1 (p. 565). Use your text and Exercise 21-1 in this unit for reference.

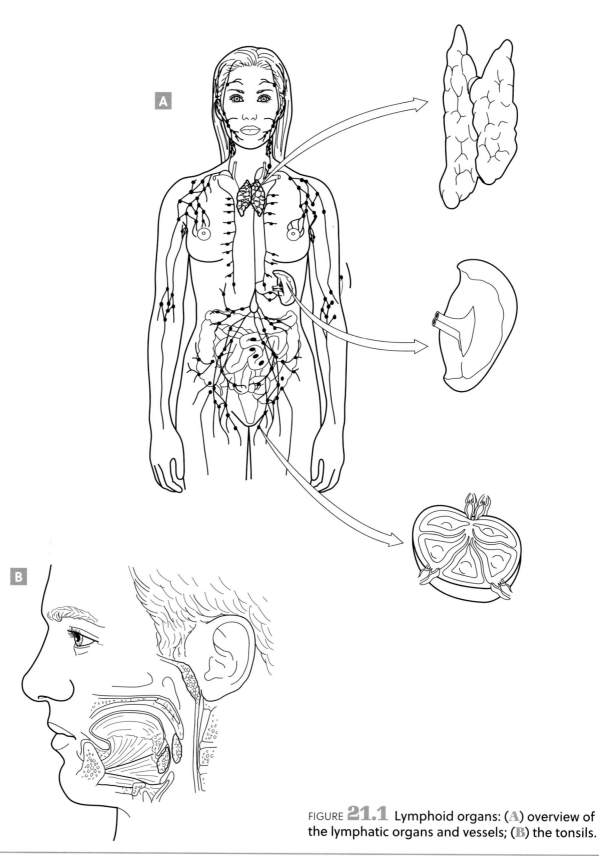

FIGURE **21.1** Lymphoid organs: (**A**) overview of the lymphatic organs and vessels; (**B**) the tonsils.

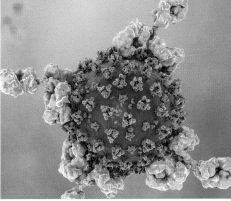

The **lymphatic system** (limf-Ă-tik) is a diverse group of organs, tissues, and vessels that serves numerous functions in the body. For one, it is an important part of the immune system and combats harmful agents in the internal and external environments. It also works with the cardiovascular system to maintain fluid homeostasis in the extracellular fluid and with the gastrointestinal system to absorb fats.

The exercises in this unit introduce you to this important system. In the first exercise, you will study the lymphatic system's anatomy, and trace the flow of lymph throughout the body. In the second exercise, you will examine different types of lymph tissue on microscope slides. Finally, in the last two exercises you will explore the immune system response.

Antibodies responding to SARS-CoV-2, illustration.

EXERCISE
21-1

MATERIALS

❏ Anatomical models and diagrams:
  ▪ human torso
  ▪ head and neck
  ▪ intestinal villus
❏ Laminated outline of the human body
❏ Water-soluble marking pens
❏ Colored pencils

Lymphatic System Anatomy

As you have learned, the lymphatic system consists of a diverse group of organs that have the following three primary functions:

1. **Transporting excess interstitial fluid back to the heart.** The process of filtration pushes water out of the blood and into the interstitial fluid. Approximately 1.5 mL/min of fluid is lost from the circulation in this manner. This may not sound like a lot, but if this fluid were not returned to the blood vessels, we would lose our entire plasma volume in about a day. Fortunately, the lymphatic system picks up this lost fluid, carries it through lymphatic vessels, and returns it to the cardiovascular system.

   The water in the interstitial fluid first enters small, blind-ended **lymph capillaries** (LIMF; *lymph* = "water") that surround blood capillary beds. These lymph capillaries have highly permeable walls that allow large substances and large volumes of fluid to enter and exit. Once inside the lymph capillaries, the fluid is called **lymph** and is delivered to larger **lymph-collecting vessels,** which contain valves to ensure that lymph flows in a single direction. Lymph-collecting vessels drain into larger **lymph trunks.** There are nine main lymph trunks that drain lymph from major body regions (Fig. 21.2A): the **jugular trunks,** which drain the head and the neck; the **subclavian trunks,** which drain the upper limbs; the **bronchomediastinal trunks** (brongk-oh-mee-dee-uh-STYN-uhl), which drain the thorax; the **intestinal trunk,** which drains the abdomen; and the **lumbar trunks,** which drain the pelvis and lower limbs.

   The lymph trunks then drain into the final vessels of the lymphatic circuit—**lymph ducts.** Note in Figure 21.2A that there are two lymph ducts: the **right lymphatic duct,** which drains the right upper limb and the right side of the head, neck, and thorax, and the **thoracic duct,** which drains lymph from the remainder of the body. The right lymphatic duct delivers lymph to the blood at the junction of the right subclavian and right internal jugular veins. Similarly, the thoracic duct drains lymph into the blood at the junction of the left subclavian and left internal jugular veins (Fig. 21.2B).

2. **Absorbing dietary fats.** Fats are not absorbed from the small intestine directly into the blood capillaries because they are too large to enter these small vessels. Instead, fats enter a lymphatic capillary called a **lacteal** (lak-TEEL; see Fig. 24.19, p. 654). The lacteal delivers fats to lymph-collecting vessels and intestinal trunks, after which the fatty lymph enters a large lymphatic vessel called the **cisterna chyli** (sis-TUR-nuh KY-lee; "juice box"). The cisterna chyli then drains into the thoracic duct, at which point the fats join the rest of the lymph.

3. **Activating the immune system.** Several lymphatic organs activate the *immune system,* a group of cells and proteins that protects the body from cellular injury such as trauma or pathogens (disease-causing organisms, cells, or chemicals). The lymphatic organs include the following:

   a. **Thymus.** The **thymus** is an organ composed of two lobes and many small lobules that is located in the anterior mediastinum (Fig. 21.2C). Recall from Unit 16, the endocrine system, that the thymus secretes the hormones thymosin and thymopoietin in order to stimulate T lymphocyte maturation. The thymus is also the site of T cell "selection," where T cells that react to self-antigens are destroyed. This prevents the release of T cells that may bind and attack our own cells.

      The thymus is largest and most active in infants and young children. In adults, it atrophies (shrinks) and becomes filled with adipose and other connective tissue. (Note that the adult thymus is smaller and less distinct than what is shown in Fig. 21.2C; the thymus is shown larger and more distinct here for clarity.)

21

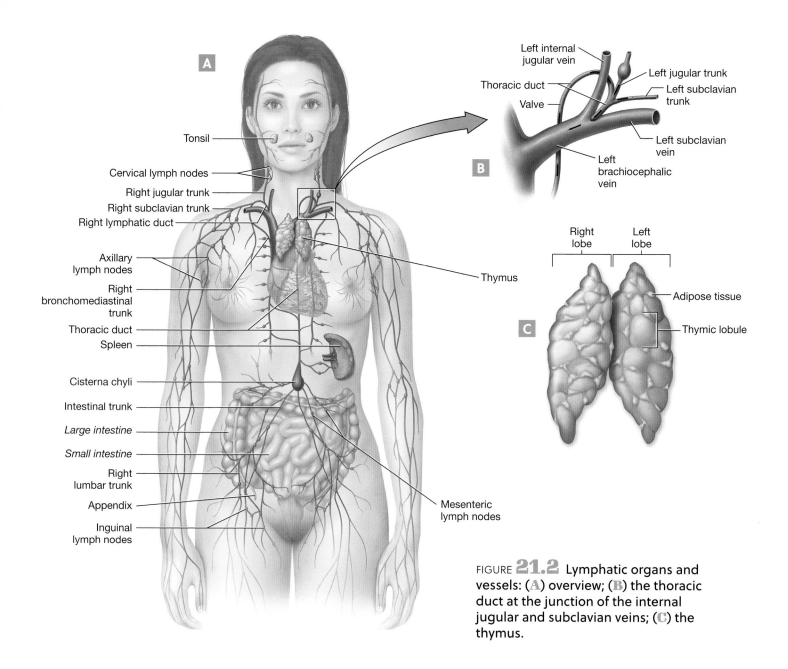

FIGURE **21.2** Lymphatic organs and vessels: (**A**) overview; (**B**) the thoracic duct at the junction of the internal jugular and subclavian veins; (**C**) the thymus.

Labels in figure:

- Tonsil
- Cervical lymph nodes
- Right jugular trunk
- Right subclavian trunk
- Right lymphatic duct
- Axillary lymph nodes
- Right bronchomediastinal trunk
- Thoracic duct
- Spleen
- Cisterna chyli
- Intestinal trunk
- *Large intestine*
- *Small intestine*
- Right lumbar trunk
- Appendix
- Inguinal lymph nodes
- Thymus
- Mesenteric lymph nodes

(B)
- Left internal jugular vein
- Thoracic duct
- Valve
- Left jugular trunk
- Left subclavian trunk
- Left subclavian vein
- Left brachiocephalic vein

(C)
- Right lobe
- Left lobe
- Adipose tissue
- Thymic lobule

b. **Lymph nodes.** The lymphatic organs called **lymph nodes** are arrangements of lymphatic tissue surrounded by a connective tissue capsule. Lymph nodes are often called "lymph glands," but this is a misnomer—they are not glands because they do not secrete any products. Instead, they act as filters that remove potential pathogens from the lymph before it is delivered to the blood. Lymph nodes are found along lymphatic vessels, where lymph is delivered by *afferent lymphatic vessels* and drained by an *efferent lymphatic vessel*. As lymph percolates through the node, it is filtered, pathogens are removed, and cells of the immune system are activated. All lymph nodes are individual, but there are clusters of them that are named as a group. Notice in Figure 21.2A that we find lymph nodes in clusters in specific areas; these groupings are referred to as the **cervical, axillary, inguinal** (IN-gwin-uhl), and **mesenteric** (or intestinal) **lymph nodes.**

Figure 21.3 shows the internal structure of a lymph node, which consists of an outer **cortex** and an inner **medulla.** In the cortex, immune cells such as lymphocytes and macrophages are arranged into clusters called **lymphoid follicles,** which are separated from one another by inward extensions of the capsule called *trabeculae.* In the center of lymphoid follicles are lighter areas called **germinal centers** where large numbers of B lymphocytes reside.

c. **Spleen.** The **spleen** is a lymphatic organ that resides in the upper left quadrant of the abdominopelvic cavity. Unlike lymph nodes, which filter lymph, the spleen filters blood. As you can see in Figure 21.4, it has two histologically distinct regions: red pulp and white pulp. The **red pulp,** found surrounding *trabecular veins,* contains macrophages that destroy old, damaged, and abnormal erythrocytes. **White pulp** contains T lymphocytes, B lymphocytes, macrophages, and dendritic cells that surround branches of the splenic artery called **central arteries.** Blood flows through the central arteries

21

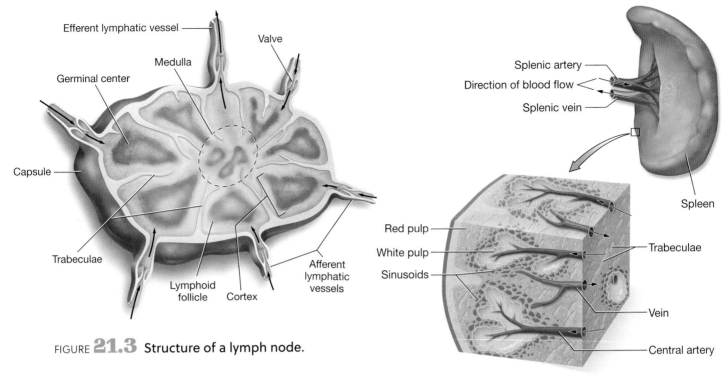

FIGURE **21.3** Structure of a lymph node.

FIGURE **21.4** Anatomy and microanatomy of the spleen.

and a series of arterioles until it gets to the spleen's very leaky capillaries: the *sinusoids*. From here, pathogens leak from the blood into the white pulp, where they encounter the many immune cells that attempt to remove them from the blood.

d. **Mucosa-associated lymphatic tissue and tonsils.** Clusters of loosely organized, unencapsulated lymphatic tissue are scattered throughout mucous membranes in locations such as the gastrointestinal tract. These clusters are known as **mucosa-associated lymphatic tissue**, or **MALT**. Most MALT lacks a connective tissue capsule; however, some types of MALT, known as specialized MALT, are partially encapsulated. The most prominent examples of specialized MALT are the **tonsils**, which are found in the posterior oropharynx and nasopharynx (Fig. 21.5). Notice in the figure the three named tonsils: the **pharyngeal tonsil** (or **adenoid**), located in the posterior nasopharynx; the paired **palatine tonsils**

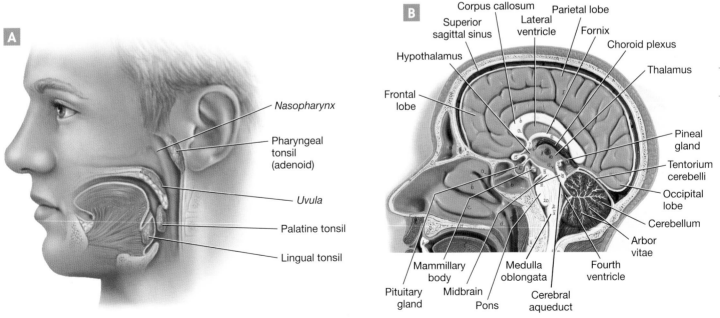

FIGURE **21.5** Anatomy of the tonsils: (**A**) midsagittal section of the oral cavity, illustration; (**B**) midsagittal section of the head, anatomical model photo.

(PAL-uh-ty'n), located in the oropharynx posterior to the soft palate; and the **lingual tonsil** (LING-yoo-uhl; *ling-* = "tongue"), located at the base of the tongue. There is another small pair of *tubal tonsils* adjacent to the opening of the pharyngotympanic tubes that may or may not be present in every individual.

In the following activities, you will identify structures of the lymphatic system, and then trace the flow of lymph through the vessels on its way back to the cardiovascular system. Your instructor may also wish you to dissect a preserved small mammal to identify some of the structures difficult to see on models, such as the thymus.

1 PROCEDURE
Model Inventory for the Lymphatic System

Identify the following structures of the lymphatic system on models and diagrams, using your textbook and this unit for reference. As you examine the anatomical models and diagrams, record the name of the model and the structures you were able to identify on the model inventory in Table 21.1. When you have completed this activity, answer Check Your Understanding Questions 1 through 3 (p. 585).

1. Lymph vessels
   a. Lymph-collecting vessels
   b. Lymph trunks: jugular, subclavian, bronchomediastinal, intestinal, lumbar trunks
   c. Right lymphatic duct
   d. Thoracic duct
   e. Lacteal
   f. Cisterna chyli
2. Blood vessels: internal jugular vein, subclavian vein, brachiocephalic vein
3. Thymus (this may be best viewed on a fetal model)

4. Lymph nodes
   a. Cervical lymph nodes
   b. Axillary lymph nodes
   c. Inguinal lymph nodes
   d. Mesenteric lymph nodes
5. Spleen
6. Mucosa-associated lymphatic tissue (MALT)
7. Tonsils
   a. Pharyngeal tonsil
   b. Palatine tonsils
   c. Lingual tonsil

TABLE **21.1** Model Inventory for the Lymphatic System

Model/Diagram	Structures Identified

2 PROCEDURE
Tracing the Flow of Lymph Through the Body

In this procedure, you'll trace the pathway of lymph flow from the starting location to the point at which the lymph is delivered to the cardiovascular system. You will trace the flow through the major lymph-collecting vessels, trunks, and ducts, and highlight clusters of lymph nodes through which the lymph passes as it travels.

1 Write the sequence of the flow.

2 Then, use differently colored water-soluble markers to draw the pathway on a laminated outline of the human body. If no outline is available, use colored pencils and Figure 21.6.

3 Trace the flow from the following locations:

Start: Left Foot _____

_____

_____

_____

_____

_____

Start: Right Side of the Head _____

_____

_____

_____

_____

_____

Start: Intestines (with Fat) _____

_____

_____

_____

_____

_____

_____

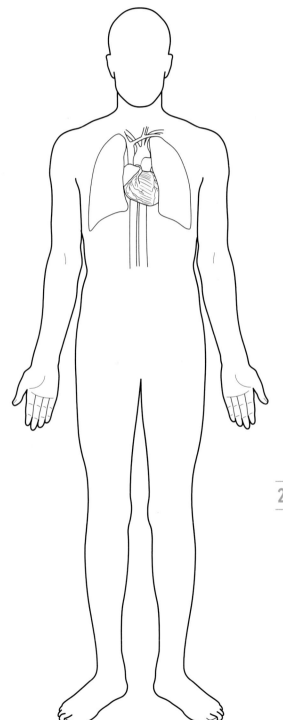

FIGURE **21.6** Outline of human body, anterior view.

EXERCISE 21-2

Lymphatic Organ Histology

In this exercise, you will examine the microscopic anatomy of four different lymphatic organs and tissues: the spleen, a lymph node, a special type of MALT found in the terminal portion of the small intestine called a **Peyer's patch**, and the **palatine tonsil**. Following are some hints regarding what to look for on each slide.

1. **Spleen.** As you read in Exercise 21-1, the spleen consists of two types of tissue: **red pulp**, which is involved in the destruction of old and worn-out red blood cells, and **white pulp**, which contains phagocytes and lymphocytes that play a role in the immune system. Notice in Figure 21.7A that the red pulp is reddish in color, but the white pulp doesn't appear on the slide as white; instead, it appears as purplish "islands" within the red pulp. The purple color is caused by the presence of white blood cells, which have prominent nuclei that stain purple with commonly used stains.

2. **Lymph node.** Recall that lymph nodes have an outer **cortex** that contains spherical clusters of immune cells (primarily B lymphocytes) called lymphoid follicles. In the center of the follicle is a lighter-staining region consisting of B lymphocytes, dendritic cells, and macrophages called a **germinal center** (Fig. 21.7B). Deep to the lymphoid follicles, we find an area of the cortex that houses primarily T lymphocytes. The innermost region of the node, called the **medulla**, houses primarily macrophages. The entire lymph node is surrounded by a capsule made of dense irregular connective tissue. Start first on low power and find the lymphoid follicles, then advance to higher powers to see them in greater detail.

3. **Peyer's patch. Peyer's patches** are clusters of MALT located in the terminal portion of the small intestine, which is called the *ileum.* This portion of the small intestine is continuous with the large intestine, which contains a large number of bacteria. The small intestine normally contains no bacteria, so these Peyer's patches play an important role in protecting it from any bacteria that migrate in from the large intestine. The Peyer's patches somewhat resemble lymph nodes, although their lymphoid follicles and germinal centers are less well defined, and their capsules are incomplete or absent (Fig. 21.7C). To have the best chance of finding them, examine your section on low power, and look for the epithelial lining of the small intestine. Scroll downward (deep to the epithelium) into the connective tissue, where you will note large, oval or teardrop-shaped, purplish clusters. These are Peyer's patches.

4. **Tonsil.** As tonsils have similar functions to MALT and lymph nodes, they also have a similar structure (Fig. 21.7D). Internally, they also consist of lymphoid follicles with germinal centers. Externally, however, they are lined with stratified squamous epithelium and feature deep indentations called **tonsillar crypts** that help to trap pathogens in the oral cavity. You will have the best chance of finding all these structures by examining your slide on low power.

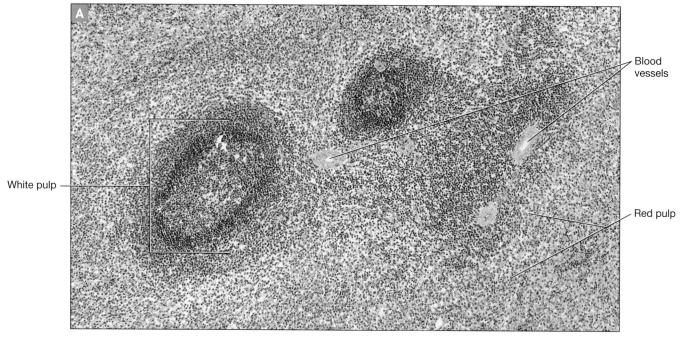

White pulp

Blood vessels

Red pulp

FIGURE **21.7** Lymphatic organs, photomicrographs: (**A**) spleen; *(continues)*

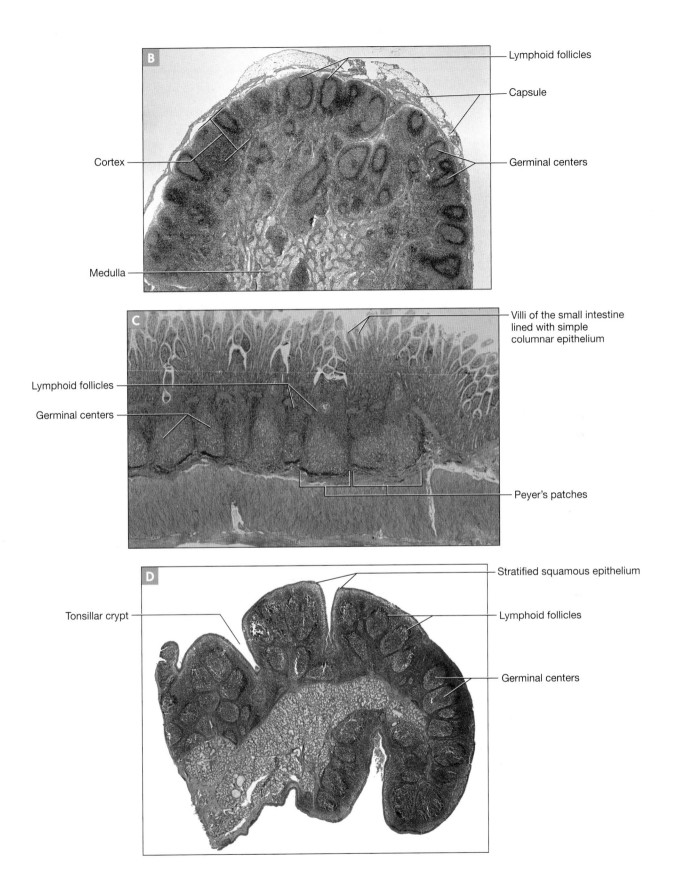

Lymphoid follicles

Capsule

Cortex

Germinal centers

Medulla

Villi of the small intestine lined with simple columnar epithelium

Lymphoid follicles

Germinal centers

Peyer's patches

Stratified squamous epithelium

Tonsillar crypt

Lymphoid follicles

Germinal centers

FIGURE **21.7** Lymphatic organs, photomicrographs (*cont.*): (**B**) lymph node; (**C**) Peyer's patches in the ileum; (**D**) palatine tonsil.

21

Obtain prepared slides of the spleen, a lymph node, the small intestine (the *ileum*), and the palatine tonsil. Use your colored pencils to draw what you see in the field of view, and label your drawing with the listed terms. When you have completed the activity, answer Check Your Understanding Question 4 (p. 585).

1 Spleen

- ■ Red pulp
- ■ White pulp

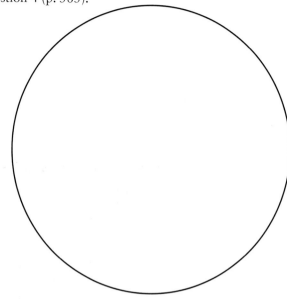

2 Lymph Node

- ■ Capsule
- ■ Cortex
- ■ Medulla
- ■ Lymphoid follicle
- ■ Germinal center

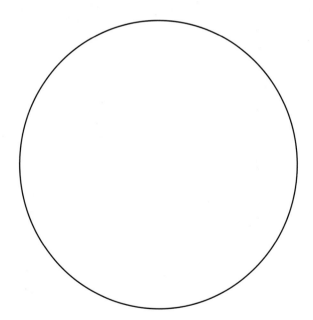

21

3 Peyer's Patch

- ■ Mucosa (simple columnar epithelium)
- ■ Peyer's patch
- ■ Lymphoid follicle
- ■ Germinal center

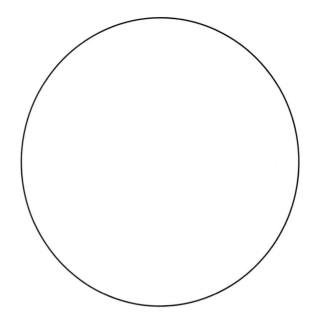

4 Palatine Tonsil

- ■ Stratified squamous epithelium
- ■ Tonsillar crypt
- ■ Lymphoid follicle
- ■ Germinal center

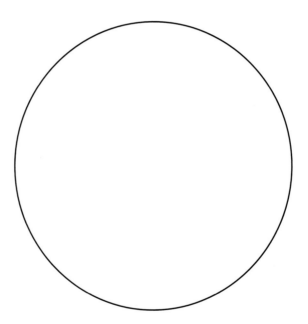

The Immune Response

The immune system may be divided into three lines of defense against tissue injury:

- The first line of defense involves **surface barriers** that prevent the entry of pathogens into the body. Surface barriers include the skin and mucous membranes. Both provide continuous, avascular surfaces. In addition, they secrete substances to deter the growth of microorganisms, wash away pathogens, and/or trap foreign particles.

- The second line of defense consists of the responses of the cells and proteins that are collectively known as **innate immunity**, which reacts the same way to any invading organism or cellular injury. The components of innate immunity are named as such because we are born with these responses, and they do not require exposure to a foreign cell or molecule to be produced.

- The third line of defense consists of the responses of the cells and proteins of **adaptive immunity**, which respond to foreign cells and molecules with a unique set of cells and molecules for each individual threat. The components of adaptive immunity do require exposure to a foreign agent to be produced, and for this reason they are often referred to as **acquired immunity**.

The responses of innate immunity may be subdivided into the following:

- **Inflammation and fever.** When cells are damaged by microorganisms, foreign cells, toxins, viruses, or trauma, the injured cells release chemicals called **inflammatory mediators**. The inflammatory mediators first attract local immune cells—which are primarily macrophages as they reside in many tissues—to the area. Inflammatory mediators also stimulate local *vasodilation*, which causes the area to become red and warm; *increased capillary permeability*, which causes the area to become swollen; and *increased sensitivity to pain*. As this occurs, activated macrophages continue to release inflammatory mediators that attract other phagocytes, particularly neutrophils, to the damaged area in large numbers in a process called *chemotaxis*. Macrophages and other cells also produce inflammatory mediators called **pyrogens** (PY-roh-jenz; *pyro-* = "fire") that act on the hypothalamus to raise the body temperature "set point." This results in the elevated temperatures known as **fever**.

- **Cells.** Several cell types function in innate immunity. First are the body's main phagocytic cells: the **macrophages** (mature monocytes) and the **granulocytes** (**neutrophils, basophils,** and **eosinophils**). These cells nonspecifically ingest and destroy any damaged cells as well as foreign cells such as bacteria. Macrophages are the first to arrive on the scene, and can perform this task repeatedly. Neutrophils arrive later. They can ingest a cell only once, after which they die. When tissue damage is extensive, many neutrophils in one area will die and accumulate, leaving a whitish liquid called **pus**. Note that eosinophils and basophils can function as phagocytes, but their main role is to secrete inflammatory mediators such as histamine.

    Another type of phagocytic cell is the **dendritic cell** (*dendr-* = "branches"). These cells, named for their spiky processes, reside in the skin, mucous membranes, and lymphatic organs such as lymph nodes and the spleen. When they encounter foreign cells, they ingest them and process the foreign antigens. Dendritic cells then display a portion of the antigen on their surfaces and migrate to lymphatic organs such as lymph nodes. Here, they activate T lymphocytes of adaptive immunity. In this way, dendritic cells are **antigen-presenting cells** that link the innate and adaptive immune responses.

    Nonphagocytic cells also function in innate immunity. One such cell is the **natural killer** or **NK** cell—a type of lymphocyte that can recognize cancerous cells and cells infected with viruses. NK cells release substances that destroy their target cells and other substances that attract phagocytes.

- **Antimicrobial proteins.** Several proteins in the blood will nonspecifically attack and lyse invading organisms when activated. The largest such system is the **complement system**, a collection of more than 20 proteins, most of which are made by the liver. Complement proteins perform a variety of functions, including lysing foreign cells, enabling phagocytes to function better, and enhancing the inflammatory response.

    Another important group of antimicrobial proteins is the **interferons** (in-ter-FEER-ahnz; abbreviated **IFN**). Interferons are produced by macrophages, dendritic cells, NK cells, and cells of adaptive immunity—generally in response to cancer cells or intracellular pathogens (viruses or intracellular bacteria). The name "interferon" comes from their ability to "interfere" with pathogens as they attempt to infect additional cells. They do this by inhibiting viral replication inside infected cells and activating components of both innate and adaptive immunity.

Adaptive immunity involves primarily B and T lymphocytes (generally referred to as *B* and *T cells*), which respond specifically to unique **antigens**, or chemical markers. Antigens are present in many molecules, such as toxins and allergens,

21

and on the surfaces of all cells, including our own cells. Each population of T and B cells has a unique receptor that binds to a unique antigen.

There are two branches of adaptive immunity: *humoral* and *cell-mediated immunity*. **Humoral immunity**, which is also known as *antibody-mediated immunity*, is a response brought about by B cells and proteins they produce called **antibodies**. The humoral response is initiated when an antigen binds a B cell. This, along with help from T cells, causes the B cell to activate and differentiate into two cell types: **plasma cells**, which secrete antibodies, and **memory cells**, which will "remember" the antigen and permit a more rapid antibody response upon subsequent exposures. This phenomenon of **immunological memory** is the basis for vaccines—an individual is intentionally exposed to an antigen to stimulate the production of antibodies and memory cells.

As you learned in the blood unit, antibodies are proteins that bind and **agglutinate** antigens, causing them to clump together. This facilitates their destruction by phagocytes and other components of the immune system. Antibodies also activate innate defenses, particularly complement defenses, and neutralize toxins such as venoms.

As its name implies, **cell-mediated immunity** is mediated by cells—specifically T cells—rather than by antibodies. Of the several different kinds of T cells, we will consider two here: the **CD4**, or **helper T cells** (T_H cells), and the **CD8**, or **cytotoxic T cells** (T_C cells). The cell-mediated response begins when an antigen-presenting cell, such a dendritic cell, ingests an antigen. It then presents the antigen to the T_H cell that has a receptor for that specific antigen. The T_H cell then secretes chemicals called **cytokines** (SY-toh-kyn'z), which attract cells of innate immunity such as macrophages; encourage inflammation; activate B cells; and activate T_C cells. The activated T_C cells bind to cells whose antigens correspond to their receptors. The T_C cells then release proteins called *perforins* that lyse and destroy their target cells. The cells targeted by T_C cells may include cancer cells, transplanted cells, and those infected with viruses or intracellular bacteria. Both T_H and T_C cells may become **memory T cells**, which "remember" the antigen and mount a stronger, faster response upon subsequent exposure.

Note that any kind of cell damage or invading organism is potentially met with all three lines of defense. For example, cancer cells are prevented from spreading by surface barriers; are phagocytized by granulocytes and macrophages in the blood and in the lymph nodes; are lysed by antimicrobial proteins released when healthy cells are damaged; cause local and systemic inflammation and fever; are met with an antibody response from B cells; and are located and lysed by T_C cells. This same cascade of responses is seen with viral infections, bacterial infections, envenomations, severe burns, major trauma, organ and tissue transplantations, fungal infections, parasitic infections, and more.

Let's look at an example of how all the parts function together. Figure 21.8 walks through the immune response to SARS-CoV-2, the virus that causes COVID-19. This is, of course, a simplification of the overall response, but it provides a general overview of some of the main parts and how they interact. The general steps proceed as follows:

1. **The infected cells are damaged by the virus, which triggers an inflammatory response and interferon secretion.** When SARS-CoV-2 particles are inhaled, they bind to receptors on local cells called ACE-2 receptors. The particles then enter the cell, where their RNA hijacks the host cell's ribosomes and other cellular machinery to make more copies of SARS-CoV-2. In response to infection, the damaged cells secrete interferons and inflammatory mediators.

2. **Interferons protect neighboring cells and activate NK cells, which lyse infected cells. Dendritic cells in the nasal mucosa ingest infected cells by phagocytosis.** Interferons act on neighboring cells, preventing SARS-CoV-2 from entering and infecting them. In addition, interferons bind and activate NK cells, which secrete chemicals that perforate infected cells, thus killing them. The death of infected cells prevents the virus from using those cells to make more copies of itself. Local dendritic cells in the nasal mucosa ingest infected cells, processing the SARS-CoV-2 antigens and displaying them on their surface.

3. **Dendritic cells migrate to lymphatic tissues, where they activate T_H and T_C cells.** These dendritic cells enter the lymph and migrate to lymphatic tissues such as lymph nodes. Here, the dendritic cells act as antigen-presenting cells, activating T_H cells.

4. **T_H cells activate B cells, which differentiate into plasma cells and memory cells. Plasma cells secrete antibodies, which neutralize the virus.** The activated T_H cells in turn activate B cells that have bound to viral particles. When activated, B cells differentiate into plasma cells and memory B cells. The plasma cells become "antibody factories," secreting antibodies that bind to the viral particles. This effectively neutralizes the SARS-CoV-2 particles, rendering them unable to infect cells.

5. **T_H cells secrete cytokines to enhance both innate and adaptive immunity. They also secrete cytokines that activate T_C cells, which lyse infected cells.**

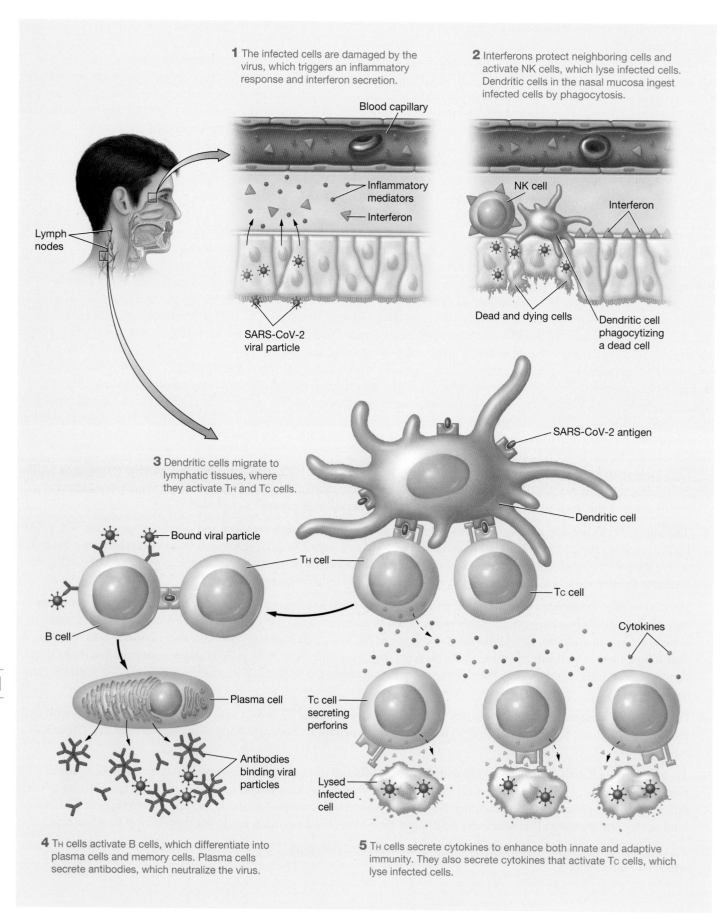

1 The infected cells are damaged by the virus, which triggers an inflammatory response and interferon secretion.

2 Interferons protect neighboring cells and activate NK cells, which lyse infected cells. Dendritic cells in the nasal mucosa ingest infected cells by phagocytosis.

Blood capillary

Inflammatory mediators

Interferon

Lymph nodes

NK cell

Interferon

Dead and dying cells

Dendritic cell phagocytizing a dead cell

SARS-CoV-2 viral particle

3 Dendritic cells migrate to lymphatic tissues, where they activate TH and Tc cells.

SARS-CoV-2 antigen

Dendritic cell

Bound viral particle

TH cell

Tc cell

Cytokines

B cell

Plasma cell

Tc cell secreting perforins

Antibodies binding viral particles

Lysed infected cell

4 TH cells activate B cells, which differentiate into plasma cells and memory cells. Plasma cells secrete antibodies, which neutralize the virus.

5 TH cells secrete cytokines to enhance both innate and adaptive immunity. They also secrete cytokines that activate Tc cells, which lyse infected cells.

FIGURE **21.8** The overall immune response to SARS-CoV-2.

21

PROCEDURE

Time to Trace!

In this procedure, you will be tracing two invaders: bacteria in the extracellular fluid and a virus that has infected cells. To keep things simple, you will trace the *main* pathway and the *main* immune response to the pathogen. Do note, however, that the actual response is much more complex, and your instructor may wish you to include more information. You are provided with hints and the number of steps you should aim to include for each organism, but you will likely want to consult your textbook for more help. After you have completed the activity, answer Check Your Understanding Questions 5 and 6 (p. 586).

Start: bacteria in the extracellular fluid → bacteria damage local macrophages and damaged macrophages release

_____ _____ that attract _____ to the area

→ these cells phagocytize _____ and bacteria and secrete

chemicals to attract granulocytes called _____ → at the same time, cells called _____

_____ cells ingest bacteria and migrate to _____ → these

cells present antigens to T_H cells → T_H cells activate _____ cells , which differentiate into _____

_____ cells and _____ cells → _____ cells proliferate

and secrete proteins called _____ , which _____ and

_____ the bacteria → **End**

Start: viruses infect cells and cause cellular damage → damaged cells release _____

_____ and _____ → _____ cells

arrive and _____ infected cells → _____ protects neighboring cells →

_____ cells ingest infected cells by _____ and process viral

_____ → _____ cells migrate to _____

_____ → _____ cells present antigens to _____

cells → T_H cells activate _____ cells, which differentiate into _____ cells

and _____ cells → _____ cells proliferate and secrete proteins called

_____ , which _____ and _____

the viral particles → T_H cells secrete _____ , which activate _____

cells → _____ cells secrete _____ , which _____

infected cells **End**

MATERIALS

- ☐ ELISA well plate
- ☐ Micropipettor and tips
- ☐ Microcentrifuge tube with "blood" sample
- ☐ Empty microcentrifuge tube
- ☐ Antibody solution
- ☐ Colorant solution
- ☐ Washing solution
- ☐ Permanent marker

ELISA Test for Antigens: Tracking the Spread of a Viral Outbreak

When an infectious agent is present in a population, there are well-established methods to control the spread. With the advent of the COVID-19 pandemic—caused by the virus SARS-CoV-2—we all learned more than we ever imagined about two such methods: *quarantine* (staying home when possible) and *social distancing* (remaining at least 6 feet from people not from your own household).

Like many viruses, SARS-CoV-2 spreads when people are in close contact for an extended period. This is because the virus is spread by respiratory droplets, which enter the air when an infected person coughs, sneezes, or talks. Quarantine and social distancing are especially important with SARS-CoV-2 because people can unknowingly spread the virus—it is transmissible before a person shows symptoms and by those with an asymptomatic infection.

Another well-established method to combat the spread of viruses like SARS-CoV-2 is with **contact tracing**—working with infected individuals to list everyone with whom they have been in close contact while possibly infected. Public health professionals then contact individuals on that list so those individuals can practice self-quarantine. This limits the ability of a single person to exponentially spread the infection. Extensive contract tracing can also be used to identify the original infected person, who is known as "patient zero."

The most commonly used test for SARS-CoV-2 is a technique called *RT-PCR* (reverse transcriptase polymerase chain reaction), which looks for viral RNA sequences unique to SARS-CoV-2. Another way to test for a history of infection is a laboratory test called **ELISA**, which stands for **enzyme-linked immunosorbent assay**. ELISA allows you to detect the presence of antibodies or antigens. The antibody test, which is used for SARS-CoV-2, determines whether a sample contains antibodies that bind to receptor proteins in the test. The antigen test determines whether a sample contains antigens that bind to antibodies in the test.

In this exercise, we use the type of ELISA that tests for antigens in a sample. The basic procedure is outlined in Figure 21.10. As you can see, samples are added to wells, and any antigens present in the solution bind to the base of the wells. In the next step, a solution containing antibodies is added to the wells. The antibodies will bind to the antigens at the base of the well. In the final step, a colorant is added. The colorant reacts with an enzyme associated with the antibody. Notice in Figure 21.9 that the colorants in Wells 1 and 2 react with the enzyme on the antibody and change the color of the solution. This is read as a positive result, meaning that the antigen for which you were initially testing was present in the solution. Well 3, on the other hand, has no antibodies with which the colorant can react, and so it does not change color. This is interpreted as a negative reaction, meaning your test solution did not contain the antigen in question.

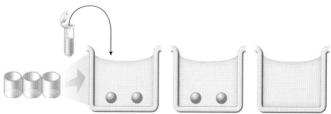

Three samples are placed in wells. Note that the samples placed in Wells 1 and 2 have antigens; the sample placed in Well 3 has no antigen.

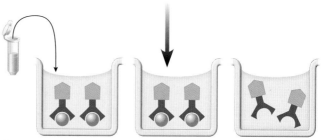

An antibody solution is added to all three wells. The antibodies bind to the antigens in Wells 1 and 2 and are not removed in the washing step. The antibodies in Well 3 do not bind to antigens and so are washed away in the washing step.

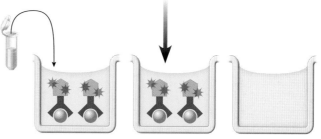

A colorant is added that binds to an enzyme associated with the antibody. This leads to a colored solution in Wells 1 and 2 and no color in Well 3.

FIGURE **21.9** The basic ELISA procedure and interpretation of ELISA results.

21

In this procedure, you will demonstrate the spread of infection of SARS-CoV-2 through your class (note that no samples have the actual virus—the antigens in the samples are harmless). Each student will be given a sample that represents his or her own body fluids. One or two random members of your class will receive a sample with the antigen; these samples represent the "infected" individuals. During the first part of the procedure, you'll mimic a non-socially distanced event, exchanging portions of your "body fluids" sample with three classmates. For the second part (Step 5), you'll run the ELISA and determine who among your classmates has become infected with SARS-CoV-2. At the end of the procedure, you'll perform contact tracing to attempt to determine who had the original infected sample. When you have completed the procedure, answer Check Your Understanding Question 7 (p. 586).

> **Hypothesis:** What percent of the class will become infected if the class is provided with 1–2 positive "patient zero" samples?

1. Obtain two microcentrifuge tubes from your instructor: one tube containing a fluid to be your "body fluid" sample and one empty tube. Use a marker to write your initials on each tube. Label the fluid sample tube "1" and the empty tube "2."

2. Use a micropipettor to withdraw 200 μL of your sample from Tube 1. Transfer this 200 μL to the empty Tube 2. Set Tube 2 aside for now. (**Note:** If you don't have a micropipettor, 200 μL is about 4 drops of liquid.)

3. At your instructor's prompt, begin the swapping portion of the lab, which mimics a gathering such as a party. Note that you should choose partners from the entire lab, not just your immediate lab group.

   a. Randomly choose a partner in your lab. Use a micropipettor to withdraw 100 μL of your sample from Tube 1, and place it into your partner's Tube 1. Your partner will do the same: They will use a micropipettor to withdraw 100 μL of the sample in their Tube 1, and transfer it to your tube. (**Note:** If you don't have a micropipettor, 100 μL is about 2 drops of liquid.)

   b. Mix the solution in your Tube 1—which should contain 100 μL of your sample and 100 μL of your partner's sample—with a stirring rod or the micropipettor tip.

   c. Choose another partner in your lab, and repeat the procedure. Your tube should now contain your original sample and portions from two classmates' samples.

   d. Choose your third and final partner, and repeat the procedure. At the end, your microcentrifuge tube will contain four total samples: yours and three from your classmates. Record the names of each partner here:

   ■ Partner 1: _____

   ■ Partner 2: _____

   ■ Partner 3: _____

4. Ensure your sample is thoroughly mixed, using a stirring rod or the micropipettor tip. Write your initials at the top of one column on your group's ELISA plate. Use a micropipettor to transfer 100 μL of the thoroughly mixed sample into the first well of the column. Transfer another 100 μL to the second well of the column; and transfer a final 100 μL to the third well of the column (300 μL total). You are running three tests to ensure accurate results.

5. When all partners have added their samples to the wells, follow the ELISA procedural steps illustrated in Figure 21.10:

   a. Set a timer for 5 minutes. Allow the plate to sit undisturbed on your lab table for those 5 minutes.

   b. After 5 minutes have passed, empty the contents of the plate into a sink or designated container. If antigens were present in your solution, they will be bound to the bottom of the well.

   c. Rinse the wells with washing solution. Discard the fluid in the sink or designated container. Repeat this procedure three times.

   d. Use a micropipettor to add 100 μL of antibody solution to each well. When all partners have added antibody solution to the wells, set a timer for 5 minutes. Allow the plate to sit undisturbed on your lab table for those 5 minutes.

e After 5 minutes have passed, empty the contents of the plate into the sink or designated container. Rinse the wells with washing solution and discard the fluid in the sink or designated container. Repeat this procedure three times.

f Use a micropipettor to add 100 µL of colorant solution to each well. Set a timer for 5 minutes. Allow the plate to sit undisturbed on your lab table for those 5 minutes.

6 Interpret your results. Who among your group was infected with the SARS-CoV-2?

_____

_____

7 Compile the results for your class to perform contact tracing.

a How many were infected? _____

b Determine as a class who you believe had the initial infected sample(s).

_____

8 Determine to whom the initial infected sample belonged by running an ELISA on the contents of Tube 2. Repeat Step 5 of this procedure with this uncontaminated sample.

9 Compile the data for your class and interpret your results.

a Who in your class had the initial infected sample(s), according to these results?

_____

b What percentage of the class was infected at the beginning? _____

c What percentage of the class was infected following the "party"? _____

d What does this say about the importance of quarantine and social distancing in reducing the spread of infection?

_____

_____

_____

10 Compare your results to your hypothesis.

_____

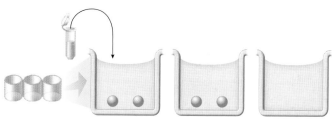

Step 5a: When everyone has added samples to the wells, allow the plate to sit undisturbed on your lab table for 5 minutes.

Step 5b: After 5 minutes have passed, empty the contents of the plate into a sink or designated container. If antigens were present in your solution, they will be bound to the bottom of the well.

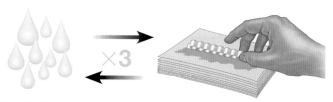

Step 5c: Rinse the wells with washing solution, and discard the fluid in the sink or designated container. Repeat this procedure three times.

Step 5d: Add about three drops (100 µl) of antibody solution to each well. Allow the plate to sit undisturbed on your lab table for 5 minutes.

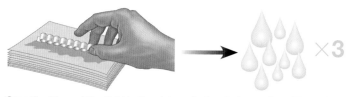

Step 5e: Discard the fluid in the sink or designated container. Rinse the wells with washing solution three times.

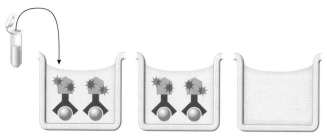

Step 5f: Add about three drops (100 µl) of colorant solution to each well. Allow the plate to sit undisturbed on your lab table for 5 minutes.

FIGURE **21.10** ELISA procedure.

Check Your Recall

1 **Label** Figure 21.11 **with the following terms.**

- ❏ Axillary lymph nodes
- ❏ Cervical lymph nodes
- ❏ Cisterna chyli
- ❏ Inguinal lymph nodes

- ❏ Left brachiocephalic vein
- ❏ Left internal jugular vein
- ❏ Left jugular trunk
- ❏ Left subclavian vein

- ❏ Right lymphatic duct
- ❏ Spleen
- ❏ Thoracic duct
- ❏ Thymus

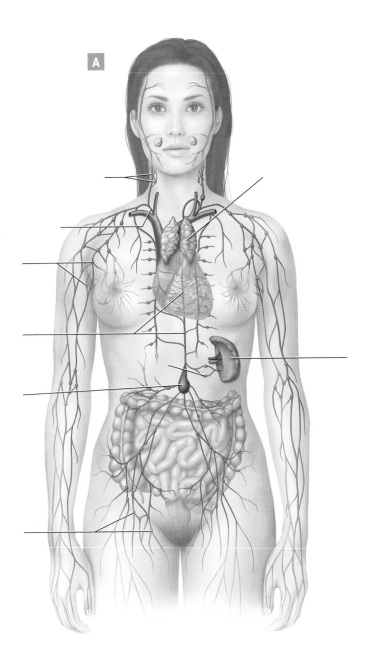

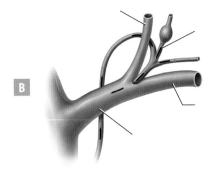

FIGURE **21.11** Lymphatic organs and vessels: (**A**) overview; (**B**) close-up of vessels.

2 Label Figure 21.12 with the following terms.

- ❏ Cortex
- ❏ Germinal center
- ❏ Lingual tonsil
- ❏ Lymphoid follicle
- ❏ Medulla
- ❏ Palatine tonsil
- ❏ Pharyngeal tonsil
- ❏ Red pulp
- ❏ Sinusoids
- ❏ White pulp

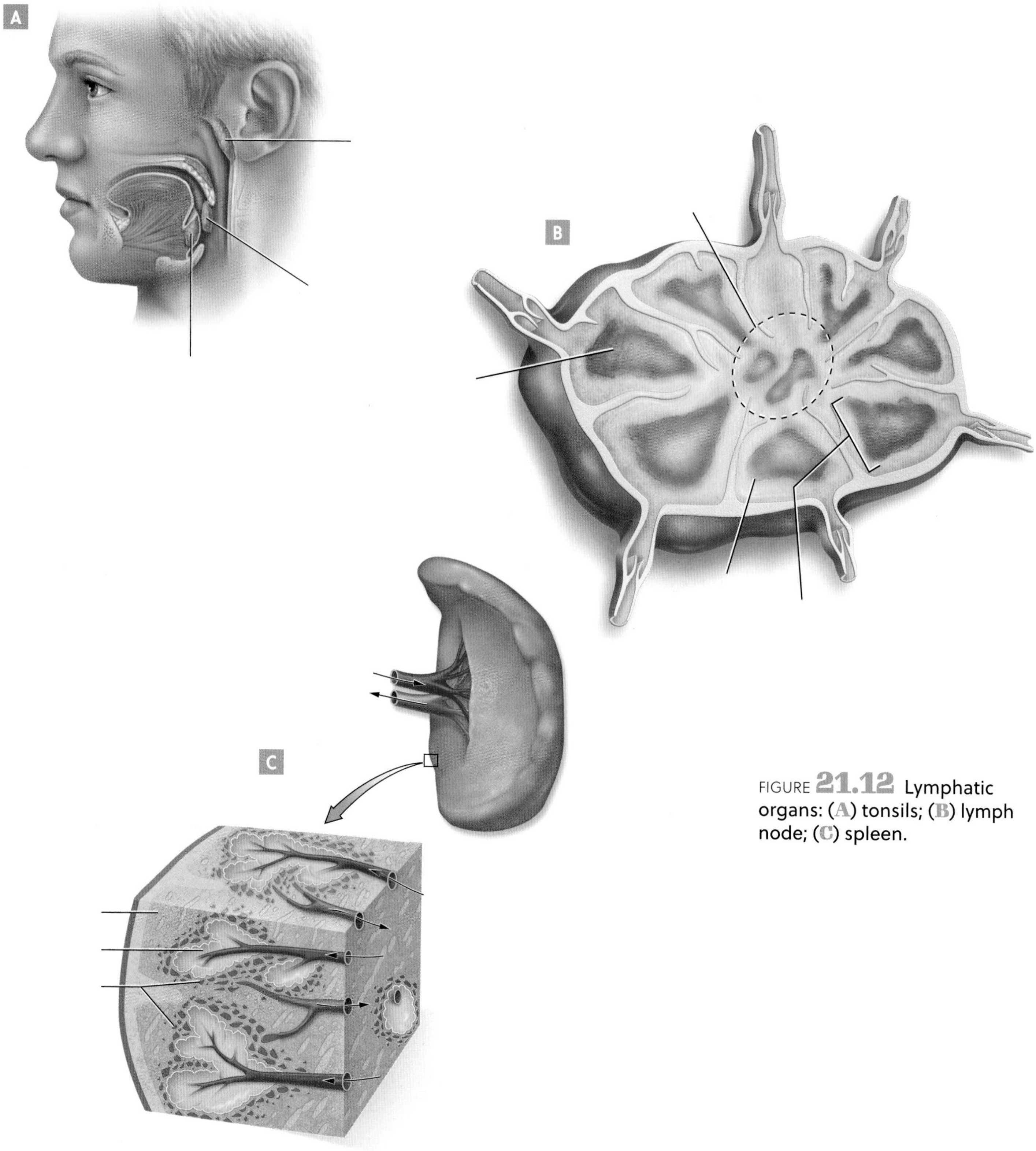

FIGURE **21.12** Lymphatic organs: (**A**) tonsils; (**B**) lymph node; (**C**) spleen.

3 Which of the following is not drained by the right lymphatic duct?

    a. Right side of the head.
    b. Right side of the thorax.
    c. Right lower limb.
    d. Right upper limb.

4 *True/False:* Mark the following statements as true (T) or false (F). If the statement is false, correct it to make it a true statement.

_____ a. Vessels of the lymphatic system absorb dietary carbohydrates and deliver them to the blood.

_____ b. The spleen's red pulp contains macrophages that destroy old or damaged erythrocytes.

_____ c. B lymphocytes migrate to the thymus to mature.

_____ d. Lymph nodes filter lymph and activate the immune system.

5 Tonsils are defined as

    a. lymph nodes in the posterior nasopharynx and oropharynx.
    b. partially encapsulated clusters of mucosal-associated lymphatic tissue in the posterior nasopharynx and oropharynx.
    c. encapsulated clusters of mucosal-associated lymphatic tissue lining mucous membranes.
    d. lymph nodes lining mucous membranes.

6 In the center of a lymphoid follicle is a _____, containing B lymphocytes, dendritic cells, and macrophages.

    a. germinal center
    b. Peyer's patch
    c. tonsillar crypt
    d. medulla

7 Which of the following is *not* a phagocytic cell?

    a. Dendritic cell.
    b. Neutrophil.
    c. NK cell.
    d. Macrophage.

8 How do dendritic cells link innate and adaptive immunity?

_____

_____

_____

_____

21

9 Which of the following are the main component of humoral immunity?

a. Antibodies and T_H cells.

b. Antibodies and B cells.

c. T_H and T_C cells.

d. Cytokines and T_H cells.

10 Inflammatory mediators that increase the set point of the hypothalamic temperature are called

a. interferons.

b. cytokines.

c. complement proteins.

d. pyrogens.

21

Check Your Understanding

Critical Thinking and Application Questions

1 Why do you think we find clusters of lymphatic tissue associated with mucous membranes? (*Hint:* Think about where mucous membranes are located in the body.)

_____

_____

_____

_____

2 Explain why diseases that damage erythrocytes tend to cause enlargement of the spleen.

_____

_____

_____

_____

3 Melva has a diagnosis of breast cancer of the left breast. Four weeks ago, she underwent surgery to remove the left breast and all axillary lymph nodes on the left side. She is now reporting extensive swelling in her left upper limb. What is causing the swelling, and why?

_____

_____

_____

_____

4 Juliet just had her palatine tonsils removed due to recurrent infections. A histological examination of the removed tonsils reveals they have abnormally deep tonsillar crypts. How does this help explain her recurrent infections?

_____

_____

_____

_____

5 The drug ibuprofen blocks the production of inflammatory mediators, including pyrogens. Why does this make ibuprofen a good drug to treat fever?

6 Like many pathogens, *SARS-CoV-2* enhances its ability to cause severe disease by evading or suppressing certain aspects of the immune response. For example, studies have found that the virus can impair dendritic cell activity during the acute phase of infection. How would this affect the immune response to SARS-CoV-2?

7 A YouTube video suggests that ELISA tests for SARS-CoV-2 are fraudulent because they can detect RNA from any type of coronavirus. What is this YouTuber fundamentally misunderstanding about ELISA tests?

Respiratory System Anatomy

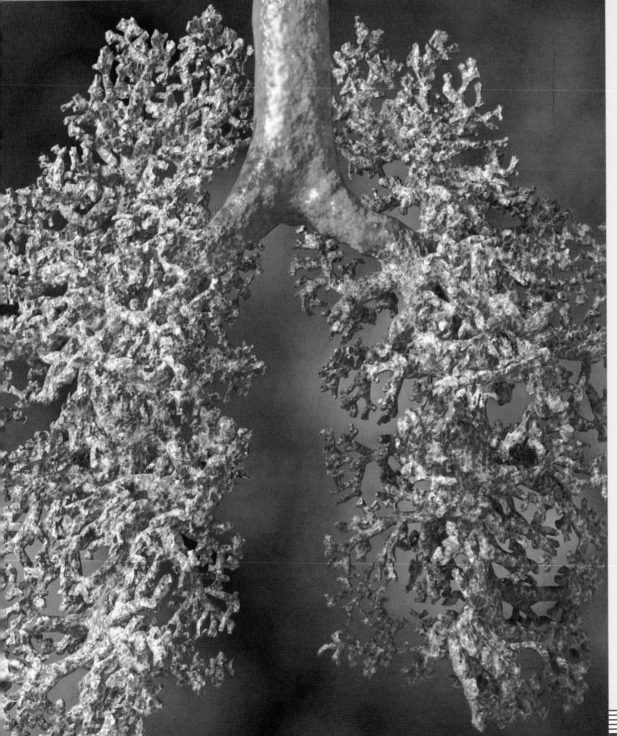

When you have completed this unit, you should be able to:

1 Describe and identify structures of the respiratory system.

2 Trace the pathway of gases through the respiratory system.

3 Identify the microscopic anatomy of the respiratory system on microscope slides.

PRE-LAB EXERCISES

Complete the following exercises prior to coming to lab, using your lab manual and textbook for reference.

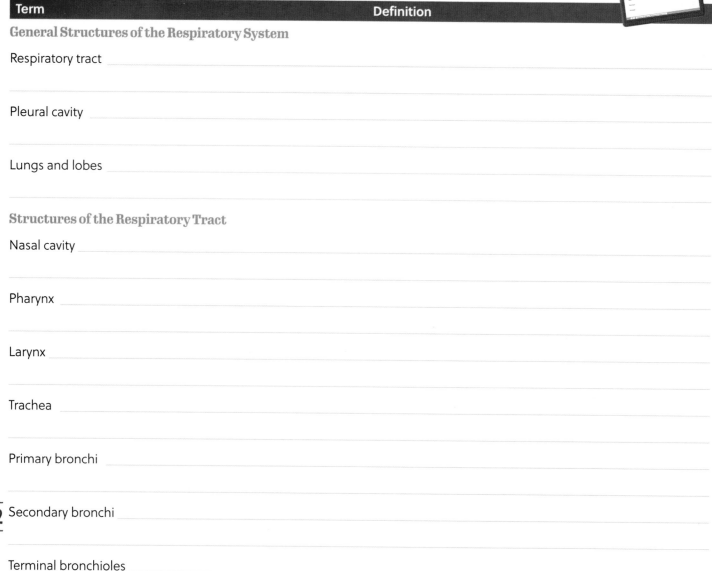

PRE-LAB

22-1 Key Terms

You should be familiar with the following terms before coming to lab.

Term	Definition

General Structures of the Respiratory System

Respiratory tract _____

Pleural cavity _____

Lungs and lobes _____

Structures of the Respiratory Tract

Nasal cavity _____

Pharynx _____

Larynx _____

Trachea _____

Primary bronchi _____

Secondary bronchi _____

Terminal bronchioles _____

Respiratory bronchioles _____

Alveolar ducts _____

Alveoli _____

22

PRE-LAB

22-2

Respiratory System Anatomy

Color the structures of the respiratory system in Figure 22.1, and label them with the terms from Exercise 22-1 (p. 591). Use your text and Exercise 22-1 in this unit for reference.

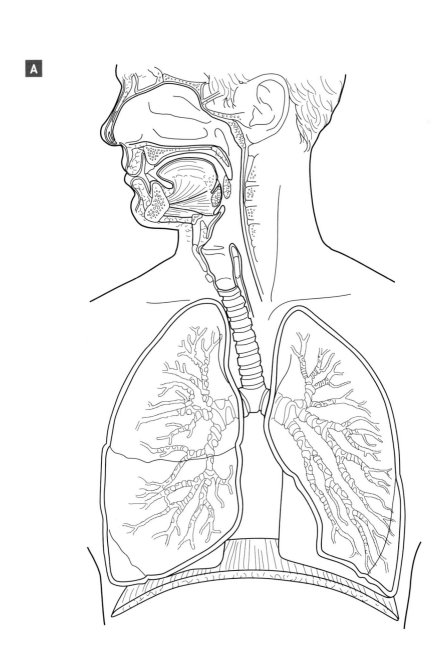

FIGURE **22.1** Structures of the respiratory system: (**A**) anatomy of the lungs and respiratory tract; (*continues*)

22

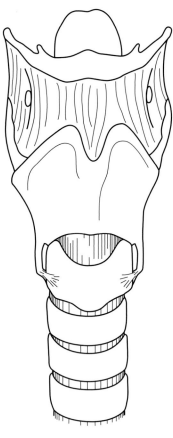

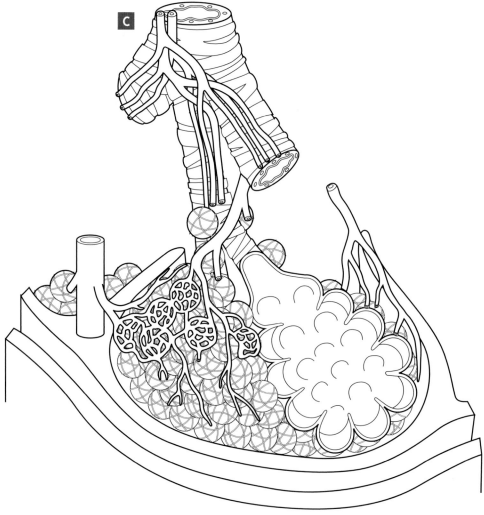

FIGURE **22.1** Structures of the respiratory system (*cont.*): (**B**) anterior view of the larynx; (**C**) bronchiole and alveolar sac.

Trachea and bronchi of the lungs.

EXERCISES

Cells require oxygen to synthesize ATP, and these reactions produce carbon dioxide as a waste product. The organs of the **respiratory system** carry out parts of the process of **respiration**, which provides cells with this needed oxygen and removes carbon dioxide. There are four separate processes that make up respiration: (1) pulmonary ventilation, (2) pulmonary gas exchange, (3) gas transport in the blood, and (4) tissue gas exchange.

The first two processes of respiration are carried out within the respiratory system. During **pulmonary ventilation** (PUL-muh-nehr-ee; *pulmon-* = "lung"), air moves in and out of the lungs. It consists of two phases: *inspiration*, the movement of oxygen-rich air into the lungs, and *expiration*, the movement of carbon dioxide-rich air out of the lungs. Oxygen and carbon dioxide are exchanged in the lungs during **pulmonary gas exchange**— the movement of oxygen from the air to the blood, and of carbon dioxide from the blood to the air.

The remaining two processes of respiration are functions of the cardiovascular system. During **gas transport,** the blood moves gases through the body. In systemic capillary beds, **tissue gas exchange** takes place between the blood and the tissues— oxygen is dropped off within the tissues, and the blood picks up carbon dioxide.

The exercises in this unit will familiarize you with the organs and histology of the respiratory system, including the paired *lungs* and the collection of airway passages known as the *respiratory tract*. In the next unit, we examine how these organs carry out pulmonary ventilation and pulmonary gas exchange.

EXERCISE
22-1

MATERIALS

- ☐ Anatomical models and diagrams:
  - lung
  - larynx
  - alveolar sac
  - head and neck
- ☐ Colored pencils

Respiratory System Anatomy

The lungs are composed of elastic connective tissue and tiny air sacs, called **alveoli** (al-vee-OH-lye; "small cavities"), where pulmonary gas exchange takes place. Each lung is divided into smaller structures called **lobes**. The right lung has three lobes (upper, middle, and lower), and the left lung has two lobes (upper and lower) (Fig. 22.2). The lobes are separated from one another by deep indentations called **fissures**. The **horizontal fissure** separates the right upper and right middle lobes; the **right oblique fissure** separates the right middle and right lower lobes; and the **left oblique fissure** separates the left upper and left lower lobes. The left upper lobe has a groove, called the **cardiac notch**, on its medial surface where it comes into contact with the heart. Each lung has an **apex** that sits just above the clavicle and a **base** that rests on the **diaphragm muscle**, the main muscle for pulmonary ventilation.

Each lung is surrounded by serous membranes, similar in structure and function to the pericardial membranes, known as the **pleural membranes** (PLOO-ruhl; *pleura* = "side of the body"). There are two layers of the pleural membranes:

1. **Parietal pleura.** The outer **parietal pleura** lines the interior of the thoracic cavity and the superior surface of the diaphragm.

2. **Visceral pleura.** When the parietal pleura reaches the structures of the mediastinum, it folds inward to become the **visceral pleura.** The visceral pleura adheres tightly to the surface of the lung.

The very thin potential space between the parietal and visceral pleurae is the **pleural cavity.** The space is only a "potential" space because it is filled with a thin layer of serous fluid that reduces friction as the lungs change in shape and size during pulmonary ventilation.

If we flip a lung on its side and examine its medial or mediastinal surface (the surface that faces the mediastinum), as we do in Figure 22.3, we can see an area called the **hilum** (HY-lum) of the lung. This is an indentation where the pulmonary vessels, nerves, lymphatic vessels, and airway passages called *primary bronchi* enter and exit the lungs.

Air is delivered to the lungs' alveoli through the passageways of the **respiratory tract**. The respiratory tract may be divided into two regions according to both structure and function. Structurally, it is divided into (1) the *upper respiratory tract*, which consists of the passages from the nasal cavity to the larynx; and (2) the *lower respiratory tract*, which consists of the passages from the trachea to the alveoli. Functionally, it is divided into the conducting zone and the respiratory zone. The *conducting zone* consists of passages that carry, or "conduct," air to where pulmonary gas exchange takes place. Most of the respiratory tract belongs to the conducting zone. The *respiratory zone* consists of the passages in which pulmonary gas exchange takes place, located in the terminal respiratory tract.

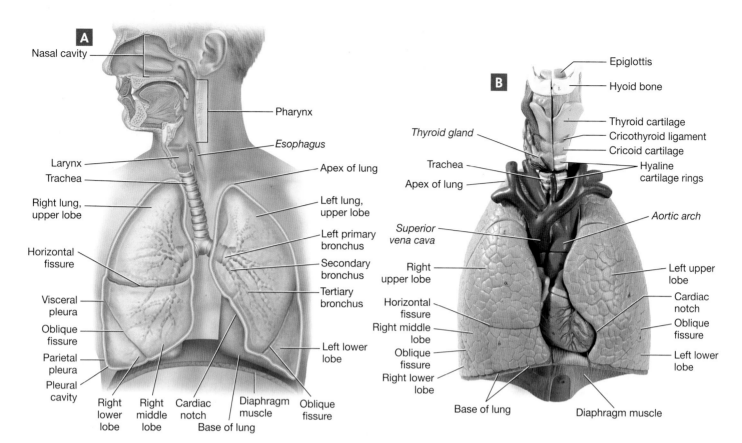

FIGURE **22.2** Anatomy of the lungs and respiratory tract: (**A**) illustration; (**B**) anatomical model photo.

The conducting zone begins with the **nasal cavity** (Fig. 22.4), which warms, filters, and humidifies the incoming air. Air first enters through the **nares** (or nostrils) and the hair-lined *vestibule*, then enters the actual nasal cavity. Lining the walls of the nasal cavity are three projections known as the **superior**, **middle**, and **inferior nasal conchae** (KAHN-kee). These projections make airflow turbulent. The turbulent airflow removes dust and other debris from the inhaled air. The nasal cavity is lined with pseudostratified ciliated columnar epithelium with copious mucus-secreting **goblet cells**, a type of tissue known as **respiratory epithelium**.

Air flow is continuous between the nasal cavity and the **paranasal sinuses**. The sinuses assist in filtering, warming, and humidifying the inhaled air. Recall from Unit 8 that there are four paranasal sinuses: the **frontal, maxillary, ethmoid,** and **sphenoid sinuses** (see Fig. 8.12, p. 199, for a review).

From the nasal cavity, air next enters the **pharynx** (FEHR-inks), also known as the throat, which has the following three divisions:

1. **Nasopharynx.** The **nasopharynx** (nayz-oh-FEHR-inks; *pharyng-* = "throat") is the region posterior to the nasal cavity, color-coded green in Figure 22.4A. The muscles of the soft palate and *uvula* move superiorly to close off the nasopharynx during swallowing to prevent food from entering the passage. Sometimes this mechanism fails (such as when a person is laughing and swallowing simultaneously), and the unfortunate result is that food or liquid comes out of the nose. Like the nasal cavity, the nasopharynx is lined with respiratory epithelium.

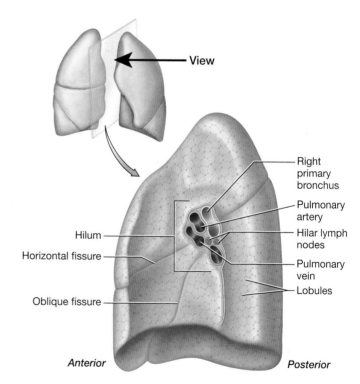

FIGURE **22.3** Mediastinal surface of the right lung.

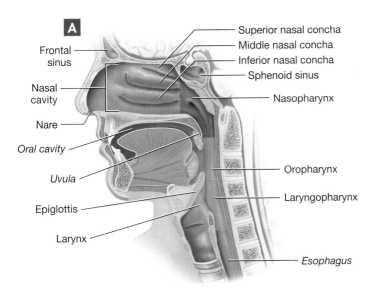

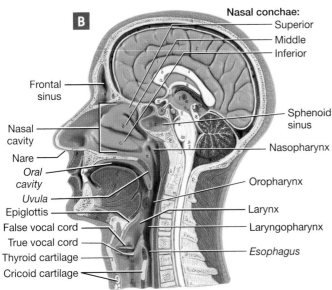

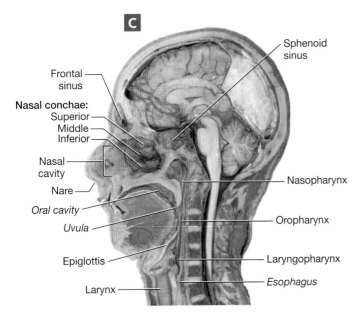

FIGURE **22.4** Midsagittal section of the head and neck: (**A**) illustration; (**B**) anatomical model photo; (**C**) cadaver dissection.

2. **Oropharynx.** The **oropharynx** (ohr-oh-FEHR-inks) is the region posterior to the oral cavity, color-coded yellow in Figure 22.4A. Both food and air pass through the oropharynx, and it is therefore lined with stratified squamous epithelium. This tissue provides more resistance to mechanical and thermal stresses.

3. **Laryngopharynx.** The **laryngopharynx** (lah-ring-oh-FEHR-inks) is the intermediate region between the larynx and the esophagus, color-coded light blue in Figure 22.4A. As with the oropharynx, both food and air pass through the laryngopharynx, and it is lined with stratified squamous epithelium.

Next, air passes from the pharynx to the **larynx** (LEHR-inks), a short passage framed by the hyoid bone and nine cartilages (Fig. 22.5). The "lid" of the larynx is a piece of elastic cartilage called the **epiglottis** (ep-ih-GLAH-tiss; *epi-* = "on top;" *glott-* = "tongue"). During swallowing, muscles of the pharynx and larynx move the larynx superiorly, and the epiglottis seals off the larynx from food and liquids. The largest cartilage of the larynx is the shieldlike **thyroid cartilage** (THY-royd; "shield"), which is inferior to the hyoid bone and forms the larynx's anterior and lateral walls. Inferior to the thyroid cartilage is the smaller **cricoid cartilage** (KRY-koyd; *cric-* = "ring"), which is the only cartilage in the respiratory tract that is a complete ring—the remainder are C-shaped. The thyroid and cricoid cartilages are united by a connective tissue membrane called the **cricothyroid ligament** (kry-koh-THY-royd). The smaller cartilages of the larynx include the **arytenoid** (uh-RIT-uh-noyd), **corniculate** (kor-NIK-yoo-lit; "horn like"), and **cuneiform cartilages** (kyoo-NEE-ih-form; "wedge shaped"), which are found in its posterior and lateral walls (Fig. 22.5C).

As its common name "voice box" implies, the larynx is the structure where sound is produced. As you can see in Figure 22.4B, it contains two sets of elastic ligaments known as the **vocal folds** or **vocal cords.** The superior set of vocal folds, the **false vocal cords** (also called the *vestibular folds*), plays no role in sound production. The folds do, however, serve an important sphincter function and can constrict to close off the larynx. The inferior set of vocal folds, called the **true vocal cords,** vibrates as air passes over it to produce sound. Superior to the vocal cords, the larynx is lined with stratified squamous epithelium; inferior to the vocal cords, it is lined with respiratory epithelium, as is the remainder of the respiratory tract until we reach much smaller passageways.

Inspired air passes from the larynx into a passage supported by C-shaped rings of hyaline cartilage called the **trachea** (TRAY-kee-uh; Fig. 22.6). The trachea bifurcates in the mediastinum at its final cartilage ring, which is called the **carina** (kuh-RY-nuh), into two **primary bronchi** (BRONG-kye) that begin the large and branching **bronchial tree** (BRONG-kee-uhl; *bronch-* = "windpipe"). The right primary bronchus is short, fairly straight, and wide, and the left primary bronchus is long, more horizontal, and narrow due to the position of the heart.

22

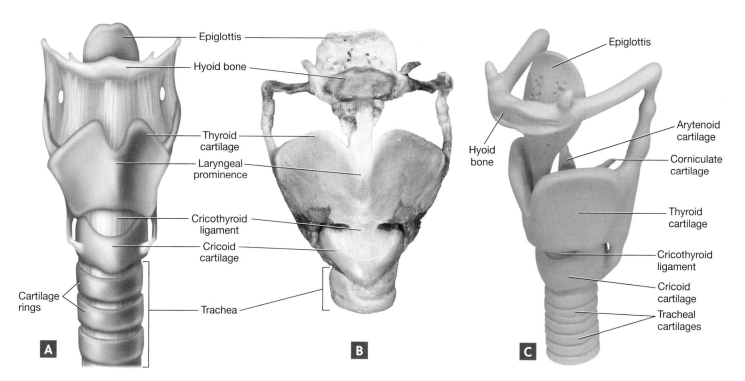

FIGURE **22.5** Larynx: (**A**) anterior view; (**B**) anterior view from a cadaver; (**C**) anterolateral view from an anatomical model.

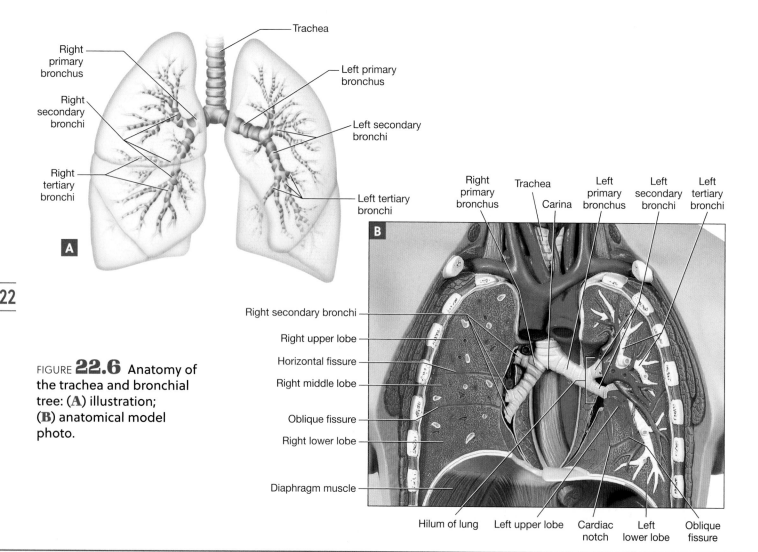

FIGURE **22.6** Anatomy of the trachea and bronchial tree: (**A**) illustration; (**B**) anatomical model photo.

22

Each primary bronchus divides into smaller **secondary bronchi,** each of which serves one lobe of the lung. The two left secondary bronchi serve the two lobes of the left lung, while the three right secondary bronchi serve the three lobes of the right lung. The bronchi continue to branch and become tertiary bronchi, quaternary bronchi, and so on until the air reaches tiny air passages smaller than 1 mm in diameter called **bronchioles** (BRONG-kee-ohlz; Fig. 22.7). At this level, the epithelium changes to simple cuboidal epithelium.

Bronchioles smaller than 0.5 mm in diameter are called the **terminal bronchioles;** these mark the end of the conducting zone. The respiratory zone begins with small branches called **respiratory bronchioles** that have alveoli in their walls. As the respiratory bronchioles progressively branch, the number of alveoli in their walls increases until the walls are made up exclusively of alveoli, at which point they are termed **alveolar ducts** (al-vee-OH-luhr). The terminal portions of the respiratory zone, called **alveolar sacs,** are grapelike clusters of alveoli.

The alveoli are surrounded by **pulmonary capillaries,** which are fed by pulmonary arterioles and drained by pulmonary venules. The capillary-alveolus junction, along with the fused capillary and alveolar basal laminae, forms a structure known as the **respiratory membrane,** which is where pulmonary gas exchange takes place. During pulmonary gas exchange, oxygen from the air in the alveoli diffuses into the blood, and carbon dioxide from the blood diffuses into the air in the alveoli to be exhaled. Alveolar walls and capillary walls are both composed of simple squamous epithelium with abundant elastic fibers. The thin epithelium gives gases only a short distance to diffuse, which is critical to effective pulmonary gas exchange. In addition, the grapelike structure of the alveolar sacs creates a huge surface area (around 1,000 square feet on average), another factor that allows pulmonary gas exchange to take place rapidly and efficiently.

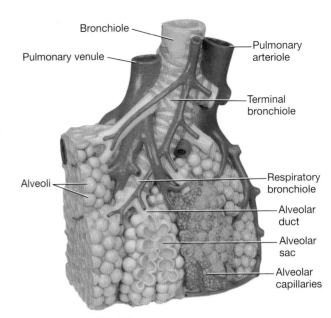

FIGURE **22.7** Bronchiole and alveolar sac, anatomical model photo.

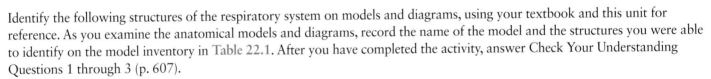

1 PROCEDURE
Model Inventory for the Respiratory System

Identify the following structures of the respiratory system on models and diagrams, using your textbook and this unit for reference. As you examine the anatomical models and diagrams, record the name of the model and the structures you were able to identify on the model inventory in Table 22.1. After you have completed the activity, answer Check Your Understanding Questions 1 through 3 (p. 607).

1. Right lung
   a. Upper, middle, and lower lobes
   b. Horizontal fissure
   c. Oblique fissure
2. Left lung
   a. Upper and lower lobes
   b. Oblique fissure
   c. Cardiac notch
3. Lungs, general
   a. Apex
   b. Base
   c. Diaphragm muscle
   d. Pleurae
      (1) Parietal pleura
      (2) Visceral pleura
      (3) Pleural cavity
   e. Hilum
4. Nasal cavity
   a. Nares

b. Nasal conchae
   (1) Superior nasal conchae
   (2) Middle nasal conchae
   (3) Inferior nasal conchae
c. Paranasal sinuses
   (1) Frontal sinus
   (2) Maxillary sinus
   (3) Ethmoid sinus
   (4) Sphenoid sinus
5. Pharynx
   a. Nasopharynx
   b. Oropharynx
   c. Laryngopharynx
6. Larynx
   a. Hyoid bone
   b. Epiglottis
   c. Thyroid cartilage
   d. Cricoid cartilage
   e. Cricothyroid ligament

f. Arytenoid cartilages
   g. Corniculate cartilages
   h. Cuneiform cartilages
   i. False vocal cords
   j. True vocal cords
7. Trachea
   a. Hyaline cartilage rings
   b. Carina
8. Bronchi
   a. Right and left primary bronchi
   b. Secondary bronchi
   c. Tertiary bronchi
9. Bronchioles
   a. Terminal bronchioles
   b. Respiratory bronchioles
   c. Alveolar duct
10. Alveoli and alveolar sacs

22

TABLE **22.1** Model Inventory for the Respiratory System

Model/Diagram	Structures Identified

2 PROCEDURE
Time to Draw

In the space provided, draw, color, and label one of the respiratory system models that you examined. In addition, write the function of each structure that you label.

Time to Trace!

In this next procedure, you will trace the pathway taken by oxygen and carbon dioxide molecules through the respiratory tract and through parts of the systemic and pulmonary vascular circuits. When you have completed your tracings, answer Check Your Understanding Question 4 (pp. 607–608).

Part 1

You are a molecule of oxygen floating happily through the atmosphere when all of a sudden you are inhaled by Ms. Magenta.

1 Trace your pathway through Ms. Magenta's respiratory tract, beginning in her nasal cavity to the point at which you cross the respiratory membrane and enter the pulmonary capillaries.

Start: Nasal Cavity →

_____ pharynx (one word) →

_____ pharynx (one word) →

_____ pharynx (one word) →

_____ →

_____ →

_____ bronchus →

_____ bronchus →

bronchial tree →

_____ →

_____ bronchiole →

_____ bronchiole →

_____ duct →

_____ sac →

_____ membrane →

End: Pulmonary Capillaries

2 Trace your pathway from Ms. Magenta's pulmonary capillaries through the blood, beginning in the pulmonary circuit in her lungs, going through her heart, then through her systemic arteries to your final destination in a hepatocyte (liver cell). You likely will have to review Unit 18 (p. 481) for some help with this.

Start: Pulmonary Capillaries →

_____ veins →

_____ →

_____ valve →

_____ →

_____ valve →

ascending _____ →

_____ arch →

descending _____ →

_____ trunk →

_____ artery →

_____ capillaries →

End: Hepatocyte

22

Part 2

While in her hepatocyte, you notice that a molecule of carbon dioxide has just been produced.

1 Trace the carbon dioxide's pathway from Ms. Magenta's hepatocyte through the systemic veins to her heart, then through her heart to the pulmonary circuit, and, finally, through the pulmonary circuit to her pulmonary capillaries. You will likely need to review Unit 18 (p. 481) for some help with this.

Start: Hepatocyte →

_____ capillaries →

_____ vein →

_____ →

_____ atrium →

_____ valve →

_____ →

_____ valve →

_____ →

_____ artery →

End: Pulmonary Capillaries

2 Trace the pathway of the carbon dioxide molecule from the pulmonary capillaries through the respiratory tract to the point at which it exits from Ms. Magenta's body through her nares.

Start: Pulmonary Capillaries →

_____ membrane →

_____ →

_____ sac →

_____ duct →

_____ bronchiole →

_____ bronchiole →

_____ →

bronchial tree →

_____ bronchus →

_____ bronchus →

_____ →

_____ →

_____ pharynx (one word) →

_____ pharynx (one word) →

_____ pharynx (one word) →

_____ cavity →

End: Nares

MATERIALS

- ☐ Slides:
  - ▪ trachea
  - ▪ lung tissue
  - ▪ bronchiole
- ☐ Light microscope
- ☐ Colored pencils

Histology of the Respiratory Tract

As you learned in Exercise 22-1 (p. 591), the respiratory tract is a series of branching passages that conduct air to and from the respiratory zone for pulmonary gas exchange. The "tubes" of the respiratory tract are similar in structure histologically to other hollow organs of the body and consist of three tissue layers. Figure 22.8A uses the example of the trachea to show these layers: the mucosa, the submucosa, and the adventitia.

1. **Mucosa.** Mucous membranes, or **mucosae**, line all passageways that open to the outside of the body, including the passages of the respiratory tract. Mucosae consist of epithelial tissue overlying the basement membrane. As we have seen elsewhere in the body, there is a clear relationship between structure and function. This is also true in the respiratory tract, because the epithelial tissue of the mucosae are adapted for each region's function. Some examples of the epithelia found in different regions include the following:

   a. **Pseudostratified ciliated columnar epithelium with goblet cells.** The nasopharynx, larynx (inferior to the vocal cords), trachea, and bronchi are lined with **respiratory epithelium** or pseudostratified ciliated columnar epithelium with mucus-secreting cells called **goblet cells**. Figure 22.8B shows you an example of respiratory epithelium from the nasal cavity, but note that you can see respiratory epithelium in Figure 22.8A in the trachea, as well. The cilia of respiratory epithelium sweep dust and other particulates that become trapped in the mucus out of the respiratory tract. Some of the dust and debris is removed from the body via sneezing or coughing, but most is simply pushed toward the laryngopharynx and esophagus and swallowed. The actions of the cilia prevent this material from reaching the deeper parts of the respiratory tract.

   b. **Stratified squamous epithelium.** The oropharynx, laryngopharynx, and larynx (superior to the vocal cords) are lined with stratified squamous epithelium. This helps to protect these areas from mechanical abrasion from food.

   c. **Simple cuboidal epithelium.** The bronchioles are lined with simple cuboidal epithelium, which is shown in Figure 22.9. These small passageways need fewer goblet cells and cilia because most dust and debris have already been removed by the time air reaches them.

   d. **Simple squamous epithelium.** Alveoli are lined with simple squamous epithelium. Note in Figure 22.10 that the alveoli consist of a mucosa only—having no other tissue layers—which minimizes the distances gases must diffuse across the alveoli and into the pulmonary capillaries. As you read earlier, the structure through which gases must diffuse, which is called the **respiratory membrane**, consists of the squamous alveolar epithelial cells, the endothelial cells of the pulmonary capillaries, and their fused basal laminae.

2. **Submucosa.** Deep to the mucosa we find the **submucosa**, a layer of loose connective tissue. The submucosa contains specialized **seromucous glands** (seer-oh-MYOO-kuhs) that secrete watery mucus. The submucosa of larger passages contains hyaline cartilage for support; it also contains smooth muscle that controls the diameter of the airways.

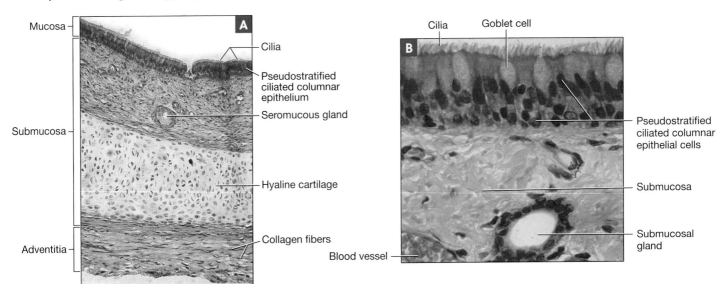

FIGURE **22.8** Histology of the respiratory tract: (**A**) trachea, photomicrograph; (**B**) nasal mucosa with goblet cells, photomicrograph.

22

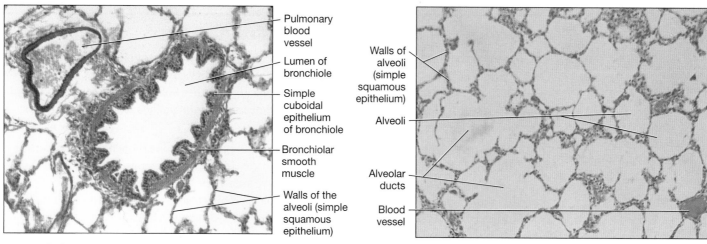

FIGURE **22.9** Bronchiole, photomicrograph.

Labels (Figure 22.9):
- Pulmonary blood vessel
- Lumen of bronchiole
- Simple cuboidal epithelium of bronchiole
- Bronchiolar smooth muscle
- Walls of the alveoli (simple squamous epithelium)

FIGURE **22.10** Alveoli and lung tissue, photomicrograph.

Labels (Figure 22.10):
- Walls of alveoli (simple squamous epithelium)
- Alveoli
- Alveolar ducts
- Blood vessel

3. **Adventitia.** The outermost layer of the respiratory tract, the **adventitia** (ad-ven-TISH-uh), consists of dense irregular connective tissue with elastic fibers for support.

As you examine different regions of the respiratory tract, you will note a few trends:

- The epithelial tissue changes from taller (pseudostratified) in the upper passages to shorter (cuboidal) in the lower passages and, finally, to flat (squamous) in the alveoli.

- The amount of hyaline cartilage gradually decreases as the passages of the bronchial tree become smaller (it is absent in bronchioles), as does the number of goblet cells.

- The amount of smooth muscle tissue and elastic fibers increases as we move deeper into the respiratory tract. The elastic fibers allow the respiratory passages and alveoli to stretch without becoming damaged, which is critical to their ability to expand during inspiration. In addition, they cause the passages and alveoli to recoil to their original size when the stretching forces are removed. Without this elastic recoil, expiration becomes difficult.

These trends can help you to determine the portion of the respiratory tract from which the section on your slide was taken. In the following procedure, you will be able to see these trends as you examine photomicrographs of the trachea, a bronchiole, and the alveoli.

1 PROCEDURE

Examining Respiratory Tissues with Microscopy

View prepared slides of a section of the trachea, a bronchiole, and alveoli. Note that the bronchiole may be on the same slide as the alveoli. Begin your examination of the slides on low power, and advance to medium and high power to observe details. Use colored pencils to draw what you see under the microscope, and label your drawings with the terms listed. When you have completed the activity, answer Check Your Understanding Questions 5 and 6 (p. 608).

1 Trachea

- Pseudostratified columnar epithelium
- Cilia
- Goblet cells
- Submucosa
- Seromucous glands
- Hyaline cartilage

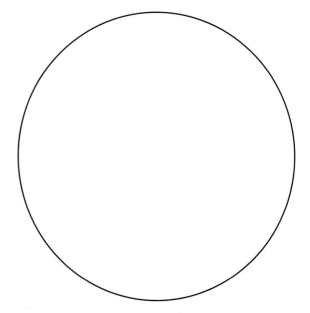

2 Bronchioles

- Simple columnar or cuboidal epithelium
- Smooth muscle
- Pulmonary arteriole

3 Alveoli

- Simple squamous epithelium
- Alveolar duct
- Alveolus

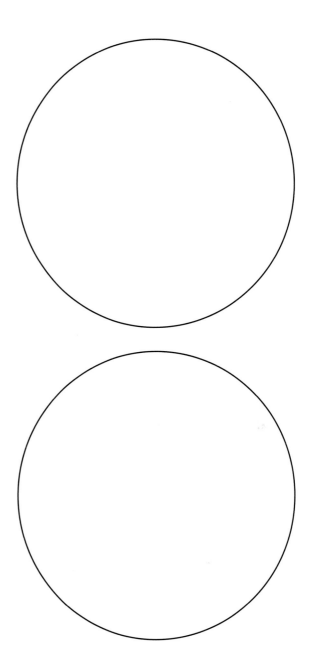

MATERIALS

❑ Tray
❑ Air hose
❑ Fresh lungs
❑ Air pump

Lung Inflation

How does a healthcare provider help a patient breathe when the patient is unable to do so? The answer is via a process called **endotracheal intubation** (in-doh-TRAY-kee-uhl), during which a plastic tube—an *endotracheal* or *ET tube*—is inserted into the trachea. The ET tube is generally inserted into the trachea through the mouth or nasal cavity, which are known as *orotracheal intubation* and *nasotracheal intubation*, respectively.

In emergency situations, such as when a patient is choking, an ET tube may be inserted using a procedure called a **cricothyroidotomy** (kry-koh-thy-royd-AH-toh-mee). During a cricothyroidotomy, an incision is placed in the cricothyroid ligament, the soft spot between the thyroid and cricoid cartilages, and the ET tube is inserted into the larynx. When longer-term placement of an ET tube is needed, it may be inserted via a *tracheostomy*, during which the hole and tube are placed directly into the trachea.

After the tube is placed, a balloon cuff on the outside of the tube is inflated to hold it in place and prevent gases from leaking out of the lungs. The patient can then be ventilated, meaning air is forced into the lungs, which artificially inflates them. Patients may be ventilated with a bag valve mask, which relies on someone squeezing it repeatedly to drive air into the lungs. Longer-term ventilation may be provided by a mechanical ventilator.

In this exercise, you will see what it looks like when fresh lungs are manually inflated and deflated with an air pump. In place of an ET tube, you will use an air hose inserted into the larynx. After you have completed both procedures, answer Check Your Understanding Question 7 (p. 608).

---

1 PROCEDURE

Inflating Fresh Lungs

1 Obtain a fresh specimen and a large air hose.

2 Place the specimen on a tray and examine it, identifying the structures covered in Exercise 22-1 (p. 591). In particular, you should be able to see the epiglottis, the vocal folds, the laryngeal cartilages, the trachea and its hyaline cartilage rings, and the pleural membranes.

⚠ **SAFETY NOTE**

Safety glasses and gloves are required!

3 Squeeze the deflated lungs between your fingertips and record their texture in the space provided. Deflated lungs are shown in Figure 22.11A.

_____

4 Perform your endotracheal intubation by inserting the air hose into the larynx.

5 Attach the hose to the air outlet or air pump and turn it on slowly. The air hose doesn't have a balloon cuff to secure the hose or prevent air leakage, so you will have to squeeze the larynx and the hose.

6 Observe the lungs as they inflate, as shown in Figure 22.11B. You may inflate the lungs quite fully. Don't worry—they're very unlikely to pop.

7 Squeeze the inflated lungs between your fingers and note their texture in the space provided.

_____

8 Crimp the air hose and watch the lungs deflate. Again, feel the lungs, and note changes in texture:

_____

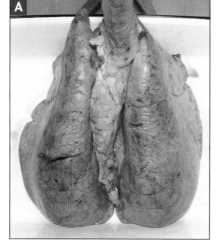
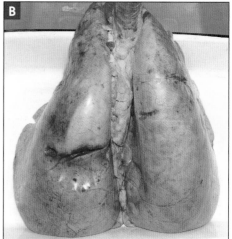

FIGURE **22.11** Fresh lungs: **(A)** deflated; **(B)** inflated.

1 Label Figure 22.12A and 22.12B with the following terms.

- ❏ Carina
- ❏ Cricoid cartilage
- ❏ Diaphragm muscle
- ❏ Horizontal fissure
- ❏ Hyoid bone
- ❏ Left primary bronchus
- ❏ Oblique fissure
- ❏ Right primary bronchus
- ❏ Secondary bronchi
- ❏ Thyroid cartilage
- ❏ Trachea

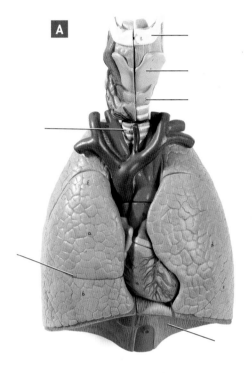

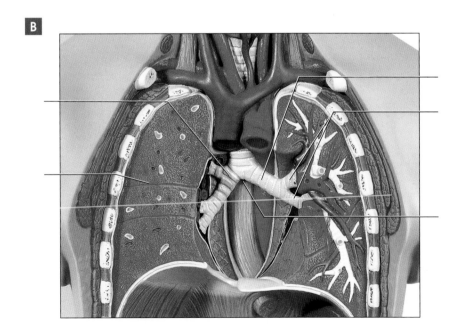

FIGURE **22.12** Respiratory structures: (**A**) anatomy of the lungs and respiratory tract, anatomical model photo; (**B**) anatomy of the respiratory tract, anatomical model photo.

2 Label Figure 22.13 with the following terms.

- ❏ Alveolar duct
- ❏ Alveolar sac
- ❏ Alveoli
- ❏ Bronchiole
- ❏ Pulmonary arteriole
- ❏ Pulmonary capillaries
- ❏ Pulmonary venule
- ❏ Respiratory bronchiole
- ❏ Terminal bronchiole

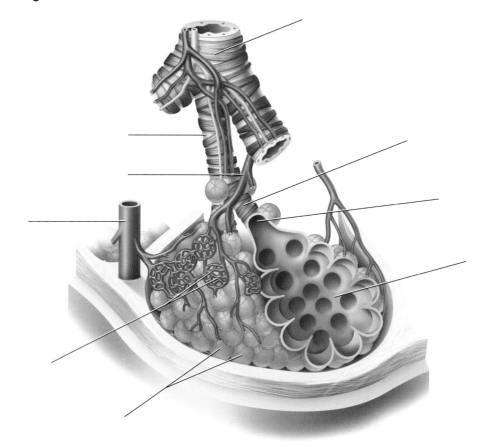

FIGURE **22.13** Microanatomy of the respiratory tract.

3 Label Figure 22.14 with the following terms.

- ❏ Epiglottis
- ❏ False vocal cord
- ❏ Frontal sinus
- ❏ Nare
- ❏ Nasal conchae
- ❏ Nasopharynx
- ❏ Oropharynx
- ❏ Sphenoid sinus
- ❏ True vocal cord

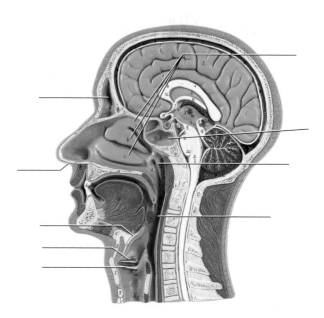

FIGURE **22.14** Midsagittal section of the head and neck, anatomical model photo.

4 The pleural cavity contains a thin layer of _____ , which functions to _____ .
    a. air; increase pressure on the lungs during pulmonary ventilation
    b. serous fluid; reduce friction as the lungs change shape and size
    c. mucus; reduce friction as the lungs change shape and size
    d. serous fluid; increase pressure on the lungs during pulmonary ventilation
    e. air; reduce friction as the lungs change shape and size

5 *True/False:* Mark the following statements as true (T) or false (F). If the statement is false, correct it to make it a true statement.

    _____ a. The trachea is lined with O-shaped rings of hyaline cartilage.

    _____ b. The paranasal sinuses filter, warm, and humidify inhaled air.

    _____ c. The superior vocal folds are the true vocal cords.

    _____ d. The left primary bronchus is shorter, straighter, and wider than the right primary bronchus.

    _____ e. Bronchioles are passages of the respiratory tract that are less than 1 mm in diameter.

6 What are the functional differences between the conducting zone and the respiratory zone?

_____

_____

7 The final passages of the respiratory zone, which have walls made of alveoli, are called
    a. terminal bronchioles.
    b. respiratory bronchioles.
    c. alveolar ducts.
    d. primary bronchioles.

8 Which of the following is *not* a trend we find in the respiratory tract?
    a. The epithelium gradually increases in height as we move deeper into the respiratory tract.
    b. The amount of smooth muscle and elastic fibers increases as we move deeper into the respiratory tract.
    c. The number of goblet cells progressively decreases as we move deeper into the respiratory tract.
    d. The amount of hyaline cartilage decreases as we move deeper into the respiratory tract.

9 Which of the following statements about the alveoli is true?
    a. The walls of alveoli contain abundant cilia and goblet cells.
    b. The grapelike structure of the alveolar sacs creates a huge surface area for pulmonary gas exchange.
    c. The walls of alveoli are composed of simple cuboidal epithelial cells.
    d. Alveoli have few elastic fibers so as to maximize the surface area for pulmonary gas exchange.

22

10 Which of the following is *not* one of the components of the respiratory membrane?

   a. Simple squamous epithelial cells.
   b. A fused basal lamina.
   c. Smooth muscle fibers.
   d. Capillary endothelial cells.

22

Check Your Understanding

Critical Thinking and Application Questions

1 The condition *asthma* is characterized by contraction of the smooth muscle lining the bronchioles, which causes them to constrict and narrow. It also causes excessive mucus secretion and inflammation of the bronchioles. How would this affect a person's ability to breathe, and why?

2 How does the structure of alveoli fit their function?

3 Eva has developed shortness of breath. An x-ray reveals her pleural cavities are filled with infectious fluid (pus), a condition called *pyothorax*. Why would infectious fluid in Eva's pleural cavities cause shortness of breath?

4 Henry accidentally inhales a fragment of a carrot, and it lodges deep in his respiratory tract, in the respiratory bronchioles of his right lower lobe.

  a Trace the pathway the piece of carrot had to take from his mouth to his respiratory bronchiole.

b The carrot has caused inflammation around the alveoli in the affected area, which has collapsed the alveoli. How would this affect his ability to exchange gases?

5 Regarding the histology of the respiratory tract:

   a Why does pulmonary gas exchange occur at the alveoli and not in the nasal cavity or trachea?

   b Why do we find no hyaline cartilage in the alveoli?

6 Some of the chemicals in cigarette smoke damage the elastic fibers of the alveoli. How will this affect pulmonary gas exchange, and why?

7 You are riding with paramedics, who are called to a restaurant after a diner chokes on his food and loses consciousness. In providing emergency care, the paramedic cuts a small hole in the diner's throat and inserts a tube. After the tube is placed, she attaches a bag and begins squeezing it rhythmically. Into what anatomical structure did the paramedic cut? What is the tube she inserted, and why?

22

Respiratory System Physiology

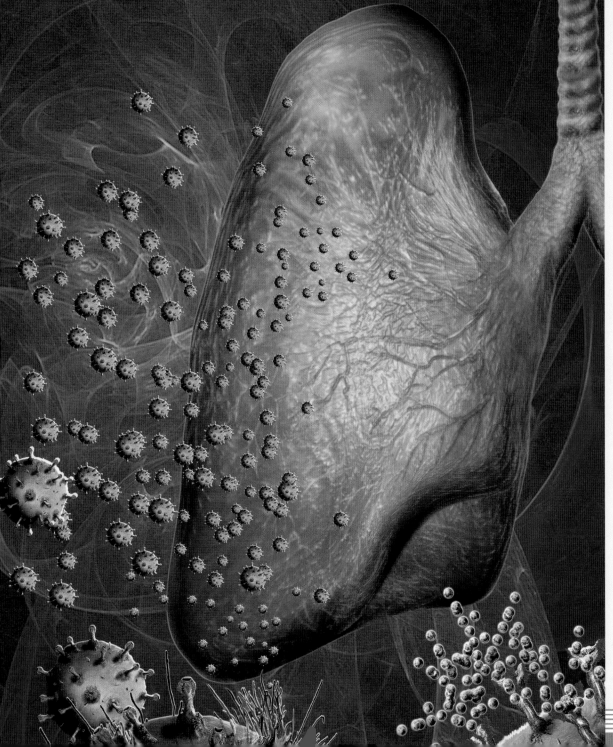

When you have completed this unit, you should be able to:

1. Describe the pressure-volume relationships in the lungs.

2. Describe and measure respiratory volumes and capacities.

3. Explain the effects of carbon dioxide concentration on blood pH.

PRE-LAB EXERCISES

Complete the following exercises prior to coming to lab, using your lab manual and textbook for reference.

PRE-LAB

23-1 Key Terms

You should be familiar with the following terms before coming to lab. Please note that the respiratory volumes and capacities are covered in Pre-Lab Exercises 23-2 and 23-3.

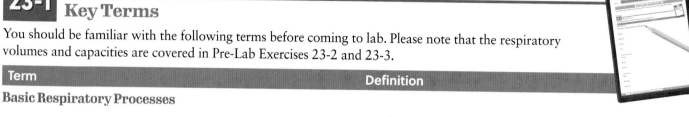

Term	Definition

Basic Respiratory Processes

Respiration _____

Pulmonary ventilation _____

Pulmonary gas exchange _____

Gas transport _____

Tissue gas exchange _____

Pulmonary Ventilation Terms

Inspiration _____

Expiration _____

Boyle's law _____

Intrapulmonary pressure _____

Atmospheric pressure _____

Gas Transport Terms

Carbonic acid–bicarbonate buffer system _____

Name _____ Section _____ Date _____

Carbonic anhydrase _____

Hyperventilation _____

_____

Hypoventilation _____

_____

Defining Pulmonary Volumes and Capacities

Define and give the normal value for adult males and females for each of the following pulmonary volumes and capacities listed in Table 23.1.

TABLE **23.1** Pulmonary Volumes and Capacities

Volume/Capacity	Definition	Normal Value
Tidal volume		Male: _____ mL Female: _____ mL
Inspiratory reserve volume		Male: _____ mL Female: _____ mL
Expiratory reserve volume		Male: _____ mL Female: _____ mL
Residual volume		Male: _____ mL Female: _____ mL
Inspiratory capacity		Male: _____ mL Female: _____ mL
Functional residual capacity		Male: _____ mL Female: _____ mL
Vital capacity		Male: _____ mL Female: _____ mL
Total lung capacity		Male: _____ mL Female: _____ mL

23-3

Labeling Pulmonary Volumes and Capacities

Color the respiratory volumes and capacities in Figure 23.1, and label them using the terms from Exercise 23-2 (p. 615). Use your text and Exercise 23-2 in this unit for reference.

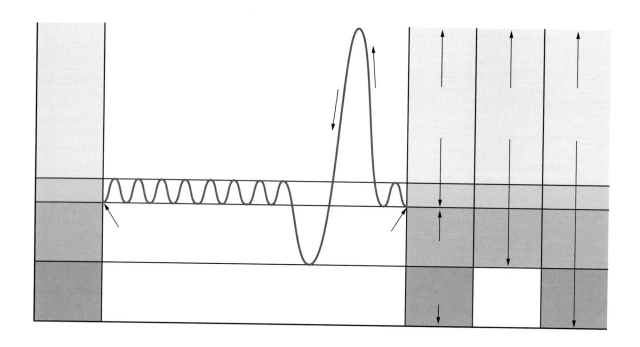

FIGURE **23.1** Pulmonary volumes and capacities.

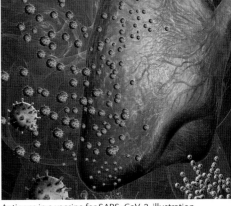

Antigens in a vaccine for SARS-CoV-2, illustration.

EXERCISES

In the previous unit, we covered respiratory system anatomy, and now we turn our attention to respiratory system physiology. Recall that **respiration** consists of four basic physiological processes:

1. *Pulmonary ventilation*, the physical movement of air into and out of the lungs;
2. *Pulmonary gas exchange*, the diffusion of gases across the respiratory membrane in the pulmonary capillaries or into the alveoli;
3. *Gas transport*, the movement of gases through the blood; and
4. *Tissue gas exchange*, the diffusion of gases between the blood in the systemic capillaries and the tissues.

In this unit, we examine the first three processes by studying a model of the lungs, measuring respiratory volumes, and measuring the effect of exercise on carbon dioxide exchange.

EXERCISE 23-1

MATERIALS

☐ Bell-jar model of the lungs

Pressure-Volume Relationships in the Lungs

Pulmonary ventilation, the physical movement of air into and out of the lungs, consists of two phases: (1) **inspiration**, during which air is brought into the lungs, and (2) **expiration**, during which air is expelled from the lungs. The movement of air during inspiration and expiration is driven by changes in the lungs' volume and pressure (Fig. 23.2). The relationship of gas pressure and volume is expressed in what is known as **Boyle's law**, expressed mathematically as:

$$P_1V_1 = P_2V_2 \text{ or } P = 1/V$$

Stated simply, this means that pressure (P) and volume (V) are inversely proportional: As the volume of a container increases, the pressure inside the container decreases, and as the volume of a container decreases, the pressure inside the container increases.

The changes in volume during the phases of ventilation are driven by the **inspiratory muscles**. The main inspiratory muscle is the **diaphragm muscle**, and it is assisted by the **external intercostal muscles** (see Fig. 10.6, p. 273, for a review). During forced inspiration, several other muscles, termed *accessory muscles of inspiration*, assist the diaphragm and external intercostal muscles. Accessory muscles include the sternocleidomastoid, pectoralis major, pectoralis minor, serratus anterior, and scalene muscles.

When the inspiratory muscles contract, they increase both the height and the diameter of the thoracic cavity and lungs, which increases their volume. Recall that the lungs are attached to the thoracic cavity directly by the pleural membranes. For this reason, the lungs' height and diameter increases as well, as does their volume. As the lungs' volume increases, the pressure within

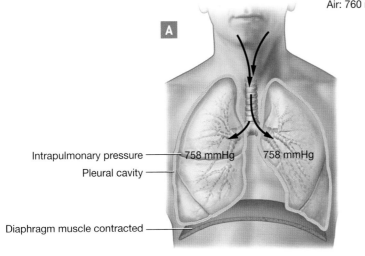

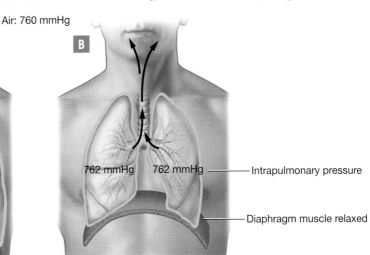

Air: 760 mmHg

A

Intrapulmonary pressure — 758 mmHg   758 mmHg

Pleural cavity

Diaphragm muscle contracted

Inspiration: Lung volume increases and intrapulmonary pressure decreases.

B

762 mmHg   762 mmHg — Intrapulmonary pressure

Diaphragm muscle relaxed

Expiration: Lung volume decreases and intrapulmonary pressure increases.

FIGURE **23.2** Pressure-volume relationships in the lungs: (**A**) during inspiration; (**B**) during expiration.

the alveoli, called the **intrapulmonary pressure**, decreases. When intrapulmonary pressure is lower than the **atmospheric pressure**, inspiration occurs, and air rushes into the lungs.

Passive expiration is achieved primarily by the elastic recoil of the lungs. As the inspiratory muscles relax, the lungs' elastic tissue causes them to recoil to their original, smaller size. This decreases the volume of the lungs and increases the intrapulmonary pressure. When the intrapulmonary pressure is higher than the atmospheric pressure, air exits the lungs, and expiration occurs. In the event of forced expiration, several accessory muscles of expiration, including the **internal intercostal muscles**, will further decrease the height and diameter of the thoracic cavity.

1 PROCEDURE
Modeling Ventilation with the Bell-Jar Model

In this procedure, we will use a bell-jar model of the lungs, shown in Figure 23.3, to view the effects of pressure and volume on ventilation. The bell-jar model has two balloons, each representing one lung, and a flexible membrane on the bottom, which represents the diaphragm muscle. When you have completed the activity, answer Check Your Understanding Questions 1 and 2 (p. 625).

1 Apply upward pressure to the membrane. This represents how the diaphragm muscle looks when it is relaxed. What has happened to the pressure of the system (has it increased or decreased)? What happened to the volume of the lungs? Explain.

_____

_____

_____

_____

2 Now, slowly release the membrane. This represents the diaphragm muscle flattening out as it contracts. What is happening to the pressure as you release the membrane? What happened to the volume of the lungs?

FIGURE **23.3** Bell-jar model of the lungs, simulated inspiration.

_____

_____

_____

3 If your bell-jar model has a rubber stopper in the top, you can use it to demonstrate the effects of a **pneumothorax** (noo-moh-THOHR-ax) on lung tissue. A pneumothorax generally is caused by a tear in the pleural membranes that allows air to enter the pleural cavity. With the membrane flat and the lungs (balloons) inflated, loosen the rubber stopper. What happens to the lungs? Why?

_____

_____

_____

MATERIALS

☐ Wet or handheld spirometer

☐ Disposable mouthpiece

Pulmonary Volumes and Capacities

Pulmonary volumes are the volumes of air that are exchanged with each breath. The pulmonary volumes, which can be measured with an instrument called a **spirometer** (spih-RAH-meh-ter; *spiro-* = "to breathe"), include the following (Fig. 23.4):

- **Tidal volume (TV).** The **tidal volume**, or TV, is the amount of air exchanged with each breath during normal, quiet breathing. It measures about 500 mL in a healthy adult.
- **Expiratory reserve volume (ERV).** The **expiratory reserve volume**, or the ERV, is the volume of air that may be expired after a tidal expiration. It averages between 700 and 1,200 mL of air.

- **Inspiratory reserve volume (IRV).** The **inspiratory reserve volume**, or the IRV, is the amount of air that may be inspired after a tidal inspiration. It averages between 1,900 and 3,100 mL of air.

Note that there is a fourth volume, called the **residual volume (RV)**, which is defined as the amount of air that remains in the lungs after maximal expiration, and is generally equal to about 1,100 to 1,200 mL of air. The RV cannot be measured with general spirometry, but its value can be estimated by subtracting the ERV from the IRV (e.g., IRV − ERV = RV).

Two or more pulmonary volumes may be combined to give **pulmonary capacities**. As you can see in Figure 23.4, there are four pulmonary capacities:

- **Inspiratory capacity (IC).** The **inspiratory capacity**, or IC, is equal to the TV plus the IRV, and is the amount of air that a person can maximally inspire after a tidal expiration. It averages between 2,400 and 3,600 mL of air.
- **Functional residual capacity (FRC).** The **functional residual capacity**, or the FRC, is the amount of air that is normally left in the lungs after a tidal expiration. It is the sum of the ERV and the RV, and averages between 1,800 and 2,400 mL of air. It is not measurable with general spirometry.
- **Vital capacity (VC).** The **vital capacity**, or VC, represents the total amount of exchangeable air that moves in and out of the lungs. It averages between 3,100 and 4,800 mL of air, and is equal to the sum of the TV, IRV, and the ERV.
- **Total lung capacity (TLC).** The **total lung capacity**, or TLC, represents the total amount of exchangeable and non-exchangeable air in the lungs. It is the total of all four respiratory volumes, and is not measurable with general spirometry. It averages between 4,200 and 6,000 mL of air.

Spirometry is a useful tool with which to assess pulmonary function. The pulmonary volumes and capacities are especially helpful in differentiating the two primary types of respiratory disorders: restrictive diseases and obstructive diseases.

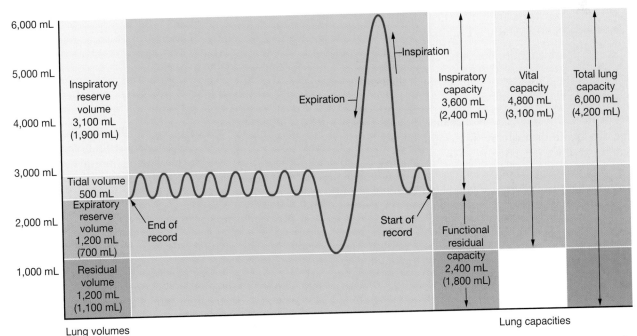

FIGURE **23.4** Pulmonary volumes and capacities (note that the top value in the figure is the average value for males, and the value in parentheses is the average value for females).

23

Restrictive diseases are characterized by a loss of lung, alveolar, or chest distensibility, meaning that the lungs or chest are unable to stretch and increase in size. Examples include pneumoconiosis (coal-miner's lung), tuberculosis, and *atelectasis* (ă-tuh-LEK-tuh-sis; collapse of the alveoli). Restrictive diseases cause difficulty with *inspiration*. This results in a decreased IRV, IC, VC, and TLC.

Obstructive diseases, such as chronic obstructive pulmonary disease (COPD) and asthma, are characterized by increased airway resistance caused by narrowing of the bronchioles, increased mucus secretion, and/or an obstructing body such as a tumor. It may seem counterintuitive, but obstructive diseases make *expiration* difficult. This is because the increased intrapulmonary pressure during expiration naturally tends to shrink the diameter of the bronchioles. When the bronchioles are already narrowed, as in an obstructive disease, the increased intrapulmonary pressure can actually collapse the bronchioles and trap oxygen-poor air in the distal respiratory passages. Therefore, patients with obstructive diseases often exhale slowly and through pursed lips to minimize the pressure changes and maximize the amount of air exhaled. Obstructive diseases decrease the ERV and VC and increase the RV and FRC.

---

1 | **PROCEDURE**

Measuring Respiratory Volumes with a Wet or Handheld Spirometer

Three types of spirometers are commonly found in anatomy and physiology labs: (1) a bell, or "wet" spirometer; (2) a computerized spirometer; and (3) a handheld spirometer (shown in Fig. 23.5). Many types of wet and handheld spirometers allow you to assess only expiratory volumes, whereas computerized spirometers typically allow you to assess both inspiratory and expiratory volumes. All types of devices allow measurement of one or more respiratory capacities.

The following procedure is intended for a wet or handheld spirometer. If your lab has a computerized spirometer, however, you can either follow the procedure steps or follow the prompts by the computer program. When you have completed the activity, answer Check Your Understanding Questions 3 and 4 (pp. 625–626).

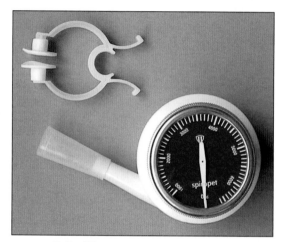

FIGURE **23.5** Handheld spirometer.

> ⚠ **SAFETY NOTE**
>
> You should not be the subject of this experiment if you have cardiovascular or pulmonary disease, are prone to dizziness or fainting, or have had symptoms of COVID-19 in the past 14 days.

1 Obtain a disposable mouthpiece, and attach it to the end of the tube.

2 Before you begin, practice exhaling through the tube several times. Note that you are supposed to only *exhale* into the tube, as the tube likely has no filter.

3 *Measure the tidal volume*: Sit in a chair with your back straight and your eyes closed. Inhale a normal tidal inspiration, and exhale this breath through the tube. Getting a true representation of the tidal volume is often difficult, because people have a tendency to force the expiration. To get the most accurate tidal volume, take several measurements and average the numbers. Note that some handheld spirometers are not terribly sensitive and so give a value for the tidal volume that is too low. If you find that this is the case, you may need to take extra readings to get an approximately accurate measurement.

Measurement 1: _____   Measurement 3: _____

Measurement 2: _____   Average Tidal Volume: _____

4 *Measure the expiratory reserve volume*: Before taking this measurement, inhale and exhale a series of tidal volumes. Then, inspire a normal tidal inspiration, breathe out a normal tidal expiration, put the mouthpiece to your mouth, and exhale as forcibly as possible. Don't cheat by taking in a large breath first! As before, perform several measurements and average the numbers.

Measurement 1: _____   Measurement 3: _____

Measurement 2: _____   Average Expiratory Reserve Volume: _____

5 *Measure the vital capacity*: As before, inhale and exhale a series of tidal volumes. Then, bend over and exhale maximally. Once you have exhaled as much air as you can, raise yourself upright and inhale as much air as you possibly can (until you feel like you are nearly about to "pop"). Quickly place the mouthpiece to your mouth and exhale as forcibly and as long as possible. Take several measurements (you may want to give yourself a minute to rest between measurements), and record the data in the spaces provided.

Measurement 1: _____

Measurement 2: _____

Measurement 3: _____

Average Vital Capacity: _____

6 *Calculate the inspiratory reserve volume*: Even though the bell or handheld spirometer cannot measure inspiratory volumes, you can calculate this volume now that you have the vital capacity (VC), tidal volume (TV), and expiratory reserve volume (ERV). Recall that VC = TV + IRV + ERV. Rearrange the equation: IRV = VC − (TV + ERV).

Average IRV: _____

7 How do your values compare with the average values? What factors, if any, do you think may have affected your results?

_____

_____

_____

_____

2	**PROCEDURE**

Comparing Results of Tobacco Users with Nonusers

It's widely known that tobacco use—with both regular and electronic cigarettes—negatively affects lung function. Here, you will measure the effects by comparing spirometry data from tobacco users and nonusers.

Hypothesis: How will tobacco use affect spirometry results?

_____

1 Pool the results for your class, and divide the results into four categories: female tobacco users, female nonusers, male tobacco users, and male nonusers. (Note that tobacco use includes regular and electronic cigarettes.) Calculate the average TV, ERV, and VC for each group, and record these data in Table 23.2.

TABLE **23.2** Pulmonary Volumes and Capacities for Tobacco Users and Nonusers

Group	Tidal Volume	Expiratory Reserve Volume	Inspiratory Reserve Volume	Vital Capacity
Female tobacco users				
Female nonusers				
Male tobacco users				
Male nonusers				

23

2 Interpret your results:

a How did the average values differ for males and females?

b How did the average values differ for tobacco users and nonusers?

c What disease pattern would you expect to see with the tobacco users? Did your results follow this expectation?

3 Compare your hypothesis to your results.

❑ 200 mL beaker (1)

❑ Deionized water

❑ pH meter

❑ Drinking straw

pH and Ventilation

Pulmonary ventilation is required not only to bring oxygen into the body but also to remove carbon dioxide from the body. Carbon dioxide is a nonpolar gas that does not dissolve fully in the water of plasma, so only about 7 to 10% of the carbon dioxide that we produce is transported in this manner. Another 20% of the carbon dioxide entering the blood binds to hemoglobin to form a molecule called *carbaminohemoglobin*. The remainder of the carbon dioxide is transported as another compound entirely: the weak base called the **bicarbonate ion** (HCO_3^-).

When carbon dioxide encounters water, it undergoes a reversible reaction to form the weak acid **carbonic acid** (H_2CO_3). Most carbonic acid dissociates to form hydrogen and bicarbonate ions, which form a system known as the **carbonic acid–bicarbonate buffer system**. In the body, this reaction is catalyzed by an enzyme called **carbonic anhydrase** (kar-BAH-nik an-HY-dray'z) and proceeds as follows:

$$H_2O + CO_2 \Longleftrightarrow H_2CO_3 \Longleftrightarrow HCO_3^- + H^+$$

Recall from the chemistry unit that a solution's concentration of hydrogen ions determines whether it is acidic, basic, or neutral, which is a value that is represented by the solution's **pH**. As you can see from this reaction, the amount of carbon dioxide in the blood is a major determinant of the concentration of hydrogen ions in the blood. As the amount of carbon dioxide in the blood is determined directly by the rate and depth of ventilation, anything that affects ventilation can change the hydrogen ion concentration and so the pH of the blood.

Let's figure out what happens to the pH of the blood when the rate and depth of ventilation increase during **hyperventilation**.

During hyperventilation, what happens to the amount of carbon dioxide expired (i.e., does it increase or decrease)?

_____

How will this affect the concentration of carbon dioxide in the blood (i.e., will it increase or decrease)?

_____

How will this affect the number of hydrogen ions released from carbonic acid (i.e., will it increase or decrease)?

_____

How does the change in the number of hydrogen ions affect the pH of the blood? _____

So, how will hyperventilation affect the pH of the blood? _____

Let's now walk through what happens when the rate and depth of ventilation decrease during **hypoventilation**.

During hypoventilation, what happens to the amount of carbon dioxide expired (i.e., does it increase or decrease)?

_____

How will this affect the concentration of carbon dioxide in the blood (i.e., will it increase or decrease)?

_____

How will this affect the number of hydrogen ions released from carbonic acid (i.e., will it increase or decrease)?

_____

How does the change in the number of hydrogen ions affect the pH of the blood? _____

So, how will hypoventilation affect the pH of the blood? _____

Imbalances in the pH of the body's fluids can rapidly become deadly, so the body controls pH very tightly through negative feedback loops. One of the fastest-acting loops involves the respiratory system and the brainstem. When the pH of the blood

23

increases, the brainstem attempts to correct this pH imbalance by decreasing the rate and depth of ventilation. This causes retention of carbon dioxide, which lowers the pH back to normal. Conversely, when the pH of the blood decreases, the brainstem triggers hyperventilation to expire more carbon dioxide and remove it from the blood. This loss of carbon dioxide increases the pH back to normal. This latter response is something you witness when you engage in moderate to strenuous exercise—as you exercise, you produce more metabolic acids such as carbon dioxide and lactic acid. This triggers the negative feedback loop and the elevated respiratory rate you experience during exercise.

⚠ **SAFETY NOTE**

You should not be the subject of this experiment if you have cardiovascular or pulmonary disease, are prone to dizziness or fainting, or have had symptoms of COVID-19 in the past 14 days.

1 PROCEDURE
Measuring the Effect of Carbon Dioxide on the pH of a Solution

We can't measure the effects of ventilatory rate on blood pH directly in the lab because it requires an analysis of arterial blood. However, we can observe and measure the effects of carbon dioxide on the pH of water and correlate this with the changes you would see in the blood, which is what you will do in the following experiment. When you have completed the activity, answer Check Your Understanding Questions 5 and 6 (p. 626).

Hypothesis: How will an elevated ventilatory rate affect the pH of water?

1 Measure your partner's respiratory rate while seated and resting. Measuring the respiratory rate can be tricky because as soon as you tell people to breathe normally, they automatically become conscious of breathing and alter the rate. A trick you may want to try is to place two fingers on your partner's radial artery and take a pulse rate. This will cause your partner to focus more on the pulse rate and breathe more naturally. Record this value in Table 23.3.

2 Fill a 200 mL beaker about half-full of deionized water. Measure the pH of the water with a pH meter. Record this value in the space provided:

pH of deionized water: _____

3 Place a drinking straw into the water, and have your partner exhale through the straw into the water (the water should bubble) for 20 seconds. Repeat the pH measurement of the water with the pH meter, and record the value in Table 23.3.

4 Empty your beaker, and refill it with new water. Have your partner do vigorous exercise for at least 5 minutes (running up and down stairs or doing jumping jacks usually does the job). The longer and more vigorously your partner exercises, the better results you will obtain from the procedure. Immediately upon finishing the exercise, have your partner blow through the straw into the beaker of water for 20 seconds. Measure the pH of the water with the pH meter, and record the value in Table 23.3.

5 After you record the pH, measure your partner's respiratory rate (you may want to use the pulse trick again), and record the value in Table 23.3.

6 Empty your beaker again, and refill it with new water. Allow your partner to have a (well-deserved) rest for at least 5 minutes. Again, have your partner blow through the straw into the beaker of water for 20 seconds, and measure the pH of the water with the pH meter. Record the value in Table 23.3.

7 After you record the pH, measure your partner's respiratory rate, and record the value in Table 23.3.

TABLE **23.3** pH of Water and Rate of Ventilation

Setting	Respiratory Rate	pH
At rest		
Immediately after exercise		
After 5 minutes of rest		

8 Interpret your results:

a Start with the basics: What happens to the metabolic rate during exercise? What is generated as a waste product of glucose catabolism?

b What does this waste product do to the pH of the blood? Why?

c What sort of ventilatory response does this change in pH cause (increase or decrease in rate/depth of ventilation)? Why?

d Now apply this information to your results:

(1) What happened to the respiratory rate during and after exercise? Why? (**Hint:** See question 8c.)

(2) What happened to the pH of the water after exercise? Why?

(3) What happened to the respiratory rate and the pH of the water after resting? Why?

9 Compare your results to your hypothesis.

23

Check Your Recall

1 Pulmonary gas exchange is best defined as
   a. the movement of gases across the respiratory membrane.
   b. the exchange of gases between the blood in the systemic capillaries and the tissues.
   c. the physical movement of air into and out of the lungs.
   d. the movement of gases through the blood.

2 Which of the following correctly describes the relationship of pressure and volume according to Boyle's law?
   a. Pressure and volume are directly proportional—as volume increases, so does pressure.
   b. Pressure and volume are inversely proportional—as volume increases, pressure decreases.
   c. Pressure and volume are directly proportional, but only if temperature increases.
   d. Pressure and volume are not directly correlated.

3 The muscles of inspiration
   a. increase lung volume and increase intrapulmonary pressure.
   b. decrease lung volume and increase intrapulmonary pressure.
   c. increase lung volume and decrease intrapulmonary pressure.
   d. decrease lung volume and decrease intrapulmonary pressure.

4 The lungs' elastic recoil is responsible for
   a. active inspiration.
   b. passive inspiration.
   c. active expiration.
   d. passive expiration.

5 *Fill in the blanks.* Carbon dioxide is transported through the blood primarily as _____

_____ due to a reaction catalyzed by the enzyme _____

_____ .

6 What happens to the pH of the blood during hyperventilation, and why?

_____

_____

_____

_____

7 Label Figure 23.6 with the following terms.

❑ Expiratory reserve volume   ❑ Inspiratory reserve volume   ❑ Total lung capacity
❑ Functional residual capacity   ❑ Residual volume   ❑ Vital capacity
❑ Inspiratory capacity   ❑ Tidal volume

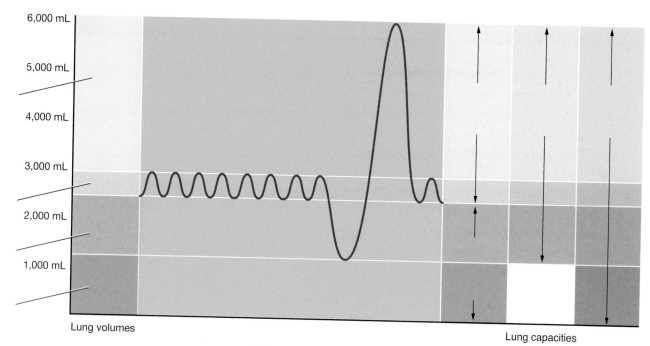

FIGURE **23.6** Pulmonary volumes and capacities.

8 What are the key differences between a restrictive and an obstructive disease?

9 Calculate the inspiratory capacity, vital capacity, and total lung capacity for a patient with the following pulmonary volumes:

- Tidal Volume = 600 mL
- Expiratory Reserve Volume = 1,450 mL
- Inspiratory Reserve Volume = 2,650 mL
- Residual Volume = 1,300 mL

Inspiratory Capacity = _____

Vital Capacity = _____

Total Lung Capacity = _____

10 The equation for the carbonic acid-bicarbonate buffer system is

a. $H_2O + CO_2 \Longleftrightarrow H_2CO_3 \Longleftrightarrow HCO_3^- + H^+$
b. $H_2O + O_2 \Longleftrightarrow C_6H_{12}O_6 \Longleftrightarrow H_2CO_3 + H^+$
c. $H_2CO_3 \Longleftrightarrow H_2O + CO_2 \Longleftrightarrow HCO_3^- + H^+$
d. $H_2O + HCO_3^- \Longleftrightarrow H_2CO_3 \Longleftrightarrow CO_2 + H^+$

Check Your Understanding

Critical Thinking and Application Questions

1 A *pleural effusion* is an accumulation of pleural fluid, blood, pus, or other fluid within the pleural cavity. This condition increases pressure on the lungs. Explain why a pleural effusion makes pulmonary ventilation difficult in terms of pressure and volume.

_____

_____

_____

_____

_____

2 Your patient Kaylee has been hospitalized with *COVID-19*, the respiratory disease caused by the virus SARS-CoV-2. While caring for her, you notice she is struggling to breathe, and she is using her chest and neck muscles. Explain which muscles she is using, and why, in terms of pressure and volume.

_____

_____

_____

_____

_____

3 A male patient presents with the following pulmonary volumes and capacities: TV = 400 mL, ERV = 800 mL, IRV = 1,200 mL. What is this patient's VC? What is the estimated RV? Are these values normal? If not, are they more consistent with an obstructive or restrictive disease pattern? Explain.

_____

_____

_____

_____

_____

4 Kaylee's COVID-19 has resulted in inflammation of her alveoli, which caused them to fill with fluid and partially collapse. Has this given Kaylee a restrictive or obstructive disease pattern? Predict the values you would expect to see on her spirometry examination.

_____

_____

_____

_____

_____

5 How will the fluid in Kaylee's alveoli affect her pulmonary gas exchange? What effect will this have on the pH of her blood? Explain.

_____

_____

_____

_____

_____

6 Leda is a diabetic patient who presents after having forgotten her past two insulin doses. You do an assessment and determine that she has a type of metabolic acidosis called _ketoacidosis_. Is her respiratory rate likely elevated or depressed? Explain.

_____

_____

_____

_____

_____

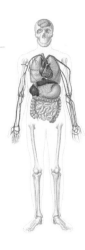

Lab Practical Practice Quiz 3

1 The structure marked number 1 in Figure Q.3.1 is the
   a. thymus gland.
   b. thyroid gland.
   c. parathyroid gland.
   d. thyroid cartilage.

2 The glands located on the posterior surface of structure number 2 in Figure Q.3.1 are the
   a. thymus glands.
   b. adrenal glands.
   c. thyroid glands.
   d. parathyroid glands.

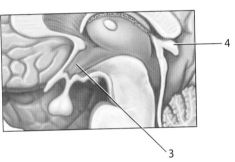

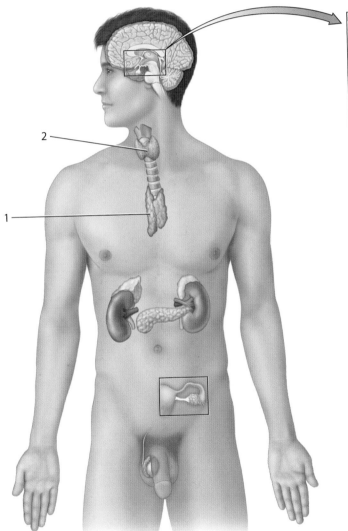

3 The structure marked number 3 in Figure Q.3.1 is the
   a. anterior pituitary gland.
   b. adrenal gland.
   c. hypothalamus.
   d. thymus gland.

4 The structure marked number 4 in Figure Q.3.1 is the
   a. anterior pituitary gland.
   b. posterior pituitary.
   c. hypothalamus.
   d. pineal gland.

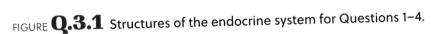

FIGURE **Q.3.1** Structures of the endocrine system for Questions 1–4.

5 The structure marked number 5 in Figure Q.3.2 is the
   a. mitral valve.
   b. tricuspid valve.
   c. aortic valve.
   d. pulmonary valve.

6 The vessel marked number 6 in Figure Q.3.2 is the
   a. superior vena cava.
   b. ascending aorta.
   c. pulmonary trunk.
   d. pulmonary vein.

7 The structure marked number 7 in Figure Q.3.2 is the
   a. chordae tendineae.
   b. papillary muscle.
   c. right auricle.
   d. coronary sinus.

8 The structure marked number 8 in Figure Q.3.2 is the
   a. interatrial septum.
   b. chordae tendineae.
   c. papillary muscle.
   d. trabeculae carneae.

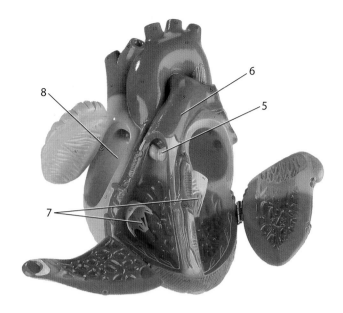

FIGURE **Q.3.2** Frontal dissection of the heart for Questions 5–8.

9 The chamber marked number 9 in Figure Q.3.3 is the
   a. right atrium.
   b. right ventricle.
   c. left atrium.
   d. left ventricle.

10 The chamber marked number 10 in Figure Q.3.3 contains
   _____ and pumps into the _____.
   a. oxygenated blood; pulmonary trunk
   b. deoxygenated blood; pulmonary trunk
   c. deoxygenated blood; aorta
   d. oxygenated blood; left ventricle

11 The structure marked number 11 in Figure Q.3.3 is the
   a. anterior interventricular artery.
   b. right coronary artery.
   c. posterior interventricular artery.
   d. circumflex artery.

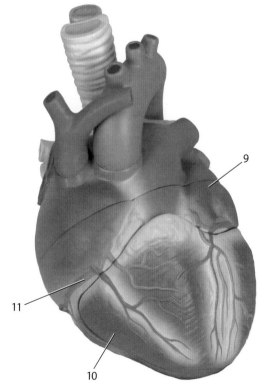

FIGURE **Q.3.3** Anterior view of the heart for Questions 9–11.

12 The vessel marked number 12 in Figure Q.3.4 is the
   a. axillary artery.
   b. brachial artery.
   c. radial artery.
   d. ulnar artery.

13 The vessel marked number 13 in Figure Q.3.4 is the
   a. external jugular vein.
   b. left common carotid artery.
   c. internal jugular vein.
   d. vertebral artery.

14 The vessel marked number 14 in Figure Q.3.4 is the
   a. femoral artery.
   b. common iliac artery.
   c. femoral vein.
   d. external iliac vein.
   e. great saphenous vein.

15 The vessel marked number 15 in Figure Q.3.4 is the
   a. basilic vein.
   b. brachiocephalic vein.
   c. subclavian vein.
   d. cephalic vein.

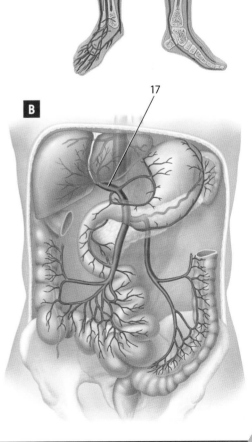

FIGURE **Q.3.4** Major arteries and veins of the body for Questions 12–15.

16 The structure marked number 16 in Figure Q.3.5A is the
   a. celiac trunk.
   b. gonadal artery.
   c. renal artery.
   d. internal iliac artery.

17 The vessel marked number 17 in Figure Q.3.5B is the
   a. splenic vein.
   b. common iliac vein.
   c. hepatic portal vein.
   d. inferior mesenteric vein.

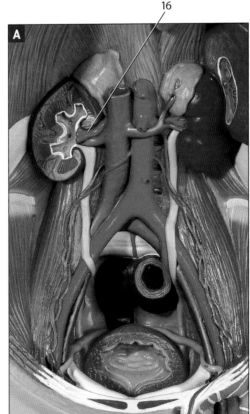

FIGURE **Q.3.5** Blood vessels of the abdomen for Questions 16–17: (**A**) arteries and veins of the abdomen; (**B**) veins of the abdomen.

18 The bracketed structure marked number 18 in Figure Q.3.6 is known as the

  a. middle cerebral artery.
  b. basilar artery.
  c. vertebral artery.
  d. cerebral arterial circle.

19 The structure marked number 19 in Figure Q.3.6 is the

  a. basilar artery.
  b. internal carotid artery.
  c. vertebral artery.
  d. anterior communicating artery.

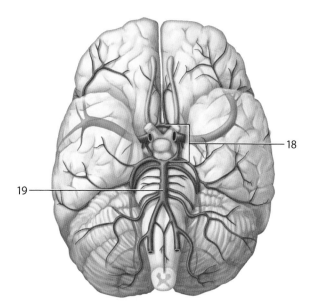

FIGURE **Q.3.6** Inferior view of the vessels of the brain for Questions 18–19.

20 The structure marked number 20 in Figure Q.3.7 is the

  a. thyroid cartilage.
  b. spleen.
  c. thoracic duct.
  d. thymus.

21 The structure marked number 21 in Figure Q.3.7 is a/an

  a. axillary lymph node.
  b. inguinal lymph node.
  c. intestinal lymph node.
  d. cervical lymph node.

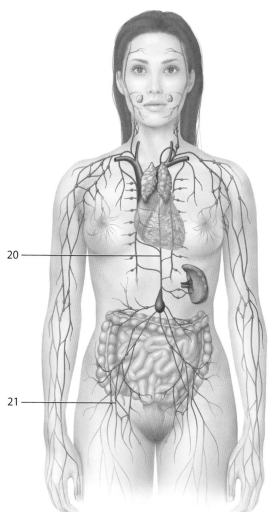

FIGURE **Q.3.7** Structures of the lymphatic system for Questions 20–21.

22 The structure marked number 22 in Figure Q.3.8A is the
   a. laryngopharynx.
   b. nasopharynx.
   c. larynx.
   d. oropharynx.

23 The structure marked number 23 in Figure Q.3.8A is the
   a. cricoid cartilage.
   b. true vocal cord (fold).
   c. hyoid bone.
   d. false vocal cord (fold).

24 The structure marked number 24 in Figure Q.3.8B is the
   a. cricoid cartilage.
   b. thyroid cartilage.
   c. hyoid bone.
   d. epiglottis.

25 The structure marked number 25 in Figure Q.3.8B is the
   a. oblique fissure.
   b. hilum of the lung.
   c. horizontal fissure.
   d. cardiac notch.

26 The structure marked number 26 in Figure Q.3.8B is a/the
   a. primary bronchus.
   b. secondary bronchus.
   c. pharyngeal tonsil.
   d. trachea.

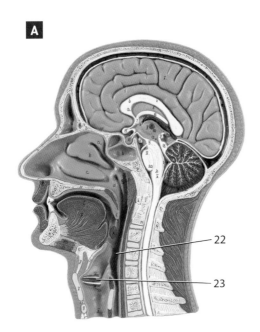
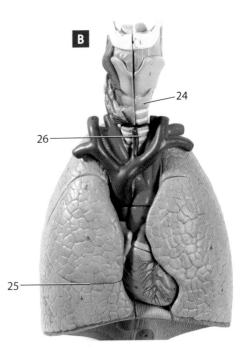

FIGURE **Q.3.8** Respiratory structures for Questions 22–26: (**A**) midsagittal section through the head for Questions 22–23; (**B**) anterior dissection of the thorax for Questions 24–26.

27 The structure marked number 27 in Figure Q.3.9 is a/the
   a. pulmonary venule.
   b. pulmonary arteriole.
   c. pulmonary capillary bed.
   d. pulmonary vein.

28 The structure marked number 28 in Figure Q.3.9 is a/an
   a. alveolar duct.
   b. terminal bronchiole.
   c. respiratory bronchiole.
   d. alveolar sac.

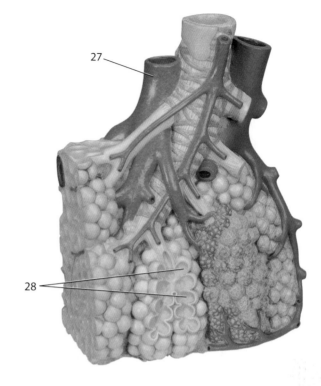

FIGURE **Q.3.9** Microscopic structures of the lung for Questions 27–28.

29 The blood cell marked number 29 in Figure Q.3.10 is a/an
   a. neutrophil.
   b. eosinophil.
   c. lymphocyte.
   d. monocyte.

30 The blood sample in Question 29 reacted with anti-Rh antiserum, but not with anti-B or anti-A antisera. What *antigens* do the blood cells in this sample have on their surfaces?
   a. A antigen.
   b. B antigen.
   c. Rh antigen.
   d. Both responses a and b are correct.
   e. Both responses b and c are correct.

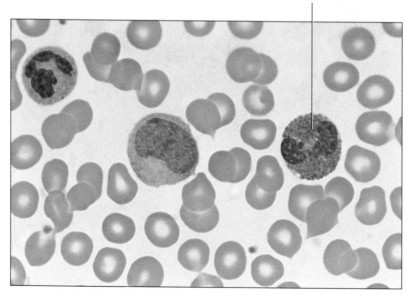

FIGURE **Q.3.10** Peripheral blood smear for Question 29.

Digestive System

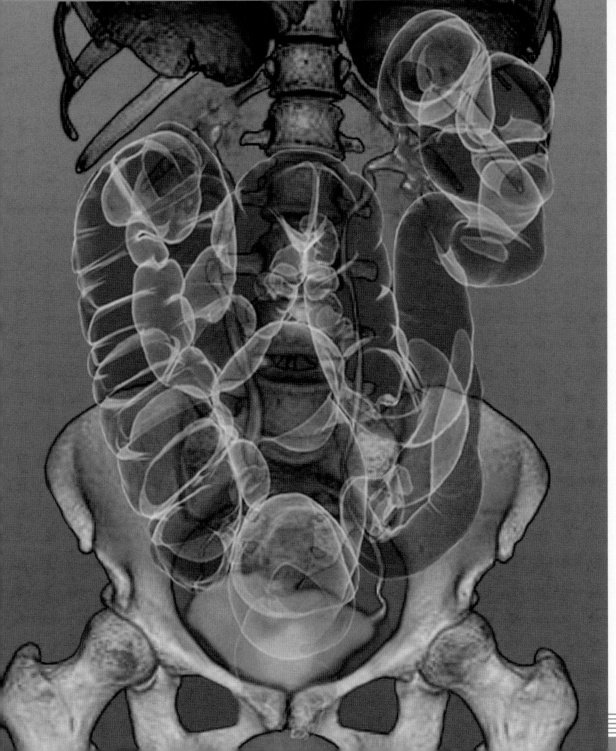

When you have completed this unit, you should be able to:

1 Describe and identify structures of the digestive system.

2 Describe and identify the microscopic anatomy of the digestive system.

3 Explain how emulsifying agents act on lipids.

4 Explain the factors that influence the functions of digestive enzymes.

5 Trace the anatomical pathway taken by carbohydrates, proteins, and lipids as they are digested and absorbed into the blood.

6 Trace the physiological processes that physically and chemically break down carbohydrates, proteins, and lipids as they are digested.

PRE-LAB EXERCISES

Complete the following exercises prior to coming to lab, using your lab manual and textbook for reference.

PRE-LAB

24-1 Key Terms

You should be familiar with the following terms before coming to lab. Please note that this list is not all-inclusive, because the terminology for the digestive system is extensive. Digestive enzymes are covered separately in Pre-Lab Exercise 24-3 (p. 640).

Term	Definition

Digestive System Structures

Alimentary canal (gastrointestinal tract) _____

_____

Accessory organ _____

_____

Peritoneal cavity _____

_____

Gastroesophageal sphincter _____

_____

Pyloric sphincter _____

_____

Duodenum _____

_____

Jejunum _____

_____

Ileum _____

_____

Colon _____

_____

Salivary glands _____

_____

Pancreas _____

_____

Liver _____

Gallbladder _____

_____

Digestive Histology

Mucosa _____

_____

Submucosa _____

_____

Muscularis externa _____

_____

Serosa _____

_____

Acinar cells _____

_____

Pancreatic islet _____

_____

Liver lobule _____

_____

Digestive Physiology

Digestive enzyme _____

_____

Chemical digestion _____

_____

Emulsification _____

_____

Bile _____

_____

Color the structures of the digestive system in Figures 24.1 through 24.4, and label them with the terms from Exercise 24-1 (p. 641). Use your text and Exercise 24-1 in this unit for reference.

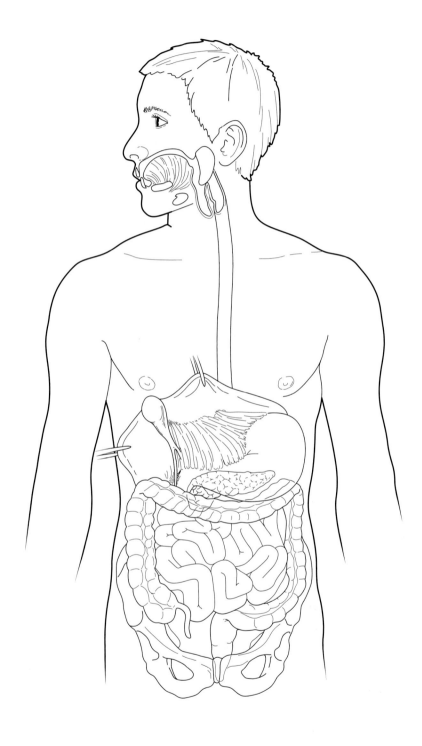

FIGURE **24.1** Anatomy of the digestive system.

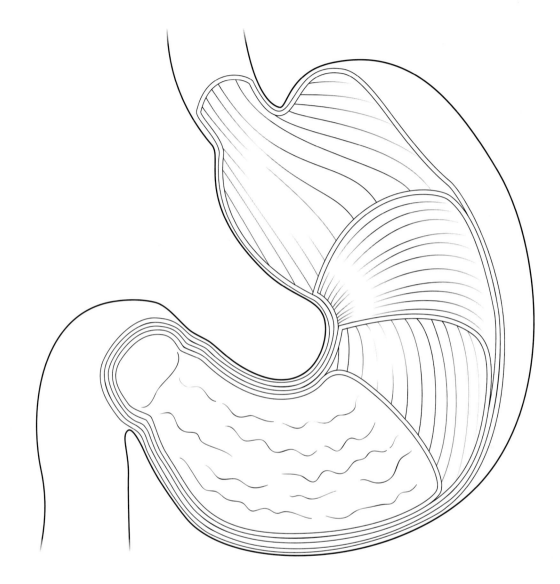

FIGURE **24.2** **Anatomy of the stomach.**

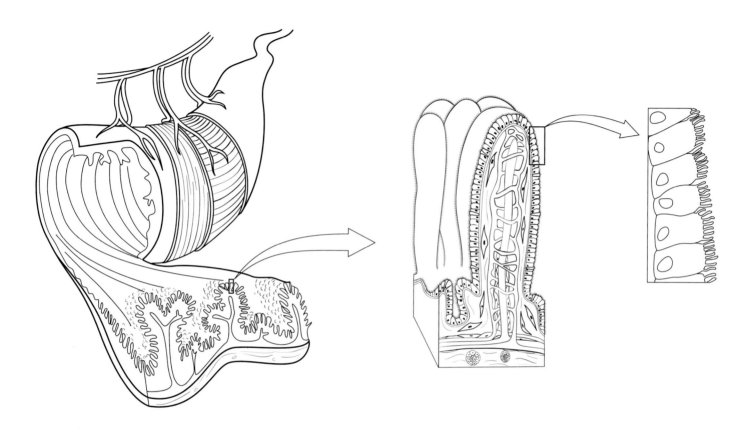

FIGURE **24.3** Gross and microscopic anatomy of the small intestine.

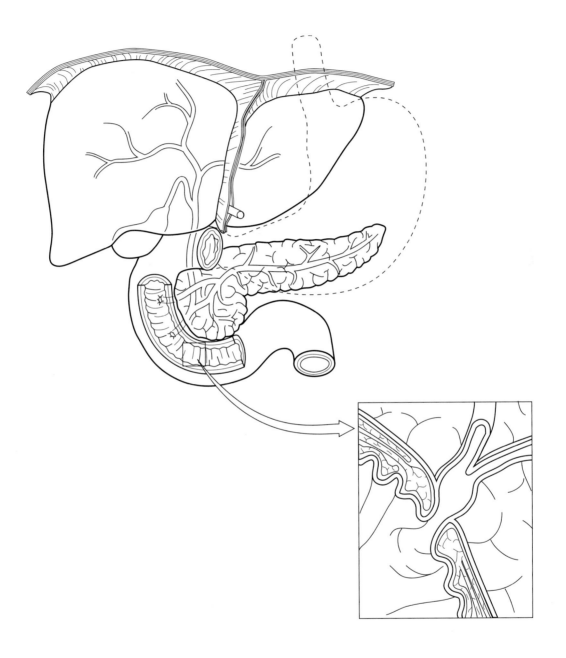

FIGURE **24.4** Anatomy of the liver, gallbladder, pancreas, and duodenum.

Digestive Enzymes

Chemical digestion is one of the main functions of the digestive system and is carried out with the help of numerous digestive enzymes. Record the organ that produces each enzyme and the enzyme's function in Table 24.1.

TABLE **24.1** Digestive Enzymes

Enzyme	Source	Function
Salivary amylase		
Pepsin		
Trypsin		
Pancreatic lipase		
Brush border enzymes		

EXERCISES

The food we eat contains nutrients our cells use to build and repair body tissues and to make ATP. Food macromolecules, however, are typically too large for the body to absorb and utilize, so the body must break them down into smaller molecules. This process of breaking down foods into smaller substances that can enter body cells is called **digestion** and is carried out by the **digestive system**. In general, the functions of the digestive system include:

- **Ingestion**, or bringing food into the body;
- **Propulsion**, or the movement of food through the organs of the digestive system;
- **Mechanical digestion**, or breaking food apart physically into smaller pieces;
- **Chemical digestion**, or breaking the food apart chemically via enzyme-catalyzed reactions;
- **Absorption** of digested nutrients into the bloodstream; and
- **Defecation**, or the elimination of indigestible substances.

We begin this unit with an introduction to the anatomy and histology of the organs of the digestive system. Next, we examine the physiological processes of chemical digestion and emulsification. We conclude with a "big picture" view of digestion through a tracing exercise.

3D computed tomography scan of an abdomen.

EXERCISE 24-1

MATERIALS

- ❑ Anatomical models and diagrams:
  - digestive system
  - head and neck
  - human torso
  - intestinal villus
  - tissue layers of the alimentary canal
  - digestive organs (stomach, pancreas, liver, and duodenum)
- ❑ Human skulls with teeth
- ❑ Colored pencils

Digestive System Anatomy

The digestive system is composed of two groups of organs: (1) the organs of the **alimentary canal** (al-uh-MEN-tuh-ree; *aliment-* = "nourishment"), also known as the **gastrointestinal** or **GI tract** (*gastr-* = "stomach"), through which food travels; and (2) the **accessory organs**, which assist in mechanical or chemical digestion (Fig. 24.5). The organs of the alimentary canal include the *oral cavity*, *pharynx*, *esophagus*, *stomach*, *small intestine*, and *large intestine*. The accessory organs include the *teeth*, *tongue*, *salivary glands*, *liver*, *gallbladder*, and *pancreas*. We discuss the structure of each in greater detail shortly.

Much of the alimentary canal and many of the accessory organs reside inside a cavity known as the **peritoneal cavity** (pehr-ih-toh-NEE-uhl; *peri-* = "around;" *ton-* = "stretched"), shown in Figure 24.6. Like the pleural and pericardial cavities, the peritoneal cavity is found between a double-layered serous membrane. The membrane secretes serous fluid to enable the organs within the cavity to slide over one another without friction. Organs that are within the peritoneal cavity are known as *intraperitoneal*, while those that are behind the cavity are *retroperitoneal* (*retro-* = "behind"). You can see in Figure 24.6 how widespread the peritoneal cavity is, and how many of the abdominal organs are located either partially or totally within it.

The two layers of the peritoneal membranes are as follows:

- **Parietal peritoneum.** The outer **parietal peritoneum** is a thin membrane functionally fused to the abdominal wall and certain organs.

- **Visceral peritoneum.** The inner **visceral peritoneum** adheres to the surface of many abdominal organs. The visceral peritoneum around the intestines folds over on itself to form a thick membrane known as the **mesentery** (MEZ-en-tehr-ee), which is shown in Figure 24.7. The mesentery houses blood vessels, nerves, and lymphatic vessels, anchoring these structures and the intestines in place. Mesenteries in different regions have specific names, such as the **greater omentum** (oh-MEN-tum; "apron"). True to its name, this mesentery covers the abdominal organs like an apron. The smaller **lesser omentum** runs from the liver to the lesser curvature of the stomach (visible in Figs. 24.5 and 24.6). The mesentery attached to the large intestine is often called the *mesocolon*; for example, the *transverse mesocolon* is attached to the transverse colon, and the *sigmoid mesocolon* is attached to the sigmoid colon.

Let's now turn to the alimentary canal, which is a hollow passageway that extends from the mouth to the anus. Ingested food within the alimentary canal is broken down mechanically and chemically into nutrient molecules. The nutrients, along with water, vitamins, ions, and other substances, then cross the epithelium of the canal to enter the body and be absorbed into the blood or lymph.

24

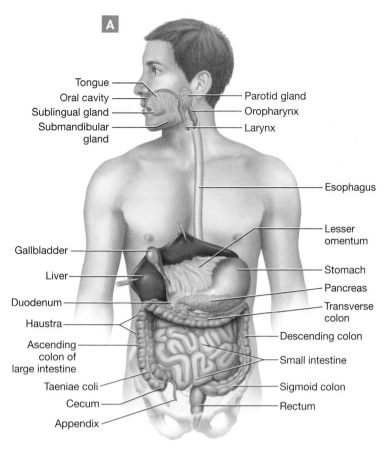

A

Tongue
Oral cavity
Sublingual gland
Submandibular gland

Parotid gland
Oropharynx
Larynx

Esophagus

Lesser omentum

Gallbladder

Liver

Duodenum

Haustra

Ascending colon of large intestine

Taeniae coli

Cecum

Appendix

Stomach

Pancreas

Transverse colon

Descending colon

Small intestine

Sigmoid colon

Rectum

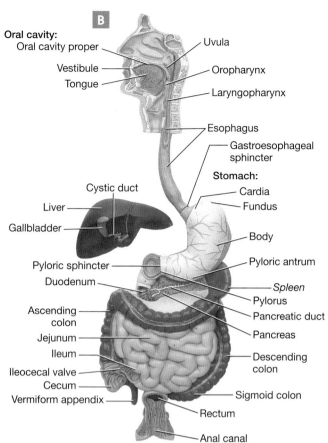

B

Oral cavity:
  Oral cavity proper
  Vestibule
  Tongue

Uvula
Oropharynx
Laryngopharynx

Esophagus

Gastroesophageal sphincter

Cystic duct

Liver

Gallbladder

Stomach:
  Cardia
  Fundus

Body

Pyloric sphincter

Duodenum

Ascending colon

Jejunum

Ileum

Ileocecal valve

Cecum

Vermiform appendix

Pyloric antrum

Spleen

Pylorus

Pancreatic duct

Pancreas

Descending colon

Sigmoid colon

Rectum

Anal canal

FIGURE **24.5** Overview of the digestive system:
(**A**) illustration; (**B**) anatomical model photo;
(**C**) a dissected abdominopelvic cavity.

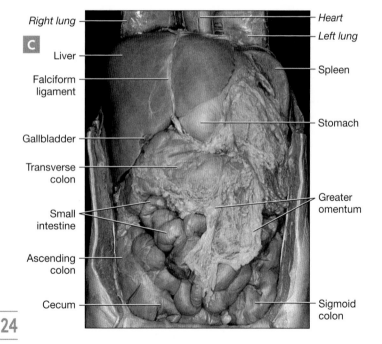

C

Right lung

Liver

Falciform ligament

Gallbladder

Transverse colon

Small intestine

Ascending colon

Cecum

Heart

Left lung

Spleen

Stomach

Greater omentum

Sigmoid colon

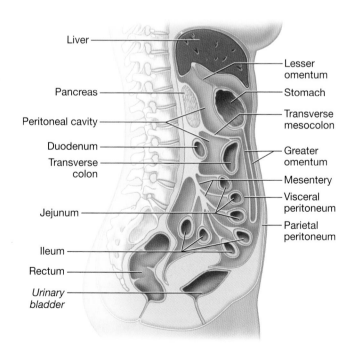

Liver

Pancreas

Peritoneal cavity

Duodenum

Transverse colon

Jejunum

Ileum

Rectum

Urinary bladder

Lesser omentum

Stomach

Transverse mesocolon

Greater omentum

Mesentery

Visceral peritoneum

Parietal peritoneum

FIGURE **24.6** Structure of the peritoneal membranes and cavity.

24

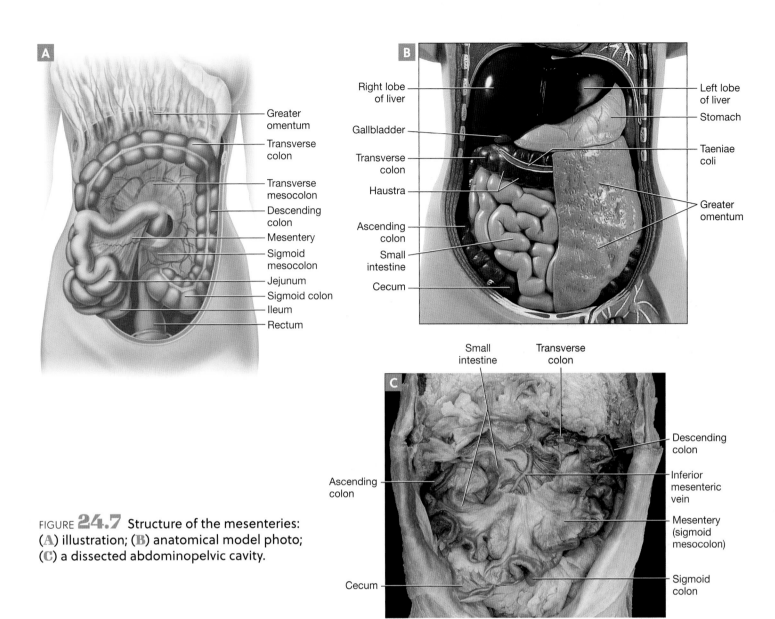

FIGURE **24.7** Structure of the mesenteries:
(**A**) illustration; (**B**) anatomical model photo;
(**C**) a dissected abdominopelvic cavity.

The alimentary canal consists of the following organs:

■ **Mouth.** The alimentary canal begins with the **mouth**, which has two internal regions: the vestibule and the oral cavity (Fig. 24.8). The **vestibule** is the space between the lips and the teeth. Within the vestibule, we find the **gingivae** (JIN-jih-vay; *gingiv-* = "gums"), or *gums*, and the maxilla and mandible, where the teeth are housed. We also find a narrow band of mucosa called the **labial frenulum** (LAY-bee-uhl FREN-yoo-lum; *lab-* = "lip") on each of the lips (both upper and lower) that attaches their internal surfaces to the upper and lower gums.

Posterior to the vestibule, we find the **oral cavity**, which is defined as the area posterior to the teeth and bounded by the palate, cheeks, and tongue. The "roof" of the mouth is the **palate** (PAL-it), which consists of two portions. The first, which makes up the anterior two-thirds of the palate, is the bony **hard palate**. Recall from the skeletal unit that the hard palate is formed by the palatine processes of the maxillary bones and the palatine bones. The second portion of the palate, which makes up its posterior one-third, is the muscular, arch-shaped **soft palate** (you can see this shape in Fig. 24.8A). Extending inferiorly from the soft palate is the **uvula** (YOO-vyoo-luh)—both move posteriorly to prevent food from entering the nasopharynx and nasal cavity when we swallow.

■ **Pharynx.** The food next enters the **pharynx** (FEHR-inks), also known as the throat. Food passes through two divisions of the pharynx: the **oropharynx** (ohr-oh-FEHR-inks) and the **laryngopharynx** (lah-ring-oh-FEHR-inks; Fig. 24.8B). The muscles surrounding the pharynx propel swallowed food, which is known as a *bolus*, into the next portion of the alimentary canal. Recall from the lymphatic and immune unit that two sets of tonsils are located in the oropharynx—the lingual tonsil and the palatine tonsil—which protect the alimentary canal from ingested pathogens.

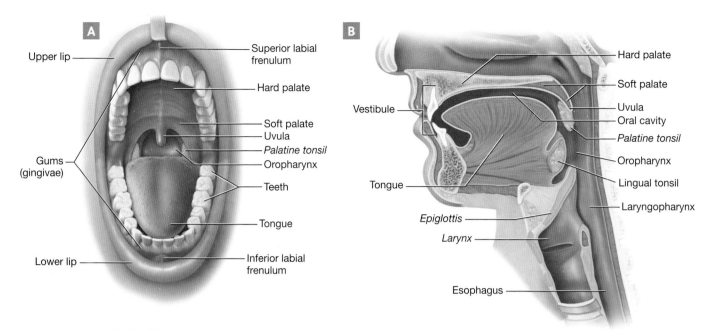

FIGURE **24.8** Structure of the mouth and oral cavity: (**A**) anterior view; (**B**) midsagittal section.

■ **Esophagus.** The bolus next enters the **esophagus** (eh-SAHF-uh-guhs), a narrow tubular organ posterior to the heart and the trachea in the thoracic cavity. Smooth and skeletal muscle in the wall of the esophagus propel the bolus toward the stomach via rhythmic contractions called **peristalsis** (pehr-ih-STAHL-sis; "wrap around"). At the inferior end of the esophagus is a ring of smooth muscle called the **gastroesophageal sphincter** (gas-troh-eh-sahf-uh-JEE-uhl), also known as the *lower esophageal sphincter* or *cardiac sphincter*. Several sphincters are found in the alimentary canal, where they regulate the flow of materials from one section of the canal to another. The gastroesophageal sphincter normally remains closed, which prevents the contents of the stomach from regurgitating into the esophagus.

■ **Stomach.** The **stomach**, shown in Figure 24.9, has five regions: the **cardia** near the gastroesophageal sphincter, the dome-shaped **fundus**, the middle **body**, the inferior **pyloric antrum**, and the terminal portion of the stomach, which is called the **pylorus** (py-LOHR-uhs). At the pylorus, we find another sphincter, called the **pyloric sphincter**. As implied by its name— which means "gatekeeper"—it controls the flow of material from the stomach to the initial portion of the small intestine.

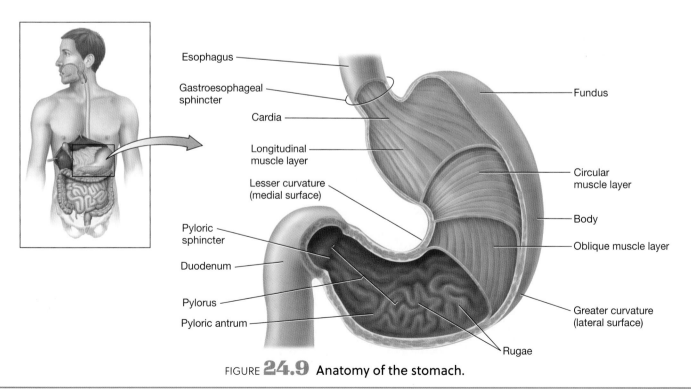

FIGURE **24.9** Anatomy of the stomach.

24

Note in Figure 24.9 that the stomach has interior folds called **rugae** (ROO-ghee; "wrinkles") that allow it to expand considerably when it is filled with food and liquid. In addition, notice that the wall of the stomach has three layers of smooth muscle (inner oblique, middle circular, and outer longitudinal layers). These three muscle layers perform a motion called **churning** that mechanically digests the bolus into a liquid material called **chyme** (KY'M; "juice").

The stomach also participates in chemical digestion by secreting acid and enzymes, which are collectively known as *gastric juice*. The stomach contains abundant mucus-secreting goblet cells that protect its lining from the contents of the gastric juice.

■ **Small intestine.** Chyme passes through the pyloric sphincter to enter the **small intestine**, the portion of the alimentary canal where most chemical digestion and absorption take place. It has three divisions: the initial **duodenum** (doo-AH-den-um), the middle **jejunum** (jeh-JOO-num), and the terminal **ileum** (ILL-ee-um; Fig. 24.10).

Of the three divisions, the duodenum is the shortest, measuring only about 10 in. The jejunum and the ileum measure about 8 ft. and 12 ft. long, respectively. Notice in Figure 24.10 that at the terminal ileum there is a sphincter called the **ileocecal valve** (ill-ee-oh-SEE-kuhl) that abuts the first portion of the large intestine, the *cecum*. This valve helps to prevent bacteria in the large intestine from reaching the normally sterile small intestine.

The chyme is further mechanically digested in the small intestine by a motion called **segmentation**. This mixes the incoming chyme with intestinal and pancreatic secretions, which catalyze the reactions that chemically digest the ingested nutrients. Most absorption of digested nutrients occurs in the small intestine, particularly the jejunum.

■ **Large intestine.** Material from the small intestine that was not digested or absorbed moves to the terminal part of the alimentary canal—the **large intestine**, which is named for its large diameter rather than its length (about 5.5 ft.). Here,

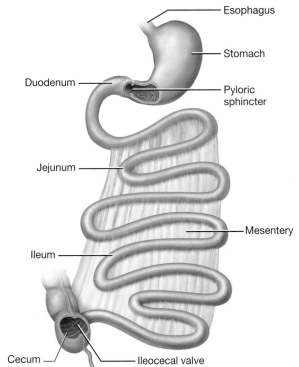

FIGURE **24.10** Small intestine, spread out to show the divisions.

water, electrolytes, and vitamins are absorbed, and any material not absorbed is eliminated by defecation. In addition, the remaining undigested food material is processed by bacteria called the *normal flora* that reside in the alimentary canal.

There are an incredible number of bacteria in the large intestine—as many as one trillion per gm of intestinal contents. The normal flora perform several functions: they produce enzymes that catalyze reactions to break down carbohydrates humans enzymes can't digest; they synthesize fatty acids and vitamins; aid in the development of the immune system; and they protect against disease-causing bacteria.

Notice in Figures 24.11A and B that much of the large intestine features ribbonlike bands of longitudinal smooth muscle called **taeniae coli** (TEE-nee-ee KOHL-aye; "colon ribbon"). These smooth muscle bands have a drawstring effect on the large intestine, pulling it into pouches called **haustra** (HAH-struh; *haustr-* = "scoop"). Extending from the external surface of the large intestine are fat-filled pouches of visceral peritoneum called *epiploic appendages* (ep-ih-PLOH-ik).

The large intestine may be divided into four regions:

▪ The **cecum** (SEE-kum; "blind") is the blind pouch that receives contents from the ileum, from which it is separated by the ileocecal valve. It features an extension called the **vermiform appendix** ("wormlike"), also visible in Figure 24.11C, which is a blind-ended sac that contains lymphoid follicles.

▪ The next segment is the **colon**, which itself has four divisions. It begins as the **ascending colon**, which turns left at the **hepatic flexure** (*hepat-* = "liver) and crosses the superior abdomen as the **transverse colon**. At the spleen, the colon turns inferiorly at the **splenic flexure** to become the **descending colon**, which curves into an "S" shape as it approaches the sacrum to become the **sigmoid colon** ("S-shaped").

▪ The **rectum** is the straight part of the large intestine that runs anterior to the sacrum. Its walls have *rectal valves* that help to control the passage of flatus and feces.

▪ The terminal portion of the large intestine is the **anal canal** (*anus* = "ring"). It has two sphincters: the involuntary **internal anal sphincter** and the voluntary **external anal sphincter**.

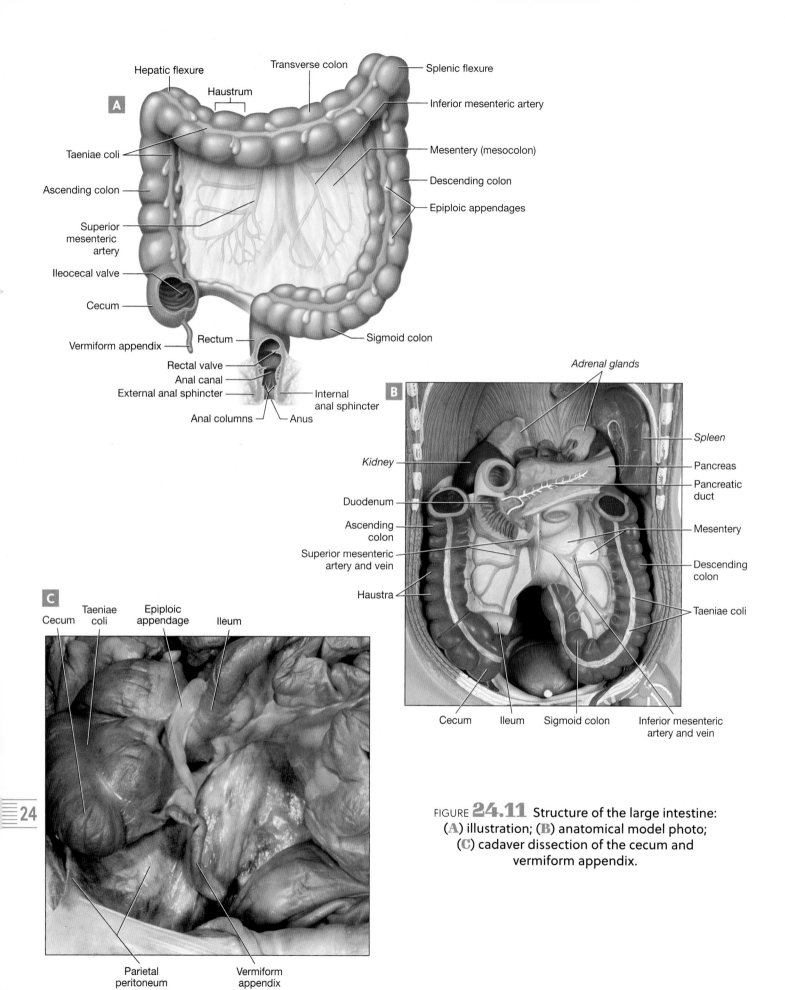

FIGURE **24.11** Structure of the large intestine: (**A**) illustration; (**B**) anatomical model photo; (**C**) cadaver dissection of the cecum and vermiform appendix.

The accessory digestive organs generally do not come into direct contact with the ingested food (the teeth and tongue are exceptions). Most of them instead secrete substances such as bile salts and enzymes that travel through a duct to the alimentary canal. The accessory digestive organs are as follows:

■ **Teeth and tongue.** The **teeth** and the **tongue** are accessory organs located in the mouth that assist in mechanical digestion of ingested food. The tongue's surface features keratinized papillae called **filiform papillae** that provide a rough surface to help break down food physically. Note that filiform papillae do not contain taste buds, which are located only on circumvallate, foliate, and fungiform papillae (for a review of tongue anatomy, see Unit 15, p. 393).

The **teeth** are located within the mandible and maxilla in bony sockets known as *alveoli*. They are held in place by bands of collagen fibers known collectively as the *periodontal ligament* (pehr-ee-oh-DAHN-tuhl). There are three classes of teeth:

  ▪ **Incisors.** The **incisors** are the broad and flat central teeth. There are four incisors: the two *central incisors*, and the two *lateral incisors*.

  ▪ **Canines.** The **canines** (KAY-nynz), also known as *cuspids*, are the pointed teeth located to the sides of the lateral incisors.

  ▪ **Molars.** There are two sets of molars. First are the **premolars**, located lateral to the canines, and second are the larger **molars**, which are the posterior teeth.

As you are no doubt aware, humans normally have two sets of teeth: one set of "baby teeth" and one set of "permanent teeth." The "baby teeth," shown in Figure 24.12A, are known as the **primary dentition** or **deciduous teeth** (dih-SIJ-oo-uhs; "falling off"). Notice that there are 20 deciduous teeth: 4 incisors, 2 canines, and 4 molars each in the maxilla and mandible. The **secondary dentition** or **permanent teeth** generally begin to erupt at about 6 years of age when these teeth enlarge and cause the roots of the deciduous teeth to dissolve. There are 32 permanent teeth, shown in Figure 24.12B: 4 incisors, 2 canines, 4 premolars, and 6 molars each in the maxilla and mandible. Generally, by age 12, all deciduous teeth have fallen out and all but the third set of molars, the "wisdom teeth," have erupted. These third molars tend to erupt later, around age 17, although they often remain embedded in the bone, which is a condition called *impaction*.

■ **Salivary glands.** The **salivary glands** are exocrine glands located around the mouth (Fig. 24.13). There are three sets of salivary glands:

  ▪ The largest salivary glands are the paired **parotid glands** (puh-RAHT-id; *para-* = "beside;" *ot-* = "ear"), which are located superficial to the masseter muscles. The secretions of the parotid gland pass through a duct called the **parotid duct**, which enters the oral cavity by piercing the buccinator muscle.

  ▪ The smaller **submandibular glands** are located just medial to the mandible. They secrete saliva through the **submandibular ducts**, which open into the floor of the oral cavity under the tongue.

  ▪ The **sublingual glands** (sub-LING-gwuhl; *ling-* = "tongue") are located under the tongue, as their name implies. They secrete saliva through multiple **sublingual ducts**.

All three types of glands secrete **saliva**, which contains water, mucus, an enzyme called *salivary amylase*, and antimicrobial proteins such as *lysozyme*.

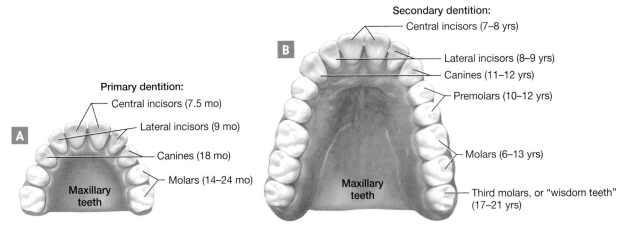

FIGURE **24.12** Teeth: (**A**) primary dentition of the maxilla; (**B**) secondary dentition of the maxilla.

- **Liver.** The liver is located in the right upper quadrant of the abdominal cavity. The **liver** consists of four lobes: the large **right** and **left lobes**, as well as the small **caudate** (KAH-dayt) and **quadrate lobes**, which are located on the posterior side of the right lobe (Fig. 24.14). The liver is wrapped in a thin connective tissue capsule, and most of it is covered by the visceral peritoneum. On the liver's anterior side, shown in Figure 24.14A, we find the **falciform ligament** (FALL-sih-form), which is a fold of visceral peritoneum that separates the right and left lobes and anchors the liver to the abdominal wall. Inferior to the falciform ligament is the **round ligament**, which is a remnant of a structure called the *umbilical vein*, which brings oxygenated blood to the fetus.

  On the liver's posterior side near the quadrate lobe, shown in Figure 24.14B, is an area called the **porta hepatis** (POHR-tuh heh-PĂ-tis; *porta* = "door"). This area serves as a main "gateway" into and out of the liver, as the hepatic artery, the hepatic portal vein, and the common hepatic duct all enter and exit via the porta hepatis. Note the exception is the hepatic veins, which exit at the superior side of the liver, where they drain into the inferior vena cava.

  The liver has multiple functions in the body, most of which are metabolic in nature. For example, recall from Unit 18 that all blood from the digestive organs and the spleen travels via the hepatic portal vein to the hepatic portal system of the liver. There, the absorbed nutrients and other substances are processed before they enter the general circulation. One of the liver's main digestive functions is to produce a chemical called *bile*, a substance required for the digestion and absorption of fats.

- The **gallbladder** is a small, saclike organ on the posterior side of the liver that stores and concentrates bile. Bile leaves the right and left lobes of the liver by the *right* and *left hepatic ducts*, which merge to form the **common hepatic duct**. Some bile may be released into the duodenum depending on hormonal signals, but most of it enters the gallbladder for storage (Fig. 24.15). When stimulated by certain hormones, the gallbladder contracts, and the bile contained within it is ejected through the **cystic duct** (SIS-tik; *cyst-* = "gallbladder"). Notice that the cystic duct joins with the common hepatic duct to form the **common bile duct**, which empties into the duodenum at the **hepatopancreatic ampulla** (heh-PĂ-toh-payn-kree-at-ik am-POOL-ah). A sphincter controls the release of bile from the ampulla to the duodenum.

- **Pancreas.** The **pancreas** (PAYN-kree-uhs) is an exocrine and endocrine gland that sits posterior and inferior to the stomach. Its exocrine functions are digestive, whereas its endocrine functions are metabolic. The exocrine portion of the pancreas produces a fluid called **pancreatic juice** that contains water, bicarbonate ions to neutralize the acid produced by the stomach, and multiple digestive enzymes. Pancreatic juice is released through the **pancreatic duct** and enters the duodenum at the hepatopancreatic ampulla.

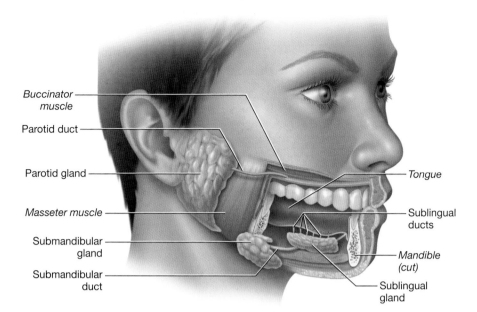

Buccinator muscle
Parotid duct
Parotid gland
Masseter muscle
Submandibular gland
Submandibular duct
Tongue
Sublingual ducts
Mandible (cut)
Sublingual gland

FIGURE **24.13** Salivary glands.

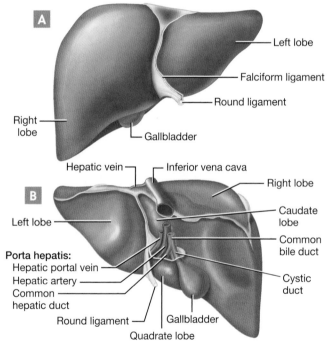

A
Left lobe
Falciform ligament
Round ligament
Right lobe
Gallbladder

B
Hepatic vein
Inferior vena cava
Right lobe
Caudate lobe
Common bile duct
Cystic duct
Left lobe
Porta hepatis:
Hepatic portal vein
Hepatic artery
Common hepatic duct
Round ligament
Gallbladder
Quadrate lobe

FIGURE **24.14** Anatomy of liver: (**A**) anterior view; (**B**) posterior view.

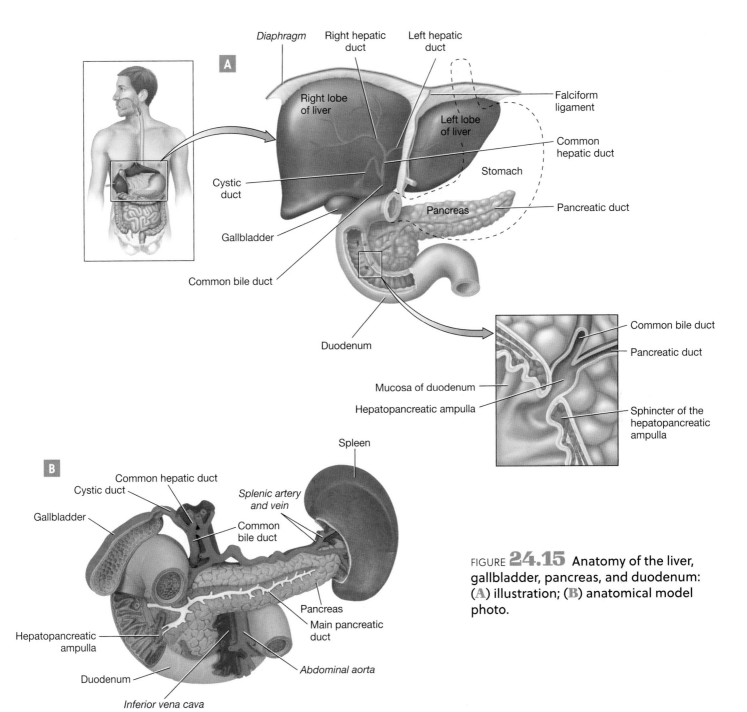

A

Diaphragm

Right hepatic duct

Left hepatic duct

Right lobe of liver

Left lobe of liver

Falciform ligament

Common hepatic duct

Stomach

Cystic duct

Pancreas

Pancreatic duct

Gallbladder

Common bile duct

Duodenum

Common bile duct

Pancreatic duct

Mucosa of duodenum

Hepatopancreatic ampulla

Sphincter of the hepatopancreatic ampulla

Spleen

B

Common hepatic duct

Cystic duct

Splenic artery and vein

Gallbladder

Common bile duct

Hepatopancreatic ampulla

Pancreas

Main pancreatic duct

Abdominal aorta

Duodenum

Inferior vena cava

FIGURE **24.15** Anatomy of the liver, gallbladder, pancreas, and duodenum: (**A**) illustration; (**B**) anatomical model photo.

Model Inventory for the Digestive System

Identify the following structures of the digestive system on models and diagrams, using your textbook and this unit for reference. As you examine the anatomical models and diagrams, record the name of the model and the structures you were able to identify on the model inventory in Table 24.2. After you have completed the activity, answer Check Your Understanding Questions 1 through 3 (p. 673).

Peritoneum
1. Peritoneal cavity
2. Parietal peritoneum
3. Visceral peritoneum
4. Mesentery
5. Greater omentum
6. Lesser omentum

Accessory Organs
1. Tongue
   a. Filiform papillae
2. Teeth
   a. Incisors
   b. Canines
   c. Premolars
   d. Molars
   e. Primary dentition
   f. Secondary dentition
3. Salivary glands
   a. Parotid gland with parotid duct
   b. Submandibular gland with submandibular duct
   c. Sublingual gland with sublingual ducts
4. Liver
   a. Right lobe, left lobe, caudate lobe, and quadrate lobe
   b. Falciform ligament
   c. Round ligament

   d. Porta hepatis
   e. Hepatic arteries
   f. Hepatic portal vein
   g. Hepatic veins
   h. Common hepatic duct
5. Gallbladder
   a. Cystic duct
   b. Common bile duct
   c. Hepatopancreatic ampulla
6. Pancreas
   a. Pancreatic duct

Alimentary Canal
1. Mouth
   a. Vestibule
   b. Gingivae (gums)
   c. Labial frenulum
   d. Oral cavity
   e. Hard palate
   f. Soft palate
      (1) Uvula
2. Pharynx
   a. Oropharynx
   b. Laryngopharynx
3. Esophagus
   a. Gastroesophageal sphincter (or lower esophageal sphincter)
4. Stomach
   a. Cardia

   b. Fundus
   c. Body
   d. Pyloric antrum
   e. Pylorus
   f. Pyloric sphincter
   g. Rugae
5. Small intestine
   a. Duodenum
   b. Jejunum
   c. Ileum
   d. Ileocecal valve
6. Large intestine
   a. Taeniae coli
   b. Haustra
   c. Cecum
      (1) Vermiform appendix
   d. Colon
      (1) Ascending colon
      (2) Hepatic flexure
      (3) Transverse colon
      (4) Splenic flexure
      (5) Descending colon
      (6) Sigmoid colon
   e. Rectum
   f. Anal canal
      (1) Internal anal sphincter
      (2) External anal sphincter

Your instructor may wish to omit certain structures or add structures not included in these lists. List any additional structures here:

TABLE **24.2** Model Inventory for the Digestive System

Model/Diagram	Digestive Structures Identified

(continues)

24

TABLE **24.2** **Model Inventory for the Digestive System** (*cont.*)

Model/Diagram	Digestive Structures Identified

2 **PROCEDURE**

Time to Draw

In the space provided, draw, color, and label the arrangement of the liver, gallbladder, pancreas, and duodenum. In addition, write the function of each structure that you label.

MATERIALS

- ❑ Anatomical models and diagrams: layers of the alimentary canal
- ❑ Slides:
  - ▪ esophagus
  - ▪ stomach
  - ▪ duodenum
  - ▪ pancreas
  - ▪ liver
  - ▪ tooth
- ❑ Light microscope
- ❑ Colored pencils

Digestive System Histology

The organs of the alimentary canal follow the same basic pattern we have seen for other hollow organs: an inner layer of epithelial tissue that rests on connective tissue, a middle layer of smooth muscle, and an outer layer of supportive connective tissue. The tissue layers of the alimentary canal, shown in Figure 24.16, are named as follows:

1. **Mucosa.** The inner epithelial tissue lining of the alimentary canal is called the **mucosa.** Throughout most of the alimentary canal, it consists of simple columnar epithelium overlying a lamina propria and a thin layer of smooth muscle called the **muscularis mucosa.** The mucosa contains a collection of lymphoid follicles called **mucosa-associated lymphatic tissue (MALT)**, mucus-secreting goblet cells, and other glands that secrete products such as hydrochloric acid and enzymes. The mucosa is generally covered with a layer of mucus, which protects the underlying epithelium from the effects of acid and digestive enzymes.

2. **Submucosa.** Deep to the mucosa we find the **submucosa,** a layer of connective tissue that houses blood vessels, nerves, lymph vessels, and elastic fibers.

3. **Muscularis externa.** The **muscularis externa** in most regions of the alimentary canal has two layers of smooth muscle: an inner circular layer and an outer longitudinal layer. These two layers contract alternately to produce the rhythmic contractions of peristalsis, which propel digesting food through the alimentary canal. The muscularis externa also assists in mechanical digestion in the stomach, via *churning*, and in the small intestine, via *segmentation*.

4. **Serosa** or **adventitia.** The outer layer of the alimentary canal is called the **serosa** in the locations where it is composed of the visceral peritoneum and the **adventitia** in places where it is composed of dense irregular connective tissue.

Although this pattern is followed throughout most of the alimentary canal, there are some notable differences in some organs, particularly in the esophagus (Fig. 24.17). The mucosa of the esophagus is composed of stratified squamous epithelium with no goblet cells or thick mucus layer. In addition, the esophagus' muscularis externa changes as it progresses toward the

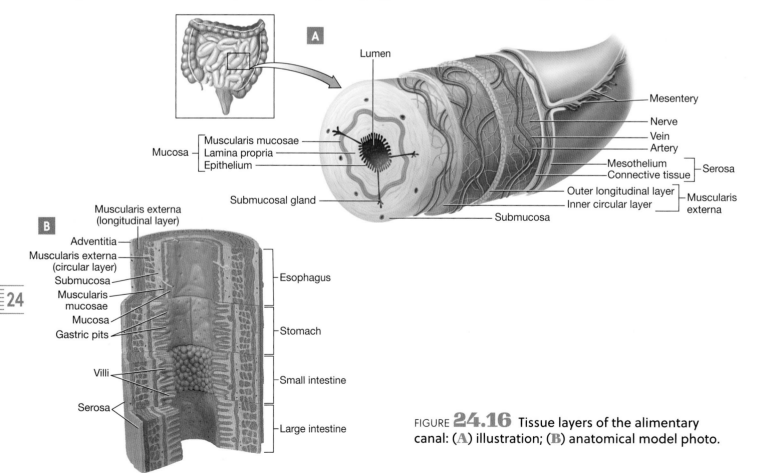

FIGURE 24.16 Tissue layers of the alimentary canal: (**A**) illustration; (**B**) anatomical model photo.

stomach. The upper one-third of the esophagus is skeletal muscle, the middle one-third is about half skeletal muscle and half smooth muscle, and the lower one-third is smooth muscle. These differences in the muscularis externa help you to determine the location of the section you are examining.

You will also find variations in the pattern in the stomach. Recall from Exercise 24-1 (p. 641) that the muscularis externa of the stomach has three layers of smooth muscle, with an additional oblique layer. In addition, the stomach's mucosa is heavily indented, which reflects the presence of numerous **gastric pits** that lead to **gastric glands** (Fig. 24.18). Recall that these glands

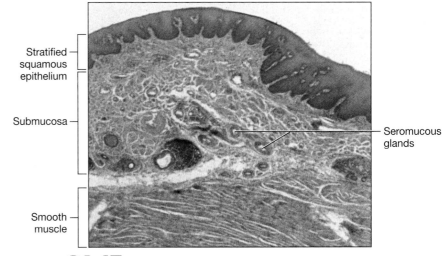

FIGURE **24.17** Microanatomy of the esophagus, photomicrograph.

secrete products for digestion into the stomach, including hydrochloric acid and enzymes, that are known collectively as **gastric juice**. Certain cells within the glands also produce hormones that are secreted into the blood. The stomach mucosa between the gastric pits contains a large number of goblet cells.

The structure of the small intestinal wall also features numerous specializations. For example, the submucosa of the duodenum houses *duodenal glands*, which secrete a protective alkaline mucus to coat the mucosa. Also, notice in Figure 24.19 that the wall of the small intestine is highly folded, an adaptation that increases the surface area available for absorption. There are three sets of folds:

1. **Circular folds**. The **circular folds**, also known as *plicae circulares*, are folds of the mucosa and submucosa. They are visible as ridges along the surface of the small intestinal wall.

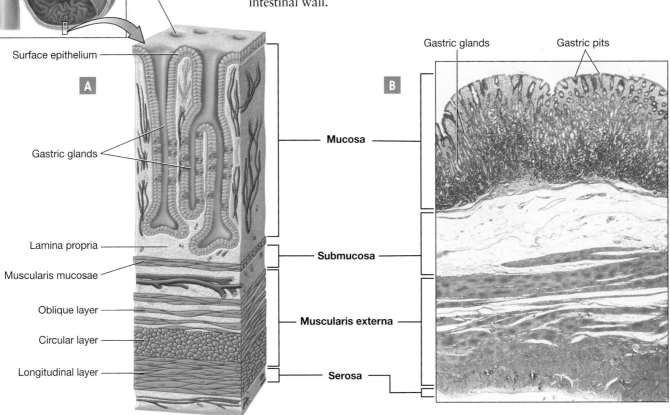

FIGURE **24.18** Microanatomy of the stomach and gastric glands: (**A**) illustration; (**B**) photomicrograph.

2. **Villi.** The fingerlike **villi** (VILL-aye; *villus* = "hair") are folds of the mucosa, and they make up the "fringe" on the circular folds. Note in Figure 24.19 that between the villi are glands called **intestinal crypts**. Each villus consists of an outer layer of simple columnar epithelial cells called **enterocytes** (IN-tuh-roh-syt'z; *enter-* = "intestine") surrounding a connective tissue core. Within the core of the villus we find blood vessels and a lymphatic vessel called a **lacteal** (lak-TEEL).

3. **Microvilli.** The smallest folds are **microvilli**, which are extensions of the enterocytes' plasma membranes. The enterocytes and their microvilli are often collectively referred to as the *brush border*.

The three accessory digestive organs we will examine in this exercise—the pancreas, liver, and a tooth—are not hollow organs, so they do not follow the same histological pattern as the alimentary canal. The pancreas is a gland that consists of clusters of cells that produce exocrine and endocrine secretions (Fig. 24.20). The exocrine cells of the pancreas, called **acinar cells** (AY-sin-ahr), produce and secrete pancreatic juice (digestive enzymes, bicarbonate ions, and water) into ducts. The endocrine cells of the pancreas, called **pancreatic islets** (AYE-lets), secrete hormones such as insulin into the bloodstream. They are visible as small, circular groups of cells that stain less darkly than the surrounding acinar cells.

The liver is composed of hepatocytes organized into hexagonal plates of cells called **liver lobules** (Fig. 24.21). At the center of each lobule is a central vein that will eventually drain into a hepatic vein. At each of the six corners of a liver lobule, we find three small vessels collectively called **portal triads**. The three vessels are: (1) a **bile duct**, which carries bile made by hepatocytes and drains into the hepatic duct; (2) a **portal venule**, which is a tiny branch off the hepatic portal vein that delivers nutrient-rich blood to the liver for processing and detoxification; and (3) a **hepatic arteriole**, which delivers oxygen-rich blood to the hepatocytes.

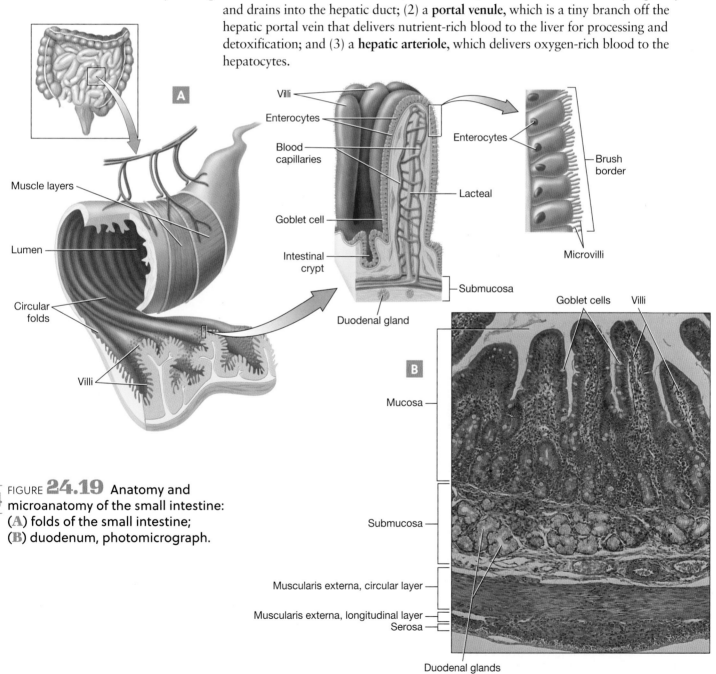

FIGURE **24.19** Anatomy and microanatomy of the small intestine: (**A**) folds of the small intestine; (**B**) duodenum, photomicrograph.

The last slide you will examine is a tooth, which has two components: the **crown**, which is the visible portion above the gum line, and the **root**, which is embedded within the bone (Fig. 24.22). The outer layer of the tooth in the crown is composed of **enamel**, which is the hardest substance in the body, given that it is made almost completely of calcium hydroxyapatite crystals. In the root, the outer layer of the tooth is called **cementum**; its composition is similar to bone, and so it is about as hard as bone tissue. Collagen fibers from the *periodontal ligament* extend into the cementum to help hold the tooth in place. Both enamel and cementum cover the next layer of the tooth, the **dentin** (*dent-* = "tooth"), which is the second hardest material in the body. Dentin covers the soft, inner **pulp** that resides in the **pulp cavity** along with nerves and blood vessels. The pulp cavity, blood vessels, and nerves extend into the root of the tooth via the **root canal**.

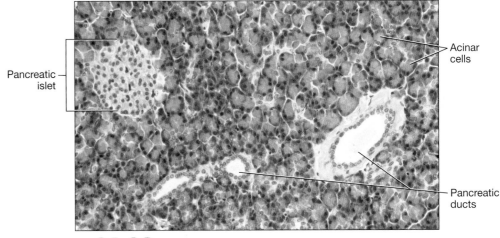

Pancreatic islet

Acinar cells

Pancreatic ducts

FIGURE **24.20** Microanatomy of the pancreas, photomicrograph.

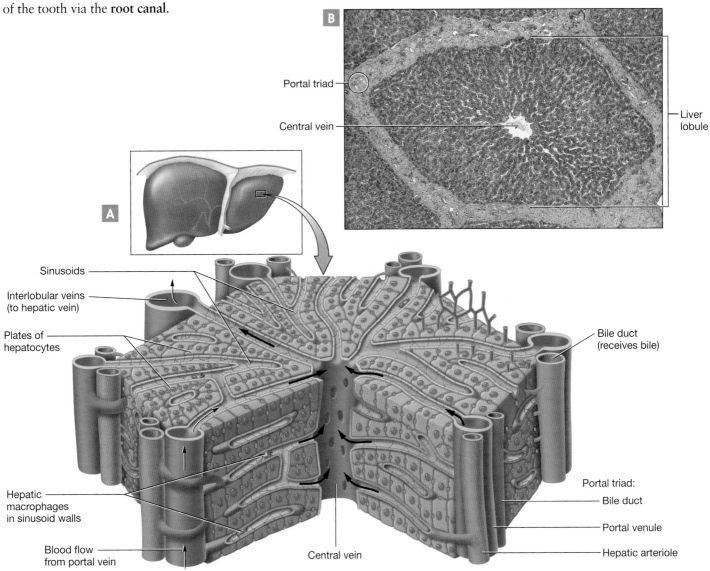

Portal triad

Central vein

Liver lobule

Sinusoids

Interlobular veins (to hepatic vein)

Plates of hepatocytes

Hepatic macrophages in sinusoid walls

Blood flow from portal vein

Central vein

Bile duct (receives bile)

Portal triad:

Bile duct

Portal venule

Hepatic arteriole

FIGURE **24.21** Microanatomy of the liver: (**A**) liver lobule; (**B**) liver section from a pig, photomicrograph.

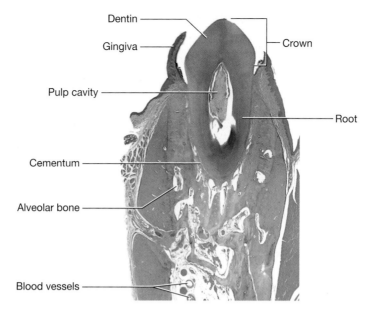

FIGURE **24.22** Microanatomy of a human tooth.

1

PROCEDURE
Model Inventory for the Microscopic Anatomy of the Digestive System

Identify on models and diagrams the following microscopic anatomical structures of the digestive system, using your textbook and this unit for reference. As you examine the models and diagrams, record the name of the model and the structures you were able to identify on the model inventory in Table 24.2 (pp. 650–651—note that this is the model inventory in Exercise 24-1).

1. Mucosa
   a. Epithelial tissue (simple columnar epithelium)
   b. Muscularis mucosae
   c. MALT
   d. Glands
2. Submucosa
   a. Blood vessels
   b. Nerves
   c. Lymphatic vessels
   d. Microvilli

3. Muscularis externa
   a. Inner circular layer
   b. Outer longitudinal layer
   c. Inner oblique layer (stomach only)
4. Serosa or adventitia
5. Intestinal villi
   a. Enterocytes
   b. Lacteal

PROCEDURE

Examining the Digestive Organs with Microscopy

Obtain prepared slides of the esophagus, the fundus of the stomach, the duodenum, the pancreas, the liver, and a tooth. You will have the best results viewing most of the slides on low power. Use your colored pencils to draw what you see and label your drawing with the listed terms. When you have completed the activity, answer Check Your Understanding Questions 4 and 5 (p. 674).

1 Esophagus

- Stratified squamous epithelium
- Submucosa with blood vessels
- Muscularis externa
  - Smooth muscle
  - Skeletal muscle
- Adventitia

2 Fundus of the Stomach

- Mucosa with goblet cells and gastric glands
- Submucosa with blood vessels
- Muscularis externa with smooth muscle layers
- Serosa

3 Duodenum

- Villi
- Mucosal-associated lymphatic tissue
- Enterocytes
- Microvilli (visible as small "hairs" projecting from the cells); may only be visible on oil immersion
- Duodenal glands

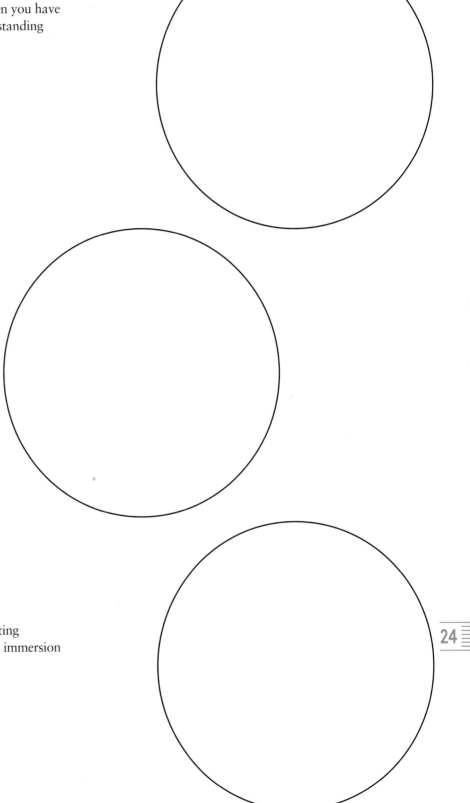

24

4 Pancreas
- Acinar cells
- Pancreatic ducts
- Pancreatic islets

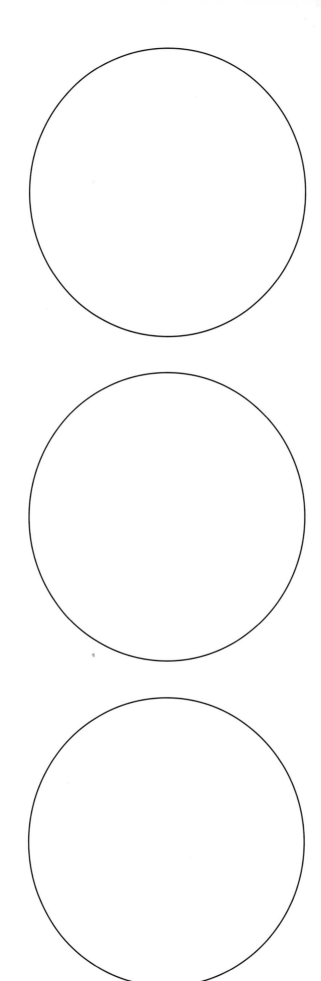

5 Liver
- Liver lobule
- Portal triad
- Central vein

6 Tooth (best viewed on low power)
- Crown
- Root
- Dentin
- Pulp cavity
- Cementum
- Gingiva

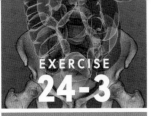

MATERIALS

Procedure 1
- ❏ Spot plate
- ❏ Lugol's iodine solution
- ❏ Test tubes (4)
- ❏ Test tube rack
- ❏ Stopwatch
- ❏ Glass stirring rod
- ❏ 0.5% starch solution
- ❏ Amylase solution
- ❏ Distilled water
- ❏ 37°C water bath
- ❏ Pipettes (4)
- ❏ Permanent marker

Procedure 2
- ❏ Test tubes (4)
- ❏ Powdered albumin
- ❏ Scoop
- ❏ Pepsin solution
- ❏ pH 8 buffer solution
- ❏ 0.01 M HCl solution
- ❏ Distilled water
- ❏ Biuret reagent
- ❏ Stirring rod
- ❏ 37°C water bath
- ❏ Permanent marker

Procedure 3
- ❏ Rubber stopper
- ❏ Test tubes (4)
- ❏ Test tube rack
- ❏ Liquid detergent
- ❏ Distilled water
- ❏ Vegetable oil
- ❏ Sudan red stain

Procedure 4
- ❏ Test tubes (4)
- ❏ 0.1 M Sodium hydroxide
- ❏ Bile salts
- ❏ Powdered lipase
- ❏ Vegetable oil
- ❏ Phenol red
- ❏ Distilled water
- ❏ 37°C water bath
- ❏ Measuring spoon (1/4 tsp.)
- ❏ Permanent marker

Digestive System Physiology

We now turn our attention to the physiology of food breakdown and absorption. Three major types of nutrients are broken down and absorbed in the alimentary canal: *carbohydrates*, *proteins*, and *lipids*. Carbohydrate digestion begins in the mouth with the enzyme **salivary amylase** (AM-uh-layz; *amyl-* = "starch"), which catalyzes the reactions that digest polysaccharides into smaller oligosaccharides. The remaining polysaccharides and oligosaccharides are digested in the small intestine. These reactions are catalyzed by **pancreatic amylase** and enzymes associated with the enterocytes of the small intestine called **brush border enzymes** (including lactase, maltase, and sucrase).

Protein digestion begins in the stomach with the enzyme **pepsin** (*pep-* = "digestion"), secreted by chief cells in the gastric glands as the inactive pre-enzyme **pepsinogen**. Pepsinogen becomes the active enzyme pepsin when it encounters an acidic environment. Pepsin catalyzes the reactions that begin digesting proteins into polypeptides and some free amino acids.

The remainder of protein digestion occurs in the small intestine with pancreatic enzymes, such as **trypsin** and **chymotrypsin**. These enzymes are released by pancreatic cells in an inactive form so they don't damage the proteins in pancreatic cells. The reaction that activates trypsin is catalyzed by an enzyme made by the duodenum called *enterokinase*. Activated trypsin then catalyzes the activation of the other pancreatic enzymes. These activated enzymes, along with brush border enzymes such as *carboxypeptidase* and *aminopeptidase*, catalyze the reactions that break proteins and polypeptides into amino acids.

Most lipid digestion begins when lipids reach the small intestine. The process is more complicated than it is for protein or carbohydrate digestion because lipids are nonpolar molecules that do not dissolve in the water-based environment of the small intestine. This causes the lipids to clump together and form fat "globules" in the small intestine. In this form, it is extremely difficult for the enzyme **pancreatic lipase** (LYE-payz; *lip-* = "fat") to catalyze the breakdown of lipids into monoglycerides and free fatty acids because it has only a small surface area on which to work. Therefore, the first step in lipid digestion is to break up fat globules into smaller pieces, a process called **emulsification** (Fig. 24.23).

Emulsification is accomplished by chemicals called **bile salts**, which are produced by the liver and stored in the gallbladder. Bile salts are amphipathic molecules that have both nonpolar and

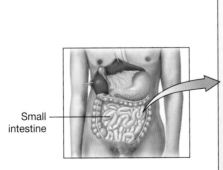

Small intestine

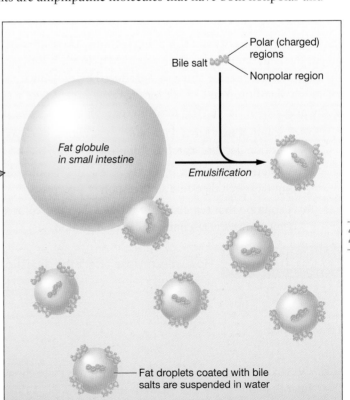

Bile salt

Polar (charged) regions

Nonpolar region

Fat globule in small intestine

Emulsification

Fat droplets coated with bile salts are suspended in water

FIGURE **24.23** Emulsification of fats by bile salts.

24

polar parts. Notice in Figure 24.23 what happens to a fat globule when bile salts come into contact with it: The bile salts' nonpolar parts interact with the lipids, but their polar parts repel other lipids. The overall effect is that the fat globule is physically broken down into smaller fat pieces. Note that this is entirely a physical process—it does not change the lipids' chemical composition. However, as the lipids are physically broken apart by emulsification, they are also chemically digested in reactions catalyzed by pancreatic lipase. These reactions chemically break triglycerides into monoglycerides and free fatty acids.

When chemical digestion is complete, all three nutrients are absorbed through the plasma membranes of the enterocytes lining the intestinal villi. Most such absorption (about 90%) occurs in the jejunum. Both monosaccharides and amino acids are absorbed into the enterocytes via facilitated diffusion or secondary active transport mechanisms. These nutrients then exit the other side of the enterocytes and enter the intestinal capillaries in the core of the villus. Nutrients in the intestinal capillaries are then delivered to the superior mesenteric vein. Remember from Exercise 24-1 (p. 641) that all blood from the small intestine and other abdominal organs is delivered to the hepatic portal system before being delivered to the general circulation. Therefore, both monosaccharides and amino acids travel first to the liver via the hepatic portal vein, after which they enter the blood in the hepatic veins to be delivered to the inferior vena cava.

Lipid absorption, like lipid digestion, is more complicated because lipids are nonpolar and cannot be transported as free fatty acids through the water-filled plasma of the blood. In the small intestinal lumen, digested lipids remain associated with bile salts to form clusters of lipids and other nonpolar chemicals called **micelles** (my-SELLZ). Micelles escort the lipids to the enterocytes' plasma membranes; they can do so because of their polar outer surface, which allows them to move freely between the enterocytes' microvilli. The lipids then leave the micelles and enter the enterocytes by simple diffusion. Note that in the absence of bile salts, nearly all the lipids will simply pass through the small intestine unabsorbed and be excreted in the feces.

In the enterocytes, lipids associate with other nonpolar substances and proteins to assemble protein-coated droplets called **chylomicrons** (ky-loh-MY-krahnz). Chylomicrons exit the enterocytes into the core of the villus by exocytosis, but they are too large to enter blood capillaries. Instead, they enter the lacteal and join the lymph in the lymphatic system. For this reason, lipids are not delivered to the hepatic portal system like carbohydrates and amino acids are. Chylomicrons travel within the lymphatic vessels until they enter the blood at the junction of the left subclavian vein and the left internal jugular vein.

In this exercise, we examine the processes of chemical digestion using many of the enzymes we just discussed. We also look at how various factors affect the efficiency of chemical digestion. When you have completed the procedures, answer Check Your Understanding Question 6 (p. 674).

1 PROCEDURE
Testing Carbohydrate Digestion

As you've learned, enzymes speed up reactions. These are reactions that would occur without an enzyme, but would take place very slowly. In the following procedure you will examine the effects of the enzyme amylase—produced by the salivary glands and by the pancreas—on starch digestion. You'll check for digestion using Lugol's iodine, which turns dark blue in the presence of starch. You may interpret the results of your tests as follows:

⚠ **SAFETY NOTE**
Safety glasses and gloves are required!

- A solution that turns dark blue-black with Lugol's iodine demonstrates no starch digestion because starch is still present (Fig. 24.24).

- A solution that turns light blue with Lugol's iodine demonstrates limited starch digestion or digestion in progress.

- A solution that remains light brown (the same color as the iodine) demonstrates near-complete starch digestion.

Hypothesis: How will amylase affect the digestion of starch?

_____

_____

1 Obtain a spot plate and a pipette or dropper. Place three drops of Lugol's iodine in each of 12 wells. Label the wells 1 through 12 with a marker.

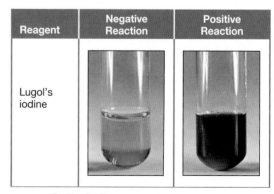

FIGURE **24.24** Possible results for Lugol's iodine, which turns dark purple in the presence of starch.

Reagent	Negative Reaction	Positive Reaction
Lugol's iodine		

24

2 Obtain a stopwatch, four pipettes, and four glass test tubes, and number them 1 through 4 with a marker.

3 Place 5 mL of 0.5% starch solution into Tube 1 and Tube 2.

4 Place 5 mL of amylase solution into Tube 3.

5 Place 5 mL of distilled water into Tube 4.

6 Add 5 mL of amylase solution to Tube 1. Mix the contents thoroughly with a stirring rod.

7 Add 5 mL of distilled water to Tube 2. Rinse the stirring rod you used in Step 6, and use the clean stirring rod to mix the contents of Tube 2 thoroughly.

8 Set Tubes 1 through 4 into a 37°C water bath. As soon as the tubes are in the water bath, use a pipette to transfer four drops from Tube 1 to Well 1, which, like all 12 wells, contains iodine. Then, repeat the process three times, using a clean pipette each time: Transfer four drops from Tube 2 to Well 2, four drops from Tube 3 to Well 3, and four drops from Tube 4 to Well 4. In Table 24.3, record the color each well turns.

9 Set a timer for 15 minutes. After 15 minutes have passed, return to the tubes. Using a clean pipette each time, transfer four drops from Tube 1 to Well 5, four drops from Tube 2 to Well 6, four drops from Tube 3 to Well 7, and four drops from Tube 4 to Well 8. In Table 24.3, record the color each well turns.

10 Set a timer for another 15 minutes. After 15 minutes have passed, return to the tubes. Using a clean pipette each time, transfer four drops from Tube 1 to Well 9, four drops from Tube 2 to Well 10, four drops from Tube 3 to Well 11, and four drops from Tube 4 to Well 12. In Table 24.3, record the color each well turns.

TABLE **24.3** Results of Carbohydrate Digestion Experiment

Tube	Color from Reaction with Iodine at Time Zero	Color from Reaction with Iodine at Time 15 Minutes	Color from Reaction with Iodine at Time 30 Minutes
1: starch + amylase			
2: starch + water			
3: amylase			
4: water			

11 Interpret your results:

a In which tube(s) did carbohydrate digestion occur? How do you know?

b In which tube(s) did no carbohydrate digestion occur? How do you know?

c What conclusions can we draw about the activity of amylase?

12 Compare your hypothesis to your results.

2 PROCEDURE
Testing Protein Digestion

Next, you will examine protein digestion with the enzyme pepsin. Recall that pepsin is produced in gastric glands by chief cells. It is secreted as the inactive enzyme *pepsinogen* and requires certain conditions to be active. You will assess for protein digestion with the chemical Biuret reagent, which turns blue in the presence of undigested proteins and lavender-purple in the presence of amino acids (Fig. 24.25).

⚠ **SAFETY NOTE**
Safety glasses and gloves are required!

Hypothesis: How will pH affect protein digestion with pepsin?

1 Obtain four test tubes and number them 1 through 4 with a permanent marker.

2 Add one scoop of powdered albumin to each test tube.

3 To Tube 1, add:
   a 5 mL of pepsin solution
   b 5 mL of pH 8 buffer solution

4 To Tube 2, add:
   a 5 mL of pepsin solution
   b 5 mL of 0.01M HCl solution

5 To Tube 3, add 5 mL of 0.01M HCl solution.

6 To Tube 4, add 5 mL of water.

7 Stir each tube well with a stirring rod, rinsing the rod between each tube.

8 Place each tube in a 37°C water bath for one hour.

9 Remove the tubes and place them in a test tube rack. Add 6–7 drops of Biuret reagent to each tube. In Table 24.4, record the color change that you observe in each tube.

10 Interpret your results:
   a In which tube(s) did protein digestion occur? How do you know?

   b In which tube(s) did no protein digestion occur? How do you know?

   c What effect does pH have on protein digestion with pepsin? Why?

Reagent	Negative Reaction	Positive Reaction
Biuret reagent		

FIGURE **24.25** Possible results with Biuret's test: light blue indicates no protein digestion, while light purple indicates amino acids are present.

TABLE **24.4** Results of Protein Digestion Experiment

Tube	Color of Mixture after Adding Biuret Reagent
1: albumin + pepsin + pH 8 buffer	
2: albumin + pepsin + HCl	
3: albumin + HCl	
4: albumin + water	

d   What other effects does acid have in the stomach?

11   Compare your hypothesis to your results.

3	PROCEDURE

Demonstrating Lipid Emulsification

Let's examine what happens during the process of emulsification. In this procedure, you will use four substances to observe emulsification in action:

- *Lipids*: The source of lipids for this exercise is vegetable oil.
- *Emulsifying agent*: Detergents are emulsifiers because they have both polar parts and nonpolar parts, similar to bile salts. The emulsifying agent in this procedure is a liquid detergent.
- *Distilled water.*
- *Sudan red stain*: This is a stain that binds only to lipids. The sole purpose of this stain is to make the lipids more visible during the procedure.

⚠ **SAFETY NOTE**

Safety glasses and gloves are required!

Hypothesis: How will an emulsifying agent affect lipid distribution in water?

1   Obtain two glass test tubes and add approximately 2 mL of distilled water to each tube.

2   Add about 2 mL of vegetable oil to each tube. What happens to the oil and water?

3   Add three or four drops of Sudan red stain to each tube. What color is the oil? What color is the water?

4   Add about 1 mL of liquid detergent to Tube 1. Shake both tubes vigorously for 15 seconds, then allow them to stand undisturbed for 2 minutes. What has happened to the mixture in Tube 1? How does it compare to the mixture in Tube 2? Explain your results.

5   Compare your hypothesis to your results.

24

4	PROCEDURE

Testing Lipid Digestion

In the following procedure, you will be comparing the ability of four solutions to digest vegetable oil: lipase and bile, lipase alone, bile alone, and water. You will check for the presence of digestion using an indicator called **phenol red**. Phenol red appears pink at an alkaline (basic) pH, changes to an orange-red color at a neutral pH, and changes to a yellow color when the pH becomes acidic (Fig. 24.26). If fat digestion has occurred, fatty acids will be released that will decrease the pH of the contents of your tube and turn them orange-red or yellow. You may interpret your results in the following way:

- Pink color = the pH is basic and no (or limited) fat digestion occurred
- Red-orange color = the pH is neutral and some fat digestion occurred
- Yellow color = the pH is acidic and significant fat digestion occurred

Hypothesis: How will bile affect the ability of lipase to catalyze the breakdown of lipids?

1 Obtain four glass test tubes and number them 1 through 4 with a marker.
2 Add 3 mL of vegetable oil to each test tube.
3 Add 8–10 drops of the pH indicator phenol red to each test tube. The oil now should appear pink. If it does not appear pink, add drops of 0.1 M NaOH to each tube until the indicator turns pink.
4 Add ¼ teaspoon (tsp.) of powdered lipase and ¼ tsp. of bile salts to Tube 1. Use separate spoons for the lipase and bile salts to avoid cross-contamination.
5 Add ¼ tsp. of powdered lipase to Tube 2.
6 Add ¼ tsp. of bile salts to Tube 3.
7 Add 1 mL of distilled water to Tube 4.
8 Place each tube in a 37°C water bath for 30 minutes.
9 Remove the tubes from the water bath and record the color of each tube in Table 24.5.
10 Interpret your results:
  a In which tube(s) did lipid digestion occur? How do you know?

  _____

  _____

  b In which tube(s) did limited or no lipid digestion occur? How do you know?

  _____

  _____

  c What effect does bile have on lipid digestion? Why?

  _____

  _____

11 Compare your results to your hypothesis.

  _____

  _____

  _____

  _____

⚠ **SAFETY NOTE**

Safety glasses and gloves are required!

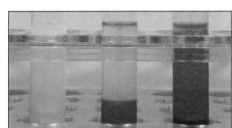

FIGURE **24.26** Possible results with phenol red test: pink indicates no/limited fat digestion, red-orange indicates some fat digestion, and yellow indicates significant fat digestion.

TABLE **24.5** Results of Lipid Digestion Experiment

Tube	Color	pH (Acidic, Neutral, or Alkaline)
1: oil + lipase + bile		
2: oil + lipase		
3: oil + bile		
4: oil + water		

24

MATERIALS

❏ Laminated outline of the human body
❏ Water-soluble marking pens

Time to Trace!

Now, it's time to put all the digestive anatomy and physiology together to get a "big picture" view of the digestive system. In this exercise, you will trace the pathway that three different nutrients take from their ingestion at the mouth to their arrival at the heart. You will trace a cookie (primarily carbohydrates), a protein shake (primarily protein), and greasy fried food (primarily lipids).

Along the way, detail the following for each:

- The *anatomical pathway* that each takes, from ingestion, through its passage through the alimentary canal, to its absorption into the blood, and, finally, to its passage through the blood until it reaches the heart.

- The *physical* and *chemical processes* that break down each substance, including enzyme-catalyzed chemical digestion and processes of mechanical digestion, such as churning, chewing, and emulsification.

Some hints:

- Don't forget that carbohydrates and amino acids travel through the hepatic portal system before they enter the general circulation.

- Remember that digestion and absorption are quite different for lipids. For example, fats are not absorbed into the intestinal blood capillaries.

- Use the text in Exercise 24-3 (p. 659) and your list of enzymes you completed in Pre-Lab Exercise 24-3 (p. 640) for reference.

- Refer to the tracing exercises from Unit 18 (p. 481) and Unit 21 (p. 561) to review the pathway of blood and lymph flow through the body.

- You may find it helpful to physically trace the pathway on a laminated outline of the human body to better visualize the processes.

Tracing Steps

1 **Cookie:** **Start:** Mouth →

mechanical digestion with _____ →

chemical digestion with

_____ →

_____ pharynx (one word) →

_____ pharynx (one word) →

_____ →

_____ sphincter →

_____ →

mechanical digestion via _____ →

_____ sphincter →

_____ →

_____ →

chemical digestion by _____

_____ and

_____ →

absorption into _____ by

_____ →

absorption into _____ capillaries →

_____ vein →

_____ vein →

_____ vein →

_____ cava →

Heart End

24

2 Protein shake: Start: Mouth →

mechanical digestion with _____ →

_____ pharynx (one word) →

_____ pharynx (one word) →

_____ →

_____ sphincter →

_____ →

mechanical digestion via _____ →

chemical digestion with _____ →

_____ sphincter →

_____ →

_____ →

chemical digestion by pancreatic enzymes such as

_____ and _____ →

chemical digestion with _____

_____ →

absorption into _____ by

_____ →

absorption into _____ capillaries →

_____ vein →

_____ vein →

_____ vein →

_____ cava →

→ **Heart End**

3 **Greasy fried food: Start:** Mouth →

mechanical digestion with _____ →

_____ pharynx (one word) →

_____ pharynx (one word) →

_____ →

_____ sphincter →

_____ →

mechanical digestion via _____ →

_____ sphincter →

_____ →

_____ →

chemical digestion by pancreatic _____

after emulsification by _____ _____ →

_____ escort the lipids to the plasma membrane →

absorption into _____ by

_____ →

assembly into _____ →

absorption into a _____ →

_____ trunk →

_____ chyli →

_____ duct →

_____ vein →

_____ cava →

→ **Heart End**

24

Name _____

Section _____ Date _____

Check Your Recall

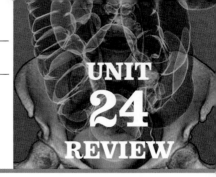

1 Label the following structures on Figure 24.27.

- ❏ Anal canal
- ❏ Cecum
- ❏ Fundus
- ❏ Gallbladder
- ❏ Gastroesophageal sphincter
- ❏ Mesentery
- ❏ Pancreatic duct
- ❏ Pyloric sphincter
- ❏ Rectum
- ❏ Sigmoid colon
- ❏ Taeniae coli
- ❏ Vermiform appendix

A

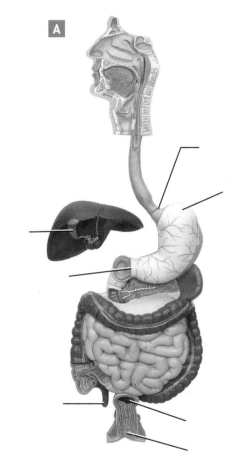

FIGURE **24.27** Organs of the digestive system: (**A**) overview of the digestive system, anatomical model photo; (**B**) interior view of abdomen, anatomical model photo.

B

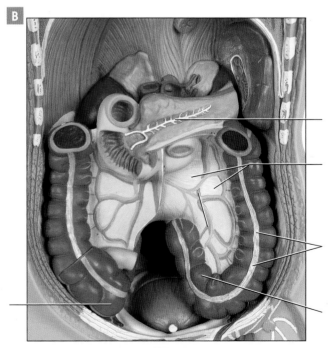

2 **Label the following structures on** Figure 24.28.

❑ Esophagus   ❑ Parotid duct   ❑ Uvula

❑ Laryngopharynx   ❑ Parotid gland   ❑ Vestibule

❑ Oral cavity   ❑ Sublingual gland

❑ Oropharynx   ❑ Submandibular gland

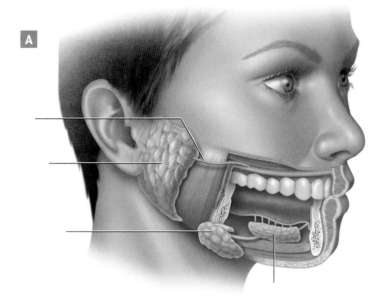

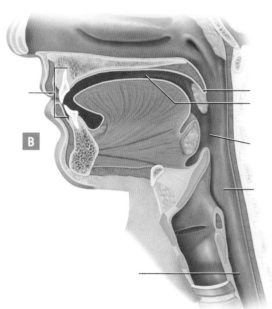

FIGURE **24.28** Anatomy of the head and neck: (**A**) lateral view; (**B**) midsagittal section.

3 The folds of the stomach are known as

a. villi.

b. microvilli.

c. rugae.

d. circular folds.

4 *True/False:* Mark the following statements as true (T) or false (F). If the statement is false, correct it to make it a true statement.

_____ a. The mesentery is a double fold of parietal peritoneum.

_____ b. The longest segment of the small intestine is the duodenum.

_____ c. Circumvallate papillae are located at the posterior tongue and house taste buds.

_____ d. Bile is produced by the gallbladder.

_____ e. The pyloric sphincter regulates flow from the esophagus to the stomach.

_____ f. The three smooth muscle layers of the stomach allow it to perform churning motions.

5 *Fill in the blanks:* Bile drains from the gallbladder via the _____ duct and drains from the

liver via the _____ duct. These two ducts unite to form the

_____ duct.

6 Label the following structures on Figure 24.29.

❏ Caudate lobe of liver   ❏ Duodenum   ❏ Hepatopancreatic ampulla
❏ Common bile duct   ❏ Falciform ligament   ❏ Pancreas
❏ Common hepatic duct   ❏ Hepatic artery   ❏ Porta hepatis
❏ Cystic duct   ❏ Hepatic portal vein   ❏ Round ligament

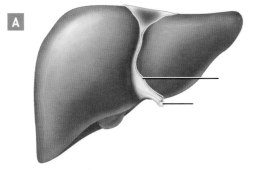

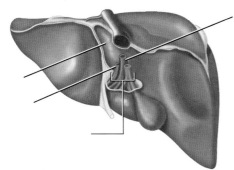

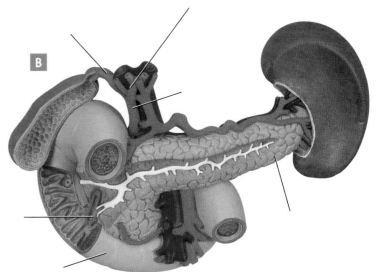

FIGURE **24.29** Accessory organs of the digestive system: (**A**) anterior and posterior views
of the liver, illustration; (**B**) accessory organs, anatomical model photo.

7 Label the following structures on Figure 24.30.

- ❏ Circular folds
- ❏ Enterocytes
- ❏ Lacteal
- ❏ Mucosa
- ❏ Muscularis externa
- ❏ Muscularis mucosae
- ❏ Serosa
- ❏ Submucosa
- ❏ Villi

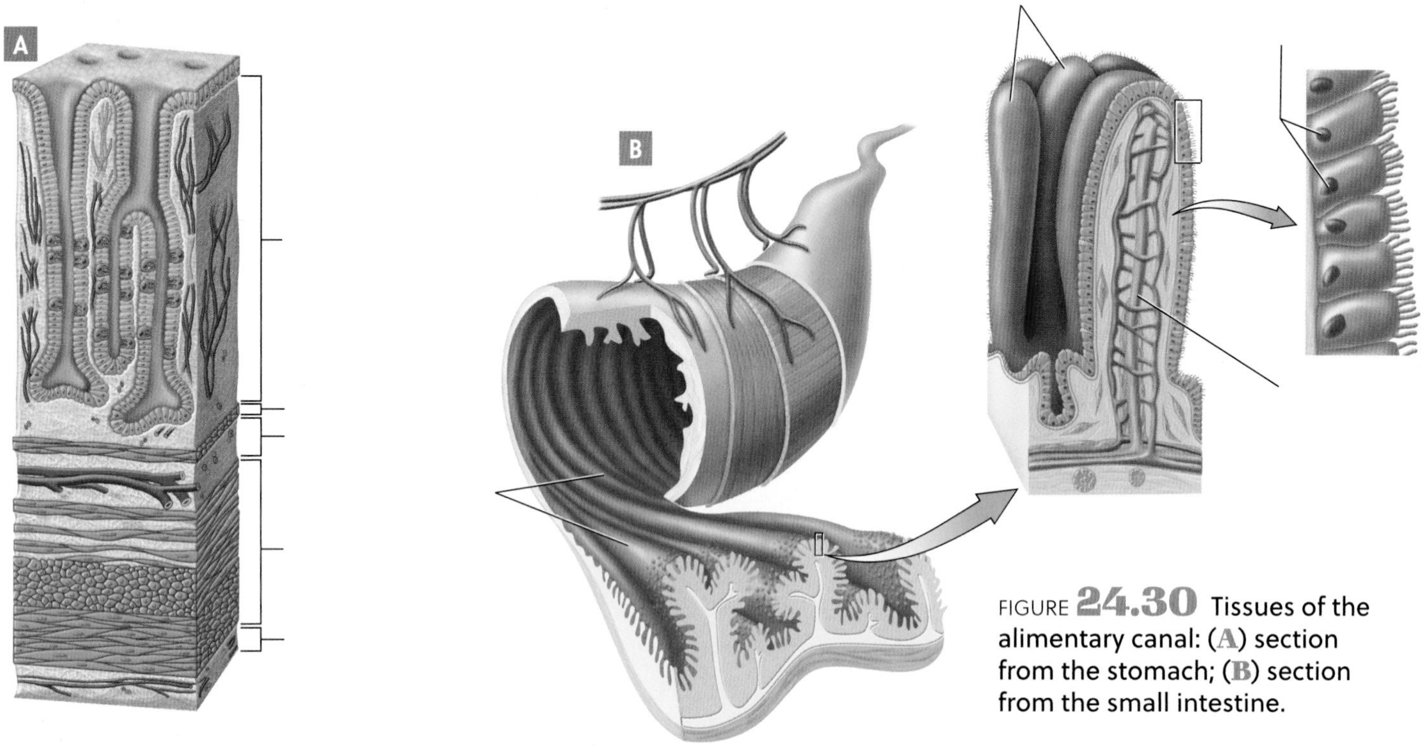

FIGURE **24.30** Tissues of the alimentary canal: (**A**) section from the stomach; (**B**) section from the small intestine.

8 Clusters of bile salts, digested lipids, and other nonpolar substances that escort lipids to enterocytes are called

- a. micelles.
- b. chylomicrons.
- c. lacteals.
- d. pancreatic lipase.

9 The enzyme that catalyzes the reaction that breaks down carbohydrates is

- a. pancreatic lipase.
- b. pepsin.
- c. trypsin.
- d. amylase.

10 Explain why lipids are absorbed into a different structure than are carbohydrates and proteins.

Name _____

Section _____ Date_____

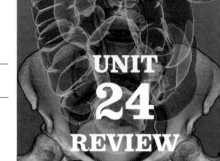

Check Your Understanding

Critical Thinking and Application Questions

1 Lourdes has been diagnosed with gallstones that are blocking her cystic duct.

a What functional impairment will Lourdes face with a blockage of the cystic duct?

b Will a blockage of the cystic duct interfere with the production of bile? Why or why not?

2 Your friend is drinking water when you suddenly say something funny. Your friend laughs as she is swallowing, and water comes out of her nose. What happened to cause this? (**Hint:** Which anatomical structure normally prevents food from entering the nasopharynx?)

3 *Acid reflux* occurs when acid from the stomach regurgitates into the esophagus.

a Which structure normally prevents acid reflux? How does it prevent acid reflux?

b Why does gastric acid "burn" the esophagus but not the stomach?

4   The condition *Crohn's disease* is a disease of the immune system that results in inflammation of different parts of the digestive tract. One of the most commonly affected sites is the small intestine, resulting in loss of intestinal villi. How would this affect the functions of the small intestine? Predict the symptoms of this form of Crohn's disease.

5   Sadaf has developed a condition called *paralytic ileus*, or paralysis of the smooth muscle of the alimentary canal.

   a   Which tissue layer is affected specifically in paralytic ileus?

   b   Sadaf's paralytic ileus is affecting her small intestine and her large intestine. Predict what symptoms Sadaf is experiencing from intestinal paralysis. Explain your reasoning.

6   In the condition *pancreatitis*, pancreatic enzymes become activated within the pancreas instead of within the small intestine.

   a   Why would this cause inflammation and disease of the pancreas?

   b   Sometimes pancreatitis is caused by a stone blocking the hepatopancreatic ampulla. How would such a stone affect digestion, and why?

24

Urinary System Anatomy

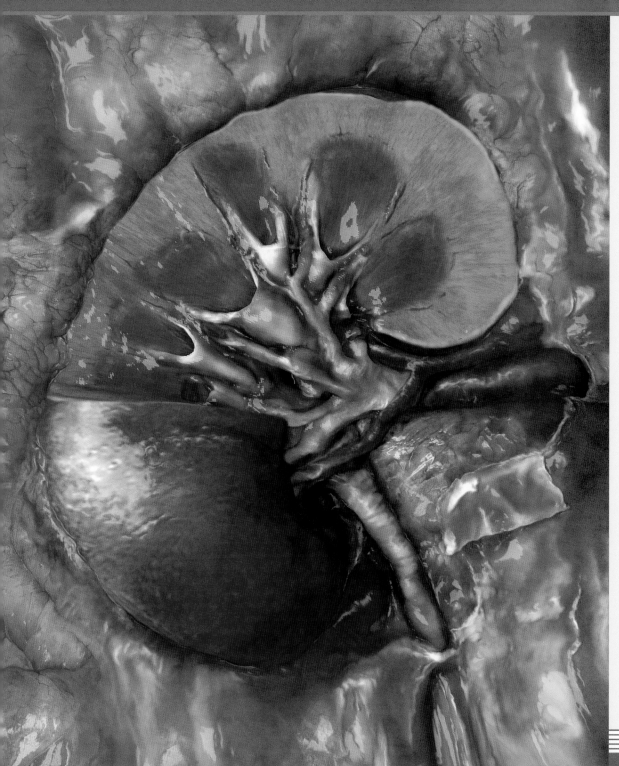

When you have completed this unit, you should be able to:

1 Describe and identify gross structures of the urinary system.

2 Describe and identify structures of the nephron.

3 Identify the microscopic anatomy of the urinary system on microscope slides.

PRE-LAB EXERCISES

Complete the following exercises prior to coming to lab, using your lab manual and textbook for reference.

PRE-LAB

25-1 Key Terms

You should be familiar with the following terms before coming to lab.

Term	Definition

Gross Structures of the Kidney

Renal cortex _____

Renal medulla _____

Renal pyramid _____

Renal pelvis _____

Major and minor calyces _____

Other Structures of the Urinary System

Ureter _____

Urinary bladder _____

Urethra _____

Microanatomy of the Kidney

Nephron _____

Glomerulus _____

Peritubular capillaries _____

25

Name _____   Section _____   Date _____

Proximal tubule _____

Nephron loop _____

Distal tubule _____

Cortical collecting duct _____

Medullary collecting duct _____

Papillary duct _____

Structures of the Urinary System

Color the structures of the urinary system in Figure 25.1, and label them with the terms from Exercise 25-1 (p. 679). Use your text and Exercise 25-1 in this unit for reference.

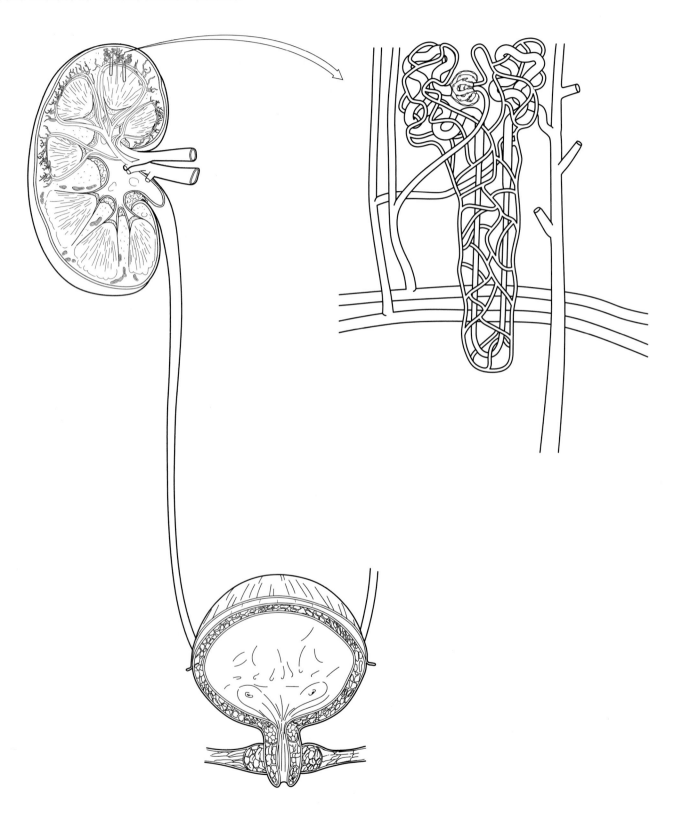

FIGURE **25.1** Overview of the anatomy of the urinary system.

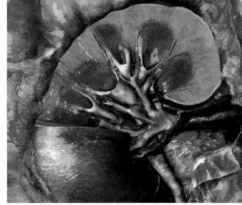

Sectioned, healthy kidney.

The **urinary system** is the group of organs that consists of the *kidneys* and the *urinary tract*—the *ureters*, *urinary bladder*, and *urethra*—and performs many functions critical to the maintenance of homeostasis. Most such functions are directly performed by the kidneys. For example, the kidneys filter the blood to remove *metabolic wastes*, which are chemicals produced by the body that the body cannot use for any purpose. The kidneys also regulate the body's fluid, electrolyte, and acid-base balance, as they can conserve or excrete water, specific electrolytes, and bicarbonate and hydrogen ions. Finally, the kidneys help the liver detoxify certain compounds, make glucose during times of starvation, and produce the hormone *erythropoietin*, which regulates blood cell formation.

In this unit, you will become acquainted with the anatomy, histology, and basic physiology of the organs of the urinary system. In the next unit, we apply this anatomy to explore the physiology of the urinary system in greater depth.

EXERCISE

25-1

MATERIALS

- ❑ Anatomical models and diagrams:
  - ▪ urinary system
  - ▪ kidney
  - ▪ nephron
- ❑ Preserved kidney
- ❑ Dissection equipment
- ❑ Dissecting tray
- ❑ Colored pencils

Urinary System Anatomy

The paired **kidneys** are situated against the posterior body wall posterior to the peritoneal membranes, meaning they are *retroperitoneal* (Fig. 25.2). Externally, they are encased within three layers of connective tissue: the superficial **renal fascia** (REE-nuhl FASH-uh; *ren-* = "kidney"), a layer of dense irregular connective tissue that anchors the kidneys to the posterior abdominal wall and the peritoneum; the **adipose capsule**, a thick layer of adipose tissue that wedges the kidneys in place; and the **renal capsule**, a very thin layer of dense irregular connective tissue that encases each kidney like plastic wrap. With the layers of connective tissue removed, the kidneys are bean-shaped and have a medial indentation where the ureter, blood vessels, nerves, and lymphatic vessels enter and exit, which is known as the **hilum** (HY-lum).

Internally, each kidney has three distinct regions (that can be seen in a frontal section as shown in Fig. 25.3):

1. **Renal cortex.** The most superficial region is known as the **renal cortex**. It is dark brown because it consists of many blood vessels that serve the tiny blood-filtering structures of the kidney, which are called the nephrons.

2. **Renal medulla.** The kidney's middle region is the **renal medulla**, which consists of triangular **renal pyramids**. The renal pyramids are separated from one another by inward extensions of the renal cortex called **renal columns**. Like the renal cortex, the renal columns contain many blood vessels. Each pyramid contains looping tubules of nephrons as well as structures that

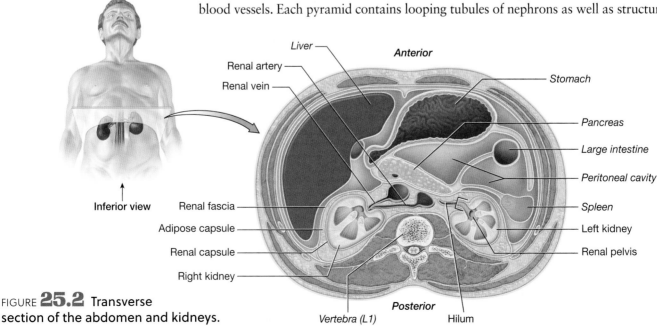

FIGURE **25.2** Transverse section of the abdomen and kidneys.

drain fluid from nephrons. These tubes give the pyramids a striped (or *striated*) appearance. The end or tip of a renal pyramid is known as a **renal papilla**.

3. **Renal pelvis.** Fluid from the renal papilla drains into tubes called **minor calyces** (KAY-lih-seez; *sing.* = "calyx," KAY-lix) that in turn drain into even larger **major calyces**. The major calyces drain into the kidney's innermost region, the **renal pelvis**, which serves as a basin for collecting urine.

The blood flow through the kidney follows a unique pattern that allows it to carry out its function of maintaining the homeostasis of the blood. The large **renal arteries** deliver about 1.2 L of blood per minute to the kidney to be filtered (Fig. 25.4). The renal arteries branch into progressively smaller arteries as they pass through the medulla to the cortex, including the **segmental arteries** in the renal pelvis, the **interlobar arteries** between the medullary pyramids, the **arcuate arteries** (ARK-yoo-it; *arc-* = "curve") that curve around the top of the pyramids, and, finally, the small **interlobular arteries** (also known as *cortical radiate arteries*) in the renal cortex. The interlobular arteries branch into tiny **afferent arterioles** (AF-uhr-int; *aff-* = "to carry toward"), each of which

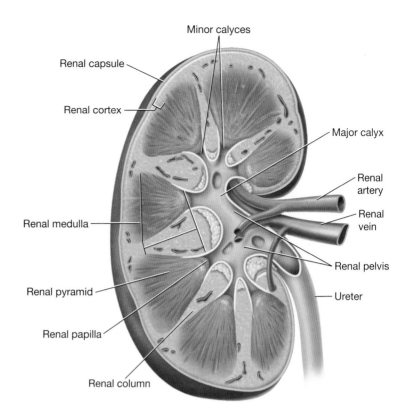

Minor calyces
Renal capsule
Renal cortex
Major calyx
Renal artery
Renal vein
Renal medulla
Renal pelvis
Renal pyramid
Ureter
Renal papilla
Renal column

FIGURE **25.3** Right kidney, frontal section.

supplies a ball of capillaries known as the **glomerulus** (gloh-MEHR-yoo-luhs; *glom-* = "ball"). This is where the blood is filtered by the process of **glomerular filtration**. Filtrate is produced at a rate of about 120 mL/min, a value known as the **glomerular filtration rate**. Note that the glomerulus is not the primary site for gas and nutrient exchange for the tissues of the kidneys.

You learned in Unit 18 (p. 481) that a capillary bed generally drains into a venule, but notice in Figure 25.4B that the capillaries of the glomerulus drain into a second *arteriole* called the **efferent arteriole** (EF-uhr-int; *eff-* = "to carry away"). The efferent arteriole then branches to form a second capillary bed known as the **peritubular capillaries**. These capillaries surround the tubules of the nephron, where the tubules provide them with oxygen and nutrients and also take substances reabsorbed by the tubules back into the blood. The peritubular capillaries then drain out through the small **interlobular veins** (also known as *cortical radiate veins*), which drain into **arcuate veins**, then into **interlobar veins**, and, finally, into the large **renal vein**. This pattern of blood flow allows the kidneys both to filter blood and to reclaim most of the fluid and solutes filtered.

Microscopically, each kidney is composed of more than a million tiny units called **nephrons** (NEF-rahns; *neph-* = "kidney"). The nephron can be divided into two parts: the *renal corpuscle* and the *renal tubule*. The **renal corpuscle** (KOHR-pus-uhl; *corpusc-* = "little body") itself consists of two parts: the glomerulus and the glomerular capsule (Fig. 25.5). As you've seen, the glomerulus is a ball of looping capillaries. The capillaries themselves are *fenestrated*, meaning that they have large slits or pores, which allows large volumes of fluid to exit them rapidly. The second portion of the renal corpuscle is the **glomerular capsule**, which has two layers: (1) the outer **parietal layer**, which is simple squamous epithelium; and (2) the inner **visceral layer**, which consists of cells called **podocytes** (POH-doh-syt'z; *pod-* = "foot") that surround the capillaries of the glomerulus. The space between the parietal and visceral layers is known as the **capsular space**. Fluid forced out of the glomerular capillaries enters this space; once in the capsular space, the fluid is called *filtrate*.

The podocytes of the visceral layer have extensions called **foot processes** that interlock to form narrow **filtration slits**. As you can see in Figure 25.5, the fenestrated glomerular endothelial cells, the podocytes, and their shared basal lamina together form a structure called the **filtration membrane**. The filtration membrane prevents large substances in the blood, such as blood cells and most proteins, from exiting the glomerular capillaries. However, water and small solutes such as electrolytes, glucose, amino acids, and urea easily cross the filtration membrane to enter the filtrate in the capsular space.

From the capsular space, the filtrate next enters the **renal tubule**, which can be likened to the "plumbing" of the kidney. In the renal tubule, the filtrate is modified by **tubular reabsorption**, during which substances in the filtrate are returned to the blood. During tubular reabsorption, about 99% of the water and solutes that enter the filtrate are reclaimed. The importance of this process can't be understated, as we would lose our entire blood volume in only 40 minutes were it to stop taking place. The filtrate is also modified by **tubular secretion**, which is the reverse of tubular reabsorption—substances that were not filtered from the blood at the glomerulus are moved from the blood to the filtrate.

25

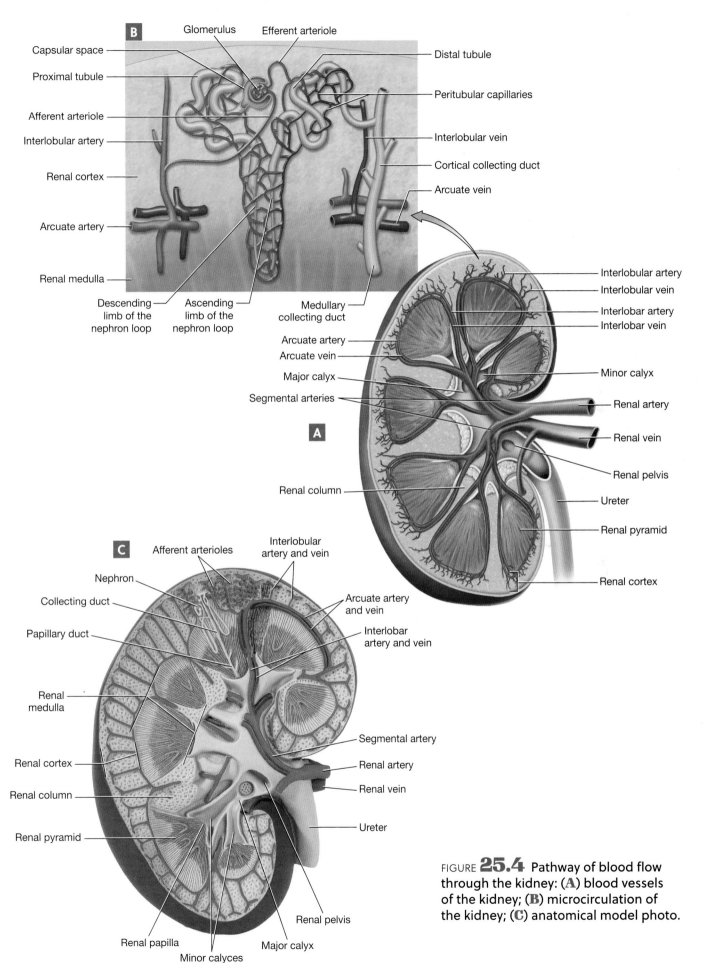

B

Capsular space

Proximal tubule

Afferent arteriole

Interlobular artery

Renal cortex

Arcuate artery

Renal medulla

Glomerulus

Efferent arteriole

Distal tubule

Peritubular capillaries

Interlobular vein

Cortical collecting duct

Arcuate vein

Descending limb of the nephron loop

Ascending limb of the nephron loop

Medullary collecting duct

Arcuate artery

Arcuate vein

Major calyx

Segmental arteries

Renal column

Interlobular artery

Interlobular vein

Interlobar artery

Interlobar vein

Minor calyx

Renal artery

Renal vein

Renal pelvis

Ureter

Renal pyramid

Renal cortex

A

C

Afferent arterioles

Interlobular artery and vein

Nephron

Collecting duct

Papillary duct

Renal medulla

Renal cortex

Renal column

Renal pyramid

Arcuate artery and vein

Interlobar artery and vein

Segmental artery

Renal artery

Renal vein

Ureter

Renal papilla

Minor calyces

Major calyx

Renal pelvis

FIGURE **25.4** Pathway of blood flow through the kidney: (**A**) blood vessels of the kidney; (**B**) microcirculation of the kidney; (**C**) anatomical model photo.

25

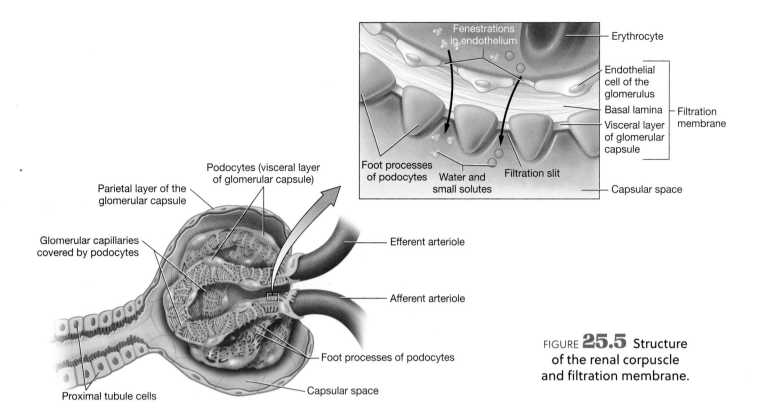

Figure 25.5 labels:

Fenestrations in endothelium

Erythrocyte

Endothelial cell of the glomerulus

Basal lamina — Filtration membrane

Visceral layer of glomerular capsule

Foot processes of podocytes

Water and small solutes

Filtration slit

Capsular space

Podocytes (visceral layer of glomerular capsule)

Parietal layer of the glomerular capsule

Glomerular capillaries covered by podocytes

Efferent arteriole

Afferent arteriole

Foot processes of podocytes

Capsular space

Proximal tubule cells

FIGURE **25.5** Structure of the renal corpuscle and filtration membrane.

The renal tubule consists of three parts, shown in Figure 25.6: (1) the **proximal tubule** (sometimes called the *proximal convoluted tubule*), (2) the descending and ascending limbs of the **nephron loop**, and (3) the **distal tubule** (sometimes called the *distal convoluted tubule*). The proximal tubule is the most metabolically active part of the nephron. Its cells have extensive microvilli to facilitate rapid reabsorption and secretion. Indeed, the cells of the proximal tubule reabsorb about 65% of the water and electrolytes in the filtrate; about 90% of the bicarbonate ions (which is critical to the maintenance of acid-base homeostasis); and nearly 100% of the glucose, amino acids, and other organic compounds.

Within the nephron loop, an additional 20–25% of the filtrate's water and ions are reabsorbed. Note that the nephron loops of certain nephrons are the only part of the nephron to dip down into the renal medulla; the remainder is confined to the renal cortex. When the filtrate reaches the distal tubule, about 85–90% of the water and solutes in the filtrate have been reclaimed. This allows for fine-tuning of water, electrolyte, and acid-base balance to occur within the distal tubule. Most of this fine-tuning is under control of hormones such as aldosterone and antidiuretic hormone.

Several distal tubules drain into one **collecting duct**, which is part of a larger **collecting system** that is not part of the nephron. Within the ducts of the collecting system, water balance is further fine-tuned. Collecting ducts in the renal cortex are **cortical collecting ducts**; those in the renal medulla are **medullary collecting ducts**. Near the renal papilla, medullary collecting ducts enlarge to form **papillary ducts**, which will drain newly formed urine into minor calyces. About 1 mL/min of urine is drained from the papillary ducts into the minor calyces, meaning the renal tubule and collecting system reclaim about 99% of the water filtered at the glomerulus.

At the junction between the ascending limb of the nephron loop and the distal tubule, we find a group of tall, closely packed cells known as the **macula densa** (MAK-yoo-lah DEN-sah; Fig. 25.7). The macula densa comes into contact with a portion of the afferent arteriole that contains specialized cells called **juxtaglomerular cells** (jux-tah-gloh-MEHR-yoo-lur; *juxta-* = "alongside"), or **JG cells**. The JG cells and macula densa together are called the **juxtaglomerular apparatus** (**JGA**). The JGA plays a role in controlling the flow of filtrate through the nephron and the blood pressure within the glomerulus.

As filtrate passes through the renal tubule and collecting system, it is heavily modified, and most of the water and solutes are reclaimed and returned to the blood. By the time the filtrate leaves the papillary ducts to enter the minor calyces, it is known as **urine**, which then drains into the major calyces and, finally, into the renal pelvis.

From the renal pelvis, urine enters the next organs of the urinary system, which are collectively called the **urinary tract**. The first portion of the urinary tract consists of the tubes called the **ureters** (YOOR-eh-terz; Figs. 25.8 and 25.9). Ureters are lined by a type of epithelium called **transitional epithelium**, and their walls contain smooth muscle that massages the urine inferiorly via peristalsis.

The ureters drain urine into the posteroinferior wall of the organ known as the **urinary bladder** at the **ureteral orifices** (yoo-REE-ter-uhl; Fig. 25.9). Like the ureters, the urinary bladder is lined with transitional epithelium and contains smooth muscle,

25

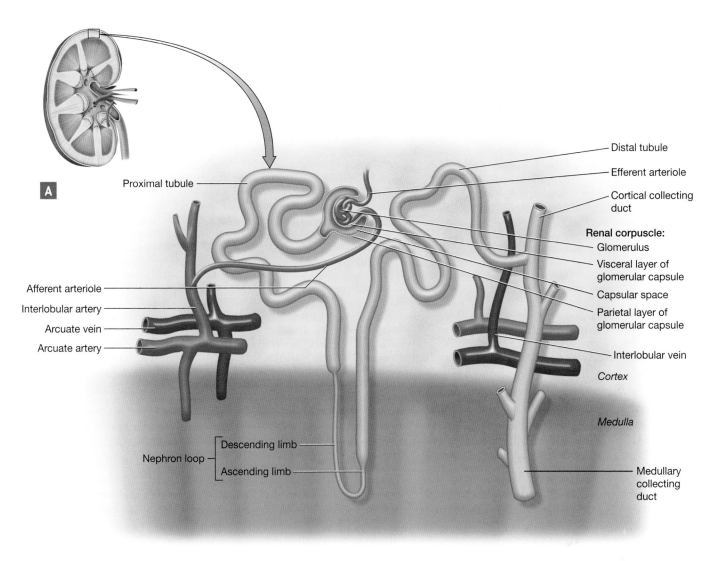

Distal tubule

Efferent arteriole

Cortical collecting duct

Renal corpuscle:

Glomerulus

Visceral layer of glomerular capsule

Capsular space

Parietal layer of glomerular capsule

Interlobular vein

Cortex

Medulla

Medullary collecting duct

Proximal tubule

A

Afferent arteriole

Interlobular artery

Arcuate vein

Arcuate artery

Nephron loop

Descending limb

Ascending limb

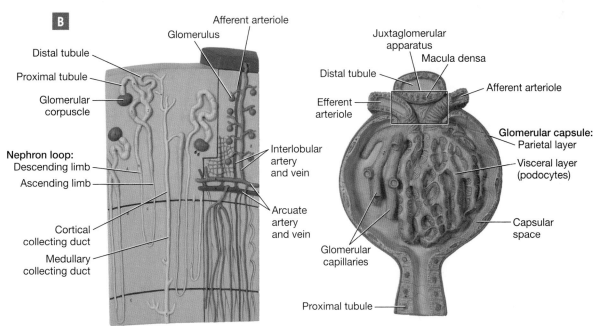

B

Afferent arteriole

Glomerulus

Distal tubule

Proximal tubule

Glomerular corpuscle

Nephron loop:

Descending limb

Ascending limb

Cortical collecting duct

Medullary collecting duct

Interlobular artery and vein

Arcuate artery and vein

Juxtaglomerular apparatus

Macula densa

Distal tubule

Afferent arteriole

Efferent arteriole

Glomerular capsule:

Parietal layer

Visceral layer (podocytes)

Capsular space

Glomerular capillaries

Proximal tubule

FIGURE **25.6** Structure of the nephron and collecting system: (**A**) illustration; (**B**) anatomical model photo.

25

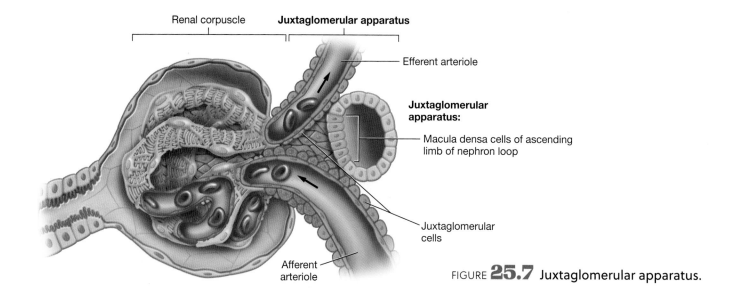

Renal corpuscle | Juxtaglomerular apparatus

Efferent arteriole

Juxtaglomerular apparatus:

Macula densa cells of ascending limb of nephron loop

Juxtaglomerular cells

Afferent arteriole

FIGURE **25.7** Juxtaglomerular apparatus.

sometimes called the **detrusor muscle** (dee-TROO-sur; *detrus-* = "thrust down"), in its wall. Most of the urinary bladder contains folds called **rugae** (ROO-ghee; *ruga-* = "wrinkle") that allow it to expand when it is filled with urine. The smooth inferior portion of the urinary bladder wall features a triangular-shaped area known as the **trigone** (TRY-gohn). This opens into the final organ of the urinary system—the **urethra** (yoo-REETH-ruh).

The urethra is surrounded by two rings of muscle: the involuntary **internal urethral sphincter**, composed of smooth muscle, and the voluntary **external urethral sphincter**, composed of skeletal muscle. The external urethral sphincter is an extension of the *levator ani muscle*, also known as the **pelvic** or **urogenital diaphragm**. When the detrusor muscle contracts and both sphincters relax, urine is expelled from the body through the **external urethral orifice**. This occurs by a process called **micturition** (mik-choo-RISH-un; *mictu-* = "urinate").

Notice in Figure 25.10 that the male and female urethras are quite different. In females, the urethra is short, measuring only about 4 cm. In males, the urethra is much longer, about 20 cm, and has three divisions: the **prostatic urethra**, which passes through the *prostate gland*; the short **membranous urethra**, which passes through the pelvic diaphragm; and the **spongy urethra**,

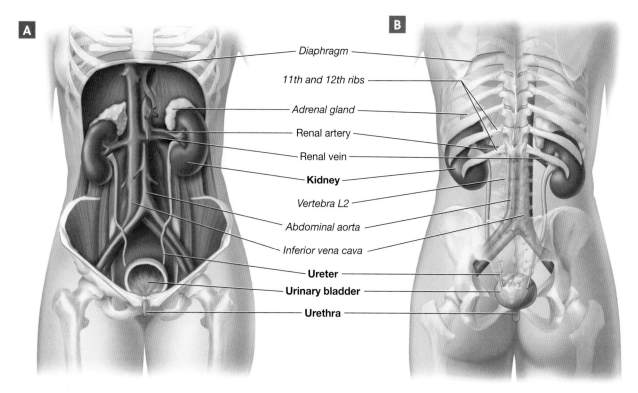

Diaphragm

11th and 12th ribs

Adrenal gland

Renal artery

Renal vein

Kidney

Vertebra L2

Abdominal aorta

Inferior vena cava

Ureter

Urinary bladder

Urethra

FIGURE **25.8** Organs of the female urinary system: (**A**) anterior view; (**B**) posterior view; (*continues*)

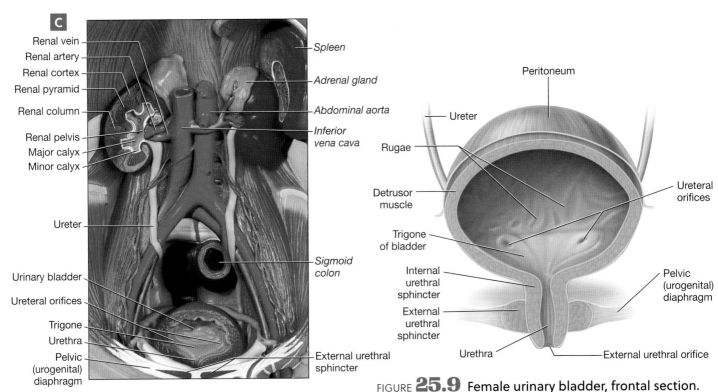

FIGURE **25.8** Organs of the female urinary system (*cont.*): (**C**) anatomical model photo.

FIGURE **25.9** Female urinary bladder, frontal section.

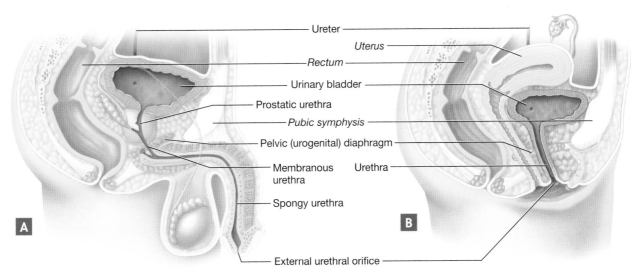

FIGURE **25.10** Organs of the male and female urinary systems, sagittal sections: (**A**) male urinary system; (**B**) female urinary system.

which passes through the penis. Another difference you may notice is the position of the urinary bladder. The urinary bladder of the male is anterior to the rectum. The urinary bladder of the female sits anterior to the vagina and inferior to the uterus. This position is one of the reasons why pregnant women have to urinate so frequently—the enlarged uterus sits right on top of the urinary bladder.

An overall view of the anatomy and physiology of the urinary system is illustrated in Figure 25.11.

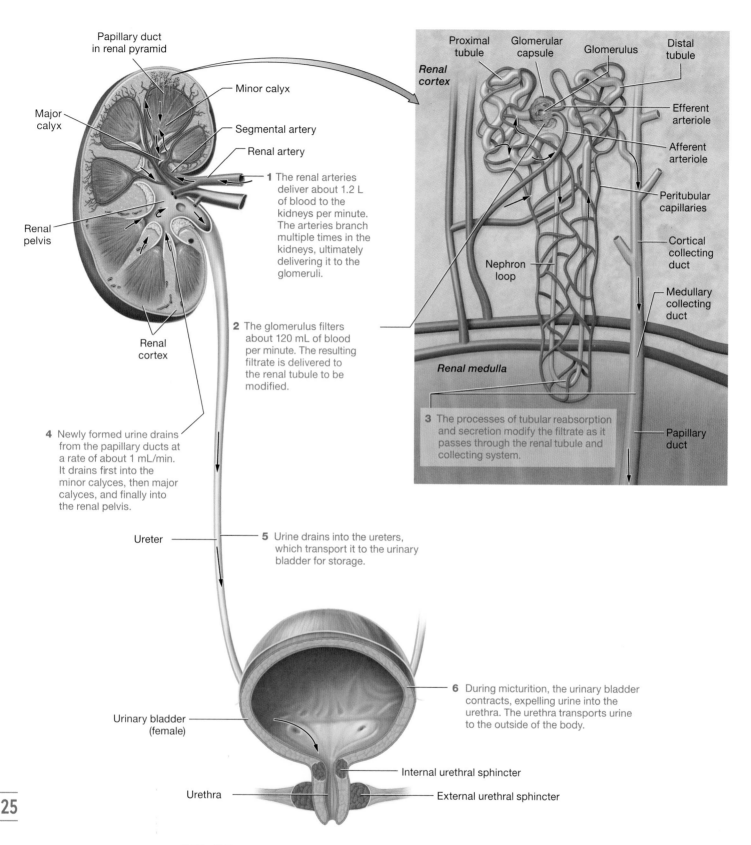

Papillary duct
in renal pyramid

Minor calyx

Major
calyx

Segmental artery

Renal artery

Renal
pelvis

Renal
cortex

1 The renal arteries
deliver about 1.2 L
of blood to the
kidneys per minute.
The arteries branch
multiple times in the
kidneys, ultimately
delivering it to the
glomeruli.

2 The glomerulus filters
about 120 mL of blood
per minute. The resulting
filtrate is delivered to
the renal tubule to be
modified.

4 Newly formed urine drains
from the papillary ducts at
a rate of about 1 mL/min.
It drains first into the
minor calyces, then major
calyces, and finally into
the renal pelvis.

Ureter

5 Urine drains into the ureters,
which transport it to the urinary
bladder for storage.

Urinary bladder
(female)

Urethra

*Renal
cortex*

Proximal
tubule

Glomerular
capsule

Glomerulus

Distal
tubule

Efferent
arteriole

Afferent
arteriole

Peritubular
capillaries

Cortical
collecting
duct

Medullary
collecting
duct

Nephron
loop

Renal medulla

3 The processes of tubular reabsorption
and secretion modify the filtrate as it
passes through the renal tubule and
collecting system.

Papillary
duct

6 During micturition, the urinary bladder
contracts, expelling urine into the
urethra. The urethra transports urine
to the outside of the body.

Internal urethral sphincter

External urethral sphincter

FIGURE **25.11** Overview of the anatomy and physiology of the urinary system.

25

Model Inventory for the Urinary System

Identify the following structures of the urinary system on models and diagrams, using your textbook and this unit for reference. As you examine the anatomical models and diagrams, record the name of the model and the structures you were able to identify on the model inventory in Table 25.1. When you have completed the activity, answer Check Your Understanding Questions 1 through 5 (pp. 697–698).

Kidney Anatomy

1. Surrounding connective tissue:
   a. Renal fascia
   b. Adipose capsule
   c. Renal capsule
2. Hilum
3. Regions:
   a. Renal cortex
   b. Renal medulla
      (1) Renal pyramids
      (2) Renal columns
      (3) Renal papilla
   c. Renal pelvis
      (1) Minor calyces
      (2) Major calyces
4. Blood supply:
   a. Renal artery
      (1) Segmental artery
      (2) Interlobar artery
      (3) Arcuate artery
      (4) Interlobular artery
   b. Renal vein
      (1) Interlobular vein
      (2) Arcuate vein
      (3) Interlobar vein

Structures of the Nephron and Collecting System

1. Renal corpuscle
   a. Glomerulus
      (1) Afferent arteriole
      (2) Efferent arteriole
      (3) Peritubular capillaries
   b. Glomerular capsule
      (1) Parietal layer
      (2) Visceral layer
      (3) Podocytes
      (4) Capsular space
2. Renal tubule
   a. Proximal tubule
   b. Nephron loop
      (1) Descending limb
      (2) Ascending limb
   c. Distal tubule
3. Collecting system
   a. Cortical collecting duct
   b. Medullary collecting duct
   c. Papillary duct
4. Juxtaglomerular apparatus
   a. Macula densa
   b. JG cells

Urinary Tract

1. Ureter
2. Urinary bladder
   a. Ureteral orifices
   b. Detrusor muscle
   c. Rugae
   d. Trigone
3. Urethra
   a. Internal urethral sphincter
   b. External urethral sphincter
      (1) Pelvic (urogenital) diaphragm
   c. External urethral orifice
   d. Prostatic urethra
   e. Membranous urethra
   f. Spongy urethra

25

TABLE **25.1** Model Inventory for Urinary Anatomy

Model/Diagram	Structures Identified

2 PROCEDURE
Time to Draw the Urinary System

In the space provided, draw, color, and label one of the overviews of the urinary system models that you examined. In addition, write the function of each structure that you label.

3 PROCEDURE
Time to Draw a Nephron

In the space provided, draw, color, and label a nephron. In addition, write the function of each structure that you label.

In this procedure, you'll dissect a preserved kidney. Here, you'll be able to identify several of the structures of the kidney that you just identified on models and diagrams.

1 Obtain a kidney specimen (fresh or preserved) and dissection supplies.

2 If the thick, surrounding connective tissue coverings are intact, note their thickness and amount of adipose tissue.

⚠ **SAFETY NOTE**

Safety glasses and gloves are required!

3 Use scissors to cut through the connective tissue coverings, and remove the kidney.

4 List surface structures you can identify (see Fig. 25.12A for reference):

_____

_____

5 Distinguishing between the ureter, the renal artery, and the renal vein is often difficult. Following are some hints:

a The renal artery typically has the thickest and most muscular wall, and it branches into several segmental arteries prior to entering the kidney.

b The renal vein is thinner, flimsier, and often larger in diameter than the renal artery. It does not branch after it has exited the kidney.

c The ureter has a thick, muscular wall, too, but it does not branch after it leaves the kidney. Also, its diameter is usually smaller than either the renal artery or the renal vein.

Keeping these points in mind, determine the location of the renal artery, the renal vein, and the ureter on your specimen. Sketch the arrangement of the three structures in the space provided.

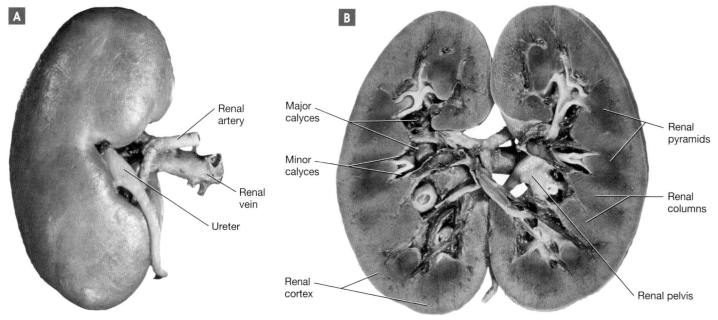

FIGURE **25.12** Preserved kidney: (**A**) anterior view; (**B**) frontal section.

25

6 Use a scalpel to make a frontal section of the kidney. Draw the kidney in the space provided and label the structures you are able to identify (Fig. 25.12B).

25

MATERIALS

Slides:
- ureter
- urinary bladder
- renal cortex
- renal medulla

Light microscope

Colored pencils

Urinary Organ Histology

Like all hollow organs, the ureters and urinary bladder consist of several tissue layers (Figs. 25.13 and 25.14). The innermost layer is the **mucosa**, which is composed of transitional epithelium and a thin layer of loose connective tissue. Recall from Unit 5 (p. 109) that transitional epithelium is stratified epithelium with cells that differ in appearance on the apical and basal sides. The cells at the apical edge are dome-shaped (or sometimes squamous) in appearance, and those nearer the basal edge are typically cuboidal. The apical cells can change shape to accommodate stretching of the urinary bladder.

The middle layer of the ureters and urinary bladder is the **submucosa**, composed of loose connective tissue and numerous glands that secrete a watery mucus. This mucus plays a critical protective role, because it prevents the chemicals in the urine from damaging and ulcerating the epithelium. The third layer is the muscularis, composed of smooth muscle that contracts to propel urine through the urinary tract. The outermost layer is the **adventitia** (ad-ven-TISH-uh), composed of dense irregular connective tissue.

In this exercise, you will also examine the tissues in two different regions of the kidney: the renal cortex and the renal medulla. Both contain many tubules made of simple epithelia. The simple epithelia of the renal tubules and collecting system provide an example of the structure-function relationship: A main function of these tubules is to reabsorb the water and solutes in the filtrate, and they could not perform this function efficiently with thick stratified epithelium. Another structural feature that aids in reabsorption is the presence of microvilli on the proximal tubule cells (and to a much lesser extent, the distal tubule). Microvilli dramatically increase the surface area available for tubular reabsorption, which ensures solutes and large volumes of water are reabsorbed rapidly from the filtrate.

Note in Figure 25.15A the abundance of small, ball-shaped glomeruli in the renal cortex.

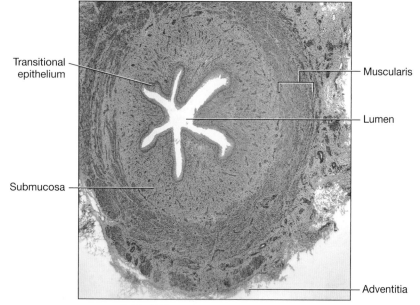

FIGURE **25.13** Tissues of the ureter.

Transitional epithelium

Submucosa

Muscularis

Lumen

Adventitia

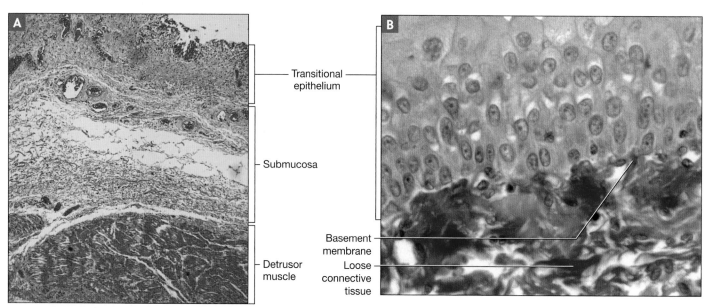

A

B

Transitional epithelium

Submucosa

Detrusor muscle

Basement membrane

Loose connective tissue

FIGURE **25.14** Urinary bladder: (**A**) bladder wall; (**B**) close-up of transitional epithelium.

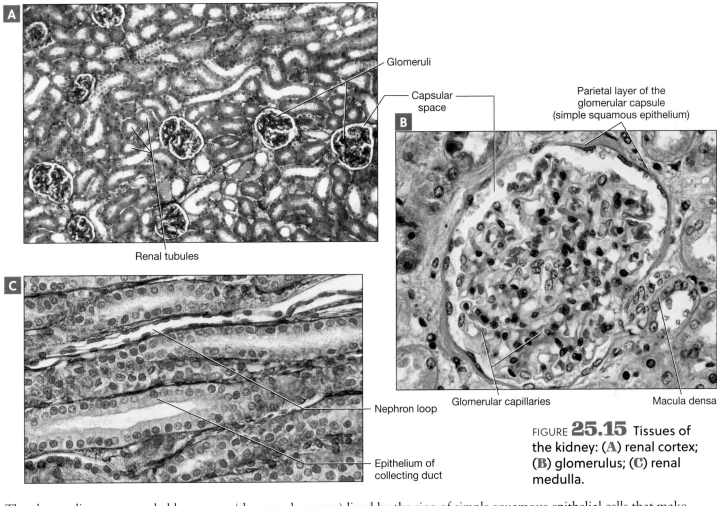

FIGURE **25.15** Tissues of the kidney: (**A**) renal cortex; (**B**) glomerulus; (**C**) renal medulla.

The glomeruli are surrounded by a space (the capsular space) lined by the ring of simple squamous epithelial cells that make up the parietal layer of the glomerular capsule (Fig. 25.15B). Between the glomeruli, note the presence of nephron tubules (the proximal and distal tubules and sections of nephron loops).

As you can see in Figure 25.15C, the renal medulla is composed mostly of collecting ducts and nephron loops. You will not see any glomeruli in the medulla, because they are confined to the cortex. This makes the renal cortex and renal medulla easily distinguishable.

1 PROCEDURE
Examining Urinary Organs with Microscopy

Now, you will view prepared slides of sections of the ureter, the urinary bladder, the renal cortex, and the renal medulla. Begin your examination of the slides on low power, and advance to medium and high power to observe details. Use colored pencils to draw what you see under the microscope, and label your drawing with the listed terms. When you have completed the activity, answer Check Your Understanding Question 6 (p. 698).

1 Ureter
- Transitional epithelium
- Submucosa
- Muscularis (smooth muscle)
- Adventitia

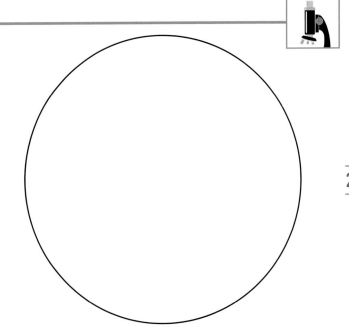

25

2 Transitional Epithelium (Urinary Bladder)

- Transitional epithelium
- Submucosa
- Muscularis (detrusor muscle)

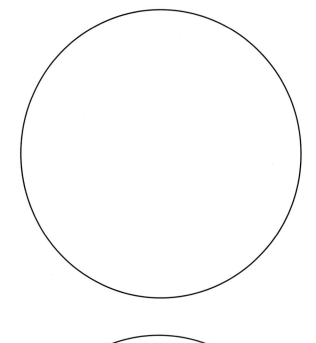

3 Renal Cortex

- Glomerulus
- Glomerular capsule with simple squamous epithelium
- Capsular space
- Renal tubules

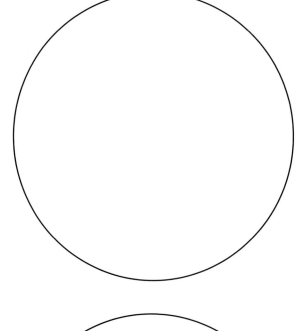

4 Renal Medulla

- Nephron loop
- Collecting ducts

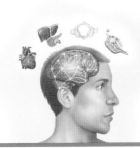

Check Your Recall

1 Label the following parts of the kidney on Figure 25.16.

❏ Afferent arteriole
❏ Distal tubule
❏ Efferent arteriole
❏ Glomerulus
❏ Minor calyx

❏ Papillary duct
❏ Peritubular capillaries
❏ Proximal tubule
❏ Renal column
❏ Renal medulla

❏ Segmental artery
❏ Ureter
❏ Urethra
❏ Urinary bladder

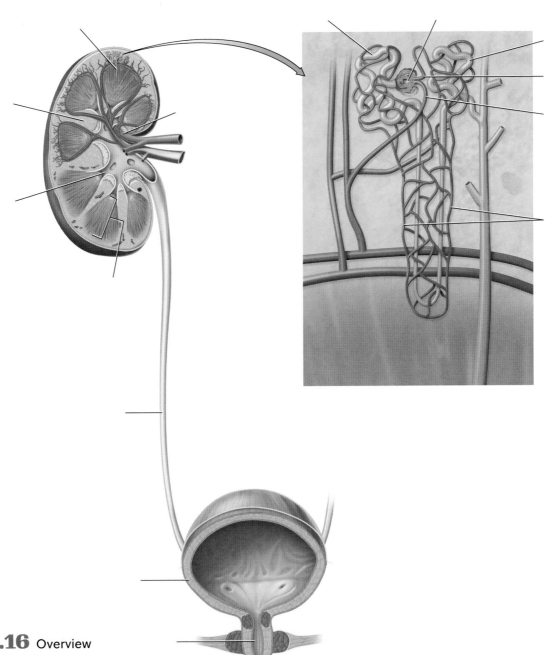

FIGURE **25.16** Overview of the urinary system.

2 Which of the following is *not* part of the nephron?

a. The proximal tubule.

b. The glomerular capsule.

c. The medullary collecting duct.

d. The nephron loop.

3 *Fill in the blanks:* The glomerulus is fed by the _____ arteriole, and drained by the _____ arteriole. Blood then flows into a set of _____ _____ .

4 *True/False:* Mark the following statements as true (T) or false (F). If the statement is false, correct it to make it a true statement.

_____ a. Nephrons consist of two parts: the renal corpuscle and the glomerular capsule.

_____ b. The visceral layer of the glomerular capsule is composed of podocytes.

_____ c. Renal columns are extensions of the renal medulla into the renal cortex.

_____ d. The renal corpuscles of only certain nephrons dip into the renal medulla.

5 The juxtaglomerular apparatus is composed of the _____ and the _____ .

a. juxtaglomerular cells; macula densa

b. macula densa; glomerular capsule

c. juxtaglomerular cells; glomerular capsule

d. glomerulus; macula densa

6 Number the following from the point the filtrate is first formed (with a number 1) to the point it drains into the renal pelvis (with a number 10).

_____ Nephron loop—descending limb

_____ Proximal tubule

_____ Cortical collecting duct

_____ Nephron loop—ascending limb

_____ Major calyx

_____ Papillary duct

_____ Medullary collecting duct

_____ Capsular space

_____ Distal tubule

_____ Minor calyx

7 Urine drains into the urinary bladder via the

a. urethra.

b. ureters.

c. renal pelvis.

d. papillary duct.

8 *Fill in the blanks:* Urine is voided by the process of _____ , and occurs when the _____ and _____ sphincters relax.

9 The inner layer of the urinary bladder is called the _____ and is composed of _____ .

a. submucosa; transitional epithelium

b. detrusor muscle; smooth muscle

c. mucosa; loose connective tissue

d. mucosa; transitional epithelium

10 The tubules of the kidney are composed of _____ , and the cells of proximal tubules feature _____ .

a. stratified epithelia; cilia

b. simple epithelia; microvilli

c. stratified epithelia; microvilli

d. simple epithelia; cilia

25

Name _____

Section _____ Date_____

Check Your Understanding

Critical Thinking and Application Questions

1 In the condition *renal artery stenosis*, the renal arteries narrow and become hardened.

   a How would this affect the amount of blood flowing to the kidney? How would it affect the glomerular filtration rate? Why?

   b How would renal artery stenosis affect blood pressure? Explain. (*Hint:* What happens to blood pressure when blood vessels narrow?)

2 Ailani develops *Fanconi syndrome* after taking herbs prescribed by a practitioner of traditional Chinese medicine. In Fanconi syndrome, the cells of the proximal tubule are unable to perform their functions. Predict the symptoms Ailani is experiencing due to her condition, and explain why.

3 You are treating a group of patients for renal failure after they contracted food poisoning with *E. coli* O157:H7 from unpasteurized juice. This bacterium produces a toxin that attacks the cells of the glomeruli. How does this explain their renal failure?

4 Individuals with damage to nerves of the sacral spinal cord may suffer from problems controlling micturition.

  a What could happen if the nerves serving the internal and external urethral sphincter were damaged? Why?

  b What could happen in the nerves serving the detrusor muscle were damaged? Explain.

5 Mr. Hadi presents with a chief complaint of having to urinate frequently and feeling as if his bladder never completely empties. A physical examination reveals that his prostate is enlarged. How does this explain his symptoms?

6 How does the form of the epithelium that lines the urinary bladder follow its function?

25

Urinary System Physiology

When you have completed this unit, you should be able to:

1 Describe the process of glomerular filtration and the structure of the filtration membrane.

2 Model the physiology of the kidney and explain why only certain substances appear in the filtrate.

3 Perform and interpret urinalysis on simulated urine specimens.

4 Explain the possible causes of abnormalities detected on urinalysis.

5 Trace various substances through the gross and microscopic anatomy of the kidney.

PRE-LAB EXERCISES

Complete the following exercises prior to coming to lab, using your lab manual and textbook for reference.

PRE-LAB

26-1 Key Terms

You should be familiar with the following terms before coming to lab.

Term	Definition
Glomerular filtration	
Glomerular filtration rate (GFR)	
Filtration membrane	
Filtrate	
Tubular reabsorption	
Tubular secretion	
Urine	
Urinalysis	
Specific gravity	
Urobilinogen	
Ketones	

26

PRE-LAB

26-2
Nephron and Collecting System Structure and Function

Review the structure of the nephron by color-coding Figure 26.1 and labeling it with the parts of the nephron and collecting system. Then, use your textbook to determine which substances are absorbed or secreted from each region, and enter this information in the blank boxes to the side of the tubules. In the boxes whose arrows are pointing toward the tubules, place substances that are secreted into the urine. In boxes whose arrows are pointing away from the tubules, place substances that are reabsorbed into the bloodstream.

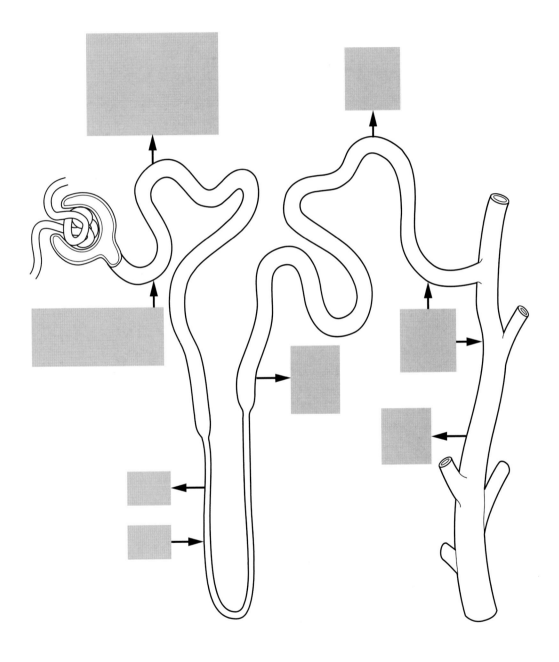

FIGURE **26.1** Anatomy of the nephron and collecting system.

26

Table 26.1 lists chemicals and cells found in blood. Do the following for each item, using your textbook for reference:

1 Determine whether each listed item is filtered at the glomerulus (i.e., whether it is able to leave the blood and enter the nephron to become part of the filtrate under normal conditions).

2 If the substance is found in the filtrate, determine whether the substance is reabsorbed into the blood or whether it is found in the urine.

3 If the substance is reabsorbed into the blood, determine where this substance is reabsorbed in the nephron (e.g., the proximal tubule, the nephron loop, etc.).

TABLE **26.1** Substances Found in the Blood and Their Filtration and Reabsorption by the Nephron

Substance	Filtered in the Glomerulus? (Yes/No)	Reabsorbed? (Yes/No)	Secreted? (Yes/No)	Location Where Reabsorption or Secretion Takes Place
Erythrocyte				
Leukocyte				
Water				
Glucose				
Proteins				
Amino acids				
Urea				
Creatinine				
Sodium and chloride ions				
Potassium ions				
Hydrogen ions				
Uric acid				
Ketones				

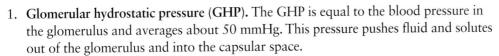

EXERCISES

The kidneys filter the blood in order to remove metabolic wastes and regulate the body's fluid, electrolyte, and acid-base balance. Recall from Unit 25 that the kidneys' filters are located within the glomerular capillaries. However, the glomerular capillaries can't filter the blood unless there is a force to push fluid and solutes through them and into the nephron tubule. This force is supplied by a pressure called the **net filtration pressure** (**NFP**).

Urine samples in a medical laboratory.

The NFP is the combination of three forces (Fig. 26.2):

1. **Glomerular hydrostatic pressure (GHP).** The GHP is equal to the blood pressure in the glomerulus and averages about 50 mmHg. This pressure pushes fluid and solutes out of the glomerulus and into the capsular space.

2. **Colloid osmotic pressure (COP).** The COP is the term that describes the osmotic pressure of solutions in which large proteins are the main solutes, and it averages about 30 mmHg. This pressure tends to oppose filtration and draws water *into* the glomerular capillaries by osmosis.

3. **Capsular hydrostatic pressure (CHP).** The final pressure, the CHP, is the force of the fluid in the capsular space. It averages about 10 mmHg, opposes filtration, and pushes fluid back into the glomerulus.

As you can see in Figure 26.2, to get the NFP, simply subtract the two forces that oppose filtration from the one force that favors filtration:

$$GHP - (COP + CHP) = NFP$$
$$50 - (30 + 10) = 10 \text{ mmHg}$$

So, there is a net pressure of 10 mmHg in the glomerulus that drives fluid from it into the capsular space. When the fluid enters the capsular space, it becomes a liquid called **filtrate**.

The rate of filtrate production averages about 120 mL/min, a value called the **glomerular filtration rate** (**GFR**). The GFR is determined largely by the three pressures that factor into the NFP. To put it simply, if the NFP increases, then the GFR generally also increases. The opposite is also true—if the NFP decreases, the GFR also generally decreases. Note that this is only true up to a point because there are many compensatory mechanisms that work to maintain a stable GFR. These compensatory mechanisms exist because the GFR is a critical determinant of kidney function; if the GFR is too low or too high, the kidneys will not be able to carry out their many functions.

The filtrate contains many substances our bodies need to reclaim, including water, glucose, amino acids, and ions. This reclamation occurs by a process known as **tubular reabsorption** (Fig. 26.3). About 99% of the water in the filtrate and most of the solutes are reabsorbed through the epithelium of the nephron tubules and returned to the blood. The importance of this function cannot be overstated. If the water were not reabsorbed in the renal tubules and the collecting ducts, we would lose our entire plasma volume in fewer than 30 minutes. This demonstrates another important reason to tightly regulate the GFR—if the GFR is too high, the nephron tubules will not have time to reabsorb all of the necessary substances in the filtrate, and we will lose much of our water and important solutes to the urine.

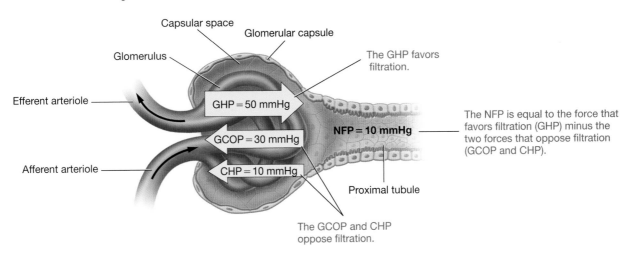

FIGURE **26.2** Net filtration pressure in the renal corpuscle.

There are certain substances that aren't filtered at the glomerulus that need to be excreted in the urine, as well as substances that the body needs to excrete in greater amounts than are filtered. Notice in Figure 26.3 that such substances can move from the blood in the peritubular capillaries to the filtrate in the nephron tubules by a process known as **tubular secretion.** Examples of secreted substances include potassium ions, hydrogen ions, and uric acid.

In the following exercises, you will examine the processes of filtration and reabsorption by constructing a model kidney and by testing samples of simulated urine (we cannot model secretion in the lab). In the final exercise, you will trace the pathway of substances through the microanatomy of the kidney to contrast the filtration and reabsorption of erythrocytes, urea, and glucose.

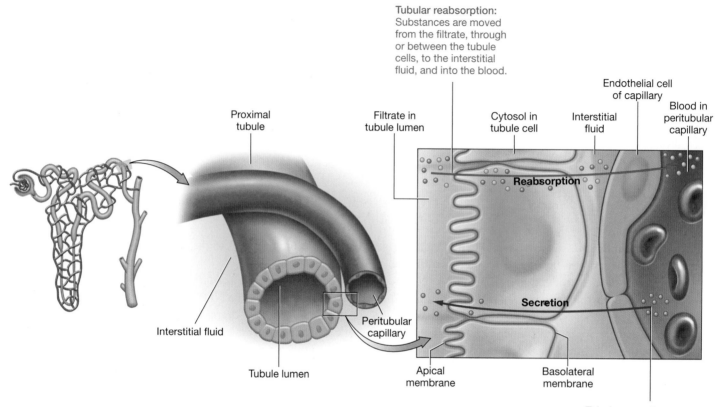

Tubular reabsorption:
Substances are moved
from the filtrate, through
or between the tubule
cells, to the interstitial
fluid, and into the blood.

Proximal tubule

Filtrate in tubule lumen

Cytosol in tubule cell

Interstitial fluid

Endothelial cell of capillary

Blood in peritubular capillary

Reabsorption

Interstitial fluid

Tubule lumen

Peritubular capillary

Apical membrane

Basolateral membrane

Secretion

Tubular secretion:
Substances are moved
from the blood, to the
interstitial fluid, through
the tubule cells, into the
filtrate.

FIGURE **26.3** Reabsorption and secretion in the renal tubule.

MATERIALS

- ☐ 4-in. piece of dialysis tubing
- ☐ Pieces of string (2)
- ☐ Animal blood or simulated blood
- ☐ 200 mL beaker
- ☐ Deionized water
- ☐ URS-10 and bottle with key

The Model Kidney

The filtrate formed by glomerular filtration is similar in composition to blood, but it lacks the formed elements and most of the proteins we find in blood. This selectivity is possible because of a structure called the **filtration membrane**, which consists of a stack of three increasingly fine and selective filters. The first and leakiest filter is formed by the fenestrated glomerular endothelial cells; the second filter is composed of the basal lamina around the endothelial cells, which contains interwoven collagen fibers; and the third and finest filter is formed by **podocytes** (POH-doh-syt′z; Fig. 26.4), specialized epithelial cells. Podocytes have extensions called *foot processes* that interlace to form very narrow **filtration slits**.

The filtration membrane acts in a similar manner to the filter in your coffeemaker. Just as a coffee filter holds back the coffee grounds while allowing water and other solutes to pass through into your coffee, the filtration membrane prevents large items, such as plasma proteins and cells, from leaving the blood. while allowing small substances, such as water, glucose, amino acids, ions, and metabolic wastes, to leave the blood and enter the filtrate. This selectivity is vitally important, as the nephron tubules and collecting system cannot reabsorb large proteins or cells. For this reason, any that entered the filtrate would be lost to the urine.

In this exercise, you will examine the process of glomerular filtration and the selectivity of the filtration membrane by constructing a model kidney and by testing for substances that appear in the filtrate. A kidney is easily modeled with either animal blood or simulated blood and simple dialysis tubing, which has a permeability similar to that of the filtration membrane. Glomerular filtration is mimicked by immersing the

FIGURE **26.4** **Structure of the filtration membrane.**

blood-filled tubing in water. Substances to which the "filtration membrane" is permeable will enter the surrounding water (the "filtrate"), whereas those to which the membrane is not permeable will remain in the tubing.

The results of this test are analyzed using **urinalysis reagent test strips** (URS-10; Fig. 26.5). Each strip consists of 10 small, colored pads that change color in the presence of certain chemicals, such as glucose or hemoglobin. The strip is interpreted by watching the pads for color changes and comparing the color changes to a color-coded key on the side of the bottle. The color that is closest to the color on the strip is recorded as your result. Please note that, for this exercise, you will read only four of the 10 boxes: blood, leukocytes, protein, and glucose.

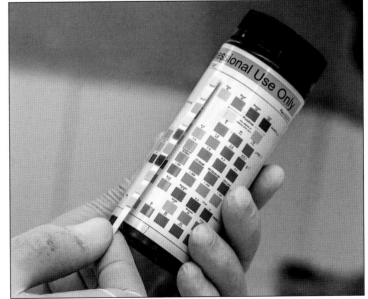

FIGURE **26.5** URS-10 strip and vial.

PROCEDURE

Making a Model Kidney and Testing Glomerular Filtration

Now, let's construct our model kidneys. The model kidney must sit in water for 25 minutes while you wait for your results. While you wait, answer Check Your Understanding Questions 1 through 3 (p. 715).

Hypothesis: Which substances will stay in the filtrate? Which will be filtered out?

1 Cut a 4-in. piece of dialysis tubing.

2 Securely tie off one end of the tubing with string and open the other end of the tubing by wetting the end of the tube and rubbing it between your fingers.

3 Fill the dialysis tubing about half-full with either animal blood or simulated blood, and securely tie off the open end of the tube with string.

4 Place the tied-off tube in a 200 mL beaker containing about 150 mL of deionized water.

5 Leave the tubing in the water for approximately 25 minutes.

6 After 25 minutes have passed, remove the tubing from the water.

7 Dip a URS-10 strip in the water and remove it quickly. Turn the bottle on its side and compare the colors of the pads for glucose, blood, leukocytes, and protein. You will notice that, on the side of the bottle, time frames are listed for each substance that is tested. Wait this amount of time to watch for a reaction; otherwise, you could obtain a false negative result. If you wait too long to read the results, though, the colors will tend to darken and may blend with adjacent colors.

8 Record your results:

   a Glucose: _____

   b Erythrocytes (blood): _____

   c Leukocytes: _____

   d Protein: _____

9 Which substances were filtered out? Which substances stayed in the tubing? Explain your results.

_____

_____

_____

10 Compare your results to your hypothesis.

26

EXERCISE 26-2

MATERIALS

- ❏ Samples of simulated urine
- ❏ Graduated cylinder or test tube
- ❏ URS-10 and bottle with key

Urinalysis

For hundreds of years, healthcare providers have recognized the utility of urinalysis as a diagnostic tool. Historically, the urine was evaluated for color, translucency, odor, and taste (yes, taste!). Today, while these characteristics are still examined (except, thankfully, taste), we also utilize urinalysis test strips, as we did in Exercise 26-1 (p. 705), to test for the presence of various chemicals in the urine. Normal and abnormal readings both can give a healthcare provider a wealth of information about a patient's renal function and overall health. Abnormal readings can be caused by changes in renal blood flow and glomerular filtration; insufficient tubular reabsorption; and excessive or insufficient tubular secretion.

In this exercise, you will analyze different urine samples using a URS-10, as in Exercise 26-1. For each urine sample, one or more results will be read as abnormal. In the second part of the exercise, you will research potential causes of the abnormalities that you detected.

1 PROCEDURE

Urinalysis Part One: Identifying Abnormalities

Test a minimum of five samples of simulated urine using your URS-10 test strips. Use a new strip for each sample, and take care to clean your graduated cylinder thoroughly between each sample that you test. Please note that this is *simulated* urine rather than real urine, although it contains the same chemicals as real urine and should be handled with equal caution. After you have completed the activity, answer Check Your Understanding Questions 4 and 5 (p. 716).

⚠ SAFETY NOTE

Safety glasses and gloves are required!

1 Randomly choose one sample of simulated urine, and pour approximately 3 mL of the sample into a test tube or graduated cylinder.

2 Submerge one URS-10 test strip in the urine, and quickly remove it.

3 Compare the resulting colors and patterns on the test strip to those on the key on the bottle. Be sure to wait the appropriate amount of time to read the results.

4 Record your results in Table 26.2, and note any anomalous results.

5 Repeat this procedure for the remaining samples.

TABLE **26.2** Urinalysis Results

Reading	Sample 1	Sample 2	Sample 3	Sample 4	Sample 5
pH					
Leukocytes					
Nitrite					
Urobilinogen					
Protein					
Blood					
Specific gravity					
Ketones					
Bilirubin					
Glucose					

Urinalysis Part Two: Researching Possible Pathologies

Each sample that you tested should have had at least one abnormality. Use your textbook or other research tools to determine which disease state(s) could lead to the abnormality you detected in each sample. Record your results in Table 26.3.

TABLE **26.3** Urinalysis Abnormalities and Disease States

Sample	Primary Abnormality	Potential Causes
1		
2		
3		
4		
5		

EXERCISE

26-3

MATERIALS

❑ Anatomical models and
diagrams:
▪ kidney
▪ nephron

Time to Trace!

Let's now trace the pathway of different substances through the vasculature and the microanatomy of the kidney. You will examine the path taken by (1) a plasma protein, (2) a molecule of water, and (3) a hydrogen ion. The path that each takes differs in key ways—and it's your job to figure out how so.

Following are some hints to help you:

■ Remember the basic rules of blood flow: You must pass through a capillary bed in order to get from an artery to a vein. Also, recall that there are two capillary beds in the microcirculation of the kidney: the glomerulus and the peritubular capillaries.

■ Reference Table 26.1 in Pre-Lab Exercise 26-3 (p. 702), which tells you three key pieces of information: (1) whether the item is filtered at the glomerulus, (2) whether a filtered item is reabsorbed or secreted, and (3) where reabsorption or secretion takes place.

■ Don't overthink things. If an item isn't filtered at the glomerulus, that means it must stay in the blood, right? Similarly, if an item is never reabsorbed, it must go through the whole nephron and collecting system to end up in the urine.

■ Refer to Figure 26.6 for help with the pathway of blood flow through the kidney and the kidney's microanatomy.

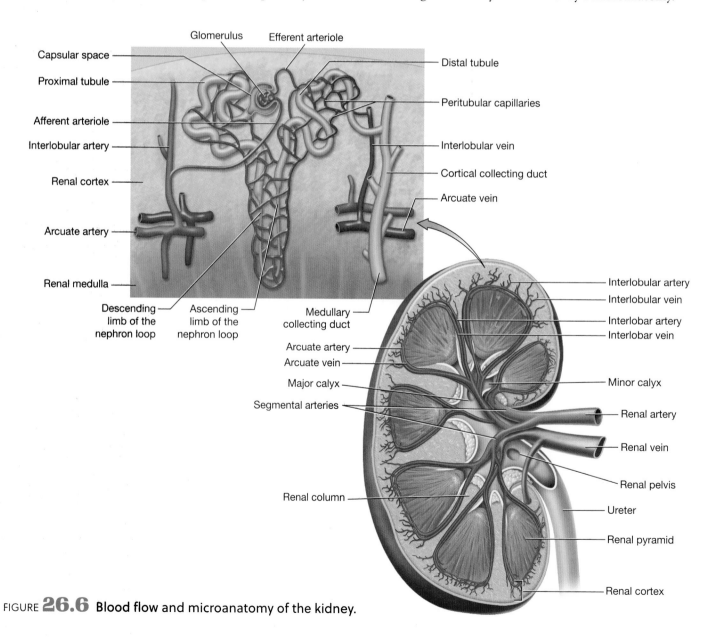

FIGURE **26.6** **Blood flow and microanatomy of the kidney.**

PROCEDURE

Tracing Substances Through the Kidney

Complete the following tracing procedures, using Figure 26.6 (p. 710) and Unit 25 for reference. When you have completed all three parts, answer Check Your Understanding Question 6 (p. 716).

Part 1 Plasma Protein

Trace a plasma protein from the renal artery to the renal vein.

Start: Renal Artery →

_____ → _____ →

_____ → _____ →

_____ → _____ →

_____ → _____ →

_____ → _____ →

_____ → **End:** Renal Vein

Part 2 Water

Trace a molecule of water from the renal artery to the renal vein. (Assume molecule of water is reabsorbed at the medullary collecting duct.)

Start: Renal Artery →

_____ → _____ →

_____ → _____ →

_____ → _____ →

_____ → _____ →

_____ → _____ →

_____ → _____ →

_____ → _____ →

_____ → _____ →

_____ → **End:** Renal Vein

Part 3 Hydrogen Ion

Trace a hydrogen ion from the renal artery to its destination outside the body of a male. (Assume it is not filtered, but is secreted into the filtrate at the distal tubule.)

Start: Renal Artery →

_____ →   _____ →

_____ →   _____ →

_____ →   _____ →

_____ →   _____ →

_____ →   _____ →

_____ →   _____ →

_____ →   _____ →

_____ →   _____ →

_____ →   _____ →

_____ →   _____ →

End: Final Destination Outside the Body of a Male

Check Your Recall

1 The force(s) that favor(s) glomerular filtration is/are known as the

a. colloid osmotic pressure.

b. capsular hydrostatic pressure.

c. glomerular hydrostatic pressure.

d. Both a and b are correct.

e. Both b and c are correct.

2 The force(s) that oppose(s) glomerular filtration is/are known as the

a. colloid osmotic pressure.

b. capsular hydrostatic pressure.

c. glomerular hydrostatic pressure.

d. Both a and b are correct.

e. Both a and c are correct.

3 *Fill in the blanks:* The three filters of the filtration membrane are the _____

_____ cells, the _____ _____ ,

and specialized cells called _____ .

4 What is the purpose of tubular reabsorption?

a. To remove substances in the blood and place them into the filtrate.

b. To reclaim 99% of the water from the filtrate.

c. To reclaim electrolytes, glucose, and amino acids from the filtrate.

d. Both a and b are correct.

e. Both b and c are correct.

5 Which is the correct pathway that a substance takes when it is secreted into the filtrate?

a. Blood in glomerular capillaries → between or through tubule cells → interstitial fluid → filtrate.

b. Blood in peritubular capillaries → interstitial fluid → between or through tubule cells → filtrate.

c. Blood in peritubular capillaries → between or through tubule cells → interstitial fluid → blood in glomerular capillaries.

d. Filtrate → interstitial fluid → cytosol of tubule cells → blood in glomerular capillaries.

6 What is the average glomerular filtration rate in a healthy person?

a. 200 mL/min

b. 120 L/min

c. 120 mL/min

d. 1 L/min

7 Why is it important that the filtration membrane be selective?

_____

_____

_____

8 Filtration slits are formed by the
   a. interlaced foot processes of podocytes.
   b. fenestrated glomerular endothelial cells.
   c. fenestrated peritubular capillary endothelial cells.
   d. parietal layer of the glomerular capsule.

9 Which of the following variables is _not_ assessed by common urinalysis?
   a. Urine pH.
   b. Urine sodium ion concentration.
   c. Urine ketone concentration.
   d. The presence of erythrocytes.

10 Which of the following substances would you expect to find in significant amounts in normal urine?
   a. Bicarbonate ions.
   b. Proteins.
   c. Urea.
   d. Leukocytes.

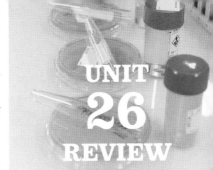

Check Your Understanding

Critical Thinking and Application Questions

1 Of the following solutes, which is *least* likely to be found in the filtrate of a person with healthy kidneys: glucose, potassium ions, plasma proteins, or amino acids? Explain why you normally wouldn't expect to find this solute in the filtrate.

2 Of the following solutes, which ones are *least* likely to be found in the urine of a healthy person: erythrocytes, glucose, sodium ions, and/or hydrogen ions? Explain why you normally wouldn't expect to find this (these) solute(s) in the urine.

3 Calculate the net filtration pressure if the glomerular hydrostatic pressure measures 36 mmHg, the colloid osmotic pressure 32 mmHg, and the capsular hydrostatic pressure 4 mmHg. Does this differ from the normal value? If so, how? What effect, if any, would this have on the GFR?

4 You test your patient's urine after he develops *dehydration, polyuria* (production of excessive volumes of urine), and *acidosis* (low pH of the body fluids). A detailed laboratory analysis finds the urine contains a high concentration of amino acids, electrolytes, glucose, and bicarbonate ions.

    a Is the abnormality in glomerular filtration, tubular reabsorption, or tubular secretion? Explain.

    _____

    _____

    _____

    b Why does the patient have acidosis? _____

    _____

    _____

5 You test another patient's urine after a complaint of discolored urine. You determine it contains erythrocytes, leukocytes, and protein. Is the abnormality in glomerular filtration, tubular reabsorption, or tubular secretion? Explain.

_____

_____

_____

_____

_____

6 In Exercise 26-3 (p. 710), you traced items that were filtered at the glomerulus. Now, consider a molecule of antibiotic that is secreted from the peritubular capillaries into the filtrate at the proximal tubule. Trace the pathway this antibiotic molecule would take from the renal artery to the point at which it exits the body of a female in the urine.

Start: Renal Artery → _____ → _____ →

_____ → _____ → _____ →

_____ → _____ → _____ →

_____ → _____ → _____ →

_____ → _____ → _____ →

_____ → _____ → _____ →

_____ → _____ → _____ →

_____ → **Exits the body in the urine.**

Reproductive System

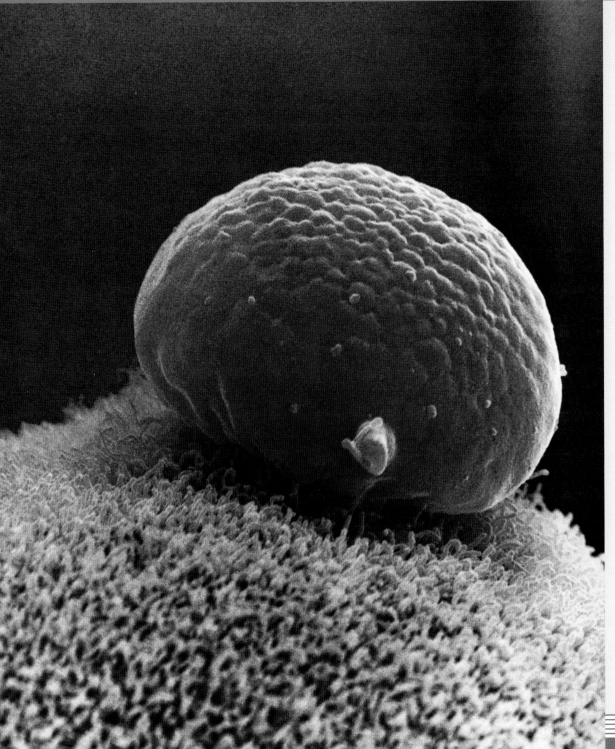

When you have completed this unit, you should be able to:

1 Describe and identify structures of the male and female reproductive systems.

2 Describe the histology of the ovary, seminiferous tubules, and spermatozoa.

3 Identify the stages of meiosis and explain how meiosis differs from mitosis.

4 Describe the basic processes of spermatogenesis and oogenesis.

5 Trace the pathway a developing gamete takes from its development to the time of fertilization.

PRE-LAB EXERCISES

Complete the following exercises prior to coming to lab, using your lab manual and textbook for reference.

PRE-LAB

27-1 Key Terms

You should be familiar with the following terms before coming to lab.

Term	Definition

Structures of the Male Reproductive System

Testes _____

Seminiferous tubules _____

Epididymis _____

Ductus deferens _____

Spermatic cord _____

Seminal vesicle _____

Prostate gland _____

Corpus spongiosum _____

Corpora cavernosa _____

Bulbourethral glands _____

Structures of the Female Reproductive System

Ovaries _____

Ovarian follicles _____

27

Name ______________________ Section __________ Date __________

Uterine tube ______________________

____

Uterus ______________________

____

Cervix ______________________

____

Vagina ______________________

____

Vulva ______________________

____

Mammary glands ______________________

____

Gametogenesis Terms

Gamete ______________________

____

Meiosis I ______________________

____

Meiosis II ______________________

____

Haploid ______________________

____

Spermatogenesis ______________________

____

Oogenesis ______________________

____

Male Reproductive Anatomy

Color the structures of the male reproductive system in Figure 27.1, and label them with the terms from Exercise 27-1 (p. 723). Use your text and Exercise 27-1 in this unit for reference.

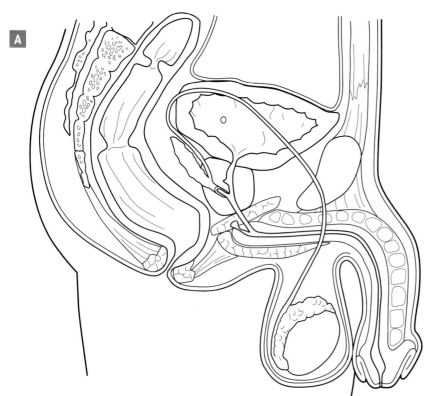

A

FIGURE **27.1** Male reproductive organs, midsagittal sections: (A) male pelvis; (B) through the testis.

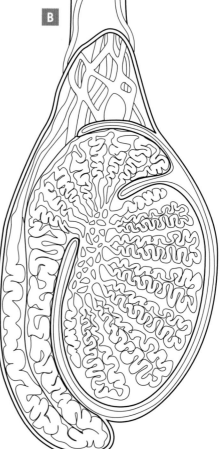

B

PRE-LAB

27-3 Female Reproductive Anatomy

Color the structures of the female reproductive system in Figure 27.2, and label them with the terms from Exercise 27-2 (p. 727). Use your text and Exercise 27-2 in this unit for reference.

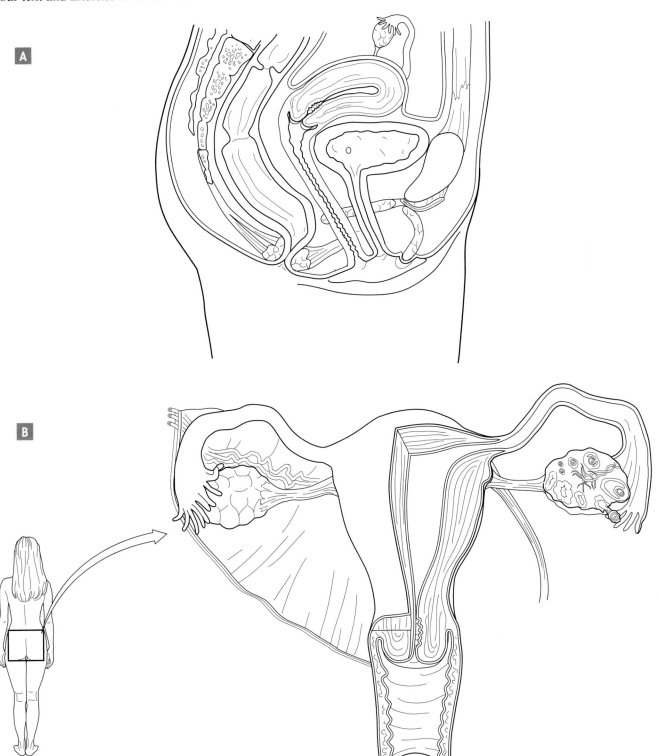

FIGURE **27.2** Female reproductive tract: (**A**) midsagittal section of the female pelvis; (**B**) partial frontal section of a posterior view of the female reproductive organs.

27-4 Stages of Mitosis

In this unit, we will discuss the process of meiosis. Meiosis proceeds similarly to mitosis, so let's review mitosis before you begin the lab. Fill in Table 27.1 with the events occurring in the cell in each of the stages of mitosis.

TABLE **27.1** Stages of Mitosis

Stage of Mitosis	Events Occurring in the Cell
Prophase	
Metaphase	
Anaphase	
Telophase	

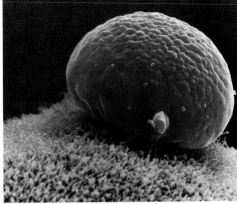

EXERCISES

The organ systems in the human body so far discussed function—in some manner—to maintain homeostasis. The **reproductive system**, however, plays a lesser role in maintaining homeostasis but a greater role in perpetuating the species. The main organs of the reproductive system are the **gonads** (GOH-nadz)—the testes and the ovaries—which produce **gametes** (GAM-eetz), or sex cells, for reproduction.

We begin this unit with the anatomy of the male (Ex. 27-1, p. 723) and female (Ex. 27-2, p. 727) reproductive systems. Then we turn to the main functions of these organs: **gametogenesis** (gah-meet-oh-JEN-uh-sis; -*genesis* = "formation"), the formation of new gametes.

EXERCISE 27-1

MATERIALS

- ☐ Anatomical models and diagrams:
  - male reproductive system
  - human torso

Male Reproductive Anatomy

The **testes**, the gamete-producing organs of the male, are situated outside the body in a sac known as the **scrotum**, which is composed of skin, connective tissue, and a layer of smooth muscle called the **dartos muscle** (Fig. 27.3). They are located externally because sperm production requires a temperature of about 34°C (about 94°F), which is lower than body temperature. Along the midline, the scrotum has a connective tissue septum that divides it into two chambers, one for each testis. Smooth muscle tissue called the **cremaster muscle** (kreh-MASS-ter; *cremaster* = "to hang") surrounds each testis in the scrotum. This muscle tissue contracts to control the testes' temperature by controlling their distance from the body.

The layer of connective tissue deep to the scrotum extends up into the pelvic cavity to form a structure known as the **spermatic cord**. Notice in Figure 27.3 that the spermatic cord surrounds the cremaster muscle, the testicular artery, a group of veins draining the testis called the **pampiniform venous plexus**, a duct known as the *ductus deferens* that transports sperm, and nerves that supply the testes. The spermatic cord passes into the pelvic cavity through the **external inguinal ring** (IN-gwin-uhl), which is the opening to a small passageway called the *inguinal canal*.

Deep to the cremaster muscle, we find two more sheaths: the superficial **tunica vaginalis** (*vagin-* = "sheath"), which is a serous membrane, and the deep **tunica albuginea** (al-byoo-JIN-ee-uh; "white membrane"), which is connective tissue that divides

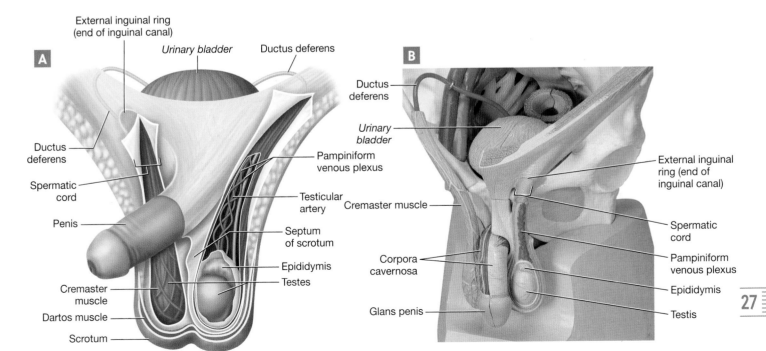

FIGURE **27.3** Structure of the scrotum and spermatic cord: (**A**) illustration; (**B**) anatomical model photo

the interior of each testis into lobules (Fig. 27.4). Each lobule contains a tightly coiled **seminiferous tubule** (sem-ih-NIF-er-uhs) where *spermatogenesis* (sper-mat-oh-JEN-ih-sis), or the formation of sperm cells, takes place.

The seminiferous tubules converge near the superior part of the testis to form a structure called the **rete testis** (REE-tee TES-tis; *ret-* = "net"). As you can see in Figures 27.4 and 27.5, the rete testis exits the testis to join the first segment of the duct system of the male reproductive tract, the **epididymis** (ep-ih-DID-ih-miss; "upon the testicle"). There are three portions of the epididymis: the initial *head*, the middle *body*, and the final *tail*. Immature sperm produced by the seminiferous tubules migrate through each of these regions of the epididymis to finish their maturation, after which they move to a long tube called the **ductus deferens** (DUHK-tuhs DEF-er-ahnz; *deferens* = "carrying off"). Notice in Figure 27.5 that the ductus deferens ascends through the pelvic cavity and curls posteriorly and superiorly around the urinary bladder. On the posterior surface of the urinary bladder, the ductus deferens widens to form its terminal portion, the *ampulla*.

The duct leaving the ampulla merges with a duct leaving a gland called the **seminal vesicle**. Together, the merged ducts form a short passage known as the **ejaculatory duct**. This duct passes through a gland on the inferior surface of the urinary bladder—the **prostate gland** (PRAH-stayt—be sure not to call it the "pros*t*rate"). Here, its contents drain into the first segment of the urethra, the **prostatic urethra**. Recall from the urinary unit that the prostatic urethra becomes the **membranous urethra** as it exits the prostate, and then becomes the **spongy urethra** as it enters the corpus spongiosum of the penis. The urethra terminates at the tip of the penis at the external urethral orifice.

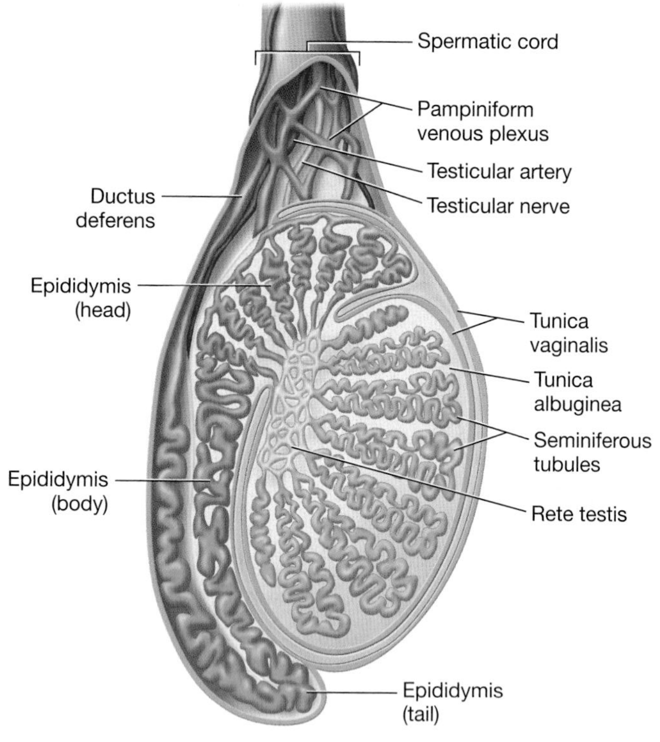

FIGURE **27.4** Midsagittal section through the testis.

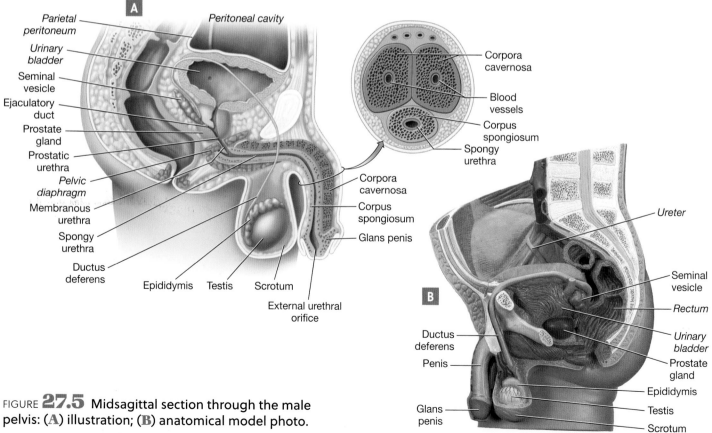

FIGURE **27.5** Midsagittal section through the male pelvis: (**A**) illustration; (**B**) anatomical model photo.

The male reproductive tract includes three exocrine glands: the previously mentioned prostate gland and seminal vesicles, and a set of two small glands located at the root of the penis called the **bulbourethral glands** (bul-boh-yoo-REETH-ruhl; Figs. 27.5 and 27.6). The seminal vesicles and the prostate gland together produce about 90% of the volume of **semen**, a fluid that contains chemicals to nourish and activate sperm. The bulbourethral glands release an alkaline fluid into the spongy urethra prior to the release of sperm during ejaculation.

The **penis** is the male copulatory organ. It is composed of three erectile bodies: the single **corpus spongiosum** (KOHR-puhs spun-jee-OH-sum; "spongy body") and the paired, dorsal **corpora cavernosa** (kohr-POHR-uh kă-ver-NOH-suh; "body with cavities"). The corpus spongiosum, which surrounds the spongy urethra, enlarges distally to form the **glans penis**. All three bodies consist of vascular spaces that fill with blood during an erection.

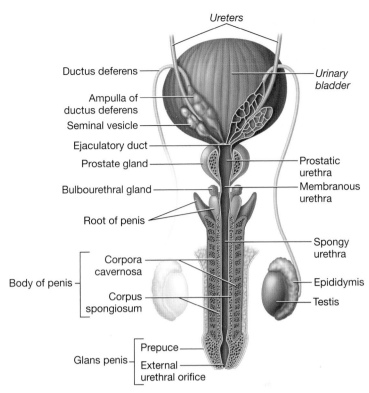

FIGURE **27.6** Posterior view of the male reproductive system with a frontal section of the penis.

 1

PROCEDURE
Model Inventory for the Male Reproductive System

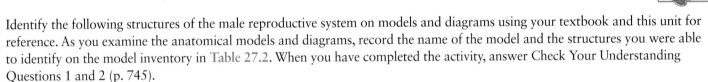

Identify the following structures of the male reproductive system on models and diagrams using your textbook and this unit for reference. As you examine the anatomical models and diagrams, record the name of the model and the structures you were able to identify on the model inventory in Table 27.2. When you have completed the activity, answer Check Your Understanding Questions 1 and 2 (p. 745).

1. Scrotum
2. Cremaster muscle
3. Spermatic cord
   a. Testicular artery
   b. Pampiniform venous plexus
   c. Inguinal canal
   d. External inguinal ring
4. Testes
   a. Tunica vaginalis
   b. Tunica albuginea
   c. Seminiferous tubules
   d. Rete testis
5. Epididymis (head, body, and tail)
6. Ductus deferens

7. Seminal vesicle
8. Ejaculatory duct
9. Prostate gland
10. Urethra
    a. Prostatic urethra
    b. Membranous urethra
    c. Spongy urethra
    d. External urethral orifice
11. Bulbourethral glands
12. Penis
    a. Corpus spongiosum
       (1) Glans penis
    b. Corpora cavernosa

27

TABLE **27.2** Model Inventory for the Male Reproductive System

Model/Diagram	Structures Identified

EXERCISE
27-2

MATERIALS

☐ Anatomical models and diagrams:
  ▪ female reproductive system
  ▪ human torso

Female Reproductive Anatomy

The female reproductive organs are located in the pelvic cavity, with the exception of the almond-shaped **ovaries** (*ova-* = "egg"), which are found in the peritoneal cavity (Figs. 27.7 and 27.8). The ovaries are the female gonads, which produce **oocytes** (OH-oh-syt′z) that travel through the reproductive tract to be fertilized. Oocytes are located within **follicles,** which are small sacs in the ovary that sit in the outer region of the ovary (known as the **ovarian cortex**). The inner region of the ovary, where we primarily find blood vessels, is the *ovarian medulla.*

Each ovary is held in place by several ligaments, including the **ovarian ligament,** which attaches the ovary to the uterus; a sheet of connective tissue called the **broad ligament,** which anchors it to the lateral pelvic wall (the part of the broad ligament attached to the ovary is called the *mesovarium*); and the **suspensory ligament,** which attaches the ovary to the posterolateral pelvic wall. Notice in Figure 27.7 that the suspensory ligaments also carry with them the ovaries' blood supply.

The duct system of the female reproductive system begins with the **uterine tube.** The uterine tube is not directly connected to the ovary. For this reason, when an oocyte is released from the ovary, it is released into the pelvic cavity and the uterine tube must "catch" it and bring it into the tube. This is accomplished by fingerlike extensions of the tube called **fimbriae** (FIM-bree-ay; "fringe") that wrap around the ovary. The next region of the uterine tube is the wide **infundibulum** ("funnel"), followed by the **ampulla** (am-PULL-uh), and finally the **isthmus** (ISS-th-muhs; "narrow passage"), where it joins the uterus. Like the ovaries, the uterine tubes are anchored by the broad ligament (a segment called the *mesosalpinx*).

The uterine tubes join the superolateral portion of the **uterus** (YOO-ter-uhs; "womb"), which is the organ in which a fertilized ovum implants, and in which a conceptus develops. As you can see in Figure 27.8, the uterus is situated posterior to the urinary bladder and anterior to the rectum. It is held in place by several ligaments: the broad ligament anchors it to the anterior and lateral pelvis (a part called the *mesometrium*); the **round ligaments** anchor it to the anterior abdominal wall (visible in Figs. 27.7 and 27.8B); and the **uterosacral ligaments** (yoo-ter-oh-SAY-kruhl) anchor it posteriorly to the sacrum.

The uterus has three regions: the dome-shaped **fundus,** the central **body,** and the narrow **cervix** (*cerv-* = "neck"). The opening of the cervix is known as the **cervical os.** The uterine wall is quite thick, and its thickness changes as it progresses through the 28-day uterine cycle. There are three layers to the uterine wall: the inner epithelial and connective tissue lining called the **endometrium** (in-doh-MEE-tree-um; *endo-* = "within;" *metr-* = "uterus"), in which a fertilized ovum implants; the middle, muscular **myometrium** (my-oh-MEE-tree-um; *myo-* = "muscle"), composed of smooth muscle tissue; and the outermost **perimetrium** (pehr-ee-MEE-tree-um; *peri-* = "around"), which is composed of a serous membrane on the posterior uterus and connective tissue on the anterior uterus.

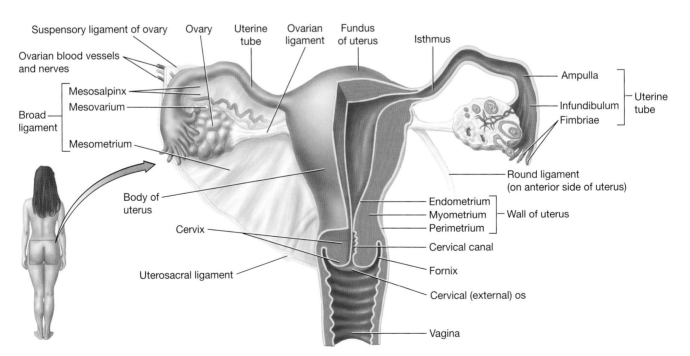

FIGURE **27.7** Posterior view of the female reproductive organs in a partial frontal section.

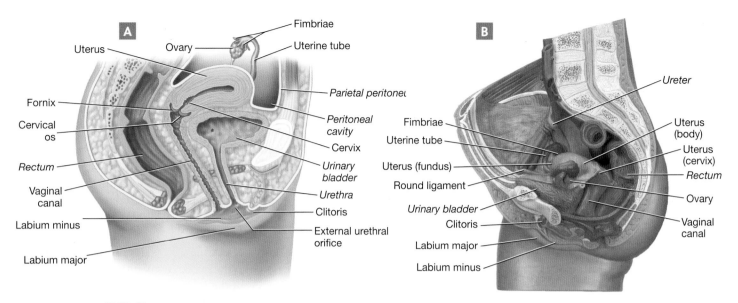

FIGURE **27.8** Midsagittal section of the female pelvis: (**A**) illustration; (**B**) anatomical model photo.

The **vagina** is a muscular passage about 8–10 cm (3.1–3.9 in.) long that extends inferiorly from the cervical os and terminates at the **vaginal orifice**. The superior end of the vagina forms a recess around the cervical os called the **fornix**. Note that the vagina is entirely internal, although it is frequently and incorrectly referred to as the female's external genitalia. Flanking the vaginal orifice are the **greater vestibular glands**, which secrete mucus to lubricate the vaginal canal during coitus (Fig. 27.9).

The external genitalia of the female are collectively called the **vulva** (Fig. 27.9), although it is quite often incorrectly called the vagina. It begins with the **mons pubis** (MAHNS PYOO-biss), the rounded area over the pubic symphysis that is covered in pubic hair after puberty. Posterior to the mons pubis are the **labia majora** and **labia minora** (LAY-bee-ah; *labi-* = "lip;" singular: labium major and minus, respectively). The labia majora are outer fatty skin folds that are analogous to the scrotum in the male; the thinner labia minora are folds of skin that enclose an area called the **vestibule**. Within the vestibule, we find the **external urethral orifice**, the vaginal orifice, and the paraurethral glands. Anterior to the urethral orifice is the **clitoris** (KLIT-uhr-iss), which is composed of erectile tissue.

The **mammary glands** are not true reproductive organs—indeed, they are modified sweat glands and part of the integumentary system—but do have an associated reproductive function in milk production (Fig. 27.10; note that this figure shows a lactating mammary gland). Mammary glands are present in both males and females, but their anatomy is most appropriately discussed with female anatomy. Internally, mammary glands consist of 15–25 **lobes**, each of which has smaller **lobules** that contain milk-producing **alveoli**. Milk leaves the alveoli through **lactiferous ducts**, which join to form storage areas called **lactiferous sinuses**. Milk leaves through the **nipple**, which is surrounded by a darkly pigmented area called the **areola** (aehr-ee-OH-lah).

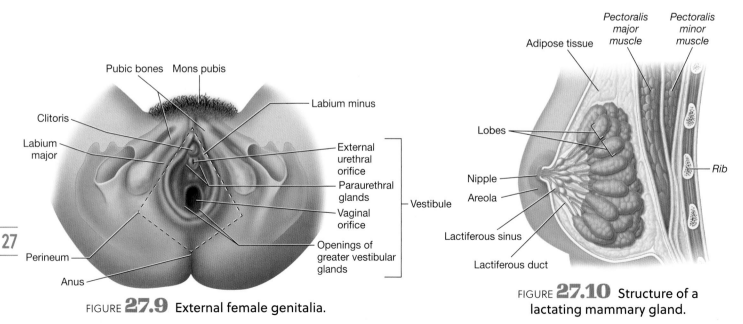

FIGURE **27.9** External female genitalia.

FIGURE **27.10** Structure of a lactating mammary gland.

Model Inventory for the Female Reproductive System

Identify the following structures of the female reproductive system on models and diagrams, using your textbook and this unit for reference. As you examine the anatomical models and diagrams, record the name of the model and the structures you were able to identify on the model inventory in Table 27.3. After you have completed the activity, answer Check Your Understanding Questions 3 and 4 (pp. 745–746).

1. Ovary
   a. Ovarian follicles
   b. Ovarian cortex
   c. Ovarian medulla
   d. Ovarian ligament
   e. Broad ligament
   f. Suspensory ligament
2. Uterine tube
   a. Fimbriae
   b. Infundibulum
   c. Ampulla
   d. Isthmus

3. Uterus
   a. Round ligaments
   b. Uterosacral ligaments
   c. Fundus
   d. Body
   e. Cervix
      (1) Cervical os
   f. Layers
      (1) Endometrium
      (2) Myometrium
      (3) Perimetrium
4. Vagina
   a. Fornix
   b. Greater vestibular glands

5. Vulva
   a. Mons pubis
   b. Labia majora
   c. Labia minora
      (1) Vestibule
      (2) External urethral orifice
      (3) Vaginal orifice
   d. Clitoris
6. Mammary glands
   a. Lobe
   b. Lactiferous duct
   c. Lactiferous sinus
   d. Nipple
   e. Areola

TABLE **27.3** Model Inventory for the Female Reproductive System

Model/Diagram	Structures Identified

27

MATERIALS

☐ Anatomical models and diagrams:
  ▪ meiosis
  ▪ mitosis
☐ Pop-bead chromosomes

Meiosis

Human somatic cells with a nucleus have 23 paired chromosomes for a total of 46. Such cells are called **diploid** (DIP-loyd; *diplo-* = "double") because the chromosomes are paired—one set of 23 comes from the mother, and the other set of 23 comes from the father. Each member of a maternal and paternal chromosome set houses the same genes; for this reason, we call the pairs **homologous chromosomes** (huh-MAH-luh-guhs; *homo-* = "same"; Fig. 27.11A). Note, however, that the matching genes aren't necessarily identical. Many genes have different variants, or **alleles** (uh-LEELZ; *alle-* = "other"). For example, if we consider the gene for blood type, the maternal chromosome may have the allele for blood type A, and the paternal chromosome may have the allele for blood type B.

As you may recall from Unit 4 (p. 79), somatic cells divide by a process called **mitosis** (my-TOH-sis). During mitosis, a diploid "mother" cell replicates its 23 pairs of homologous chromosomes. This results in a cell with two identical copies of each of its chromosomes. A chromosome and its identical "twin," known as **sister chromatids** (KROH-muh-tidz), are joined at the region of the chromatid called the *centromere* (Fig. 27.11B). After the DNA is replicated, the mother cell then divides its sister chromatids and organelles into two identical "daughter" cells (see Pre-Lab Exercise 27-4, p. 722, for a review of the stages of mitosis). Each diploid daughter cell is identical to the original mother cell.

Gametogenesis (oogenesis and spermatogenesis), however, must proceed differently for two reasons:

  ▪ Gametes must have genetic variations. If each gamete were to have the same genetic material, we all would be genetically identical to our siblings.

  ▪ Gametes must have only one set of chromosomes. During fertilization, a sperm and ovum fuse to produce a single-celled offspring called a **zygote** (ZY-goh't). If each gamete had two sets of chromosomes, the zygote would have four sets of chromosomes and be tetraploid (*tetra-* = "four").

For these reasons, gametes undergo a process known as **meiosis** (my-OH-sis), during which the cells proceed through two rounds of cell division.

Meiosis begins similarly to mitosis—with the replication of the cell's DNA, which yields 46 pairs of sister chromatids (Fig. 27.12). Also, like mitosis, cells then divide their DNA amongst daughter cells in four basic stages: prophase, metaphase, anaphase, and telophase. However, in meiosis, each of these phases occurs twice: **meiosis I** and **meiosis II**.

Meiosis I proceeds similarly to mitosis with some key differences. During prophase I, the DNA condenses into chromosomes. As the DNA condenses, we find one difference between mitosis and meiosis: The homologous chromosomes line up very tightly next to each other—a phenomenon called **synapsis** (sin-AP-sis; "connection"). Each synapse has two pairs of sister chromatids, so the entire structure is called a **tetrad**. Within a tetrad, the homologous chromosomes overlap at points called **chiasmata** (ky-az-MAH-tah; *chiasm-* = "x-shaped"), or crossover. Near the end of prophase I, alleles of sister chromatids break and DNA is exchanged between homologous chromosomes in a process called **crossing-over**.

The pairs of sister chromatids line up along the equator during metaphase I. We then move on to anaphase I, during which we find the second key difference between mitosis and meiosis: the way the genetic material is separated. Recall that during mitosis, spindle fibers attach to sister chromatids, separating them so each daughter cell has 46 unique chromosomes when mitosis completes. However, in meiosis, the spindle fibers separate the *homologous chromosome pairs*, while the sister chromatids stay together. This cuts the genetic material in half, resulting in **haploid** (HAP-loyd; *haplo-* = "single") cells. For this reason, we sometimes call meiosis I *reduction division*.

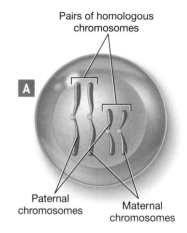

Pairs of homologous chromosomes

A

Paternal chromosomes

Maternal chromosomes

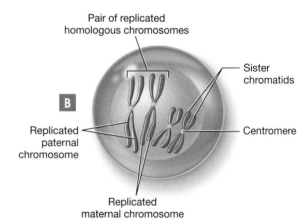

Pair of replicated homologous chromosomes

B

Replicated paternal chromosome

Replicated maternal chromosome

Sister chromatids

Centromere

FIGURE **27.11** Genetic material in a cell: **(A)** two pairs of homologous chromosomes; **(B)** two pairs of replicated homologous chromosomes.

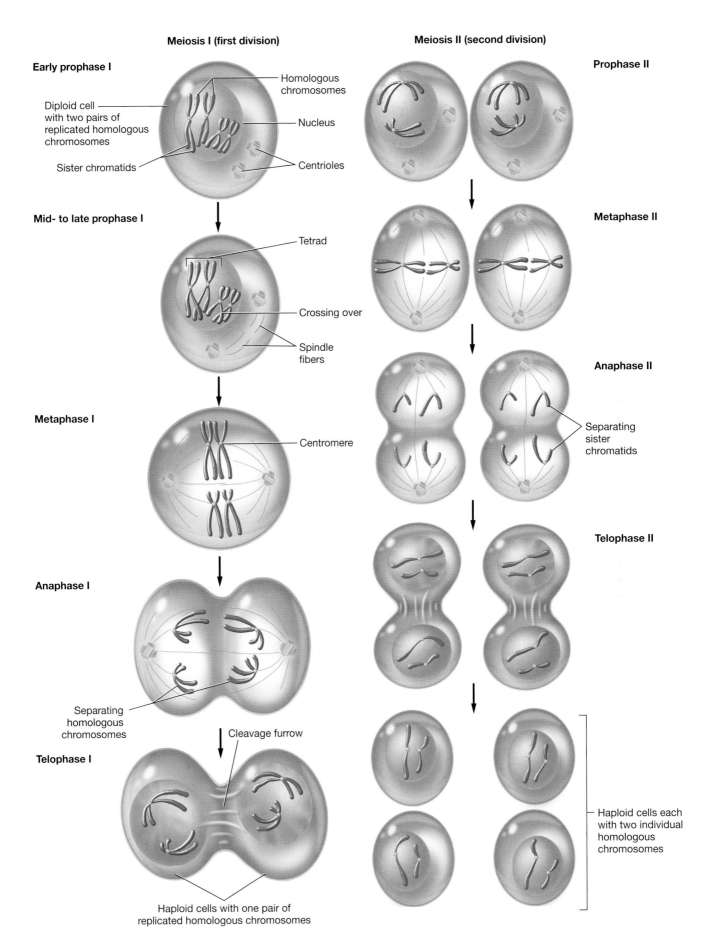

Meiosis I (first division)

Early prophase I

Diploid cell with two pairs of replicated homologous chromosomes

Sister chromatids

Homologous chromosomes

Nucleus

Centrioles

Mid- to late prophase I

Tetrad

Crossing over

Spindle fibers

Metaphase I

Centromere

Anaphase I

Separating homologous chromosomes

Telophase I

Cleavage furrow

Haploid cells with one pair of replicated homologous chromosomes

Meiosis II (second division)

Prophase II

Metaphase II

Anaphase II

Separating sister chromatids

Telophase II

Haploid cells each with two individual homologous chromosomes

FIGURE **27.12** Meiosis. (For simplicity, a cell with only two pairs of homologous chromosomes is shown.)

What's the Difference Between a Homologous Chromosome and a Sister Chromatid?

Why are the daughter cells at the end of meiosis I haploid? On a quick glance, they *seem* to have 46 chromosomes, just like the mother cell. This is where it's important to understand the difference between a homologous chromosome and a sister chromatid. A pair of homologous chromosomes consists of two unique pieces of genetic information: the maternal and paternal chromosomes. However, a pair of sister chromatids consists of one unique piece of genetic information—a single homologous chromosome and its identical twin.

You can imagine this with a simple analogy. You go to an art show with a friend. You buy two different paintings of a beach. The two paintings represent a pair of homologous chromosomes in a diploid cell, as they each contain similar scenes but with some differences. Your friend, on the other hand, picks out one painting of a beach. She likes it so much she wants to buy two: the original and a copy. Her two paintings represent a pair of sister chromatids—each painting contains the exact same scene.

So, a diploid mother cell has pairs of homologous chromosomes—or your two different beach scenes. But a cell at the end of meiosis I has pairs of sister chromatids—or your friend's two copies of the same painting. This makes the cell haploid rather than diploid, as it has half the amount of unique genetic material. (Note that this is somewhat simplified, as crossing over makes sure the sister chromatids aren't completely identical at the end of meiosis I.)

When the pairs of sister chromatids arrive at opposite poles of the cell, telophase I and cytokinesis occur, splitting the cell into two new haploid cells. Each haploid cell has 23 copied homologous chromosomes.

Meiosis II again proceeds similarly to the four stages of mitosis. However, importantly, the DNA doesn't replicate before meiosis II, so the cell starts with its 23 copied homologous chromosomes. Prophase II and metaphase II occur in the same way as during meiosis I—the chromosomes condense and line up along the cell's equator. During anaphase II, spindle fibers separate the sister chromatids of each homologous chromosome. The resulting haploid cells at the end of telophase II have only one copy of each chromatid. In this way, one diploid mother cell can divide into four genetically distinct haploid daughter cells.

---

1 PROCEDURE
Modeling Meiosis

In the following procedure, you will model meiosis with either a set of cell meiosis models or with pop-bead chromosomes. When you have completed the activity, answer Check Your Understanding Question 5 (p. 746).

1. Obtain a set of meiosis and mitosis models.

2. Arrange the mitosis models in the correct order.

3. Now, arrange the meiosis models in the correct order.

4. Compare the models of the two processes. In the space provided, list all differences you can see between meiosis and mitosis.

MATERIALS

☐ Slides:
  ▪ testis
  ▪ sperm
  ▪ epididymis
  ▪ ovary
☐ Light microscope
☐ Colored pencils

Histology of the Reproductive System

Gametogenesis is the process of producing sperm cells by the testes (*spermatogenesis*) and oocytes by the ovaries (*oogenesis*). **Spermatogenesis**, shown in Figure 27.13, begins with stem cells called **spermatogonia** (sper-mat-oh-GOH-nee-ah), which are located at the outer edge of the seminiferous tubules along the basement membrane. Before puberty, these cells undergo repeated rounds of mitosis to increase their numbers. As puberty begins, some spermatogonia divide into two different cells: one cell that remains in the basement membrane as a spermatogonium and another cell that becomes a diploid **primary spermatocyte**. The primary spermatocyte then undergoes meiosis I and divides into two haploid **secondary spermatocytes** that migrate closer to the lumen of the tubule. The two secondary spermatocytes undergo meiosis II and give rise to four haploid **spermatids**.

Note in Figure 27.14 that most of the stages of spermatogenesis are identifiable on a microscope slide of the seminiferous tubules. On the inner edge of the tubule near the lumen are small, round cells with little cytoplasm. These are the spermatozoa and spermatids. As we move to deeper layers of the tubule wall, we can see primary spermatocytes, and, on the outer edge, we can see the cuboidal spermatogonia. In between the tubules are small clusters of cells called **interstitial cells**. These cells make **testosterone**, a hormone required for spermatogenesis to take place. Note that secondary spermatocytes are not visible in Figure 27.14.

Spermatids then move to the epididymis to mature into functional gametes by a process known as **spermiogenesis** (Fig. 27.15). Notice that the mucosal lining of the epididymis is pseudostratified columnar epithelium with long projections called **stereocilia** (stehr-ee-oh-SILL-ee-uh). These projections are nonmotile microvilli that help the sperm cells to complete spermiogenesis, absorb excess fluid, and pass nutrients to the developing cells. Notice also the smooth muscle cells lining the outside of the epididymis tubule, which propel the sperm cells along as they mature. By the time the cells reach the end of the epididymis, they are mature sperm cells (or spermatozoa) that contain three parts: the **head**, in which the DNA resides; the **midpiece**, which contains an axoneme and mitochondria; and the **flagellum** (Fig. 27.16).

Like spermatogenesis, **oogenesis** (oh-oh-JEN-ih-sis) proceeds through meiosis to yield a haploid gamete, the **ovum** (Fig. 27.17). But the two processes differ in some notable ways:

■ **The number of oocytes is determined before birth.** During the fetal period, stem cells called **oogonia** (oh-oh-GOHN-ee-uh)

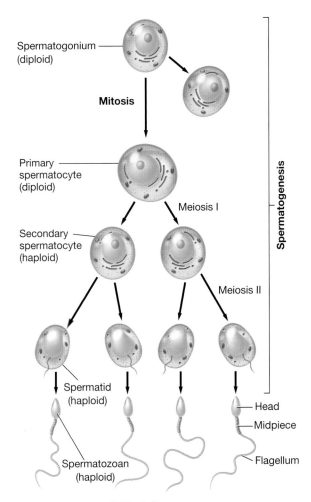

FIGURE **27.13** The process of spermatogenesis.

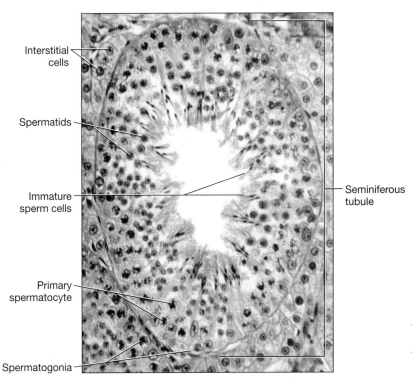

FIGURE **27.14** Microanatomy of the seminiferous tubules, photomicrograph.

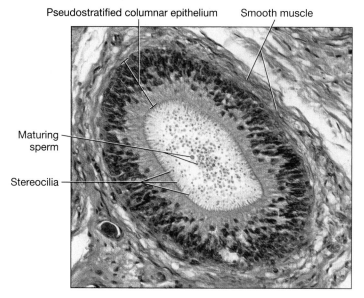

Pseudostratified columnar epithelium   Smooth muscle

Maturing sperm

Stereocilia

FIGURE **27.15** Microanatomy of the epididymis, photomicrograph.

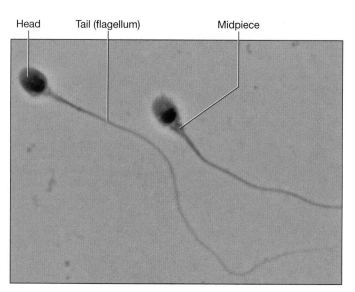

Head   Tail (flagellum)   Midpiece

FIGURE **27.16** Mature sperm cells.

undergo mitosis, increasing their numbers to between five and seven million in each ovary. This is the total number of oogonia a woman will ever produce. Oogonia and, later, primary oocytes degenerate during the fetal period and childhood; and by the time a girl reaches puberty, between 80,000 and 400,000 primary oocytes remain in each ovary. This is in sharp contrast to spermatogenesis, which begins at puberty and continues throughout a male's lifetime.

■ **Meiosis I begins during the fetal period but is arrested.** Still during the fetal period, an oogonium becomes encased in a ring of cells known as a **primordial follicle**, then enlarges and becomes a **primary oocyte** (see the ovary in Fig. 27.18). The primary oocytes begin prophase I but are arrested at this stage. Meiosis I does not resume until puberty.

■ **The first meiotic division results in one secondary oocyte and one polar body.** During childhood, some primordial follicles enlarge and begin developing into **primary follicles**. At puberty, rising levels of hormones, such as **estrogens**, trigger the beginning of the ovarian cycle, during which some primary follicles enlarge to become **secondary follicles**. As the cycle progresses, estrogens and follicle-stimulating hormone (FSH) usually trigger only one of the secondary follicles to continue growing. When the secondary follicle develops a large, fluid-filled space called the **antrum**, it's called a **vesicular follicle**. Under the influence of luteinizing hormone (LH), the primary oocyte then completes meiosis I to produce a **secondary oocyte** and a small bundle of nuclear material called a **polar body**.

Oogonium (diploid)

Mitosis

Primary oocyte (diploid)

Meiosis I

Secondary oocyte (haploid), ovulated

Polar body

Sperm contacts secondary oocyte

Meiosis II

Polar bodies degenerate

Fertilization with male gamete induces meiosis II to form an ovum and second polar body

FIGURE **27.17** The process of oogenesis.

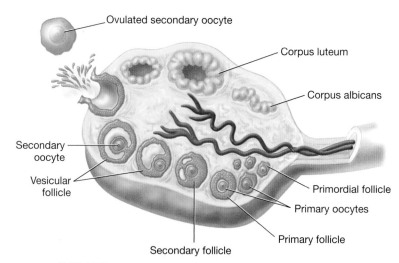

Ovulated secondary oocyte

Corpus luteum

Corpus albicans

Secondary oocyte

Vesicular follicle

Primordial follicle

Primary oocytes

Primary follicle

Secondary follicle

FIGURE **27.18** Anatomy of the ovary and ovarian follicles.

734 Exploring Anatomy and Physiology in the Laboratory

27

The formation of a polar body allows the oocyte to conserve cytoplasm, which will have to sustain the newly formed conceptus for several days if fertilization occurs.

- **The secondary oocyte undergoes meiosis II only if fertilization takes place.** Rising levels of LH, called the *LH surge*, stimulate the secondary oocyte to begin meiosis II, but the process is arrested in metaphase II. The LH surge also stimulates rupture of the vesicular follicle and release of the secondary oocyte during ovulation. But the secondary oocyte only completes meiosis to form an ovum and a second polar body if fertilization occurs. If fertilization doesn't occur, the secondary oocyte degenerates.

You can easily see some of the different follicles on a slide of the ovary (Fig. 27.19). In addition, you can determine the stage of the oocyte by looking at the surrounding follicle: Primary oocytes are encased in primordial and primary follicles; secondary oocytes are encased in secondary and vesicular follicles. Note that we cannot see oogonia in the ovary because these cells begin meiosis I and become primary oocytes during the fetal period.

When the vesicular follicle ruptures, it becomes a temporary endocrine gland called a **corpus luteum** (KOHR-puhs LOO-tee-um; "yellow body;" Fig. 27.20). The corpus luteum secretes hormones, mostly **progesterone** as well as some estrogen, that maintain the endometrial lining in case fertilization takes place. When the corpus luteum stops secreting hormones, it is degraded by macrophages, leaving behind a white scar known as the **corpus albicans** ("white body").

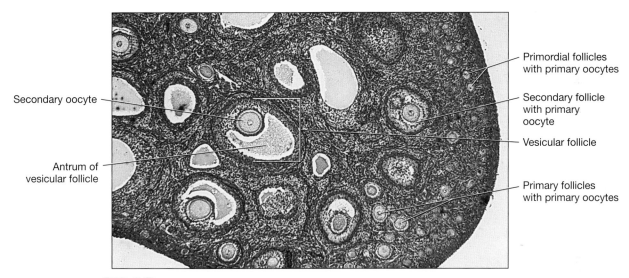

Secondary oocyte

Antrum of vesicular follicle

Primordial follicles with primary oocytes

Secondary follicle with primary oocyte

Vesicular follicle

Primary follicles with primary oocytes

FIGURE **27.19** Microanatomy of the ovary with ovarian follicles, photomicrograph.

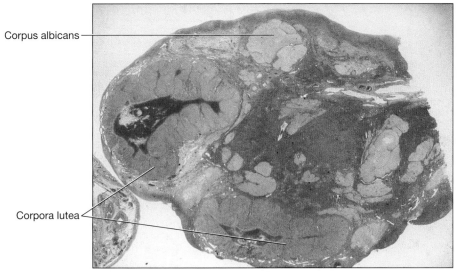

Corpus albicans

Corpora lutea

FIGURE **27.20** Microanatomy of the ovary with corpus luteum and corpus albicans, photomicrograph.

1 PROCEDURE

Examining Male Reproductive Structures with Microscopy

In this procedure, you will examine prepared slides of the testes, epididymis, and a sperm smear. You will want to examine all three slides on high power, and you may wish to examine the sperm smear with an oil-immersion lens. Because sperm cells are so small, the slide will likely have a thread or some other marker to help you find them. As you examine the slides, use colored pencils to draw what you see; label your drawings with the terms indicated. When you have completed the activity, answer Check Your Understanding Question 6 (p. 746).

1 Testes
- Seminiferous tubule
- Spermatogonia
- Primary spermatocytes
- Spermatids
- Interstitial cells

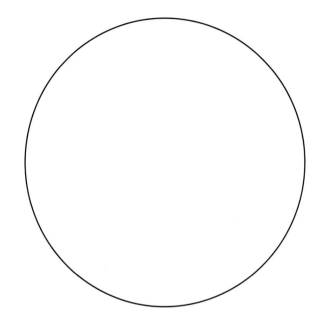

2 Epididymis
- Maturing sperm
- Stereocilia
- Pseudostratified columnar epithelium
- Smooth muscle

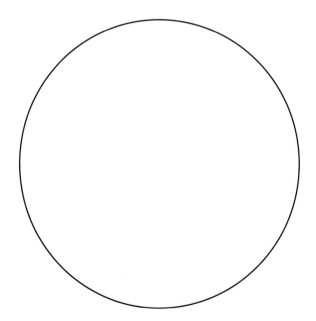

27

3 Mature Sperm

- Head
- Midpiece
- Flagellum

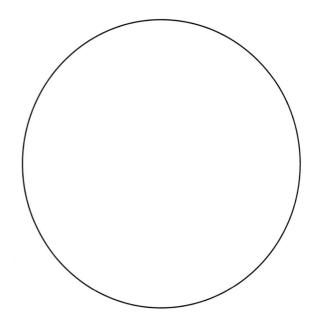

2 **PROCEDURE**

Examining the Ovary with Microscopy

Obtain a prepared slide of an ovary. Use your colored pencils to draw what you see; label your drawing with the following terms. You will have the best results if you examine the slide on low power. Please keep in mind that you may have to examine multiple slides to see all the follicular stages. When you have completed the activity, answer Check Your Understanding Question 7 (p. 746).

1 Ovary

- Primordial follicle
- Primary follicle
  - Primary oocyte
- Secondary follicle
- Vesicular follicle
  - Secondary oocyte
  - Antrum
- Corpus luteum or corpus albicans

In this procedure, you will be tracing the gametes from their production in the male and female gonads to the point at which they meet to form a zygote. This tracing involves the anatomy of the male and female reproductive systems as well as the steps of gametogenesis.

STEP 1: Male Gamete

Trace the male gamete from its earliest stage—the spermatogonium in the seminiferous tubule—through the stages of spermatogenesis to a mature sperm. Then trace the mature sperm cell through the male reproductive tract until it exits the body and enters the uterine tube of the female reproductive tract. Trace the pathway using Figure 27.21, and also write it in the space provided.

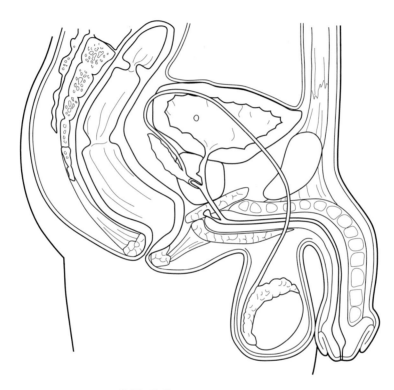

FIGURE **27.21** Male reproductive tract.

Start: Spermatogonium

End: Uterine Tube

STEP 2: Female Gamete

Trace the female gamete from its earliest stage, the oogonium in a primordial follicle, to the time at which it is ovulated and enters the uterine tube. Trace the pathway using Figure 27.22, and also write it in the space provided.

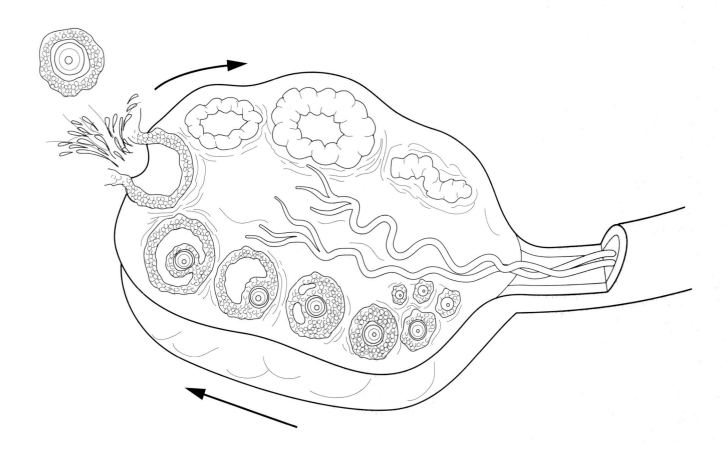

FIGURE **27.22** Ovary and ovarian follicles.

Start: Oogonium

End: Uterine Tube

27

Check Your Recall

1 Label the following structures on Figure 27.23.

- ❏ Cremaster muscle
- ❏ Ductus deferens
- ❏ Epididymis
- ❏ External inguinal ring
- ❏ Glans penis
- ❏ Pampiniform venous plexus
- ❏ Scrotum
- ❏ Spermatic cord

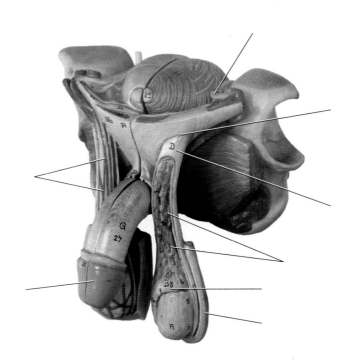

FIGURE **27.23** Male reproductive anatomy, anatomical model photo.

2 Spermatogenesis occurs in the
- a. prostate gland.
- b. spermatic cord.
- c. ejaculatory duct.
- d. seminiferous tubules.

3 About 90% of the volume of semen is produced by the
- a. prostate gland.
- b. bulbourethral glands.
- c. seminal vesicles.
- d. Both a and b are correct.
- e. Both a and c are correct.

4 **Label the following structures on** Figure 27.24.

❏ Corpora cavernosa
❏ Corpus spongiosum
❏ Ejaculatory duct

❏ External urethral orifice
❏ Membranous urethra
❏ Prostate gland

❏ Prostatic urethra
❏ Seminal vesicle
❏ Spongy urethra

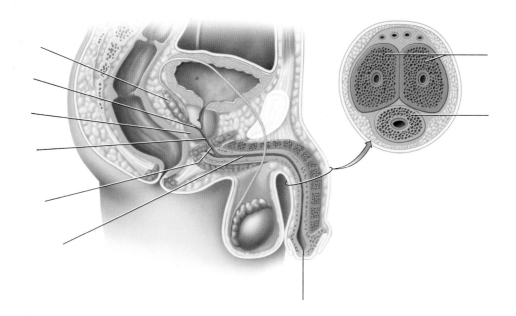

FIGURE **27.24** Midsagittal section through the male pelvis.

5 **Label the following structures on** Figure 27.25.

❏ Cervical os
❏ Clitoris
❏ External urethral orifice
❏ Fornix
❏ Fundus of uterus
❏ Labium major
❏ Labium minus
❏ Vaginal canal

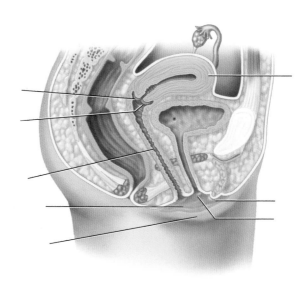

FIGURE **27.25** Midsagittal section through the female pelvis.

27

6 Label the following structures on Figure 27.26.

- ❏ Body of uterus
- ❏ Endometrium
- ❏ Fimbriae
- ❏ Myometrium
- ❏ Ovarian ligament
- ❏ Perimetrium
- ❏ Round ligament
- ❏ Uterine tube

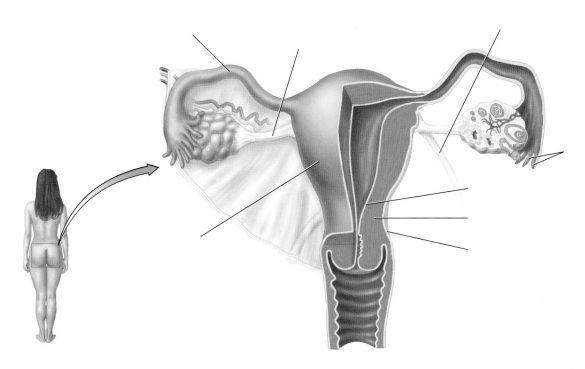

FIGURE **27.26** Posterior view of the female reproductive organs in a partial frontal section.

7 *True/False:* Mark the following statements as true (T) or false (F). If the statement is false, correct it to make it a true statement.

_____ a. Somatic cells have half the number of chromosomes compared to gametes.

_____ b. A haploid human cell has 23 chromosomes.

_____ c. A pair of sister chromatids consists of two identical copies of a single homologous chromosome.

_____ d. During anaphase I, sister chromatids are separated.

_____ e. Interstitial cells produce estrogens.

27

8 Spermatogenesis results in _____ functional gamete(s); oogenesis results in _____ functional gamete(s).

   a. 4; 4

   b. 4; 1

   c. 1; 4

   d. 1; 1

9 Why does meiosis differ from mitosis?

_____

_____

_____

_____

10 Label the following structures on Figure 27.27. In addition, on each diagram, fill in the blanks to indicate where mitosis, meiosis I, and meiosis II take place.

❑ Oogonium   ❑ Primary oocyte   ❑ Secondary spermatocyte

❑ Ovum   ❑ Primary spermatocyte   ❑ Spermatid

❑ Polar body   ❑ Secondary oocyte   ❑ Spermatogonium

                                                        ❑ Spermatozoan

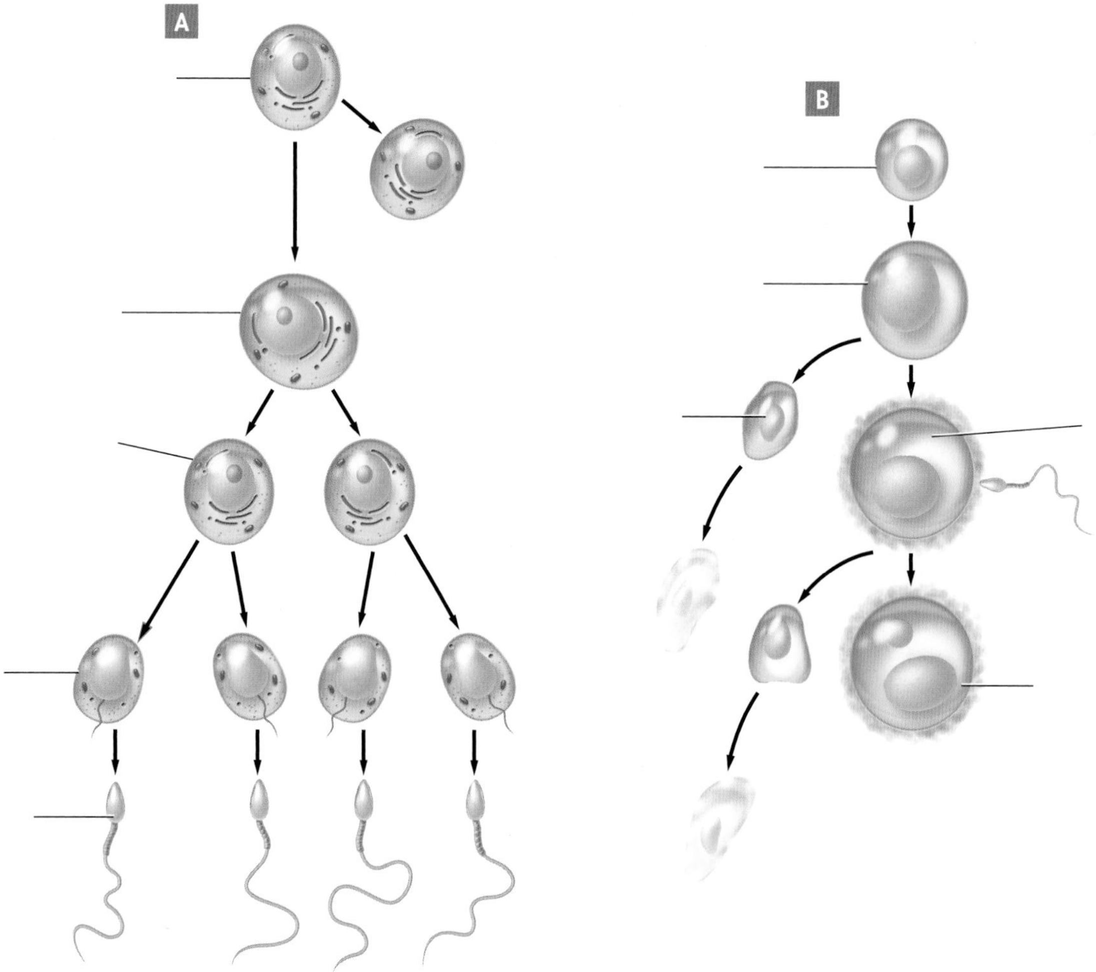

FIGURE **27.27** Gametogenesis: (**A**) spermatogenesis; (**B**) oogenesis.

Check Your Understanding

Critical Thinking and Application Questions

1 During a vasectomy, the ductus deferens is sectioned and cauterized, which renders a male infertile. Fertility can generally be restored by surgically reuniting the severed ends.

   a Why does a vasectomy render a male infertile?

   b Why is this a reversible procedure?

2 Atticus is visiting the clinic for evaluation of a low sperm count. He explains to the nurse practitioner that he is an athlete, and he spends time after each workout in a hot tub to relax his muscles. The nurse practitioner suspects this might be the cause of his low sperm count. Explain.

3 Circe has a diagnosis of *endometriosis*, a condition in which endometrial tissue grows in places other than the uterine lining. She has been unable to get pregnant for two years, despite fertility treatments. On ultrasound, it is discovered that endometrial tissue is growing in both of Circe's uterine tubes. How does this explain her infertility?

4 Frances is in the hospital delivering her first child. The physician has told her that labor is progressing slowly because her uterus isn't contracting properly. What part of her uterus, specifically, is not contracting? Explain.

5 The condition *Down syndrome* is a genetic condition of chromosome 21. It most commonly results from an individual having three homologous twenty-first chromosomes, for a total of 47 in somatic cells. Does the condition result from a problem during mitosis, meiosis I, or meiosis II? Explain.

6 Do spermatogenesis and oogenesis result in the same number of viable cells when the processes complete? Why or why not?

7 Chelsea has been researching fertility treatments on the internet. She wonders if she could take a medication that would increase the number of oogonia in her ovaries. Is this possible? Why or why not?

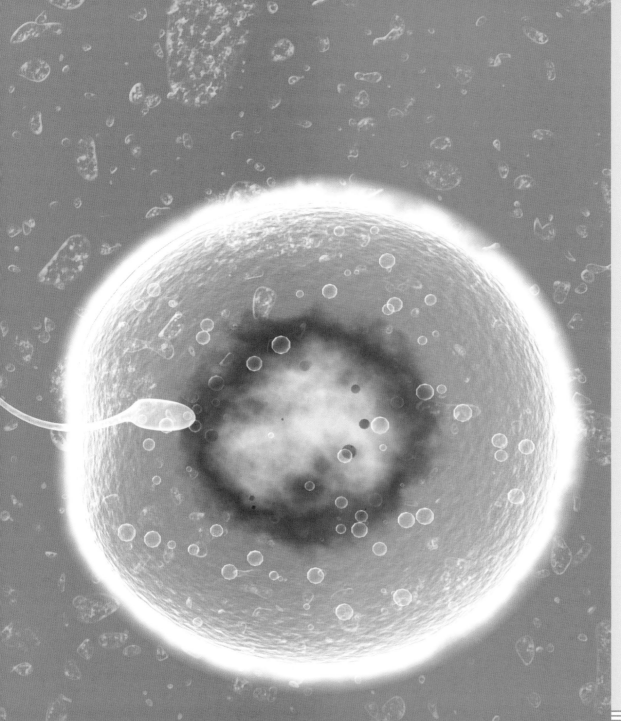

Human Development and Heredity

When you have completed this unit, you should be able to:

1 Trace a developing zygote (or conceptus) from fertilization to implantation.

2 Describe and identify structures and membranes associated with the fetus.

3 Describe and identify the stages of development and structures of the fetal circulation.

4 Define the terms phenotype and genotype, and perform analyses to determine a subject's phenotype and genotype.

5 Describe dominant, recessive, and sex-linked traits, and use Punnett squares to determine the probability of passing a trait to offspring.

PRE-LAB EXERCISES

Complete the following exercises prior to coming to lab, using your lab manual and textbook for reference.

PRE-LAB

28-1 Key Terms

You should be familiar with the following terms before coming to lab.

Term	Definition

Development

Fertilization _____

Zygote _____

Blastocyst _____

Embryo _____

Fetus _____

Fetal Structures

Chorion _____

Amnion _____

Placenta _____

Inheritance

Allele _____

Phenotype _____

Genotype _____

28

Autosomal dominant _____

_____

Autosomal recessive _____

_____

Sex-linked trait _____

_____

PRE-LAB

28-2 Fetal Membranes

Color the fetal membranes and structures in Figure 28.1, and label them with the terms from Exercise 28-2 (p. 754). Use Exercise 28-2 and your text for reference.

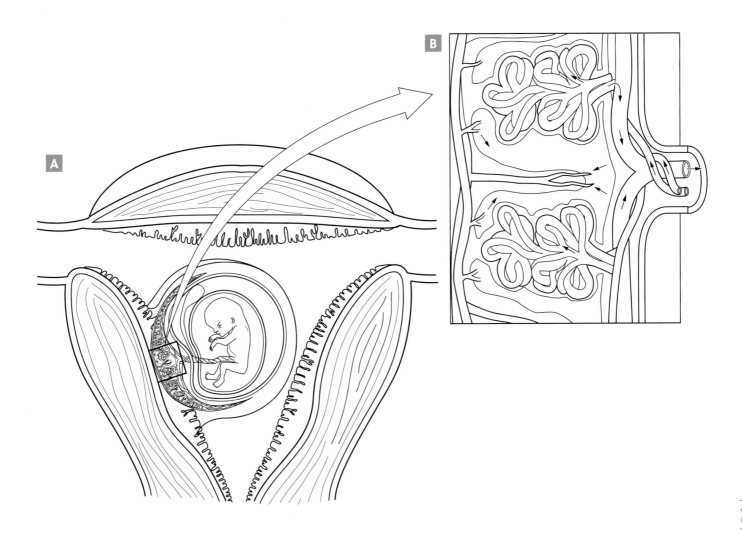

FIGURE **28.1** Embryo in membranes: (**A**) embryo in uterus; (**B**) chorionic villi.

Color the structures of the fetal cardiovascular system in Figure 28.2, and label them with the terms from Exercise 28-2 (p. 754). Use Exercise 28-2 and your text for reference.

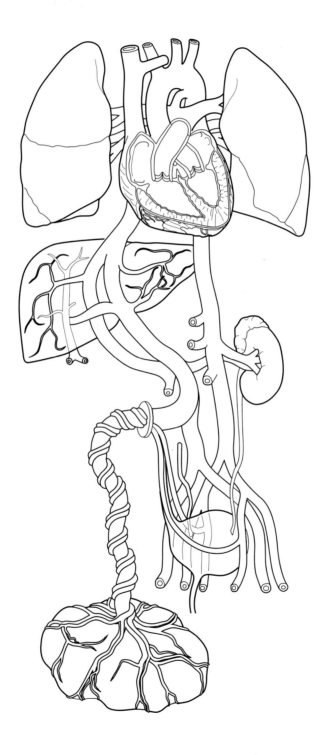

FIGURE **28.2** Fetal cardiovascular anatomy.

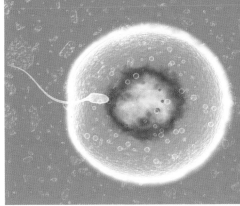

Sperm fertilizing an ovum, SEM.

When two gametes—a sperm cell from a male and an ovum from a female—unite in a process known as **fertilization**, a diploid *zygote* (ZY-goh't) forms and the incredible process of development begins. In this unit, we examine human development and the unique anatomy and structures of the developing human. We conclude by exploring the basics of **heredity**—the passing of traits from parents to offspring.

EXERCISE 28-1

MATERIALS

None required

Fertilization and Implantation

The first event in human development is fertilization, which generally takes place in the ampulla of the uterine tube when sperm cells encounter a secondary oocyte. Fertilization begins with a process called the **acrosomal reaction** (ak-roh-ZOH-muhl), in which the acrosomes in the heads of the sperm release digestive enzymes by exocytosis. The acrosomal enzymes digest the *corona radiata* and the *zona pellucida*, which are the secondary oocyte's outer coverings.

When the zona pellucida has been cleared, the head and midpiece of a single sperm enter the oocyte. Note that although mitochondria from the sperm cell (in the midpiece) enter the secondary oocyte, they are destroyed. For this reason, offspring have only maternal mitochondria.

As the sperm cell enters, the secondary oocyte completes meiosis II, yielding an ovum and a second polar body. The sperm and ovum nuclei swell to become **pronuclei**, and their nuclear membranes rupture. The two sets of exposed chromosomes then fuse to form a single-celled structure called a **zygote** (Fig. 28.3).

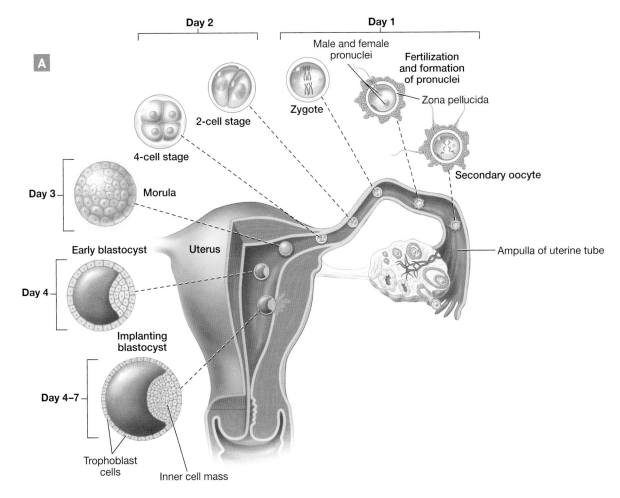

FIGURE **28.3** **Stages of development (fertilization through implantation): (A) illustration** (*continues*)

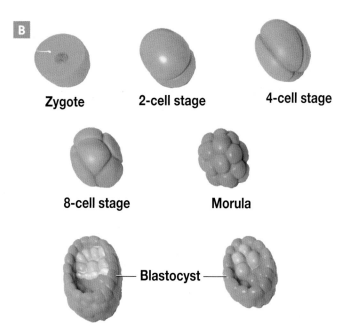

Zygote

2-cell stage

4-cell stage

8-cell stage

Morula

— Blastocyst —

Early implanting blastocyst

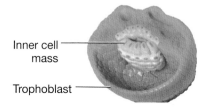

Inner cell
mass

Trophoblast

Late implanting blastocyst

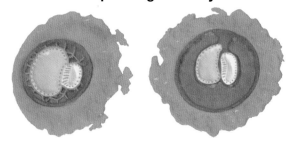

Embryo (4 weeks)   **Embryo (8 weeks)**

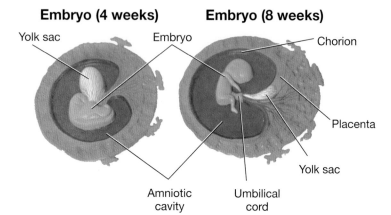

Yolk sac   Embryo   Chorion

Placenta

Yolk sac

Amniotic   Umbilical
cavity   cord

FIGURE **28.3** Stages of development (fertilization through implantation) *(cont.)*: (**B**) anatomical model photos.

The zygote, also called a **conceptus** (kuhn-SEPT-uhs), undergoes multiple changes during the period of time known as **gestation**, the 40-week period extending from the mother's last menstrual period to birth. The changes that the conceptus undergoes include an increase in cell number, cellular differentiation, and the development of organ systems.

The increase in cell number begins about 30 hours after fertilization, as the zygote travels down the uterine tube. At this time, a process called **cleavage** occurs, in which the cell undergoes a series of mitotic divisions to produce two cells, then four, and so on. As cleavage begins, the conceptus starts to migrate from the ampulla of the uterine tube, through the isthmus to the uterus. At about day 3, the conceptus reaches the uterus as a 16-cell ball called a **morula** (MOHR-yoo-luh; "little mulberry"). The morula floats around the uterus for another 2 to 3 days and continues to divide until it becomes a hollow sphere called a **blastocyst** (BLAST-oh-sist; *blast-* = "immature cell"). Notice in Figure 28.3 that the blastocyst has two populations of cells: the rounded **inner cell mass** (also called the *embryoblast*) and an outer layer of cells called the **trophoblast** (TROHF-oh-blast; *-troph* = "feed").

Around day 6, the blastocyst adheres to the endometrium and begins the process of **implantation**. The **implanting blastocyst** secretes digestive enzymes that catalyze reactions to eat away the endometrial lining, and the endometrium reacts to the injury by growing over and enclosing the blastocyst. Implantation is generally complete by the second week after fertilization, about the time a woman's menstrual period—the shedding of the inner portion of the endometrial lining—would begin if fertilization had not taken place.

28

Trace the events of development from fertilization to implantation. In your tracing, you will do two things: (1) describe the changes that the conceptus undergoes from the time that fertilization takes place until the time that it implants; and (2) trace the conceptus' location as these events occur. Trace the pathway using Figure 28.4, and also fill in the space provided. When you have completed the tracing, answer Check Your Understanding Question 1 (p. 767).

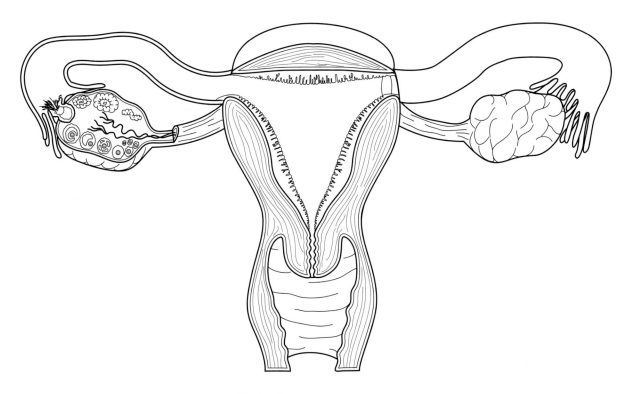

FIGURE **28.4** Female reproductive tract.

Start: Sperm and secondary oocyte meet in uterine tube ➔ _____ takes place ➔ secondary oocyte

undergoes _____ to form an _____ and a _____

_____ ➔ male and female _____ fuse to become a _____

_____ ➔ _____ cell stage ➔ _____ cell

stage ➔ _____ stage ➔ early _____ enters the _____

➔ _____ ➔ _____

_____ secretes _____ to catalyze reactions that eat away at the

_____ ➔ _____ response increases

blood flow to the _____ , which grows over the _____ ➔ **End:** Implanted

Blastocyst

MATERIALS

☐ Anatomical models and diagrams:
- sequence of embryonic development
- female reproductive system with fetus
- fetal circulation

Embryogenesis, Fetal Development, and Fetal Cardiovascular Anatomy

As the blastocyst implants, it begins undergoing a process known as **embryogenesis** (ihm-bree-oh-JEN-ih-sis) during which cellular differentiation takes place. As embryogenesis takes place, the inner cell mass differentiates into three primary tissue layers known as **germ layers**, from which all other tissues arise. The outermost germ layer is called **ectoderm** (*ecto-* = "outer"), the middle germ layer is called **mesoderm** (*meso-* = "middle"), and the innermost germ layer is called **endoderm**. These germ layers are formed by the end of the second week after fertilization, at which point the conceptus is considered an **embryo** (IHM-bree-oh).

The next six weeks of the embryonic period are marked by differentiation of the germ layers into rudimentary organ systems, formation of extraembryonic membranes, and the development of a structure called the *placenta* (Fig. 28.5). The first extraembryonic membrane to develop is the **yolk sac**, which serves as a source of cells for the digestive tract, the first blood cells and blood vessels, and *germ cells* (which are the precursors to gametes). Next, the innermost membrane, called the **amnion** (AM-nee-ahn), develops. The amnion completely surrounds the conceptus and suspends it in **amniotic fluid** within the **amniotic cavity**.

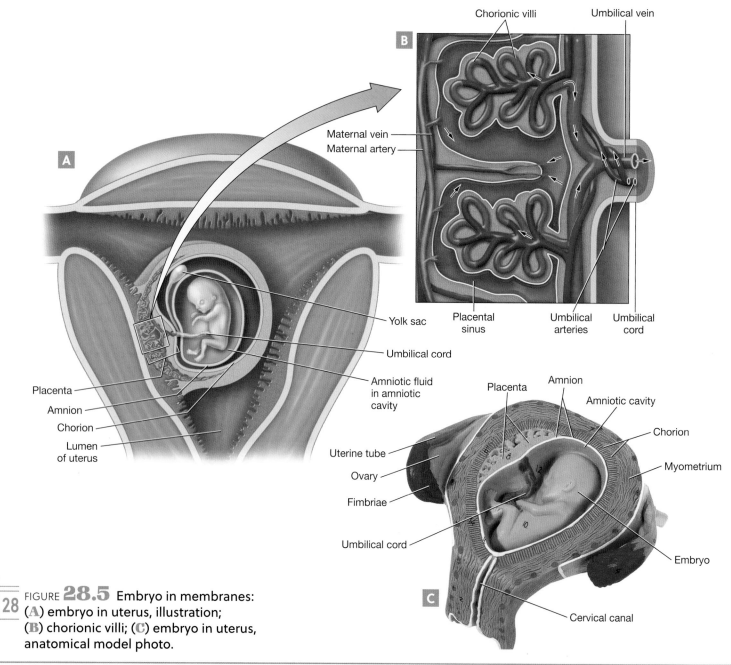

FIGURE **28.5** Embryo in membranes: (**A**) embryo in uterus, illustration; (**B**) chorionic villi; (**C**) embryo in uterus, anatomical model photo.

As the placenta and extraembryonic membranes form, the primitive organ systems develop. This process completes by the end of the eighth week after fertilization, at which point the conceptus is considered a **fetus**. For the duration of gestation, the organ systems become progressively more specialized and the fetus continues to grow and develop.

The **placenta** (plah-SIN-tuh) is the structure derived from embryonic and maternal tissues that provides oxygen and nutrients to the conceptus. It begins to form at day 11, when the trophoblast forms the outermost extraembryonic membrane, the **chorion** (KOHR-ee-ahn), the fetal portion of the placenta. As you can see in Figure 28.5B, the chorion develops elaborate projections called the **chorionic villi** (KOHR-ee-ahn-ik VILL-aye). The cells of the chorionic villi secrete enzymes that catalyze reactions to eat into uterine blood vessels. This creates the **placental sinus**, a space filled with maternal blood. Nutrients and oxygen delivered by *maternal arteries* diffuse from the placental sinuses to the chorionic villi and are delivered to the conceptus by the large **umbilical vein**. Wastes are drained from the conceptus via the paired **umbilical arteries**, which drain into the chorionic villi, diffuse into the placental sinuses, and finally back into the *maternal veins*. The umbilical arteries and vein travel to and from the conceptus through the **umbilical cord**.

The fetal cardiovascular system differs significantly from that of the neonate (Fig. 28.6). A fetus doesn't obtain oxygen directly from the air, but rather from blood delivered via the umbilical vein. Indeed, the fetal lungs are filled with amniotic fluid due to "practice" breathing movements that occur toward the end of gestation. For this reason, the amount of blood circulating within the fetal lungs is reduced to prevent pressure overload and divert blood to other parts of the body. This is accomplished by two vascular *shunts*:

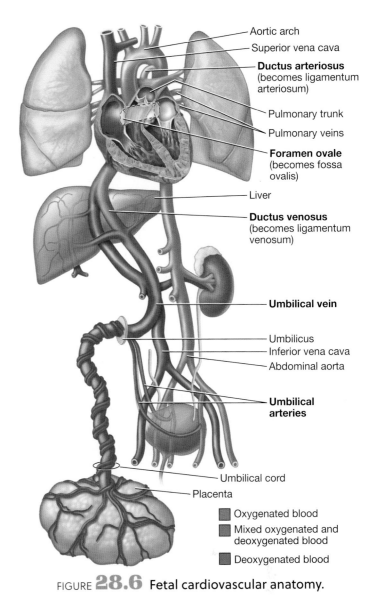

FIGURE **28.6** Fetal cardiovascular anatomy.

- **Foramen ovale.** The **foramen ovale** (oh-VAL-ay) is a hole in the interatrial septum that shunts blood from the right atrium to the left atrium. It allows blood to bypass the right ventricle and pulmonary circuit and go straight to the left heart and systemic circuit. The foramen ovale closes shortly after birth, leaving behind a dent in the interatrial septum called the *fossa ovalis*.

- **Ductus arteriosus.** The **ductus arteriosus** (ahr-teer-ee-OH-suhs) is a vascular bridge between the pulmonary trunk and the aorta. It is the second shunt that allows blood to bypass the pulmonary circuit. When the ductus arteriosus closes after birth, it leaves behind a remnant called the *ligamentum arteriosum*.

Bypassing the portal circulation in the liver is a vascular shut called the **ductus venosus** (veh-NOH-suhs). The umbilical vein delivers a small amount of blood to the portal circulation, but sends the majority of its oxygenated blood through the ductus venosus to the fetal inferior vena cava. This shunt closes about the time of birth and leaves behind a remnant called the *ligamentum venosum*.

Notice how the pattern of oxygenation differs in the conceptus versus the neonate. The umbilical vein delivers oxygenated blood to the inferior vena cava, but the blood doesn't remain fully oxygenated for long: It soon begins to mix with deoxygenated blood coming in from the inferior vena cava, and it mixes with more deoxygenated blood from the superior vena cava when it enters the right atrium. For this reason, the blood traveling through the systemic arterial circuit of the conceptus is never fully oxygenated and is represented as purple in Figure 28.6 instead of red.

Identify the following structures of development on models and diagrams, using your textbook and Exercises 28-1 (p. 751) and 28-2 for reference. As you examine the anatomical models and diagrams, record the name of the model and the structures you were able to identify on the model inventory in Table 28.1. When you have completed the activity, answer Check Your Understanding Questions 2 through 4 (p. 767).

1. Stages of development
   a. Zygote
   b. Morula
   c. Blastocyst
      (1) Inner cell mass (embryoblast)
      (2) Trophoblast
   d. Implanted blastocyst
   e. Embryo
   f. Fetus
2. Fetal membranes
   a. Yolk sac
   b. Amnion
      (1) Amniotic cavity

      (2) Amniotic fluid
   c. Chorion
      (1) Chorionic villi
3. Vascular structures
   a. Placenta
      (1) Placental sinus
      (2) Maternal arteries and veins
   b. Umbilical cord
      (1) Umbilical vein
      (2) Umbilical arteries
   c. Ductus venosus
   d. Foramen ovale
   e. Ductus arteriosus

TABLE **28.1** Model Inventory for the Stages of Development and Fetal Structures

Model/Diagram	Structures Identified

MATERIALS

- ❏ Well plate
- ❏ Simulated blood from: Ms. Rose, Ms. Magenta, Col. Lemon, Professor Purple, and Mr. Olive
- ❏ Antisera: anti-A, anti-B, and anti-Rh
- ❏ PTC tasting papers
- ❏ Ishihara chart for color blindness

Heredity

Heredity is defined as the passing of traits from parents to offspring. We refer to two properties of the cell when discussing traits:

1. **Phenotype** (FEE-noh-type; *pheno-* = "showing") is the physical expression of a specific trait, such as hair color or blood type. Traits such as "blonde hair," "brown eyes," and "type A blood" refer to an individual's phenotype.

2. **Genotype** (JEE-noh-type) is the genetic makeup of an organism, or what a cell contains genetically. When someone performs DNA analysis, he or she is examining the genotype. We have two versions of each of our genes: one from the maternal side and one from the paternal side. The varying versions of a gene are known as **alleles** (uh-LEELZ). The genotype is described using letters to stand for each of the alleles that are inherited. For example, the allele that codes for free earlobes is written as *E*, whereas the allele that codes for attached earlobes is written as *e*. A person who inherits the same allele from both parents is said to be **homozygous** (hoh-moh-ZY-guhs; *homo-* = "same;" e.g., the genotype *ee* is homozygous). A person who inherits different alleles from each parent is said to be **heterozygous** (het-er-oh-ZY-guhs; *hetero-* = "different;" e.g., the genotype *Ee* is heterozygous).

It is generally not possible to determine a person's precise genotype without doing DNA typing; however, if we know the phenotype, we can determine *possible* genotypes. Let's look at an example using blood groups:

- ■ From each parent, we can inherit one of the following ABO alleles:
  - ▪ A allele: codes for A antigens
  - ▪ B allele: codes for B antigens
  - ▪ O allele: codes for neither A nor B antigen (please keep in mind there is no "O" antigen)
- ■ From each parent, we can inherit one of the following Rh factor alleles:
  - ▪ + allele: codes for the Rh antigen
  - ▪ − allele: does not code for the Rh antigen

We can put this information into a table to determine which phenotypes accompany the possible genotypes. Fill in the remainder of Table 28.2, following the pattern from the first two examples.

Notice from this table that we need only one of each of the A, B, and + alleles to express that phenotype. For this reason, an individual with an AO+− genotype will have an A+ phenotype despite having only one A allele and one + allele.

TABLE **28.2** Phenotype and Genotype

Genotype(s)	Phenotype
AA++, AA+−, AO++, AO+−	A+
AA−−, AO−−	A−
BB++, BB+−, BO++, BO+−	
	B−
OO++, OO+−	
	O−
	AB+
AB−−	

Blood typing is a simple and quick way to determine a child's possible paternity. Following is an example:

- Child's phenotype: B+
- Mother's phenotype: O−
- Potential Father 1's phenotype: AB+
- Potential Father 2's phenotype: O−

We start by first determining the possible genotypes of each person:

- Child's potential genotypes: BB++, BB+−, BO++, BO+−
- Mother's potential genotype: OO−−
- Father 1's potential genotypes: AB++, AB+−
- Father 2's potential genotype: OO−−

Now, what we have to do is determine which alleles the child received from his mother. For the ABO gene, the mother can only give her child an O allele, because those are the only alleles she has to give. For the Rh gene, the mother can only give her child a − allele for the same reason. So, we can say definitively that the child received an O allele and a − allele from Mom.

The final step is to determine which allele(s) the child got from his father. The child has a B allele and a + allele that Mom couldn't have given him, so these B and + alleles must have come from Dad. Now, let's look at both possible fathers' potential genotypes. We see that Father 1 does have a B allele but Father 2 does not. We see also that Father 1 has a + allele, but Father 2 does not. Therefore:

- We cannot exclude Father 1 as a potential father of the child.
- We *can* exclude Father 2 as a potential father of the child.

Notice here that we can't say for certain that Father 1 is indeed the child's father. All we can say is that he cannot be excluded and that further testing is necessary. We can say for certain, however, that Father 2 is completely excluded and does not need to be tested further.

For this procedure, we return to our favorite cast of characters to sort out some sticky paternity issues using the genetics of blood typing. While investigating the murders from Unit 20 (Blood, pp. 548–550), the investigators discovered that Ms. Magenta was hiding a secret: She had a 20-year-old daughter named Ms. Rose. The investigators are uncertain as to Ms. Rose's paternity, but they are certain that there are three possible fathers: Col. Lemon, Mr. Olive, and Professor Purple. You must determine whether any of these three men may be ruled out as Ms. Rose's father on the basis of their blood types.

Following is the procedure for testing the blood samples. When you have completed the activity, answer Check Your Understanding Question 5 (p. 768).

1 Obtain a well plate, anti-A, anti-B, and anti-Rh antisera, and samples of blood from Ms. Magenta, Ms. Rose, Col. Lemon, Mr. Olive, and Professor Purple.

2 Place two drops of Ms. Magenta's blood into three separate wells.

3 Place one drop of anti-A antiserum into the first well, and watch for a reaction. Record your results in Table 28.3.

4 Place one drop of anti-B antiserum into the second well, and watch for a reaction. Record your results in Table 28.3.

5 Place one drop of anti-Rh antiserum into the third well, and watch for a reaction. Record your results in Table 28.3.

6 Repeat this procedure with the blood of Ms. Rose, Col. Lemon, Mr. Olive, and Professor Purple. Record your results in Table 28.3.

TABLE **28.3** Blood Type Results

Blood Sample	Reaction with Anti-A?	Reaction with Anti-B?	Reaction with Anti-Rh?
Ms. Magenta			
Ms. Rose			
Col. Lemon			
Mr. Olive			
Prof. Purple			

7 Use your data from Table 28.3 to complete Table 28.4.

TABLE **28.4** Phenotypes and Potential Genotypes

Blood Sample	Blood Type (Phenotype)	Potential Genotypes
Ms. Magenta		
Ms. Rose		
Col. Lemon		
Mr. Olive		
Prof. Purple		

8 Interpret your results:

a Can any of the men be excluded as Ms. Rose's potential father? Explain.

b Can any of the men *not* be excluded as Ms. Rose's potential father? Explain.

The genetic effect known as **dominance** refers to the effect that different alleles have on an individual's phenotype. An allele that can suppress or mask another allele is known as the **dominant allele,** and the allele that is suppressed is known as the **recessive allele.** Dominant alleles are nearly always represented with capital letters and recessive alleles with lowercase letters.

The example of free and attached earlobes can be used to show the effect of dominant and recessive alleles on phenotype. The gene that codes for free earlobes is dominant and written as *E*, whereas the gene that codes for attached earlobes is recessive and written as *e*. Three different combinations of genes and two phenotypes are possible:

- *EE*, or homozygous dominant individuals, will have free earlobes.
- *Ee*, or heterozygous individuals, will have free earlobes.
- *ee*, or homozygous recessive individuals, will have attached earlobes.

By using our knowledge of dominant and recessive alleles, we are able to predict the possible genotypes and phenotypes of a man and woman's offspring with a diagram called a **Punnett square.** In Figure 28.7, you can see an example of a Punnett square in which a man is heterozygous for free earlobes (*Ee*) and a woman is homozygous for attached earlobes (*ee*). As you learned in the reproductive unit, each gamete receives only one allele, and we can't know which allele the gamete will receive. For this reason, the Punnett square can only tell us the probability of having offspring with particular traits. In Figure 28.7, notice that there is a 50% chance of having offspring that are heterozygous with free earlobes (*Ee*) and a 50% chance of having offspring that are homozygous with attached earlobes (*ee*).

Now, it's your turn to complete two simple Punnett squares. In the first Punnett square, you will determine the probability of a set of parents having offspring with freckles. In the second, you will determine the probability of a set of parents having offspring with polydactyly (six fingers on one hand rather than five). When you have completed the Punnett squares, answer Check Your Understanding Question 6 (p. 768).

1 Fill in the Punnett square in Figure 28.8 using the following:

- Dominant allele, codes for freckles (*F*)
- Recessive allele, does not code for freckles (*f*)
- Father's genotype: *Ff*
- Mother's genotype: *Ff*

What is the father's phenotype?

_____

What is the mother's phenotype?

_____

What is the probability the offspring will

a   be homozygous dominant? _____

b   be heterozygous? _____

c   be homozygous recessive? _____

d   have freckles? _____

e   not have freckles? _____

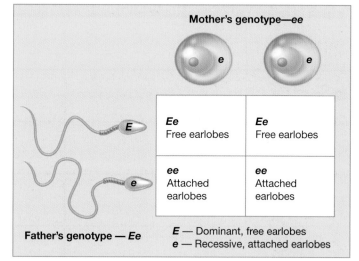

FIGURE **28.7** Punnett square for free and attached earlobes.

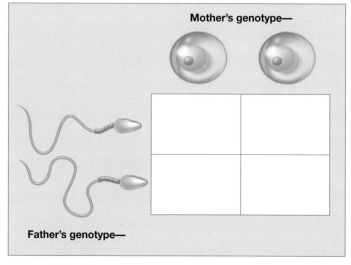

FIGURE **28.8** Punnett square.

2 Fill in the Punnett square in Figure 28.9 using the following:

- Dominant allele, codes for polydactyly (*P*; having six fingers on one hand)
- Recessive allele, does not code for polydactyly (*p*)
- Father's genotype: *PP*
- Mother's genotype: *pp*

What is the father's phenotype? _____

What is the mother's phenotype? _____

What is the probability the offspring will

a   be homozygous dominant? _____

b   be heterozygous? _____

c   be homozygous recessive? _____

d   have polydactyly? _____

e   not have polydactyly? _____

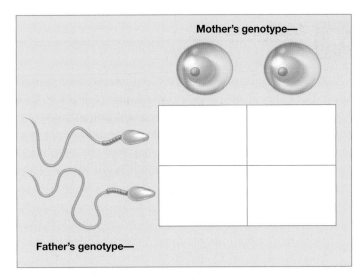

FIGURE **28.9** Punnett square.

---

3 **PROCEDURE**
Testing the Ability to Taste PTC

A dominant allele, *T*, found in about 75% of the population, determines the ability to taste **PTC** (phenylthiocarbamide), a bitter chemical found in foods such as Brussels sprouts and coffee. The remaining 25% of the population is homozygous for the recessive allele, *t*, and cannot taste PTC. In the following procedure, you will test your ability and that of your classmates to taste PTC. You will then pool your data to determine the percentage of tasters and nontasters in your class.

1 Obtain a piece of PTC paper and place it on your tongue.

2 If you can taste the PTC right away, you may remove the paper and dispose of it. If you do not taste it right away, leave the paper on your tongue for up to 1 minute. If you cannot taste the PTC after 1 minute, remove the paper and dispose of it.

Were you able to taste PTC? _____

3 Pool the data from your class and record them:

_____ Number of tasters   _____ Number of nontasters

_____ Percent of class that are tasters   _____ Percent of class that are nontasters

4 Interpret your results:

a   Which genotype(s) do the tasters have? _____

b   Which genotype(s) do the nontasters have? _____

c   How do the results from your class compare to the general population? _____

4 PROCEDURE
Testing Color Vision

Recall that humans have 23 pairs of chromosomes: Chromosomes 1 through 22 are called **autosomes** (AH-toh-sohmz), and the last pair consists of the two **sex chromosomes** known as **X** and **Y**. Females have the genotype XX and males have the genotype XY. Until now we have been discussing **autosomal traits**, or those that are passed down on autosomes. Certain traits, however, are passed down on the sex chromosomes, and these are known as **sex-linked traits**.

The inheritance of most autosomal traits is not influenced by sex; however, this is not the case with the inheritance of sex-linked traits. We can use the example of the blood disease hemophilia to see how this works. Hemophilia is the result of a recessive allele (*h*) found on the X chromosome. The normal allele is the dominant allele *H*. The possible genotypes with the resulting phenotypes include the following:

- A female with the genotype X^HX^H will not have the disease.
- A female with the genotype X^HX^b will not have the disease; however, she will be a "carrier" of the disease who is capable of passing the X^b allele to her offspring.
- A female with the genotype X^bX^b will have the disease.
- A male with the genotype X^HY will not have the disease.
- A male with the genotype X^bY will have the disease.

Notice here that because males have only one X chromosome, they require only one recessive allele on their single X chromosome to express the trait and have the disease. Conversely, females still require two recessive alleles to express the trait. For this reason, hemophilia is much more common in males than in females.

Another sex-linked trait is color blindness, or the inability to distinguish between certain colors. The allele for color blindness is a recessive allele on the X chromosome, X^b, and the allele for normal color vision is a dominant allele, X^B. The following procedure will allow you to test your vision for abnormalities in color vision, which may result from the presence of the X^b allele. The test uses a chart called an *Ishihara chart* that has a number embedded among a group of colored discs. A person with normal color vision will be able to read the number, whereas a person with color blindness will be able to see only randomly arranged colored dots. When you have completed the activity, answer Check Your Understanding Question 7 (p. 768).

1 Obtain an Ishihara chart or use Figure 28.10. Hold the chart at a comfortable reading distance. Record what you see in the space provided:

_____

Was the test negative or positive for color blindness? (Note that

"negative" means that your color vision was normal.) _____

2 Pool the results from your class and record the data:

_____ Number of females with normal color vision

_____ Number of females with impaired color vision

_____ Number of males with normal color vision

_____ Number of males with impaired color vision

3 Interpret your results:

  a What is/are the genotype(s) for females with normal color vision?

_____

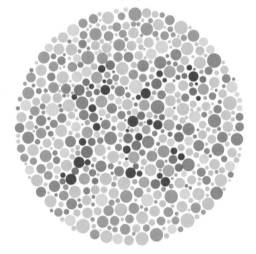

FIGURE **28.10** Ishihara chart.

  b What is the genotype for females with impaired color vision? _____

  c What is the genotype for males with normal color vision? _____

  d What is the genotype for males with impaired color vision? _____

  e How did the number of males with impaired color vision compare to the number of females with impaired color vision?

  Explain this finding. _____

Check Your Recall

1 Label Figure 28.11 with the following terms.

- ❏ Ampulla of uterine tube
- ❏ Early blastocyst
- ❏ Implanting blastocyst
- ❏ Inner cell mass
- ❏ Male and female pronuclei
- ❏ Morula
- ❏ Secondary oocyte
- ❏ Trophoblast
- ❏ Zygote

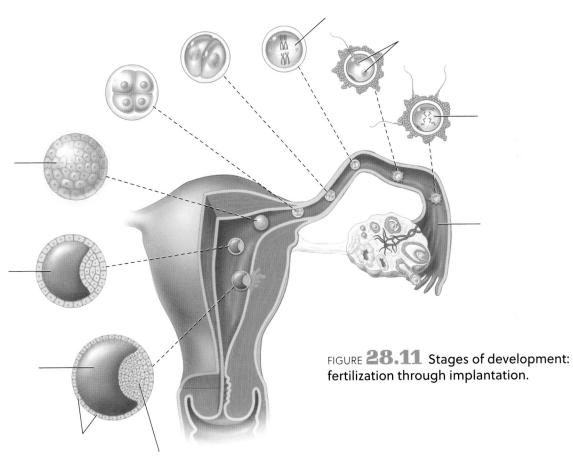

FIGURE **28.11** Stages of development: fertilization through implantation.

2 Oxygenated blood is delivered to the fetus via the

a. umbilical arteries.

b. umbilical veins.

c. ductus arteriosus.

d. ductus venosus.

3 How does a blastocyst implant in the endometrium?

4 Label Figure 28.12 with the following terms.

- ❑ Aortic arch
- ❑ Ductus arteriosus
- ❑ Ductus venosus
- ❑ Foramen ovale
- ❑ Inferior vena cava
- ❑ Placenta
- ❑ Superior vena cava
- ❑ Umbilical arteries
- ❑ Umbilical vein

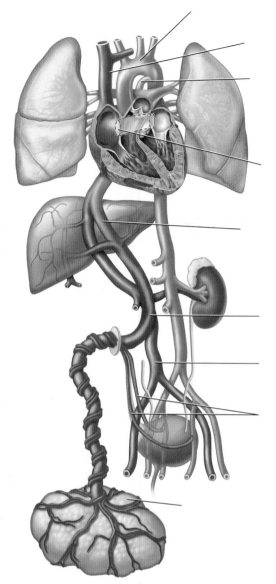

FIGURE **28.12** Fetal cardiovascular anatomy.

5 *True/False:* Mark the following statements as true (T) or false (F). If the statement is false, correct it to make it a true statement.

_____ a. Oxygen, nutrients, and wastes are exchanged between the conceptus and mother across the amnion.

_____ b. The ductus venosus is a vascular shunt from the pulmonary trunk to the aorta.

_____ c. Oxygenated blood is transported to the fetus by the umbilical arteries.

_____ d. Blood traveling through the fetal systemic arterial circuit is never fully oxygenated.

6 An allele that can mask or suppress another allele is known as a
a. dominant allele.
b. recessive allele.
c. sex-linked allele.
d. suppressive allele.

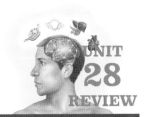

7 Label Figure 28.13 with the following terms.

- ❏ Amnion
- ❏ Amniotic cavity
- ❏ Chorion
- ❏ Chorionic villi
- ❏ Myometrium
- ❏ Placenta
- ❏ Placental sinus
- ❏ Umbilical arteries
- ❏ Umbilical vein
- ❏ Yolk sac

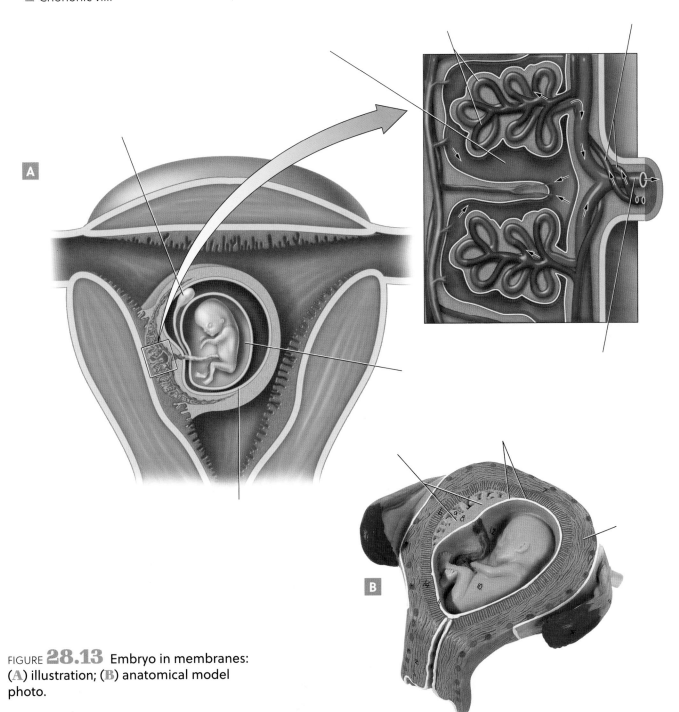

FIGURE **28.13** Embryo in membranes:
(**A**) illustration; (**B**) anatomical model
photo.

8 *Fill in the blanks:* Chromosomes 1–22 are known as _____ , while the last pair are

known as _____ .

9 Why are males at greater risk for inheriting sex-linked recessive traits than are females?

_____

_____

10 *True/False:* Mark the following statements as true (T) or false (F). If the statement is false, correct it to make it a true statement.

_____ a. An allele is a variant form of a gene.

_____ b. The phenotype is the genetic makeup of an organism.

_____ c. A person with two identical alleles is homozygous for that trait.

_____ d. A sex-linked trait is carried on autosomes.

Name _____

Section _____ Date_____

Check Your Understanding

Critical Thinking and Application Questions

1 Why do you think a woman may experience light bleeding during implantation?

2 A *breech birth* may occur when the fetus is in the uterus in a bottom-first position instead of a head-first position. A potential consequence of this position is prolapse and compression of the umbilical cord when birth initiates. Why would this be dangerous for the fetus?

3 In about 25% of the population, the foramen ovale fails to completely close, a condition called *patent foramen ovale*. While most individuals are asymptomatic, in some cases, a baby can turn blue, particularly when crying or straining. Explain why this happens.

4 *Meconium* is an infant's first bowel movement. It usually takes place shortly after birth, but sometimes a fetus expels meconium into the amniotic fluid. Why might this cause a problem for the fetus?

5 Further investigation has revealed that Ms. Magenta is in fact *not* Ms. Rose's mother. Because of a freak baby-switching accident, Mrs. Feather is really Ms. Rose's biological mother. Mrs. Feather's blood type is determined to be A−. Col. Lemon, Professor Purple, and Mr. Olive remain Ms. Rose's potential fathers.

 a What is Mrs. Feather's phenotype? What are her possible genotypes?

 b Can any of the potential fathers be excluded? Explain.

6 *Achondroplasia* is an autosomal dominant genetic disorder that results in short stature. Amy does not have achondroplasia and has a homozygous recessive genotype (*aa*). Her husband Rory has achondroplasia. Rory undergoes testing and learns that he is heterozygous dominant (*Aa*; the gene *A* codes for achondroplasia). They are seeking genetic counseling to find out their probability of having a child with achondroplasia. Use the Punnett square in Figure 28.14 to help them find answers.

What is the father's phenotype? _____

What is the mother's phenotype? _____

What is the probability the offspring will

 a be homozygous dominant? _____

 b be heterozygous? _____

 c be homozygous recessive? _____

 d have achondroplasia? _____

 e not have achondroplasia? _____

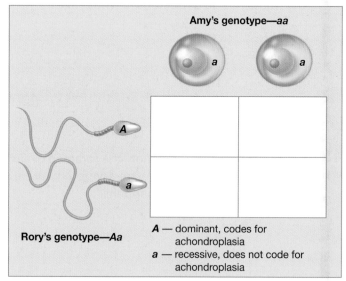

FIGURE **28.14** Punnett square.

7 A woman has given birth to two sons who both have the disease *hemophilia*. The mother does not have hemophilia. Can we conclusively determine her genotype? Explain.

The Big Picture of Human Anatomy and Physiology

When you have completed this unit, you should be able to:

1 Find physiological connections between different organs and systems in the body.

2 Review the physiology of the organ systems we have covered.

3 Trace the pathway of the physiological response to a stimulus through various body systems.

At this point in our study of anatomy and physiology, we have examined each organ system and its individual organs and have studied how the parts fit together to make the whole. Along the way, we also have developed an appreciation for how the structure of the system, organ, tissue, and cell all follow the primary functions of each part. Now, in this last unit, we will develop an appreciation for the big picture of how the organs work together to maintain homeostasis.

DNA and the human body.

EXERCISE 29-1

MATERIALS

❑ Anatomical models and diagrams: human torso

❑ Laminated outline of human body

❑ Water-soluble marking pens

Physiological Connections

In anatomy and physiology, the anatomical connections between organs and system are usually easy to see. All organs are connected by the cardiovascular system, bones are united by ligaments and cartilage, and accessory organs of the digestive system are joined to the alimentary canal by common ducts. However, the *physiological* connections that exist between all organs and organ systems are sometimes more difficult to see.

One of your final tasks in this lab manual is to find physiological connections between seemingly unrelated groups of organs or tissues. The physiological connection between the salivary glands, stomach, and duodenum is easy to find, but the connection between the heart, bone, and thyroid may be a bit less obvious. Following are some hints, and an example, to make this task easier.

- Begin each exercise by listing the functions of each organ. Some functions are obvious, and others may require a bit of digging on your part. Take, for example, the skin. The skin has the obvious functions of protection and thermoregulation. But don't forget about its other tasks: The skin also synthesizes vitamin D when it is exposed to certain wavelengths of ultraviolet radiation, it excretes small amounts of metabolic wastes, and it serves immunological functions. These less-discussed functions are easy to overlook but are vitally important.

- Beware of the tendency to fall back to anatomical connections. When given the combination "lungs, kidneys, and blood vessels," you may be tempted to say that the lungs breathe in oxygen, delivered by the blood vessels to the kidneys. That's all true, but this is an anatomical connection. With some creative thinking on your part, you could come up with something much better. Remember that lung tissue makes angiotensin-converting enzyme, and, with that said, the connection between the blood vessels and the kidneys becomes more obvious (at least I hope it does).

- When in doubt, look to the endocrine system. Remember that many different organs, not just the organs discussed in the endocrine unit, make hormones. The heart, kidneys, and even adipose tissue all function in some respects as endocrine organs. For the organs that have a primary endocrine function, don't overlook some of the hormones they make. For example, the thyroid gland makes T3 and thyroxine but also calcitonin.

Here's an example of physiological connection:

Lungs, Kidney, Bone

Connection: The lungs have the function of *gas exchange*. When this exchange is inadequate, and oxygen intake is insufficient, the kidneys detect the decreased partial pressure of oxygen in the blood. The kidneys, in turn, make the hormone *erythropoietin*, which acts on the bone marrow to stimulate increased *hematopoiesis* and an increased rate of red blood cell maturation.

Wasn't that easy?

Now it's your turn.

1 Connecting How Organs and Tissues Work Together

Part 1: Skin, Thyroid Glands, Bone

Hint: What hormone is made by the skin?

Connection:

_____

_____

_____

_____

_____

Part 2: Sympathetic Nervous System, Adrenal Gland, Blood Vessels

Hint: What are the two main parts of the adrenal gland?

Connection:

_____

_____

_____

_____

Part 3: Bone Marrow, Thymus, Lymph Node

Hint: What is the function of the thymus?

Connection:

_____

_____

_____

_____

Part 4: Large Intestine, Liver, Blood

Hint: Which vitamin is produced by the bacteria of the large intestine? What does it do?

Connection:

Part 5: Anterior Pituitary Gland, Ovary, Uterus

No hint for this one!

Connection:

The Big Picture: Tracing

Throughout this manual, you have done many different tracings of both anatomical pathways and physiological processes. Let's now put many of those tracings together to get a bigger picture of how the body functions as a whole. We are going to trace the response to a stimulus you have likely experienced: an angry wasp coming toward you. The tracing has been broken up into parts so that it is easier to manage. As with other tracings, hints have been placed throughout to help you.

1 PROCEDURE

Tracing a Reaction to a Wasp

Part 1: Sight and Sound of Wasp to Perception and Interpretation in the Brain

In this first part, Professor Purple has just seen a wasp. Trace the pathway light and sound takes from when he first sees and hears the wasp to the perception of these stimuli in the brain. This includes the anatomical path the light and sound take from the point where they enter his eye and ear to the interpretation in his brain.

Start (See Figs. 15.7, p. 403, and 14.4, p. 378, for reference): See the wasp → light enters the _____ →

light passes through _____ humor → then through the _____ → then through

_____ humor → light hits the _____ → the rods and cones hyperpolarize

→ an _____ potential is generated and propagated along the _____

nerve → some axons cross over at the _____ → the impulse is transmitted

to neurons of the _____ lobe → the stimulus is perceived and interpreted → End

Start (See Fig. 15.13, p. 408, for reference): Hear the wasp → sound enters the _____ → it

travels through the _____ canal → sound waves hit the

_____ membrane → sound waves vibrate the malleus → sound waves vibrate the next

two ossicles, the _____ and the _____ → sound

transmits through the _____ window to the _____

of the inner ear → _____ cells depolarize → an _____

potential is generated and propagated along the _____ nerve → the stimulus is delivered to the

_____ lobe → the sound is perceived and interpreted → End

Part 2: Initiation of the Sympathetic Nervous System Response

Now, let's trace Professor Purple's natural response to an angry wasp: fear. As you've learned, fear triggers activation of the sympathetic nervous system, which prepares the body for a fight or flight response.

Start (See Exercise 14-4, p. 387, for reference): Hypothalamus and cerebral cortex trigger the SNS response → sympathetic

postganglionic neurons release _____ onto target organs → the heart rate and force of contraction

_____ → the smooth muscle in bronchioles _____ → digestive and urinary

functions _____ → the blood vessels to skeletal muscles _____ → the

concentration of glucose in the blood _____ → the body primed for fight and flight → End

Part 3: Flight: Running from the Wasp

Professor Purple's body is now primed for fight or flight, so he is going to take flight and try to outrun the wasp. Let's trace a muscle contraction from its initiation by the nervous system through tension generation at the level of the muscle fiber.

Start (See Exercise 11-2, p. 312, for reference): An action potential from the _____ horn of the spinal cord travels down a lower motor neuron axon until it reaches its _____

→ the action potential triggers exocytosis of _____ → the neurotransmitter _____ diffuses across the synaptic cleft and binds to receptors on the _____ plate → an action potential is generated across the _____ of the muscle fiber → the action potential dives into the muscle fiber along the _____, and opens ion channels in the sarcoplasmic reticulum → _____ ions flood the sarcoplasm, binding to _____, which pulls tropomyosin away from actin → _____ "cocks" the myosin head → actin and myosin bind, forming a _____

→ ATP leaves the myosin head and a _____ occurs, which pulls the thin filament toward the center of the sarcomere → the process repeats as the muscle contracts → End

Part 4: Sting and Inflammatory Response

In this next part of the exercise, Professor Purple learns that it's very difficult to outrun a determined wasp, and has received a sting on his right hand. As with any tissue injury, a wasp sting leads to an inflammatory response, so you will be tracing the steps of this response.

Start (See Exercise 21-3, p. 574, for reference): Wasp stinger damages tissue → damaged cells release _____ mediators → local blood vessels _____ → capillary permeability _____

→ cells called _____ are attracted and activated → these cells attract a different cell type called _____, which ingest _____ by the process of _____ → these combined effects result in the warmth, redness, swelling, and pain of the inflammatory response → End

Part 5: Ingestion and Delivery of Medication

Now Professor Purple's right hand is sore, so he has taken an ibuprofen tablet. You will first trace the path the tablet takes through the organs of the alimentary canal to its absorption into the bloodstream. Next, you will trace its delivery to the lateral hand by arterioles and capillary beds via the radial artery. Remember that a substance that is absorbed from the alimentary canal takes a long path to get to a systemic artery: It needs to go through a capillary bed, then through the hepatic portal system, then the systemic veins, next the heart and pulmonary circuit, and finally through the systemic arteries.

Start (See Figs. 24.5, p. 642, 18.14, p. 493, 16.6, p. 441, and 18.6, p. 487, for reference): The medication is ingested at the

mouth → it travels through the alimentary canal, first the _____ , then the

_____ , next the _____ , and finally the small

_____ → an ibuprofen molecule diffuses into the enterocyte → it next diffuses out of the

enterocyte and into an intestinal _____ bed → it then enters the _____

_____ vein, and next the _____

vein → this vein leads into the liver and the _____ system

→ it drains from this system into the _____ veins and then into the inferior vena cava, which

transports it to the _____ of the heart → it next enters the

_____ ventricle, then the _____ trunk → it enters the lungs via a

_____ artery, which leads to _____ capillaries → it leaves

the lungs via the pulmonary _____ , which drains into the _____

_____ of the heart and then the _____ ventricle → the ibuprofen

molecule enters the systemic circulation via the ascending aorta, which leads to the _____

arch → it travels to the right side of the body through the _____ artery, which leads

to the _____ artery → it enters the right arm via the

_____ artery, which becomes the _____

_____ artery, and finally the right radial artery → from the systemic capillaries it diffuses out of the

blood and into the affected tissues and cells → End

Part 6: Excretion of the Medication

In this final part of the tracing, you are following the path Professor Purple's metabolized ibuprofen molecule takes as it leaves the body via the urinary system. You'll start from the capillary beds of the liver, where the ibuprofen is metabolized, and trace it through the blood vessels to the kidneys. Once it reaches the kidneys, you will trace its pathway through the nephron and out of the body.

Start (See Figs. 18.16, p. 494, 16.6, p. 441, 25.6, p. 683, and 25.10, p. 685, for reference): The metabolized ibuprofen diffuses

into the capillary beds of the hepatic portal system ⟶ it drains from this system into the hepatic veins and then the

_____ , which transports

it to the _____ of the heart ⟶ it next enters the

_____ , then the _____ trunk ⟶

it enters the lungs via a _____ , which leads to

_____ capillaries ⟶ it leaves the lungs via the _____

_____ , which drain into the _____

of the heart and then the _____ ⟶ the metabolized ibuprofen

molecule enters the systemic circulation via the _____ , which

leads to the _____ arch ⟶ it travels inferiorly via the _____ aorta,

then via the _____ aorta, and then enters the kidney through the _____

artery ⟶ in the kidney, it travels through the _____ artery, the _____

artery, the _____ artery, and finally the tiny _____ artery ⟶ it enters the

microcirculation of the kidney at the _____ arteriole, and is filtered at the _____

⟶ it next enters the filtrate in the nephron, starting with the _____ tubule, then the

_____ loop, then the _____ tubule ⟶ it then enters the collecting system,

first via the _____ collecting duct, then the _____ collecting duct, and

finally a _____ duct ⟶ it leaves the collecting system with the urine into the minor and major

_____ , which drain into the _____ pelvis ⟶ the metabolized ibuprofen

then enters the urinary tract via the _____ , then drains into the _____

_____ , and finally the _____ ⟶ the molecule exits the body in the urine

⟶ End

Lab Practical Practice Quiz 4

1 The structure marked number 1 in Figure Q.4.1 is the
- a. proximal tubule.
- b. distal tubule.
- c. ascending limb of the nephron loop.
- d. medullary collecting duct.

2 The structure marked number 2 in Figure Q.4.1 is the
- a. arcuate artery.
- b. peritubular capillaries.
- c. afferent arteriole.
- d. efferent arteriole.

3 The structure marked number 3 in Figure Q.4.1 is the
- a. afferent arteriole.
- b. glomerulus.
- c. proximal tubule.
- d. descending limb of the nephron loop.

4 The structure marked number 4 in Figure Q.4.1 is the
- a. medullary collecting duct.
- b. efferent arteriole.
- c. peritubular capillaries.
- d. glomerular capsule.

5 The structure marked number 5 in Figure Q.4.2A is the
- a. renal cortex.
- b. renal medulla.
- c. renal pelvis.
- d. renal pyramid.

6 The structure marked number 6 in Figure Q.4.2A is the
- a. interlobular artery.
- b. arcuate artery.
- c. interlobar artery.
- d. segmental artery.

7 The structure marked number 7 in Figure Q.4.2B is the
- a. urethra.
- b. ureter.
- c. urinary bladder.
- d. renal pelvis.

8 The structure marked number 8 in Figure Q.4.2B is the
- a. urethra.
- b. ureter.
- c. urinary bladder.
- d. renal pelvis.

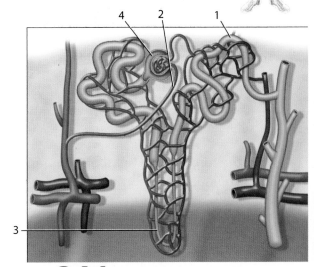

FIGURE **Q.4.1** Microanatomy of the kidney for Questions 1–4.

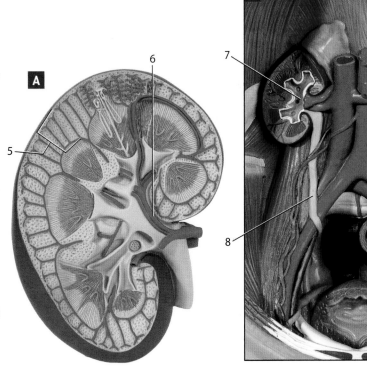

FIGURE **Q.4.2** Anatomy of the urinary system: (**A**) the kidney for Questions 5–6; (**B**) organs of the urinary system for Questions 7–8.

9 The structure marked number 9 in Figure Q.4.3 is the
   a. common bile duct.
   b. common hepatic duct.
   c. cystic duct.
   d. main pancreatic duct.

10 The structure marked number 10 in Figure Q.4.3 is the
   a. common bile duct.
   b. common hepatic duct.
   c. cystic duct.
   d. pancreatic duct.

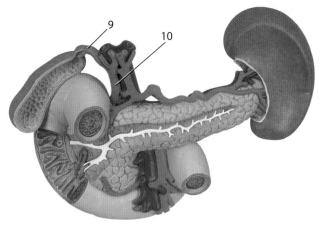

FIGURE **Q.4.3** Accessory organs of digestion for Questions 9–10.

11 The structure marked number 11 in Figure Q.4.4A is the
   a. submandibular gland.
   b. parotid duct.
   c. parotid gland.
   d. sublingual gland.

12 The structure marked number 12 in Figure Q.4.4B is the
   a. gastroesophageal sphincter.
   b. fundus.
   c. pyloric antrum.
   d. pyloric sphincter.

13 The structure marked number 13 in Figure Q.4.4B is the
   a. circular muscle layer.
   b. oblique muscle layer.
   c. rugae.
   d. lesser curvature.

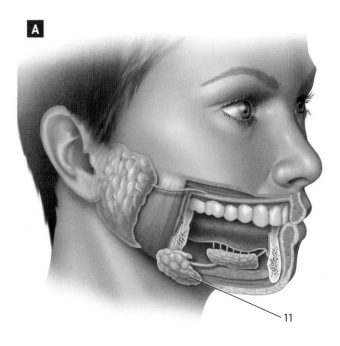

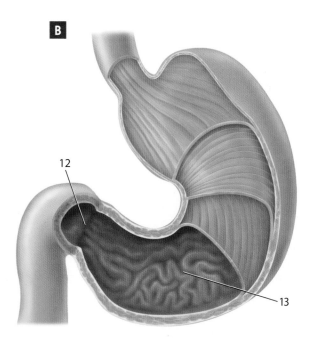

FIGURE **Q.4.4** Organs of the digestive system: (**A**) accessory digestive organs around the mouth for Question 11; (**B**) the stomach for Questions 12–13.

14 The structure marked number 14 in Figure Q.4.5 is the
   a. cecum.
   b. duodenum.
   c. sigmoid colon.
   d. ileum.

15 The structure marked number 15 in Figure Q.4.5 is the
   a. vermiform appendix.
   b. taeniae coli.
   c. haustra.
   d. cecum.

16 The structure marked number 16 in Figure Q.4.5 is the
   a. ascending colon.
   b. rectum.
   c. mesentery.
   d. pancreas.

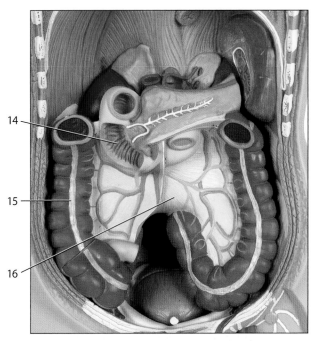

FIGURE **Q.4.5** Abdominal digestive organs for Questions 14–16.

17 The structure marked number 17 in Figure Q.4.6 is the

   a. pyloric sphincter.
   b. gallbladder.
   c. rectum.
   d. vermiform appendix.

18 The structure marked number 18 in Figure Q.4.6 is the
   a. oropharynx.
   b. parotid gland.
   c. esophagus.
   d. uvula.

19 The structure marked number 19 in Figure Q.4.6 is the
   a. duodenum.
   b. cecum.
   c. ileum.
   d. jejunum.

20 The structure marked number 20 in Figure Q.4.6 is the
   a. ileocecal valve.
   b. pyloric sphincter.
   c. gastroesophageal sphincter.
   d. uvula.

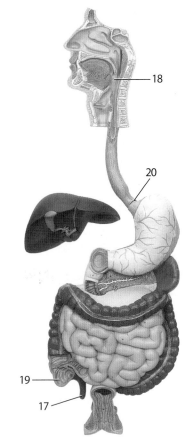

FIGURE **Q.4.6** Organs of the digestive system for Questions 17–20.

21 The structure marked number 21 in Figure Q.4.7A is the

a. prostate gland.
b. ductus deferens.
c. seminal vesicle.
d. epididymis.

22 The structure marked number 22 in Figure Q.4.7A is the

a. prostatic urethra.
b. ductus deferens.
c. spongy urethra.
d. membranous urethra.

23 The structure marked number 23 in Figure Q.4.7B is the

a. ductus deferens.
b. pampiniform venous plexus.
c. cremaster muscle.
d. spermatic cord.

24 The structure marked number 24 in Figure Q.4.7B is/are the

a. corpora cavernosa.
b. corpus spongiosum.
c. cremaster muscle.
d. spermatic cord.

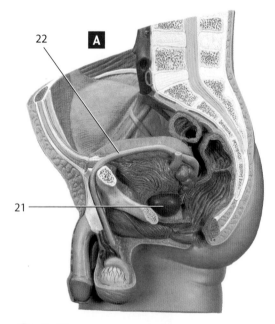 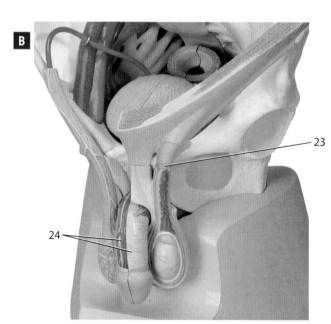

FIGURE **Q.4.7** Male reproductive organs: (**A**) midsagittal section through the male pelvis for Questions 21–22; (**B**) anterolateral view of the male reproductive organs for Questions 23–24.

25 The structure marked number 25 in Figure Q.4.8 is the
   a. ovarian ligament.
   b. broad ligament.
   c. round ligament.
   d. uterosacral ligament.

26 The structure marked number 26 in Figure Q.4.8 is/are the
   a. fornix.
   b. cervical canal.
   c. fundus.
   d. fimbriae.

27 The structure marked number 27 in Figure Q.4.8 is the
   a. perimetrium.
   b. myometrium.
   c. ampulla.
   d. endometrium.

28 The structure marked number 28 in Figure Q.4.8 is the
   a. vulva.
   b. vagina.
   c. uterine tube.
   d. cervical os.

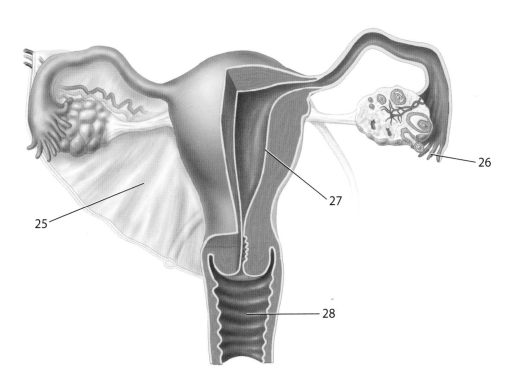

FIGURE **Q.4.8** Female reproductive structures for Questions 25–28.

29 The structure marked number 29 in Figure Q.4.9 is the
   a. placenta.
   b. amnion.
   c. chorion.
   d. cervical canal.

30 The structure marked number 30 in Figure Q.4.9 is the
   a. umbilical cord.
   b. placenta.
   c. myometrium.
   d. amniotic cavity.

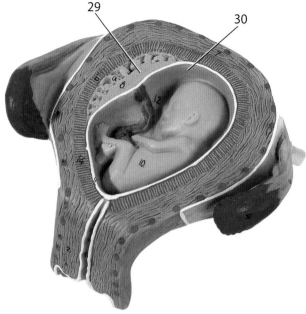

FIGURE **Q.4.9** Embryo in uterus for Questions 29–30.

Congratulations!

You've hit a major milestone by completing this manual!
I truly hope you have learned a lot and have enjoyed it
as much as I have. Best wishes with your future plans—
down whichever path they may take you.

Photo Credits

3B Scientific GmbH, Germany, 2021 www.3bscientific.com: Figures. 4.4B, 6.4B, 7.3B, Q.1.3, Q.1.6, Q.1.8, 10.14, 10.21A–B, 10.22B, 11.6, 15.4C, Q.2.5, 17.5B, 18.3, 18.17, 18.24B, 18.28, 22.5C, 22.7, Q.3.3, Q.3.4, Q.3.9, 24.5B, 24.15B, 24.16B, 24.27A, 24.29B, 25.6B, 27.3B, 27.5B, 27.8B, 28.3B, Q.4.3, Q.4.6, Q.4.7A, Q.4.7.B

Abbey, Michael/Science Source: Figures 4.11, 4.12, Q.1.4, 21.7A, 27.16

Amerman, Erin: Figures 5.5C (micrograph), 5.7A, Q.1.5B, 22.8A, 25.14A, 27.19

Anatomical Travelogue/Science Source: Figure 7.8A

Bassett, David/Science Source: Figures 8.15, Q.1.11A

Biology Pics/Science Source: Figure 5.14E

Biophoto Associates/Science Source: Figures 5.3A–B, 5.3D (micrograph), 5.4B, 5.5A, 5.6A (micrograph), 5.6B (micrograph), 5.6C, 5.9, 5.10C, 5.12B–E, 5.13A, 5.13C, 5.14C, 6.3B, 6.7, 7.9B, 8.17, Q.1.5A, Q.1.5C, 11.8B, 12.7, 13.7, 14.2B, 16.9, 16.10, 20.1, 20.2B (neutrophils, basophil, lymphocyte, and monocyte), 21.7B–C, 22.8B, 22.9, 22.10, Q.3.10, 24.17, 24.18B, 24.19B. 24.20, 25.15A, 25.15C, 27.14, 27.15, 27.20

Brown, Chuck/Science Source: Figure 5.7C

BSIP/Science Source: Figures 1.22b, 13.8C, 14.7, Q.2.7, Q.2.9, 18.18, 18.19, 19.9 (Tracing 2), 20.6, 21.5B, 22.2B, 22.4B, 22.6B, 22.12A–B, 22.14, Q.3.5A, Q.3.8A–B, 24.7B, 24.11B, 24.27B, 25.4C, 25.8C, 28.5C, 28.13B, Q.4.2A–B, Q.4.5, Q.4.9

Burger, Véronique/Science Source: Opener 26

Calvo, Jose Luis/Science Source: Opener 7; Figures 5.14B, 5.14F–G

CC Studio/Science Source: Figure 1.6D

Chambers, Keith/Science Source: Opener 23

Chillmaid, Martyn F./Science Source: Figure 23.3

Chumbley, Dr. Colin/Science Source: Figure 13.8B

CNRI/Science Source: Figures 5.4C, 10.23B, 18.24A, 25.15B

Darkin, Christian/Science Source: Opener 28

Davies, Gregory/Science Source: Figure 1.9A–B

DeLong, Garry/Science Source: Figures 6.6A, 24.22, 25.13

Denoyer-Geppert Science Company: Figures 15.13B, 17.7B, Q.3.2

Dermansky, Julie/Science Source: Figure 27.23

Du Cane Medical Imaging Ltd/Science Source: Figure 1.14B

Eye of Science/Science Source: Figure 5.3D (SEM)

Fermariello, Mauro/Science Source: Figure 26.5

Fung, K. H./Science Source: Opener 17

Furness, Dr. David; Keele University/Science Source: Figure 4.4C

Gaertner, Juan/Science Source: Openers 2, 12, 16, 22

GCA/Science Source: Figure 1.22a

Gerbier, Ph./Science Source: Figure 14.12

GIPhotoStock/Science Source: Figure 4.7

Grave, Eric/Science Source: Figure 5.10A, 11.7A, Q.2.1

Gschmeissner, Steve/Science Source: Openers 6, 15; Figures 5.4D, 5.5C (SEM), 5.6A (SEM), 5.8, 7.4, 20.7, 25.14B

Gusto/Science Source: Opener 3; Figure 2.4

Kage, Manfred/Science Source: Figures 5.10B, 11.15A

Kon, Kateryna/Science Source: Opener 21

Kulyk, Mehau/Science Source: Openers 1, 13

Landmann, Patrick/Science Source: Figure 2.16

LCJ, University of Guelph, © 2020: Figure 24.7C

LCJ, University of Guelph, © 2021: Figures 1.10, 1.11

Leboffe, Michael, *A Photographic Atlas of Histology*, 2e, © 2013 Morton Publishing Company: Figures 11.7B, Q.2.1, 17.15

Leboffe, Michael, © 2015 Morton Publishing: Figures 24.24, 24.25

Leica Microsystems: Figure 3.2

Levin, Andy/Science Source: Figure 19.4

Living Art Enterprises, LLC/Science Source: Figures 1.14A, 1.14C, 1.22c, 7.9A, 8.49

Mattei, George/Science Source: Opener 19

Moore, Justin, © 2012 Morton Publishing: Figures 2.15, 7.6A–C, 17.9B, 17.11B, 17.13B, 20.4, 22.11A–B, 24.26

Moore, Justin, © 2021 Morton Publishing: Figures 17.9A, 17.10, 17.11A, 17.12, 17.13A

Murti, Dr. Gopal/Science Source: Figure 3.3

NIH/NICDH/Dylan Burnette and Jennifer Lippincott-Schwartz/Science Source: Opener 4

Pasieka, Alfred/Science Source: Cover; Openers 11, 29

Phanie/Science Source: Figure 6.10

Phillips, David M./Science Source: Openers 5, 27; Figures 4.9A–C, 5.4A, 5.6B (SEM)

PIXOLOGICSTUDIO/Science Source: Opener 14

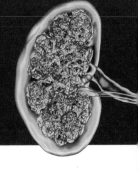

blood plasma, 130
blood types and typing, 552–555, 552t, 554–555f, 555t, 758–759, 759t
blood volume, 523
composition, 541–542, 541–542f
as connective tissue, 130, 130f
differential white blood cell count, 544, 544t
flow patterns, 499–503, 500–503f
formed elements, 540, 540f
key terms, 538–539
murder mystery game, 548–550
osmosis and, 95–96
peripheral blood smear, 543
recall check, 557–558, 557f
simulated blood testing, 546–547, 547f
skin supply, 149–150
transfusions, 551–553, 553t
understanding check, 559–600
blood-brain barrier, 328
blood glucose homeostasis, 442
blood pattern in heart, 472, 472f
blood pressure, 388, 388t, 523–524, 523f
blood vessel anatomy, 481–514
anatomical model, 497–498f
arterial anatomy, 482, 482f, 484, 484f
baroreceptor reflex, 506
basilic vein, 507, 508f
blood draw points, 507
blood flow patterns, 499–503, 500–503f
blood vessel wall histology, 504, 504f
cephalic vein, 507, 508f
clinical applications, 506–508, 506f, 507t, 508f
described, 485
intravenous catheter and access points, 507
major arteries, 485–488, 486–488f
major veins, 491–494, 491–494f
median cubital vein, 507, 508f
model inventory for arteries, 489–490, 490t
model inventory for veins, 495–496, 496t
pulse, 506–507, 506f, 507t
recall check, 509–512, 509–511f
tourniquet, 507
understanding check, 513–514
venous anatomy, 483, 483f, 484, 484f
B lymphocytes (B cells), 542, 566, 570, 574–575
body, 39–40, 39f
body cavities and membranes, 3–4, 4f, 16–22, 16–19f, 19–20t, 21f, 21t
body of epididymis, 724
body of ilium, 213
body of mandible, 193, 193f
body of scapula, 209
body of sphenoid bone, 195, 195f
body of sternum, 208
body of stomach, 644
body of uterus, 727
bolus, 643
bone (osseous) tissue, 130, 130f, 415
bone components, 175
bone markings and shapes, 176–177, 176t, 177f, 177t
bone marrow, 172
bone microscopic anatomy, 171–173, 171–173f
bony labyrinth, 408
Boyle's law, 613
brachial artery, 487
brachialis muscle, 275, 275f
brachial plexuses, 380
brachial vein, 491
brachiocephalic trunk, 485
brachiocephalic vein, 491
brachioradialis muscles, 275, 275f
bradycardia, 519
brain anatomy, 344–345, 344–345f, 347–352, 347–352f, 354–356, 354–355f

brainstem, 347, 350, 350f
broad ligament, 727
bronchial tree, 593
bronchioles, 595, 595f, 616
bronchomediastinal trunks, 565
bruits, 521
brush border, 654
brush border enzymes, 659
buccinator muscle, 271
buffers, 45–46, 46t
bulbar conjunctiva, 399
bulbourethral glands, 724–725f, 725
bulbous corpuscles, 415
bursae, 248

C (cytosine), 57
calcaneal (Achilles) tendon, 279
calcaneus, 215
calcitonin, 441
calcium hydroxyapatite crystals, 175, 175f
calcium ion homeostasis, 172
calf (gastrocnemius) muscle, 279
calvaria (cranial vault), 192
canaliculi, 172
cancer, defenses against, 575
canines (cuspids), 647
capillary beds, 485, 521, 521f
capillary permeability, 574
capillary refill time, 521–522, 521f, 522t
capitate bone, 211, 212f
capitulum, 210
capsular hydrostatic pressure (CHP), 703, 703f
capsular space, 680, 693
carbaminohemoglobin, 619
carbohydrate digestion, 659–661, 660f, 661t
carbohydrates, 55
carbon dioxide, 619–620
carbonic acid, 619
carbonic acid–bicarbonate buffer system, 45, 619
carbonic anhydrase, 619
carboxylic acid group, 56
carboxypeptidase, 659
cardia, 644
cardiac conduction system, 528
cardiac muscle histology, 473, 473f
cardiac muscle tissue, 135, 136f, 317, 317f, 474
cardiac myocytes, 317, 473
cardiac notch, 591
cardiac output, 523
cardiac sphincter, 644
cardiac veins, 465, 465f
cardiovascular physiology, 515–536
ankle–brachial index, 526–527, 526f
ANS and, 518, 518t, 524–525, 525t
auscultation, heart, 519–520, 519–520f, 520t
blood pressure, 523–524, 523f
capillary refill time, 521–522, 521f, 522t
ECGs, 528–532, 528–531f, 530t, 532t
key terms, 516–517
recall check, 533–534, 534f
understanding check, 535–536
vascular examination, 521
cardiovascular system. See blood vessel anatomy; cardiovascular physiology; heart
carina, 593
carotid bruits, 521
carotid canal, 196, 196f
carpals, 211, 212f
carpal tunnel syndrome, 382
cartilage, 128
cartilaginous joints, 245–246, 245f, 249–250, 249t, 250f, 257–258
catalase experiments, 53–54t
catalysts, 52
catecholamines, 442
cations, 40

cauda equina, 357
caudate lobe, 648, 648f
caudate nucleus, 349, 351f
cavernous sinus, 491
CD4 (helper T cells/T$_H$ cells), 575, 576f
CD8 (cytotoxic T cells/T$_c$ cells), 575, 576f
cecum, 645
celiac trunk, 487
cells
cell body, 139, 327
cell cycle, 84, 84t, 98–102, 98–99f
cell diversity, 90
cell inventory, 88–89, 89t
cell-mediated immunity, 575
cell parts, 83, 83f
cell sample preparation, 75, 75f
cell smears, 75, 75f
defined, 85
immunity and, 574
See also cytology
cementum, 655
central arteries of spleen, 566
central canal of bone, 172
central canal of brain and spinal cord, 347, 358
central incisors, 647
central nervous system (CNS), 341–366
brain anatomy, 344–345, 344–345f, 347–352, 347–352f, 354–356, 354–355f
circulation, 352f
key terms, 342–343
model inventory for brain, 353, 353t
model inventory for spinal cord, 359–360, 360t
recall check, 361–364, 361–364f
spinal cord anatomy, 346, 346f, 357–359, 357–358f
understanding check, 365–366
central process of neuron, 328
central sulcus of brain, 348
centrioles, 88
centromere, 99, 99f, 730, 730f
centrosome, 88
cephalic vein, 491, 507, 508f
cerebellar cortex, 350
cerebellum, 347
cerebral aqueduct, 347
cerebral arterial circle, 485
cerebral cortex, 348, 348f
cerebral hemispheres of cerebrum, 347
cerebrospinal fluid, 328, 347
cerebrum, 348, 348f
cervical curvature, 204, 204f
cervical enlargement, 357
cervical lymph nodes, 566, 566f
cervical os, 727
cervical plexuses, 380
cervical vertebrae, 204, 204f
cervix, 727
chemical components of bone, 175, 175f
chemical digestion, 641, 642f
chemistry, 35–66
acids and bases, 42–46
amino acids, 57f
in body, 39–40, 39f
buffers, 45–46, 46t
chemical bonds, 38, 47
chemical equation, 52
chemical reactions, 52
chemical symbols, 40
covalent bonds, 48f
enzymes and chemical reactions, 52–54, 53t, 54t, 60, 60f, 61t
ionic bonds, 48f
key terms, 36–37
lipids, 56f, 60–61, 60f, 61t
monosaccharides, 55f
nucleotides, 57f
orbital atomic model, 47f
organic compounds, 55–58
periodic table, 41f
pH scale and –logarithms, 38, 42–46, 42f, 43f, 43t, 44t

polysaccharides, 56f
recall check, 63–64
solubilities, 47–51, 50t
starches, 59, 59f
understanding check, 65–66
chemoreceptors, 413
chemosense, 413
chemotaxis, 574
chest muscle, 274, 275f, 613
chewing (mastication), 272
chiasmata, 730
choking, 602
cholesterol, 85
chondrocytes, 128
chordae tendineae, 467
chorion and chorionic villi, 755, 755f
choroid, 401, 401f
choroid plexuses, 347, 349f
CHP (capsular hydrostatic pressure), 703, 703f
chromatin, 88
chromosomes, 98
chronic obstructive pulmonary disease (COPD), 616
churning, 645, 652
chylomicrons, 660
chyme, 645
chymotrypsin, 659
cilia, 86, 87f
ciliary body, 401, 401f
ciliary muscle, 401–402, 401f
circular folds, 653–654, 654f
circumferential lamellae, 171f, 172
circumflex artery, 465
circumvallate papillae, 413
cisterna chyli, 654f
clavicle, 209, 209f
cleavage furrow, 99, 99f
clinical applications in blood vessel anatomy, 506–508, 506f, 507t, 508f
clitoris, 728
clotting cascade, 541
clotting proteins, 541
CN I: olfactory nerve, 375, 375f, 413
CN II: optic nerve, 375, 375f
CN III: oculomotor nerve, 375, 375f
CN IV: trochlear nerve, 375, 375f
CN IX: glossopharyngeal nerve, 375f, 376
CNS. See central nervous system
CN V: trigeminal nerve, 375, 375f
CN VI: abducens nerve, 375, 375f
CN VII: facial nerve, 375f, 376
CN VIII: vestibulocochlear nerve, 375f, 376
CN X: vagus nerve, 375f, 376
CN XI: accessory nerve, 375f, 376
CN XII: hypoglossal nerve, 375f, 376
coal-miner's lung (pneumoconiosis), 616
coccyx, 204, 204f, 207, 212
cochlea, 409
cochlear duct, 409
collagen fibers, 113, 113f, 175
collecting duct, 682
collecting system, 682, 701, 701f
colloid, 440, 444
colloid osmotic pressure (COP), 703, 703f
colon, 645
color vision/color blindness, 762, 762f
columnar cells, 117
common bile duct, 648
common fibular nerve, 383, 383f
common hepatic artery, 487
common hepatic duct, 648
common iliac arteries, 488, 488f
common iliac vein, 493
compact bone, 169, 169f, 172
complement system, 574
complementary base pairing, 58
compounds, 40
compressional strength, 175
computed tomography (CT) scans, 23f
computerized spirometer, 616
concentration gradient, 91, 312
concentric lamellae, 172